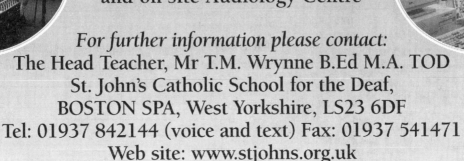

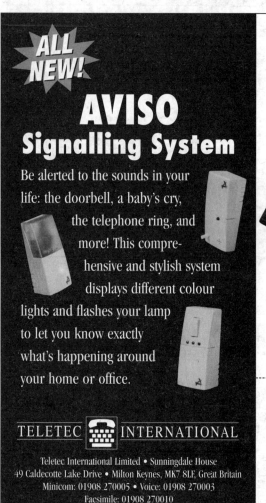

Information Update

RNID makes every effort to ensure that all details in the directory are correct at the time of going to press. Unfortunately, information can change or become out of date very quickly.

In order to keep information up to date and to ensure that we are kept abreast of new information, we would like to ask for your help. If you know of a change of address, or an organisation that is missing from these pages, please let us know by filling in this form and returning it to Tricia Harris at RNID in Featherstone Street. Alternatively, you could fill in the form on the RNID web page at www.rnid.org.uk or e-mail to tricia.harris@rnid.org.uk All the information you send us will be added to our database from which this directory is produced.

Thank you very much for your help.

To: Tricia Harris, RNID, 19-23 Featherstone Street, London EC1Y 8SL

Please note the following:

Section _____ Page Number _____

Name of organisation _____

New information _____

_____

_____

_____

Signed _____

Position _____

Address _____

_____

Telephone _____ Textphone _____

Fax _____ E-mail _____

Your views on the Information Directory

We are interested to know what people think about the directory. Is it easy to use? Does it have the information you want? Is there information missing?

Please take a few minutes to complete this short questionnaire and let us know your views. All questionnaires returned to us by the end of November 1999 will be entered into a prize draw to win a £25 Marks and Spencer gift voucher.

1. How often do you use the directory?

- ☐ Once a week
- ☐ 2-5 times a week
- ☐ 6-10 times a week
- ☐ Over 10 times a week

2. How many of the following do you agree with.

(Please tick as many boxes as apply)

- ☐ The directory is easy to use
- ☐ The index makes it easy to find the information I want
- ☐ The layout of information is helpful in finding what I want
- ☐ The directory is not easy to use
- ☐ There is too much information in the directory that is not relevant
- ☐ The information I need is not in the directory
- ☐ The balance of information is just right

I would like to see the following information/sections in the directory *(please write below the information/sections you would like to see included)*

_____

_____

_____

I think the following information/sections could be omitted from the directory *(please list below the information/sections you think should be removed from further editions)*

_____

_____

_____

3. Do you think the directory provides value for money?

☐ Yes   ☐ No

4. Would you buy the directory again?

☐ Yes   ☐ No

5. Do you have any further comments about the directory? If so, please add them here.

_____

_____

_____

Thank you for filling in this questionnaire. Please return it to Tricia Harris at the following address: RNID, Information Department, 19-23 Featherstone Street, London EC1Y 8SL.

 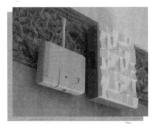

The Big Number Change

The UK telephone system has undergone its biggest reorganisation ever. This directory includes new codes for all telephone numbers and fax numbers. However, some textphone numbers may have slipped through unchanged. If you see any numbers that are incorrect, please contact RNID so that we can amend our data.

Old and new codes and numbers will operate alongside one another until 1 April 2000. Only new codes and numbers will work after Changeover Day, 1 April 2000. **Until April 2000 you will need to dial the full number including the code even if you are dialling locally.**

Six geographic regions in the UK have been given new area codes beginning with 02. They are Cardiff, Coventry, London, Portsmouth and Southampton. Each area has a new three-digit area code, followed by an eight-digit local telephone number. All numbers in Northern Ireland have been recoded. The code for Belfast is given in the examples.

Cardiff 01222 123 456	becomes **029 20**12 3456
Coventry 01203 123 456	becomes **024 76**12 3456
London 0171 123 4567	becomes **020 7**123 4567
London 0181 123 4567	becomes **020 8**123 4567
Portsmouth 01705 123 456	becomes **023 92**12 3456
Southampton 01703 123 456	becomes **023 80**12 3456
Belfast 01232 123 456	becomes **028 90**12 3456

The 01 prefix will still be used to denote most of the area codes so many numbers will remain unchanged. There is no change to international dialling codes and the prefix remains 00.

This information was kindly supplied by to us by Oftel.

New Unitary Authorities and Former Counties

From 1 April 1999 the local government status of many areas changed. Some county boundaries changed, while in others individual areas within counties gained unitary authority status. In England in particular, postal addresses have not changed and former county names are still used. However, the process is far more advanced in Scotland and Wales, where the new names are more established and in common use.

For the purpose of consistency, we have used old county names throughout this directory. In sections where the contents are broken down by country and then county, we have given the new county names with a 'See reference' to direct you to the entries for that area. For example, the former county of Avon has now been split into four unitary authorities: Bath and North East Somerset, South Gloucestershire, City of Bristol and North West Somerset. If you were looking for a particular Education Authority in Bristol or a school in South Gloucestershire, looking under South Gloucestershire in the Schools section would read: South Gloucester, see Avon.

A list of all unitary authorities is given below.

Avon
Bath and North East Somerset
City of Bristol
North West Somerset
South Gloucestershire

Bedfordshire
Luton
Milton Keynes

Berkshire
Bracknell Forest
Newbury
Reading
Slough
Windsor and Maidenhead
Wokingham

Cambridgeshire
Peterborough

Cheshire
Halton
Warrington

Cleveland
Hartlepool
Middlesbrough
Redcar and Cleveland
Stockton-on-Tees

Clwyd
Conwy
Denbighshire
Flintshire
Wrexham

County Durham
Darlington

Derbyshire
Derby

Devon
Plymouth
Torbay

Dorset
Bournemouth
Poole

Dyfed
Carmarthenshire
Ceredigion
Pembrokeshire

East Sussex
Brighton and Hove

Essex
Southend
Thurrock

Gwent
Blaenau Gwent
Caerphilly
Monmouthshire
Newport
Torfaen

Gwynedd
Anglesey

Hampshire
Portsmouth
Southampton

Humberside
East Riding of Yorkshire
Hull
North East Lincolnshire

North Lincolnshire

Kent
Gillingham and Rochester

Lancashire
Blackburn
Blackpool

Leicestershire
Leicester
Rutland

Mid Glamorgan
Bridgend
Caerphilly
Merthyr Tydfil
Rhondda Cynon Taff

North Yorkshire
York

Shropshire
Wrekin

South Glamorgan
Cardiff
Vale of Glamorgan

Staffordshire
Stoke-on-Trent

West Glamorgan
Neath Port Talbot
Swansea

Wiltshire
Thamesdown

Advertising in the RNID Directory of Services for Deaf and Hard of Hearing People

This is the most comprehensive directory of information and organisations which provide services to deaf and hard of hearing people and the professionals who work with them. An advert in these pages could reach a potential audience of 8.7 million. That's the number of people in this country with some form of hearing loss.

If you would like to consider placing an advert in future editions of the directory, contact Mongoose Communications on tel: 020 7306 0300, textphone: 020 7312 0470, fax: 020 7306 0301 for further details and a rate card.

To all users of the Directory of Services for Deaf and Hard of Hearing People

Inclusion of an advert in this directory is not an endorsement by RNID for the product or organisation concerned.

Contents

RNID Services

Information Services

RNID offers a wide range of information on all aspects of deafness and hearing loss. We have leaflets, factsheets and books, and maintain the most comprehensive database of over 6,000 services for deaf and hard of hearing people in the UK. We also produce a bi-monthly membership magazine, 'One in Seven', to help you keep fully informed.

The RNID website has over 140 pages of information including the latest news on our campaigns, projects and services, plus links to over 100 other useful websites. You can also search for services in your area on the database and read RNID factsheets and leaflets online. The website can be found at www.rnid.org.uk

The national RNID Helpline can answer any questions you may have - from hearing aids and benefits, to lipreading and sign language classes. We can also put you in touch with your nearest regional office and give you details of how to become an RNID member. The Helpline is open Monday to Friday from 9am to 5pm. Call us on tel: 0870 60 50 123, textphone: 0870 60 33 007, fax: 020 7296 8199, or e-mail: helpline@rnid.org.uk

Regional offices offer a range of RNID services and staff can put you in touch with services for deaf and hard of hearing people in your area. We have offices in Bath, Belfast, Birmingham, Cardiff, Glasgow, London and Manchester.

RNID membership is an ideal way of receiving information regularly. 'One in Seven', our bi-monthly membership magazine, has regular articles on all aspects of deafness and hearing loss. Membership is open to individuals and organisations, and all members receive discounts on our priced publications.

The RNID Tinnitus Helpline gives specialist information and support to people with tinnitus (ringing or other noises in the ears or head). They produce a free information pack, a newsletter for health professionals and tinnitus support groups, and factsheets on various aspects of tinnitus. The Tinnitus Helpline is open Monday to Friday, 10am to 3pm.

The RNID Library has specialist publications ranging from academic journals to books for children. Although the library does not lend direct to individuals, it can be accessed as a reference library, books can be borrowed on inter-library loan, and photocopies of extracts from books and journals can be supplied at a charge.

Communication Services

RNID runs a number of Communication Service Units (CSUs) throughout the UK which provide sign language interpreters, lipspeakers, notetakers, deafblind communicators and speech-to-text operators. They offer communication services for deaf, deafened, hard of hearing and deafblind people. This is a confidential and impartial service. Many of our CSUs are run in partnership with local and health authorities.

Communication Training Services

RNID offers a range of courses for people who want to embark on a career in communication services. They include sign language interpreter training, lipspeaking, electronic notetaking (SpeedText), notetaking, deafblind communication and videotelephony interpreting. We also run specialist training courses and workshops for sign language interpreters who want to update their skills and knowledge.

Disability and Deaf Awareness Training

RNID offers a range of training courses designed to make businesses more responsive to the needs of deaf people with disabilities including deaf and hard of hearing people. They give staff the practical skills and knowledge needed to improve communication with deaf colleagues and customers. Our Managing Special Needs course gives an understanding of the requirements of the Disability Discrimination Act, the barriers facing people with disabilities and how to remove them. We also offer courses on how to communicate with deaf and hard of hearing people, and communication tactics, including the use of textphones and RNID Typetalk, the national telephone relay service. Most of our trainers are deaf and can tailor courses to suit your needs.

Disability Consultancy Services

RNID's Disability Consultancy Service works with organisations to help them improve the access they offer to people who are deaf or hard of hearing or who have other disabilities. This takes in both service provision and employment, both of which are covered by the 1995 Disability Discrimination Act. The Consultancy does this by reviewing all an organisation's activity and, in the case of deafness, helping it work towards the minimum standards set down in RNID's 'Louder than Words' Charter. Recent clients include Royal

Bank of Scotland, Nationwide Building Society, Sainsburys, Yorkshire Electricity, The Employment Tribunals Service and War Pensions Agency.

Education Services

RNID is working in partnership with service providers and other agencies to improve the quality of educational provision for deaf children. We have commissioned a review of educational practice and are developing guidelines for teachers working with deaf children. We are also lobbying the government to raise awareness of the importance of education for deaf children.

Employment Services

Deaf and hard of hearing people face particular problems when trying to find a job or training opportunities. Employment Advisers from RNID's Employment and Learning Project give deaf and hard of hearing people information, advice, guidance and support to help them gain employment and/or training or to improve their promotion prospects at work. They are based in Manchester, Belfast, Colwyn Bay, Cardiff and Glasgow.

RNID advises employers and training providers on how to make their workplace or training centre suitable for deaf and hard of hearing people. We have also set up a scheme in the South West where professional deaf people act as mentors for other deaf people who are looking for work.

Medical Research

RNID has been investing in medical research for the past 20 years, particularly in the area of tinnitus therapy. Working closely with the Royal National Throat, Nose and Ear Hospital at University College London and the Institute of Hearing Research in Nottingham, we are now developing a series of research fellowships relating to deafness, hearing loss and tinnitus.

Membership Services

Joining RNID is an excellent way of receiving ongoing, up-to-date information on deafness and hearing loss as well as keeping in touch with issues that concern deaf and hard of hearing people. Membership is open to both organisations and individuals. All members receive our bi-monthly magazine, 'One in Seven', discounts on a variety of RNID products and publications, and easy access to information.

Residential and Community Services

RNID has a number of residential centres and smaller homes in the community for deaf and deafblind people of all ages who have additional social, educational or emotional difficulties. They offer vocational and educational training, respite care, community support, day services and a transition service to help residents find work when they leave the centre. Staff are trained in communication skills, so residents can communicate freely in whatever way they choose. Specialist services are available for frail older deaf and deafblind people. The centres are situated throughout the United Kingdom.

Technology

RNID researches, develops and tests new equipment for deaf and hard of hearing people. We ensure the technical quality and safety of products for sale through RNID Sound Advantage. With around a dozen technologists, we are a major source of expertise on devices, systems and aids of all kinds, maintaining close links with deaf people, professionals and equipment manufacturers. Our work includes investigating new mobile communications, developing a standard for smoke alarms for deaf people, and using computers as textphones. We are also researching digital sound processing to find ways of making speech sound clearer for hearing aid users in noisy backgrounds.

RNID Sound Advantage

RNID Sound Advantage sells a wide range of products for deaf and hard of hearing people to help them at work or in the home. There are over 150 products in our 'Solutions' catalogue - from TV listening devices and loop systems, flashing doorbells and alarm clocks to subtitling video recorders, textphones and portable telephone amplifiers. All products are tested by RNID to make sure they are safe and of a high quality.

RNID Typetalk

Typetalk is the national telephone relay service run by RNID and funded by BT. It enables deaf, deafblind and speech-impaired people to communicate with hearing people anywhere in the world over the telephone network. It is open 24 hours a day, all year round, and call charges are the same as if dialled direct. Over 500 operators relay conversations between deaf people who have textphones and hearing people. There is also a dedicated number for deaf people to access the emergency services. Typetalk is confidential and currently services around 23,000 customers.

Typetalk Customer Support can answer any questions you may have about the service, and a team of Outreach Officers provide textphone training and workshops for deaf and hard of hearing customers.

Text Users' Rebate Scheme

Typed messages can take up to six times longer than spoken ones. Deaf and deafblind people can claim substantial rebates on both BT and Typetalk calls thanks to the Text Users' Rebate Scheme. Funded by BT, deaf people registered on the scheme can claim a 60 per cent rebate, up to £160 a year, for each line. Deafblind people can claim up to £600 a year.

RNID Services

Contact details

RNID Offices

Royal National Institute for Deaf People, The

19-23 Featherstone Street, London, EC1Y 8SL

Tel: 020 7296 8000
Textphone: 020 7296 8001
Videotel: 020 7490 1641
Fax: 020 7296 8199
E-mail: helpline@rnid.org.uk
Website: www.rnid.org.uk

RNID Cymru

3rd Floor, 33-35 Cathedral Road, Cardiff, CF1 9HB

Tel: 029 2033 3034
Textphone: 029 2033 3036
Videotel: 029 2064 5298
Fax: 029 2033 3035
Website: www.rnid.org.uk

RNID Northern Ireland

Wilton House, 5 College Square North, Belfast, County Antrim, BT1 6AR

Tel: 028 9023 9619
Textphone: 028 9023 9619
Videotel: 028 9043 8354
Fax: 028 9031 2032
Website: www.rnid.org.uk

RNID Scotland

9 Clairmont Gardens, Glasgow, Lanarkshire, G3 7LW

Tel: 0141 332 0343
Textphone: 0141 332 5023
Videotel: 0141 353 2935
Fax: 0141 331 2640
Website: www.rnid.org.uk

RNID Midlands

1st Floor, Monaco House, Bristol Street, Birmingham, West Midlands, B5 7AS

Tel: 0121 622 2726
Textphone: 0121 622 1191
Fax: 0121 622 5774
Website: www.rnid.org.uk

RNID North

National Computing Centre, Armstrong House, Oxford Road, Manchester, M1 7ED

Tel: 0161 242 2313
Textphone: 0161 242 2314
Videotel: 0161 236 5687
Fax: 0161 242 2317
Website: www.rnid.org.uk

RNID South - Bath Office

13b Church Farm Business Park, Corston, Bath, Avon, BA2 9AP

Tel: 01225 874460
Textphone: 01225 874460
Videotel: 01225 874804
Fax: 01225 874246
Website: www.rnid.org.uk

RNID South - London Office

19-23 Featherstone Street, London, EC1Y 8SL

Tel: 020 7296 8000
Textphone: 020 7296-8001
Videotel: 020 7490 1641
Fax: 020 7296 8128
Website: www.rnid.org.uk

RNID Communication Service Units

RNID Communication Services Unit Bristol

ADSI, 4th Floor, Student's Union, Bristol University, Queens Road, Clifton, Bristol, BS8 1LN

Tel: 0117 954 5729
Textphone: 0117 954 5730
Fax: 0117 954 5731

RNID Communication Services Unit Central

Walton House, Walton Street, Aylesbury, Buckinghamshire, HP21 7QQ

Tel: 01296 392294
Textphone: 01296 392295
Fax: 01296 392294

RNID Communication Services Unit Cymru

Room 4, Norton Lodge, Norton Avenue, Mumbles, Swansea, SA3 5TP

Tel: 01792 402154
Textphone: 0800 622401
Fax: 01792 406090

RNID Communication Services Unit Merseyside

Merseyside Society for Deaf People, Queens Drive, West Derby, Liverpool, Merseyside, L13 0DJ
Tel: 0151 709 3663
Textphone: 0151 709 3833
Fax: 0151 228 4872

RNID Communication Services Unit North

National Computing Centre, Armstrong House, Oxford Road, Manchester, M1 7ED
Tel: 0161 242 2368
Textphone: 0161 242 2371
Fax: 0161 242 2317

RNID Communication Services Unit North East

National Computing Centre, Armstrong House, Oxford Road, Manchester, M1 7ED
Tel: 0161 242 2263
Textphone: 01642 312355
Videotel: 0161 236 2871
Fax: 0161 242 2317

RNID Communication Services Unit Northern Ireland

Wilton House, 5 College Square North, Belfast, County Antrim, BT1 6AR
Tel: 028 9023 9619
Textphone: 028 9031 2033 Text answerphone
Fax: 028 9031 2032

RNID Communication Services Unit Scotland

9 Clairmont Gardens, Glasgow, Lanarkshire, G3 7LW
Tel: 0141 332 0343
Textphone: 0141 332 4767
Fax: 0141 332 4768

RNID Communication Services Unit South East

19-23 Featherstone Street, London, EC1Y 8SL
Tel: 020 7296 8064/ 8066
Textphone: 020 7296 8065
Fax: 020 7296 8083
E-mail: se-csu@rnid.org.uk

RNID Communication Services Unit South West

13b Church Farm Business Park, Corston, Bath, Avon, BA2 9AP
Tel: 01225 873590
Textphone: 0800 622401 Freephone
Videotel: 01225 874804
Fax: 01225 874246
E-mail: sw-csu@rnid.org.uk

RNID Communication Services Unit Wolverhampton

The Methodist Centre, 24 School Street, Wolverhampton, West Midlands, WV1 4LF
Tel: 01902 423717
Textphone: 01902 423716
Videotel: 01902 310116
Fax: 01902 714456

RNID Communication Services Unit Yorkshire

Kirk House, Browning Road, Herringthorpe, Rotherham, South Yorkshire, S65 2LG
Tel: 01709 372163
Textphone: 01709 372182
Fax: 01709 372163

RNID Residential Services

RNID Brondesbury Road

113a Brondesbury Road, Queens Park, London, NW6 6RY
Tel: 020 7328 8540
Textphone: 020 7328 8544
Videotel: 020 7328 6590
Fax: 020 7328 8540

RNID Cliffe Avenue

15 Cliffe Avenue, Westbrook, Margate, Kent, CT9 5DU
Tel: 01843 232122
Textphone: 01843 230455
Fax: 01843 230455

RNID Community Outreach Services
1st and 2nd Floor, Wellington Street, St Johns, Blackburn, Lancashire, BB1 8AF
Tel: 01254 6786249
Textphone: 01254 670299
Fax: 01254 6786249

RNID Court Grange
Abbotskerswell, Newton Abbot, Devon, TQ12 5NH
Tel: 01626 353401
Textphone: 01626 367677
Videotel: 01626 353616
Fax: 01626 360895

RNID Dominion Road
30 Dominion Road, Bath, Avon, BA2 1DW
Tel: 01225 462787
Textphone: 01225 462787

RNID Ferndale Road
32 Ferndale Road, Hove, East Sussex, BN3 6EU
Tel: 01273 220949
Textphone: 01273 777692
Fax: 01273 779743

RNID Gibraltar Crescent
36a Gibraltar Crescent, Epsom, Surrey, KT19 9BT
Tel: 020 8393 0865
Textphone: 020 8393 7623
Videotel: 020 8786 7784
Fax: 020 8393 8649

RNID Harkness Gardens
1-2 Harkness Gardens, Brigade Road, Londonderry, BT47 6GG
Tel: 028 7134 1005
Textphone: 028 7134 2262
Fax: 028 7134 2262

RNID Leicester Project
Centre for Deaf People, 135 Welford Road, Leicester, LE2 6BE
Tel: 0116 255 6776
Textphone: 0116 254 5126
Fax: 0116 276 2373

RNID Mulberry House
70 Lichfield Street, Walsall, West Midlands, WS4 2BY
Tel: 01922 615218
Textphone: 01922 722658
Fax: 01922 615218

RNID Newbridge Hill
51 Newbridge Hill, Lower Weston, Bath, Somerset, BA1 3PR
Tel: 01225 443019
Textphone: 01225 443019
Fax: 01225 443019

RNID Old Oak Road
9 Old Oak Road, London, W3 7HN
Tel: 020 8740 9531
Textphone: 020 8740 1978
Videotel: 020 8746 2800
Fax: 020 8740 9531

RNID Olive Lane
60 Olive Lane, Blackheath, Halesowen, West Midlands, B62 8LZ
Tel: 0121 559 0031
Textphone: 0121 559 0280
Fax: 0121 561 1288

RNID Pendean Court
16 Pendean Court, Barras Cross, Liskeard, Cornwall, PL14 6DZ
Tel: 01579 340201
Textphone: 01579 340450
Fax: 01579 344410

RNID Poolemead
Watery Lane, Bath, Avon, BA2 1RN
Tel: 01225 332818
Textphone: 01225 332818
Fax: 01225 480825

RNID Ransdale House
Ransdale House, 54 Caversham Road, Middlesbrough, Cleveland, TS4 3NU
Tel: 01642 320785
Textphone: 01642 320785
Fax: 01642 325437

RNID Richardson House
Billinge End Road, Blackburn, Lancashire, BB2 6PT
Tel: 01254 677119
Textphone: 01254 682942
Fax: 01254 696623

RNID Roper House
St. Dunstans Street, Canterbury, Kent, CT2 8BZ
Tel: 01227 462155
Textphone: 01227 781915
Fax: 01227 452351

RNID Weatherly Close
1 Weatherly Close, John Street, Rochester, Kent, ME1 1AD
Tel: 01634 819143
Textphone: 01634 818402
Fax: 01634 819143

RNID Wilbury Gardens
13 Wilbury Gardens, Hove, East Sussex, BN3 6HQ
Tel: 01273 205044
Textphone: 01273 205044
Fax: 01273 771891

RNID Information Services

RNID Helpline
19-23 Featherstone Street, London, EC1Y 8SL
Tel: 0870 60 50 123
Textphone: 0870 60 33 007
Fax: 020 7296 8199
E-mail: helpline@rnid.org.uk
Website: www.rnid.org.uk

RNID Information and Environmental Equipment Service, Buckinghamshire
Walton House, Walton Street, Aylesbury, Buckinghamshire, HP21 7QQ
Tel: 01296 434839 information only
Textphone: 01296 436722
Fax: 01296 436358

RNID Library
The Institute of Laryngology and Otology, 330-332 Gray's Inn Road, London, WC1X 8EE
Tel: 020 7915 1553
Textphone: 020 7915 1553
Fax: 020 7915 1443
E-mail: rnidlib@ucl.ac.uk
Website: www.ucl.ac.uk/Library/RNID

RNID Sound Advice
34 The Mall, Carisbrooke Road, Newport, Isle of Wight, PO30 1BW
Tel: 01983 529533
Textphone: 01983 529533
Fax: 01983 533100

RNID Tinnitus Helpline
Castle Cavendish Works, Norton Street, Nottingham, NG7 5PN
Tel: 0345 090210 Helpline
Textphone: 0845 601 0821
Fax: 0115 978 5012
E-mail: tinnitushelpline@btinternet.com
Website: www.rnid.org.uk

RNID Employment Services

RNID Employment and Learning Project Colwyn Bay
Suite 3, Penrhos Manor, Oak Drive, Colwyn Bay, Clwyd, LL29 7YW
Tel: 01745 585589
Textphone: 01745 585541
Fax: 01745 585052

RNID Employment and Learning Project Cymru
3rd Floor, 33-35 Cathedral Road, Cardiff, CF1 9HB
Tel: 029 2033 3034
Textphone: 029 2033 3036
Fax: 029 2033 3035

RNID Employment and Learning Project Manchester
Royal School for the Deaf Manchester, Stanley Road, Cheadle Hulme, Cheadle, Cheshire, SK8 6RQ
Tel: 0161 610 0159
Textphone: 0161 610 0161
Fax: 0161 610 0160

RNID Employment and Learning Project Northern Ireland

Wilton House, 5 College Square North, Belfast, County Antrim, BT1 6AR

Tel:	028 9032 1733
Textphone:	028 9024 9462
Videotel:	028 9043 8354
Fax:	028 9023 3868

RNID Employment and Learning Project Scotland

9 Clairmont Gardens, Glasgow, Lanarkshire, G3 7LW

Tel:	0141 332 0343
Textphone:	0141 332 5023
Fax:	0141 331 2640

RNID Employment Project Bath

13b Church Farm Business Park, Corston, Bath, Avon, BA2 9AP

Tel:	01225 874460
Textphone:	01225 874460 ext 19
Fax:	01225 874246

Other RNID Services

RNID Communication Training Services

19-23 Featherstone Street, London, EC1Y 8SL

Tel:	020 7296 8000
Textphone:	0870 60 33 007
Fax:	020 7296 8199
Website:	www.rnid.org.uk

RNID Cymru Community Project

3rd Floor, 33-35 Cathedral Road, Cardiff, CF1 9HB

Tel:	029 2033 3034
Textphone:	029 2033 3036
Fax:	029 2033 3035
Website:	www.rnid.org.uk

RNID Disability and Deaf Awareness Training Services

1st Floor, Monaco House, Bristol Street, Birmingham, West Midlands, B5 7AS

Tel:	0870 240 2386
Textphone:	0121 622 1191
Fax:	0121 622 5174
E-mail:	ken.whittingham@rnid.org.uk
Website:	www.rnid.org.uk

RNID Disability Consultancy Services

19-23 Featherstone Street, London, EC1Y 8SL

Tel:	020 7296 8100
Textphone:	0870 60 33 007
Fax:	020 7296 8021
E-mail:	consultancy@rnid.org.uk
Website:	www.rnid.org.uk

RNID Membership Services

19-23 Featherstone Street, London, EC1Y 8SL

Tel:	020 7296 8049
Textphone:	020 7296 8049
Fax:	020 7296 8199
E-mail:	helpline@rnid.org.uk
Website:	www.rnid.org.uk

RNID Rotherham

Kirk House, Browning Road, Herringthorpe, Rotherham, South Yorkshire, S65 2LG

Tel:	01709 821232
Textphone:	01709 821232
Fax:	01709 821232

RNID Sandwell Community Care Project

c/o Deaf Community Social Services Centre, Dagger Lane, West Bromwich, West Midlands, B71 4BD

Tel:	0121 525 5347
Textphone:	0121 525 3092

RNID Sensory Services Redbridge

Access & Information Centre, Ground Floor, Connaught House, Broomhill Road, Woodford Green, Essex, IG8 0XR

Tel:	020 8498 9911
Textphone:	020 8498 9922
Videotel:	020 8504 0329
Fax:	020 8498 9955

RNID Sound Advantage

1 Metro Centre, Welbeck Way, Peterborough,
Cambridgeshire, PE2 7UH

Tel: 01733 361199
Textphone: 01733 238020
Fax: 01733 361161
E-mail: solutions@rnid.org.uk
Website: www.rnid.org.uk

RNID Typetalk - The National Telephone Relay Service

John Wood House, Glacier Building, Harrington
Road, Brunswick Business Park, Liverpool,
Merseyside, L3 4DF

Tel: 0151 709 9494 (admin)
                0800 7 311 888 (Helpline)
Textphone: 0800 500 888 (Helpline)
Fax: 0151 709 8119
Website: www.rnid.org.uk

Sound Advantage

The *Solutions* catalogue from RNID Sound Advantage offers quality products for deaf and hard of hearing people

Order your free catalogue now.

- Products tested by RNID

- Specialist advice available

- 28-day money back guarantee

- Credit card ordering service

- 14-day standard delivery

To receive your free catalogue please contact our Customer Service team.

RNID Sound Advantage, 1 Metro Centre, Welbeck Way, Peterborough PE2 7BR
Tel: 01733 361199 Textphone: 01733 238020 Fax: 01733 361161

THE ROYAL NATIONAL INSTITUTE FOR DEAF PEOPLE

For deaf people, it's the key to a whole new way of life

To a deaf person that 'GA' key stands for much more than 'go ahead' - it means additional independence and the benefits of the phone network that hearing people take for granted.

Typetalk's 22,000 textphone users rely on our confidential relay service to put them in contact with hearing people. A textphone is a special phone with a screen and keyboard.

Users speak directly to the hearing person or they may type their messages which are translated into speech by highly trained operators who relay them to the hearing person. Their response is then typed back to the textphone user and appears on their screen.

The service, of course, is highly confidential and FREE to join. If you could benefit from using Typetalk, or you know someone who would, then call us.

BT RNID
working together

TO FIND OUT MORE OR REGISTER FREE OF CHARGE CALL:

0800 7 311 888 (voice) or 0800 500 888 (text)

or write to **Typetalk, Registration Department,
FREEPOST, Liverpool L3 5BR**

RNID

Working in partnership

RNID's vision is a world where deafness and hearing loss are not barriers to opportunity and fulfilment.

Associate membership from £40

How your organisation can benefit from RNID Membership

- **Reduced prices on:**
  - **Priced publications**
  - **RNID Sound Advantage products**
  - **Disability Consultancy**
  - **Deaf & Disability Awareness Training**
  - **Conferences**
  - **Seminars**
  - **Leaflet Information Service**
  - **Additional magazine subscriptions**

- **Up to five copies of each bi-monthly issue of *One in Seven* magazine**

- **An invitation to members' conferences and the AGM**

- **Easy access to our Helpline and comprehensive information leaflets and factsheets**

Any organisation is welcome to join us!

To find out more or request our membership information pack, contact:
Membership Services, FREEPOST LON13186, London EC1B 1AL
Tel: 020 7296 8049 Textphone: 020 7296 8020 Fax: 020 7296 8021

THE ROYAL NATIONAL INSTITUTE FOR DEAF PEOPLE

Social Workers

Details here are of specialist social workers working with deaf people. General details of the main social services office are given where no specialist team is available.

Each social service is listed alphabetically by name within country and county sections.

England

➤ Avon

Bath and North East Somerset Social Services

7 North Parade Buildings, Bath, Avon, BA1 1NY

Tel: 01225 477000

Fax: 01225 477907

Contact: Moria Gardner, Head of Community Services

To make basic provision for deaf and hard of hearing members of the community and provide help within the limits of Social Services.

Bristol Social Services

P O Box 30, Avon House, The Haymarket, Bristol, Avon, BS99 7NB

Tel: 0117 903 7646

Fax: 0117 903 7841

Contact: Ian Tennant, Principal Officer, Adults

To enable vulnerable people to live in their own homes and, where this is not possible, to arrange good quality care in an alternative setting.

South Gloucestershire Social Services

50 Morley Road, Staple Hill, Bristol, Avon, BS16 4QS

Tel: 01454 866295

Fax: 01454 866297

Contact: Lucy Rogers

➤ Bedfordshire

Luton and Bedfordshire Social Services

Alban Neve Centre, 49 Old Bedford Road, Luton, Bedfordshire, LU2 7NX

Tel: 01582 483417

Textphone: 01582 405710

Fax: 01582 720679

Contact: Louise Clark, Acting Resource Manager

➤ Berkshire

Bracknell Social Services

Time Square, Market Street, Bracknell, Berkshire, RG12 1JD

Tel: 01344 424642

Fax: 01344 351301

Contact: Derek Simmons, Team Manager, Deaf Services

            Lytham Court, Lytham Road, Woodley, Reading, Berkshire, RG5 3PQ

Tel: 0118 927 2200

Textphone: 0118 927 2202

Fax: 0118 927 2223

Services to deaf and hard of hearing people are dealt with by the Deaf Services Team based at Lytham Court in Reading. The Deaf Services Team covers the entire county of Berkshire and provides the following services either directly or through another agency: social work support, advice and guidance, provision of equipment, interpreting services, lipspeakers and services for deafblind people. Other social service issues should be directed to the office in Bracknell.

Newbury Social Services

Pelican House, 9-15 West Street, Newbury, Berkshire, RG14 1PL

Tel: 01635 46545

Fax: 01635 516729

Derek Simmons is the Deaf Services Team Manager - all details are as for Bracknell Social Services, above.

Reading Social Services

Abbey Mill House, Abbey Square, Reading, Berkshire, RG1 3BE

Tel: 0118 955 3600

Textphone: 0118 939 0700

Fax: 0118 955 3741

Derek Simmons is the Deaf Services Team Manager - all details are as for Bracknell Social Services.

Slough Social Services

New Highfield, Wexham Road, Slough, Berkshire, SL1 1AS

Tel: 01753 690400

Fax: 01753 690413

Derek Simmons is the Deaf Services Team Manager - details are as for Bracknell Social Services.

Windsor and Maidenhead Social Services

4 Marlow Road, Maidenhead, Berkshire, SL6 7YR

Tel: 01628 798888

Fax: 01628 683100

Derek Simmons is the Deaf Services Team Manager - details are as for Bracknell Social Services.

Wokingham Social Services

Wellington House, Wellington Road, Wokingham, Berkshire, RG40 2AG

Tel: 0118 978 9656

Fax: 0118 978 9261

Derek Simmons is the Deaf Services Team Manager - details are as for Bracknell Social Services.

➢ Blackburn
See Lancashire

➢ Blackpool
See Lancashire

➢ Bournemouth
See Dorset

➢ Bracknell Forest
See Berkshire

➢ Brighton and Hove
See East Sussex

➢ Bristol, City of
See Avon

➢ Buckinghamshire

Buckinghamshire Social Services

Old County Offices, Walton Street, Aylesbury, Buckinghamshire, HP20 1EZ

Tel: 01296 395000

Fax: 01296 383182

Contact: Cathy Sandford, Service Development Officer

Easton Street, High Wycombe, Buckinghamshire, HP11 1NH

Tel: 01494 475030

Fax: 01494 475019

Milton Keynes Social Services

Saxon Court, 502 Avebury Boulevard, Central Milton Keynes, Milton Keynes, Buckinghamshire, MK9 3DS

Tel: 01908 253585

Textphone: 01908 253394

Fax: 01908 253185

Contact: Felicity Lefevre, Head of Disabilities Services Team

➢ Cambridgeshire

Cambridgeshire Social Services

Castle Court, Shire Hall, Castle Hill, Cambridge, CB3 0AP

Tel: 01223 717182

Fax: 01223 717307

Contact: Roz Hunt, Social Worker, Hearing Impaired

Seymour House, Seymour Street, Cambridge, CB1 3DQ

Tel: 01223 568801

The department provides assessment and care management for adults and children with social care needs, including people with sensory impairments. The department also provides (or purchases) a range of services to meet identified needs, subject to eligibility criteria being met.

➢ Channel Islands

Guernsey Board of Health

John Henry House, Le Vauquiedor, Guernsey, Channel Islands

Tel: 01481 725241

Fax: 01481 51350

Contact: Roy Marsden, Deputy Head, Social Work Department

Guernsey Social Security Authority

Edward T Wheadon House, Le Truchot, St Peter Port, Guernsey, Channel Islands, GY1 3WH

Tel: 01481 725241

Fax: 01481 701249

Contact: Dave Turton, Supervisor, Visiting Officers

Jersey Children's Service and Adult Social Work

Maison Le Pape, The Parade, St Helier, Jersey, Channel Islands, JE2 3PU

Tel: 01534 623500

Fax: 01534 732469

Contact: Howard White, Social Worker with Deaf People

> Cheshire

Cheshire Social Services

Commerce House, Hunter Street, Chester, Cheshire, CH1 2NJ

Tel: 01244 602424

Textphone: 01244 603213

Fax: 01244 603815

E-mail: gladdens@cheshire-cc.btx400.co.uk

Contact: Steven Gladden, Service Development and Review Manager

Policy Service, Watling Street, Northwich, Cheshire, CW9 5ET

Tel: 01606 815828

Stockport Social Services

Floor 6, Regal House, Duke Street, Stockport, Cheshire, SK1 3DA

Tel: 0161 477 3700

Textphone: 0161 474 1019

Fax: 0161 476 3521

Contact: Helen Mawson, Social Worker with Deaf People

Stockport can provide the following: general social work services, equipment, sign language interpreting services, services for deafblind people and residential services.

Tameside Social Services

Stalybridge Resource Centre, Waterloo Road, Stalybridge, Cheshire, SK15 2AU

Tel: 0161 342 2575

Textphone: 0161 342 2577

Fax: 0161 342 2584

Contact: Suzanne Robinson, Team Leader, Services for Deaf People

Tameside can provide the following: general social work services, provision of equipment, communication support services, services for deafblind people, and specialist services for deaf people from ethnic minorities.

Trafford Social Services

P O Box 16, Warbrick House, Washway Road, Sale, Cheshire, M33 7DJ

Tel: 0161 912 2778

Textphone: 0161 912 2847

Fax: 0161 912 2711

Contact: Bernard McArdle, Social Worker for the Deaf

Urmston Council Offices, Crofts Bank Road, Urmston, Manchester, Lancashire, M41 0UD

The following services are available directly or by referral from the West Area Office (Tel: 0161 875 0934): social work, equipment, interpreter support, lipspeaking, services for deafblind people, residential, hostel and other accommodation, specialist services for people from ethnic minorities and rehabilitation services. Provision of interpreters, lipspeaking and sign language communication services are also available from the RNID North Communication Support Unit.

> Cleveland

Cleveland Social Services

Melrose Avenue, Billingham, Cleveland, TS23 2JH

Tel: 01642 363222/533625

Contact: A Catchpole

Basic service provided for deaf people.

Hartlepool Social Services

P O Box 96, Civic Centre, Victoria Road, Hartlepool, Cleveland, TS24 8BR

Tel:	01429 266522
Textphone:	01429 221580
Fax:	01429 523908
Contact:	Adrian Van Loo, Team Manager, Sensory Loss Occupational Therapy

Middlesbrough Social Services

3rd Floor, Civic Centre, Middlesborough, Cleveland, TS1 2QJ

Tel:	01642 264510
Textphone:	01642 264514
Fax:	01642 262822
Contact:	Roger Shimmin, Sensory Loss Team Manager

Redcar and Cleveland Social Services

The Grange, 153 Fabian Road, Eston, Middlesbrough, Cleveland, TS6 3RQ

Tel:	01642 464610
Textphone:	01642 463598
Fax:	01642 464305
Contact:	Roger Shimmin, Sensory Loss Team Manager

Stockton-on-Tees Social Services

Council Offices, Town Square, Billingham, Cleveland, TS23 2LW

Tel:	01642 397139
Textphone:	01642 361445
Fax:	01642 397147
Contact:	Cathy Smith, Social Worker with Deaf People

➢ Cornwall

Cornwall Social Services

6 Carlyon Road, St Austell, Cornwall, PL25 4NG

Tel:	01726 63582
Textphone:	01872 240892
Fax:	01726 61858
Contact:	Mervyn Davey, Team Manager, Sensory Loss Team

The sensory loss team provides a full range of social work services for deaf people. We also provide assessment and specialised services with respect to communication support, environmental equipment and deafness management.

➢ County Durham

Darlington Social Services

Central House, Gladstone Street, Darlington, County Durham, DL3 6XJ

Tel:	01325 346200
Fax:	01325 346474
Contact:	Colin Morris, Director of Social Services

Durham Social Services

County Hall, Durham, DH1 5UG

Tel:	0191 386 4411
Textphone:	0191 383 3802
Fax:	0191 383 4182
Website:	www.durham.gov.uk

Social services for deaf people in County Durham are provided by local district offices. Details of the location of services are available from County Hall. The following services are available from the district offices: social work, equipment, interpreter support, lipspeaking and services for deafblind people.

➢ Cumbria

Cumbria Social Services

Social Services Department, 3 Victoria Place, Carlisle, Cumbria, CA1 1EH

Tel:	01228 522885
Fax:	01228 590501
Contact:	Ann Chesters, Senior Social Worker, Cumbria Deaf Association
	3 Compton Street, Carlisle, Cumbria, CA1 1HT

Social Services for deaf people in Cumbria are provided under an agency agreement by the Cumbria Deaf Association. The following services are available: social work, equipment, interpreter support, lipspeaking, services for deafblind people, and rehabilitation services.

➢ Darlington
See County Durham

➢ Derby
See Derbyshire

➢ Derbyshire
Derby Social Services
Social Services, The Coach House, 29 Kedleston Road, Derby, DE22 1FL
Tel: 01332 717567
Textphone: 01332 344358
Fax: 01332 717571
Contact: Karen Golding, Service Manager, Unit for Deaf People

D C C, Social Services, Unit for Deaf People, The Coach House, 29 Kedleston Rd, Derby, DE22 1FL

Derby City Council can provide the following: general social work services, equipment, services for deafblind people, other accommodation and rehabilitation services. Derby City Council also provide social services for deaf people in the southern half of Derbyshire through a service agreement with Derbyshire County Council.

Derbyshire Social Services
County Offices, Matlock, Derbyshire, DE4 3AG
Tel: 01629 580000
Fax: 01629 583292
Contact: Helen Best

Derwent House, Ulverston Road, Newbold, Chesterfield, Derbyshire, S41 8EW

➢ Devon
Devon Social Services
County Hall, Topsham Road, Exeter, Devon, EX2 4QR
Tel: 01392 382000
Contact: Peter Wareham, Group Manager, Sensory Services

Magdalen House, 56 Magdalen Road, Exeter, Devon, EX2 4TL
Tel: 01392 383737
Textphone: 01392 383737

Devon can provide the following: general social work services, equipment, services for deafblind people and rehabilitation services.

Plymouth Social Services
Sensory Team, 'Wolseley', Wolseley Road, Plymouth, Devon, PL2 3BW
Tel: 01752 305639
Contact: Marian Ross, Senior Social Worker

➢ Dorset
Bournemouth Social Services
3rd Floor, Oxford House, Oxford Road, Bournemouth, Dorset, BH8 8HA
Tel: 01202 458700
Textphone: 01202 458750
Fax: 01202 458740
Contact: Christine Johnson, Team Leader, Sight and Hearing Services

Dorset Social Services
County Hall, Dorchester, Dorset, DT1 1XJ
Tel: 01305 251000
Fax: 01305 224325
Contact: Rosie Ward
Tel: 01305 251414
Fax: 01305 251034

Dorset can offer the following: general social work services, equipment, communication support services, services for deafblind people, specialist services for deaf people from ethnic minorities and rehabilitation services.

Poole Social Services
Poole Borough Council, Civic Centre, Poole, Dorset, BH15 2RU
Tel: 01202 634222
Textphone: 01202 633630
Fax: 01202 633634
Contact: Andrew Creamer, Head of Sensory Loss Team

➢ East Riding of Yorkshire
See North Humberside

➤ East Sussex

Brighton and Hove Social Services

William Moon Lodge, The Linkway, Hollingdean, Brighton, East Sussex, BN1 7EJ

Tel: 01273 506368

Textphone: 01273 551006

Fax: 01273 552278

Contact: Lorna Redman, Adult Services, Disabilities

East Sussex Social Services

10 Pembury Road, Eastbourne, East Sussex, BN23 7HQ

Tel: 01323 768444

Fax: 01323 768450

Contact: Karyl Henry, Manager, Sensory Impairment Service

County Hall, St Anne's Crescent, Lewes, East Sussex, BN7 1SW

Tel: 01273 481000

The Sensory Impairment Service is a part of the Physical Disability and Sensory Impairment Team. The Sensory Impairment Service provides services to individuals or groups of people of all ages who are ordinarily resident in East Sussex, who have a permanent and substantial hearing and/or visual impairment. These services are provided to meet the County Council's statutory duty in accordance with the National Health Service/County Council and disability legislation. The overall aim is to promote and maintain daily living skills, to provide packages of care, and to facilitate the provision of specialist services to address needs arising from visual and/or hearing loss, to disabled people who wish to continue to live in the community, and their carers. Most of the work is with people who live at home, although people who live in residential care may also be seen.

➤ Essex

Barking and Dagenham Social Services

Civic Centre, Dagenham, Essex, RM10 7BW

Tel: 020 8592 4500

Contact: Elaine Williamson, Social Worker with Deaf People

Social services for deaf people in Barking and Dagenham are provided by the St George's Road Centre.

Essex Social Services

P O Box 297, County Hall, Chelmsford, Essex, CM1 1YS

Tel: 01245 434090

Textphone: 01245 434139

Fax: 01245 268580

Website: www.essexcc.gov.uk

Contact: Moira Royland, Team Leader, Physical Disabilities

Rose House, St Albright's, London Road, Colchester, Essex, CO3 5NG

Tel: 01206 768812

Fax: 01206 761776

Social services for deaf people in Essex are provided by local offices. Details of the location of services are available from Basildon Office or County Hall. The following services are available from local offices: social work services to children and adults, equipment, interpreter support, lipspeaking, services for deafblind people, specialist services for deaf people from ethnic minorities, residential, hostel and other accommodation and rehabilitation servcies. Information is also available on deaf clubs and groups for and of deaf and hard of hearing people, holiday groups, drop-in groups and youth facilities. Services are also provided under an agency agreement by The Royal Association in Aid of Deaf People (RAD). Contact: Sylvia Heys, Team Director (Tel: 01245 28377; Textphone: 01245 350333) The following services are available from RAD: social work, equipment, interpreter support, day care and services for deafblind people. RAD is also a centre for deaf clubs.

Harlow Social Services

Willowfield House, Tendring Road, Harlow, Essex, CM18 6SE

Tel: 01279 43464/ Sensory Impairment Team: 01268 643333

Havering Social Services

Whitworth Centre, Noak Hill Road, Noak Hill, Romford, Essex, RM3 7YA

Tel: 01708 772222

Fax: 01708 772935

Contact: Elizabeth Cannon, Social Worker with Deaf People

The following services are available directly: social work, equipment, services for deafblind people, and an advice service for deaf people. At the present time five members of staff at the centre have basic signing skills and three are currently undertaking advanced training.

15

Redbridge Social Services

Community Care Advice Centre, Aldborough Road North, Newbury Park, Ilford, Essex, IG2 7SR

Tel: 020 8503 8833

Fax: 020 8503 8198

Contact: Roger Hampson, Corporate Director and Director of Social Services

             Town Hall, High Road, Ilford, Essex, IG1 1DD

Tel: 020 8478 3020

Fax: 020 8478 9149

The following services are available from the Personal Services Department: assessment and provision of equipment, interpreter support, information and advice. Social work services opening hours: 9am to 1pm. Telephone: 9am to 1pm, and 2 to 4pm.

➢ Gillingham and Rochester
See Kent

➢ Gloucestershire
Gloucestershire Social Services

Shire Hall, Gloucester, GL1 2TR

Tel: 01452 425102

Fax: 01452 425149

Contact: Laurence Kitchener, Social Services Department

             Edinburgh House, Coronation Square, Cheltenham, Gloucestershire, GL51 7SA

Services in Gloucestershire are provided under an agency agreement by Gloucester Deaf Association. They provide the following: general social work services, equipment, communication support services, services for deafblind people, residential, hostel and other accomodation, mother and toddler group, social club and luncheon club. The Association will be adding specialist services for deaf people from ethnic minorities to their services.

Homecare Service Social Services

Stroud Health Centre, Beeches Green, Stroud, Gloucestershire, GL5 4BH

Tel: 01453 751691

Contact: F Fanstone

Tel: 01453 751691 ext 352

➢ Halton
See Cheshire

➢ Hampshire
Hampshire Social Services

Trafalgar House, The Castle, Winchester, Hampshire, SO23 8UQ

Tel: 01962 841841

Textphone: 01962 868639

Videotel: 01962 849554

Fax: 01962 847159

Website: www.hants.gov.uk

Contact: Roz Godfrey, Commissioning Officer, Deaf Services

Tel: 01962 847268

Textphone: 01962 877529

Fax: 01962 877681

E-mail: sssdrg@hants.gov.uk

Hampshire social services provide general social work services, equipment, services for deafblind people and community work. Communication support is provided by an independent agency.

Portsmouth Social Services

Sensory Impairment Team, Brankesmere, Queens Crescent, Portsmouth, Hampshire, PO5 3HS

Tel: 023 9277 6833

Videotel: 023 9287 5385

Contact: Ian Hiscox, Social Worker, Sensory Impairment Team

Tel: 023 9275 6321

Southampton Social Services

Archers House, 1a Archers Road, Southampton, Hampshire, SO15 2LQ

Tel: 023 8033 2861

Textphone: 023 8022 3887

Videotel: 023 8063 2083

Fax: 023 8033 8599

Contact: Jenny Tamblyn, Team Leader, Sensory Impairment

Tel: 023 8022 3855

Winchester Social Services

Corinium House, 10-14 Andover Road, Winchester, Hampshire, SO23 7BX

Tel: 01962 869313

Textphone: 01962 878209

Contact: Debbie Smith, Social Worker,
            Deafened and Hard of Hearing People

➢ Hartlepool
See Cleveland

➢ Herefordshire
Herefordshire Social Services

Garrick House, Widemarsh Street, Hereford, HR4 9EU

Tel: 01432 260000

Textphone: 01905 723351

The following services are available directly or by referral from the area specialists: social work support, equipment, lipspeaking, interpreting services for deafblind people, residential and hostel accomodation.

➢ Hertfordshire
Hertfordshire Social Services

The Woodside Centre, The Commons, Welwyn Garden City, Hertfordshire, AL7 4SE

Tel: 01707 323336

Textphone: 01707 323336

Fax: 01707 391246

E-mail: brenda.tipping@hertscc.gov.uk

Contact: Brenda Tipping, Service Manager
            Sensory Disability Team

➢ Hull
See North Humberside

➢ Isle of Man
Isle of Man Social Services

Hillary House, Prospect Hill, Douglas, Isle of Man, IM1 1EQ

Tel: 01624 686179

Fax: 01624 686198

Contact: Kath Parkinson, Disabilities Service
            Manager

Tel: 01624 686204

Isle of Man Social Services can offer the following: general social work services, equipment, services for deafblind people, rehabilitation services, and a disablement rehabilitation advisory service.

➢ Isle of Wight
Isle of Wight Social Services

The Neighbourhood Office, J S White's Building, Medina Road, Cowes, Isle of Wight, PO31 7BX

Tel: 01983 291144

Textphone: 01983 291144

Fax: 01983 281278

Contact: Roger Purton, Coordinator of Services,
            Deaf and Deafblind People

Fax: 01983 408488

The directorate offers high quality provision of specialised social work; environmental equipment assessment and issuing service, jointly run by social services and RNID; the Sound Advice Project, BSL and deafblind interpreting service (including an emergency service); deafblind and deaf awareness training, support to local hard of hearing clubs.

➢ Isles of Scilly
Isles of Scilly Social Services

Social Services Department, Town Hall, St Mary's, Isles of Scilly, TR21 0LW

Tel: 01720 422148

Full range of statutory services plus residential care.

➤ Kent

Bexley Social Services

Civic Offices, The Broadway, Bexleyheath, Kent, DA6 7LB

Tel: 020 8303 7777

Fax: 020 8301 4937

Bexley can offer the following: general social work services, equipment, communication support services, services for deafblind people, residential services, other accommodation, specialist services for deaf people from ethnic minorities, rehabilitation services and a wide range of other services. This includes access to clubs, deaf awareness courses, assisting in the statementing of children, assisting school leavers, helping clients with Disability Living Allowance applications and appeals, liaising with other professionals working with clients and facilitating the registration process of deaf and hard of hearing people. It also includes making assessments of deaf people in their own homes, and gives information about environmental equipment such as vibrating clocks, smoke alarms and door bells.

Bromley Social Services

Stockwell Building, Bromley Civic Centre, Stockwell Close, Bromley, Kent, BR1 3UH

Tel: 020 8313 4071

Textphone: 020 8313 4057

Fax: 020 8313 4620

A care management service is provided by a specialist care manager for deaf and deafblind adults living in the borough. Assessments can lead to issue of equipment and freedom travel permits. Hard of hearing people should approach area offices. Children are seen by a specialist social worker for deaf children.

Dover Social Services

Cairn Ryan, 101-103 London Road, Temple Ewell, Dover, Kent, CT16 3AA

Tel: 01304 828506

Textphone: 01304 827862

Fax: 01304 828504

Contact: Ann McMillan, Senior Practitioner, Deaf Services Bureau

Provides a full range of social work, support work and equipment services to deaf and hearing impaired people of all ages. It provides information and arranges access to interpreting services to ensure deaf people have access to a range of services and organisations. It aims to encourage and facilitate comments and feedback from service users.

Medway Social Services

Compass Centre, Pembroke Chatham Maritime, Chatham, Kent, ME4 4YH

Tel: 01634 881293

Textphone: 01634 881251

Fax: 01634 881200

Contact: Lynn Stow, Social Worker with Deaf People

A team of specialist workers provides services for deaf people and their families which include social work assessment, advice and information and the provision of equipment to enable independence. There are also services for deafblind people. Services for deafened people over 65 are currently provided under agency agreement by: Hi Kent, 18 Brewer Street, Maidstone, Kent. Contact: 01622 691151 (Voice/Text)

Sittingbourne Social Services

Avenue of Remembrance, Sittingbourne, Kent, ME10 4DD

Tel: 01795 473333

Textphone: 01795 437255

Fax: 01795 437256

Contact: Alison Horan, Sensory Disabilities Manager

Invicta House, County Hall, Maidstone, Kent, ME14 1XX

Tel: 01622 221826

Textphone: 01622 221826

The Deaf Services Bureau provides social work and support work to deaf people and their families in Kent. They also provide environmental equipment to people aged under 65. There are two teams based at Sittingbourne and Dover. All staff are skilled in sign language.

➤ Lancashire

Blackburn with Darwen Social Services

Jubilee Street, Blackburn, Lancashire, BB1 1ET

Tel:	01254 583328
Textphone:	01254 587412
Fax:	01254 587770
E-mail:	social.service@blackburn. gov.uk
Website:	www.blackburn.gov.uk
Contact:	Karen Riley, Social Worker with Deaf People

Blackburn with Darwen Social Services Department provides a variety of services for deaf people, either in their own homes or in the local community. Our department employs workers with specialist knowledge and training to offer help, advice and counselling on personal and practical matters.

Blackpool Social Services

South King Street, Blackpool, Lancashire, FY1 4TR

Tel:	01253 477666
Textphone:	01253 752384
Contact:	Sarah O'Bass, Social Worker with Deaf People

The North Zone starts in the North at Silverdale and carries on down the coast to Lytham sharing an inland boundary with the Preston area. 01524 585525 (Textphone) Lancaster. 01253 742132 (Textphone, Interpreters for deaf people).

Bolton Social Services

Le Mans Crescent, Civic Centre, Bolton, Lancashire, BL1 1SE

Tel:	01204 522311
Fax:	01204 365953
Contact:	Cath King, Principal Officer

Information, advice, and the provision of equipment are services provided by Bolton Deaf Society. Contact: Mrs Gillian Gregory. A social work service is provided by Social Services as appropriate via District Teams Duty Officer: North East District, Nessford House, Bolton, BL2 2LL. Contact: 01204 397888/ 365966 (Voice/Textphone); South East District, Great Lever Health and Social Services Centre, Rupert Street, Bolton, BL3 6RN. Contact: 01204 398000/365964 (Voice/Textphone); West District, Horwich Public Hall, Lee Lane, Horwich, Bolton, BL6 7AQ. Contact: 01204 695355/ 668172 (Voice/Textphone). Provision of interpreters, lipspeakers and sign language communication services are also available from the RNID North Communication Support Unit, funded by the 10

local authorities of Greater Manchester in partnership with the RNID.

Bury Social Services

Craig House, Bank Street, Bury, Lancashire, BL9 0BA

Tel:	0161 253 5000
Fax:	0161 253 5494

Bury Social Services provides a comprehensive and borough-wide service to all disabled people in Bury. The purpose is to ensure disabled people have access to community provisions to enable them to have more independence in their own home.

City of Salford Social Services

White Moss House, Bracken Avenue, Walkden, Manchester, Lancashire, M28 3SS

Tel:	0161 799 0888
Textphone:	0161 790 4402
Fax:	0161 799 1555
Contact:	Barrie Morecroft, Social Worker with Deaf People, Sensory Disability Team

The following services are available directly or by referral from the Sensory Impairment Section: social work, equipment and services for deafblind people. Provision of interpreter support, lipspeaking services are available from the RNID North Communication Support Unit.

Lancashire Social Services

Adult Services, Chaddesley House, Manchester Road, Burnley, Lancashire, BB11 1HW

Tel:	01772 264388
Fax:	01772 264425
Contact:	Karina McCooey, Adult Service, East Zone

Lancashire can provide the following services: general social services, equipment, communication support services and rehabilitation services.

Manchester Social Services

Gorton North Neighbourhood Office, 27 Garratt Way, Manchester, Lancashire, M18 8HE

Tel:	0161 223 1058
Textphone:	0161 230 8183
Contact:	Ian Salt, Team Manager, Physical Disabilities, Sensory Services Team

Social services in Manchester are provided jointly with St Joseph's Mission to Deaf People,

Hennessey House, Sudell Street, Collyhurst, Manchester M4. Tel: 0161 834 5888. The following services are provided: general social work services, equipment and sign language interpreting services.

Oldham Social Services

Oldham Social Services Department, Civic Centre, West Street, Oldham, Lancashire, OL1 1UW

Tel: 0161 911 4800

Textphone: 0161 911 4803

Fax: 0161 911 3803

Contact: Barbara Christopher, Team Manager, Physical and Sensory Disability Service

Sensory and Physical Disability Team, Metropolitan House, Hobson Street, Oldham, Lancashire, OL1 1UY

Fax: 020 8911 3803

Oldham can provide the following: general social work service, equipment, communication support services (via contract with RNID Communication Support Unit, Manchester), services for deaf and hard of hearing people. Duty times: Monday afternoon, Wednesday morning, Friday afternoon and usually the last Friday of each month at Oldham Deaf Society, Park Road, Oldham, from 8 to 9.30pm.

Preston Social Services

166 Tulketh Road, Ashton-on-Ribble, Preston, Lancashire, PR2 1ER

Tel: 01772 724431

Textphone: 01772 722515

Contact: Val Wilson, Senior Social Worker

Tel: 01772 724431 ext 243

Rochdale Social Services

Peine House, Hind Hill Street, Heywood, Lancashire, OL10 1JZ

Tel: 01706 867355

Textphone: 01706 867357

Fax: 01706 867393

Contact: Heather Pilling, Team Manager, Sensory Impairment Team

Rochdale can provide the following: general social work services, equipment, sign language interpreting services and residential services.

Wigan Social Services

Civic Centre, Millgate, Wigan, Lancashire, WN1 1AZ

Tel: 01942 244991

Fax: 01942 827796

Contact: Louise Leeming, Social Worker with Deaf People

Disability Resource Centre, Hamilton Square, Newtown, Wigan, Lancashire, WN5 9RX

Tel: 01942 700889

Textphone: 01942 768330

Fax: 01942 766768

Wigan can provide the following: general social work services, equipment, communication support services, services for deafblind people, residential services and hostel accommodation, specialist services for deaf people from ethnic minorities and rehabilitation services.

➤ Leicester
See Leicestershire

➤ Leicestershire
Leicestershire Social Services

County Hall, Glenfield, Leicester, LE3 8RL

Tel: 0116 232 3232

Fax: 0116 265 7440

Leicestershire can provide the following: general social work services, equipment, sign language interpreter services, services for deafblind people, residential services, specialist services for deaf people from ethnic minorities and rehabilitation services. Most of these are supplied under agreement by the Leicester Centre for Deaf People. Services for deafblind people are provided by the Society for the Blind, Leicester.

➤ Lincolnshire
Lincolnshire Deaf Services

Annex A Council Offices, Eastgate, Sleaford, Lincolnshire, NG34 7EB

Tel: 01522 527141

Textphone: 01507 525515 (answerphone)

Fax: 01522 525515

Lincolnshire Deaf Services works to support access to all services in the community and also provides equipment, community interpreting services, support for children and families, community work and CACDP deaf awareness training packages.

➢ London

Barnet Social Services

Barnet House, 1255 High Road, London, N20 0EJ
Tel: 020 8359 2000
Textphone: 020 8359 3678

Community care assessments to ensure independence in the community. Assessment for environmental equipment and adaptations for deaf and hard of hearing people.

Camden Social Services

79 Camden Road, London, NW1 9ES
Tel: 020 7413 6679
Textphone: 020 7413 6716
Videotel: 020 7267 5667
Fax: 020 7413 6089
Contact: Peter Wright, Social Worker with Deaf People
             Sensory Impairment Team, Stag House, Burnt Oak Broadway, Edgware, Middlesex, HA8 0BU
Tel: 020 8359 3669
Textphone: 020 8359 3623

The Service to Deaf and Hard of Hearing adults is within the Sensory Needs Service. This includes a social work service and equipment provisions. Duty worker available on Tuesday and Wednesday between 9.30am to 12.30pm.

Corporation of London Social Services

Milton Court, Moor Lane, London, EC2Y 9BL
Tel: 020 7332 1213
Fax: 020 7588 9173
Contact: Heather Collins, Senior Occupational Therapist
Tel: 020 7332 3689

The Corporation of London social services department provides services for people who live within the City of London (including homeless people). The department serves a small population (approximately 7000) and so does not have a specialist section for hearing impaired. People with hearing problems are assessed by the occupational therapy team and receive a full community care assessment and rehabilitation if necessary.

Ealing Social Services

Perceval House, 14-16 Uxbridge Road, London, W5 2HL
Tel: 020 8579 2424
Fax: 020 8579 5224
Contact: Phaik Choo, Team Leader, Services for People with a Disability

Greenwich Social Services

Community Sensory Services Team, Nelson House, 50 Wellington Street, Woolwich, London, SE18 6PY
Tel: 020 8854 8888
Textphone: 020 8316 6654
Fax: 020 8855 1102
Contact: John Fox, Senior Practitioner, Community Sensory Services Team

The Community Sensory Services Team aims to meet the social care needs of deaf and hard of hearing residents of the London Borough of Greenwich. Among a range of services, it provides care management, equipment and duty services. It is able to offer specialist advice and information. It also has a community sign language interpreting service. It is based at the above address and can be contacted on 020-8312 7825 (voice); 020-8312 7909 (text); 020-8855 1102 (fax).

Hackney Social Services

7 Marcon Place, London, E8 1LP
Tel: 020 8356 4283
Textphone: 020 7241 5099
Fax: 020 8356 4309
Contact: William Thornton, Head of Sensory Disability and Deaf Team

Hackney provides social work services, equipment, communication support services, services for deafblind people, residential, hostel and other accommodation, services for deaf people from ethnic minority groups and rehabilitation services.

Hammersmith and Fulham Social Services

145 King Street, London, W6 9XY
Tel: 020 8748 3020
Textphone: 020 8576 5190
Fax: 020 8576 5049
Contact: Alan Tyrer, Divisional Manager, Social Services

Hammersmith reorganised its social services provision in 1996 to provide four specialist offices for adults and children in the north and south of the borough. Details of the nearest office can be obtained from King Street. Out of hours, there is an emergency duty team on call between 5pm and 8.45am, and all day at the weekends. The team covers the whole of the borough and deals with emergencies only. The number for the emergency duty team is 020 8748 8588. Hammersmith provides general social work services, equipment, communication support services, services for deafblind people, residential accommodation, hostel and other accommodation, specialist services for deaf people from ethnic minorities and rehabilitation services.

Haringey Social Services

Civic Centre, 40 Cumberland Road, Wood Green, London, N22 4SG

Tel:	020 8975 9700
Fax:	020 8849 5915
Contact:	S Philippou, Advice and Assessments Officer
Tel:	020 8975 9700 ext 3379

Haringey provides the following services: general social work, equipment, communication support services, services for deafblind people, residential services, hostel and other accomodation and specialist services for people from ethnic minorities.

Islington Social Services

166 Upper Street, Islington, London, N1 1RE

Tel:	020 7477 3394
Textphone:	020 7477 3282
Fax:	020 7477 3279
Contact:	Ricardo Munroe, Social Worker with Deaf People

The following services are available from the special services team: social work, equipment, services for deafblind people. Sign language interpreting is provided for all the services which the council provides.

Kensington and Chelsea Social Services

Room G7, Town Hall, Hornton Street, London, W8 7NX

Tel:	020 7937 5464
Fax:	020 7938 1445
Contact:	Scott Sanders, Social Worker with Deaf People
Tel:	020 7361 2483
Textphone:	020 7937 7232

Kensington and Chelsea offer the following: general social work services, equipment, communication support services, services for deafblind people, residential services, hostel and other accommodation, specialist services for deaf people from ethnic minorities and rehabilitation services.

Lambeth Social Services

Mary Seacole House, 91 Clapham High Street, London, SW4 7TF

Tel:	020 7926 4788
Textphone:	020 7978 2811
Contact:	Jim Heron, Manager, Sensory Impairment Team

The team provides a service to deaf sign language users, the hard of hearing and deafened people. Full community care assessments will be undertaken and services provided to match people's needs in accordance with available resources. A technical officer will assess needs for specialist equipment required to facilitate clients' independence.

Lewisham Social Services

Duke House, 84-86 Rushey Green, London, SE6 4HW

Tel:	020 8695 6000
Fax:	020 8314 3089
Contact:	Desmond Hodgson, Senior Social Worker, Sensory Services Unit
Tel:	020 8314 7777
Textphone:	020 8314 3309

Lewisham provides a social work service for deaf people, technical assessment for environmental equipment, a service for deafblind people and an interpreting service for service users.

Newham Social Services

Gable House, 27a Romford Road, London, E15 4LL

Tel:	020 8534 4545
Textphone:	020 8557 8940
Fax:	020 8536 1674

We are a team of social workers working with deaf children and adults and their families/carers. We provide a full social work service, information and advice, equipment, registration and a separate interpreting service.

Southwark Social Services

151 Walworth Road, London, SE17 1RY

Tel: 020 7525 2149

Contact: David Lake, Specialist Social Worker
            with the Profoundly Deaf

Social services for hard of hearing people and deaf people in Southwark are provided by local area offices. The following services are available: social work and equipment; interpreter support provided by agency agreement.

Tower Hamlets Social Services

Mulberry Place, 5 Clove Crescent, London, E14 2BG

Tel: 020 7364 5000

Contact: Mary McHugh, Social Worker with
            Deaf People

The following services are available from the specialist section: social work and provision of equipment.

Waltham Forest Social Services

Municipal Offices, High Road, Leyton, London, E10 5QJ

Tel: 020 8527 5544

Fax: 020 8558 7162

Contact: Mary Richardson, Director of Social
            Services

The following services are available from Hatch Lane: services to deaf people, deafened people and deafblind people, social work, etc.

Wandsworth Social Services

Lyon House, 104 Wandsworth High Street, London, SW18 4LA

Tel: 020 8871 8487

Textphone: 020 8871 8485

Fax: 020 8871 8485

Contact: Mary Mears, Team Manager
            Sensory Needs Team

Tel: 020 8871 7151

A social work service to people who are deaf - principally those who need to communicate through sign language. Provides specialist assessment in liaison with other sections of the department. Provides specialist equipment, a specialist service to deafblind people including guide communicator service, in partnership with the RNID. A British Sign Language and lipspeaker interpreting service.

Westminster Social Services

Roman House, 24 Greencoat Place, London, SW1P 1DX

Tel: 020 7641 3901

Contact: Lisa Redfern, Senior Care Manager
            Mortimer Street, London, W1N 8AA

Tel: 020 7641 3943

Westminster offer the following services: general social work services, equipment, communication support services, services for deafblind people, residential services and rehabilitation services.

➢ Luton
See Bedfordshire

➢ Merseyside
Knowsley Social Services

Municipal Buildings, Cherryfield Drive, Kirkby, Merseyside, L32 1TX

Tel: 0151 443 4431

Textphone: 0151 443 4431

Fax: 0151 443 4460

Contact: Geoff Walby, Social Worker with Deaf
            People, Disability Team

Knowsley can provide the following: general social work services, equipment, interpreter support and services for deafblind people.

Liverpool Social Services

Hatton Gardens, Liverpool, Merseyside, L3 2AW

Contact: Bill Moran, Senior Manager Adults,
            Community Services Division
            St Philomena's Old School Building,
            Long Lane, Walton, Liverpool,
            Merseyside, L9 6DN

Tel: 0151 523 8855

Fax: 0151 525 5754

Social Services in Liverpool are provided under agency agreement by the Merseyside Deaf Society (Tel: 0151 228 0888). The following services are provided: general social work services, equipment, communication support services and rehabilitation services.

Sefton Social Services

Merton House, Stanley Road, Bootle, Merseyside, L20 3DL

Tel: 0151 934 3760

Textphone: 0151 934 3791

Fax: 0151 934 3755

Contact: Christine Morton, Operational Manager, Physical Disability and Sensory Impairment Services

Sefton Social Services Department contracts most of its professional services for people with hearing impairments from Merseyside Society for Deaf People (MSDP), who provide social work services, communication support, rehabilitation and specialist services for deafblind people, in addition to the use of a social centre and training courses (deaf awareness/sign language) for staff and service users. The Social Services Department directly employs two sensory impairment assistants who work in partnership with MSDP to provide recommended equipment and support to Sefton residents.

St Helens Social Services

St Helens District Society for the Deaf, 32-40 Dentons Green Lane, St Helens, Merseyside, WA10 6BQ

Tel: 01744 23887

Contact: I E Forde, Social Worker with Deaf People

Social services for deaf people in St Helens are provided under an agency agreement by the St Helens and District Society for the Deaf. The following services are available from the society: general social work services, equipment and communication support services.

Wirral Social Services

63 Hamilton Square, Birkenhead, Merseyside, L41 5JF

Tel: 0151 647 7000

Contact: Catherine Briscoe, Director of Social Services

All social services for deaf people in the Wirral area are provided by the Merseyside Society for the Deaf. Details of the availability and location of services are available from the Centre. The Society is also a centre for the deaf club.

➢ Middlesbrough
See Cleveland

➢ Middlesex
Brent Social Services

Adult Disabilities, 36 London Road, Wembley, Middlesex, HA9 7SS

Tel: 020 8937 4300

Fax: 020 8937 4630

Contact: David Quinn, Social Worker with Deaf People, Sensory Impairment Team

Brent can provide the following general social work services: equipment, services for deafblind people, residential services, and hostel and other accommodation and rehabilitation services. It also produces a comprehensive pack of information for people who are deaf or hard of hearing.

Enfield Social Services

Swan Annexe, 221 High Street, Enfield, Middlesex, EN3 4DX

Tel: 020 8379 8098

Textphone: 020 8379 7592

Fax: 020 8379 8080

Contact: Barbara Baxter, Social Worker with Deaf People

To provide a broad range of services to people who are deaf and hard of hearing. Assessment and provision of specialist equipment, repairs to equipment, income maximisation, assessment of need of individuals and families, individual social work support/carework, provision of text answerphone, registration of deaf people and a weekly drop-in service for deaf people who use BSL.

Harrow Social Services

Youngmans 1 Building, Civic Centre, Station Road, Harrow, Middlesex, HA1 2UL

Tel: 020 8424 1694

Textphone: 020 8424 2902

Fax: 020 8427 7154

Contact: Julia Redican, Team Leader, Social Work Team for Deaf People

We provide a general social work service for deaf people who communicate in sign language and who live in the London Borough of Harrow. Support can be given to deaf adults, deaf children, deaf adults or children with additional needs, hearing people who live with deaf people or deaf people who live with hearing people. We start by assessing your needs. In the case of children, we work in partnership with parents and other carers. We have contact with education, health, teachers for the deaf, audiology and voluntary organisations. We may be able to provide information, advice and support, assessment for specialist equipment and adaptations to your own equipment, support for children and adults living in residential homes, consultation with staff in other departments who can provide advice and information on deaf issues.

Hillingdon Social Services

Civic Centre, Uxbridge, Middlesex, UB8 1UW

Tel: 01895 250959

Textphone: 01895 250960/ 250298

Fax: 01895 250215

Contact: Richard Cripps, Team Manager
People With Disabilities Team

Hillingdon offers assessment and care management, equipment, provision or commissioning of other services, support to community groups and clubs, communication with people who are deaf, hard of hearing, deafblind, deafened, commitment to equal opportunity and equality of access, and assistance with benefit claims.

Hounslow Social Services

41 New Heston Road, Hounslow, Middlesex, TW5 0LW

Tel: 020 8862 6789

Textphone: 020 8862 6789

Fax: 020 8862 6776

Contact: Alex Cranwell, Social Worker with Deaf
People

Textphone: 020 8862 5750

Hounslow can provide the following; general social work services, equipment, communication support services, services for deafblind people, and information on deaf issues.

Richmond Upon Thames Social Services

Fortescue House, Stanley Road, Twickenham, Middlesex, TW2 5PZ

Tel: 020 8894 5544

Textphone: 020 8893 4404

Fax: 020 8755 1064

Contact: Abigail Monkhouse, Social Worker
with Deaf People

Part-time social worker (BSL Stage II) working with hard of hearing, deaf and deafened people, provides assessments, advice and support for

people of all ages, their families and carers. Sign language interpreters can be provided (service under review). Provision of equipment for hard of hearing and deaf people.

➤ Milton Keynes
See Bedfordshire

➤ Newbury
See Berkshire

➤ Norfolk
Norfolk Social Services

30 Unthank Road, Norwich, Norfolk, NR2 2RB

Tel: 01603 622331

Textphone: 01603 760534

Fax: 01603 619711

Contact: Verity Gibson, Team Manager,
Sensory Support Team

The Sensory Support Team provides a county-wide service from social services for adults and children with sensory disabilities. For deaf people there is equipment from the technical officer and signed communication by the social workers with deaf people. There is a separate interpreter service run by a voluntary organisation. We also provide support to deafblind people.

➤ North Humberside
East Riding of Yorkshire Social Services

47-49 Manor Road, Scarborough Road, Driffield, North Humberside, YO25 5JE

Tel: 01377 255334

Textphone: 01377 255382

Fax: 01377 255348

Contact: Lyn Stanton, Social Worker with Deaf
People

Services for deaf people are provided on the basis of assessment of need. They include social work services for both children and adults, equipment, and services for deafblind people. Provision of equipment is assessed and provided by technical assistants. Referrals are made via customer service centres.

Hull Social Services

Aneurin Bevan Lodge, 140 Hotham Road North,
Bricknell Avenue, Hull, North Humberside, HU5 4RJ
Tel: 01482 848432
Textphone: 01482 848516

Contact: Lynne Hogben, Senior Practioner with
            Deaf People

Kingston upon Hull Social Services

Bellfield House, Middlesex Road, Hull, North
Humberside, HU8 0RB
Tel: 01482 714149
Textphone: 01482 714222
Fax: 01482 714180

We offer the following services either directly or
through referral from care management: social
work, assessment for and provision of
environmental equipment, and services for
deafblind people.

➢ North Lincolnshire

See South Humberside

➢ North West Somerset

See Avon

➢ North Yorkshire

North Yorkshire Social Services

Dunslow Road, Eastfield, Scarborough, North
Yorkshire, YO11 3UT
Tel: 01723 587021
Textphone: 01723 585417
Fax: 01723 587021

Contact: Les Arrowsmith, Special Services
            Officer for Deaf and Partially Hearing
            People
Textphone: 01723 587008

York Social Services

Customer Advice Centre, P O Box 402, George
Hudson Street, York, YO1 1ZE
Tel: 01904 554051
Textphone: 01904 554136
Fax: 01904 554055

Contact: Carl Roberts, Welfare Assistant for
            Deaf People

➢ Northamptonshire

Northamptonshire Social Services

Floor 2, Oxford House, West Villa Road,
Wellingborough, Northamptonshire, NN8 4JR
Tel: 01933 220727
Textphone: 01933 223551
Fax: 01933 441390

Contact: Roger Marston, Principal Social Worker

Northamptonshire can provide the following:
general social work services, equipment, services
for deafblind people, residential services and
rehabilitation services. Interpreting and similar
services are provided under contract by RNID.

➢ Northumberland

Northumberland Social Services

Compass House, Blyth District Office, 68 Bridge
Street, Blyth, Northumberland, NE24 2BA
Tel: 01670 354316
Textphone: 01670 533825
Fax: 01670 533892
Contact: John Allan, Commissioning Manager

➢ Nottinghamshire

Nottinghamshire Social Services

County House, Dale Close, 100 Chesterfield Road
South, Mansfield, Nottinghamshire, NG19 7AQ
Tel: 01623 452233
Textphone: 01623 452045
Fax: 01623 452033
Contact: Angela Milne, Team Manager, County
            Deaf Team

County-wide service to deaf people and their
families. Environmental equipment service,
support to parents of deaf children, access to
respite care, family centres, sitting service.
Transitional planning for deaf school leavers,
community care assessment. There is a sign
language interpreting unit, free to deaf people in
Nottinghamshire.

➢ Oxfordshire
Oxfordshire Social Services

The Deaf Centre, St Ebbe's, Oxford, OX1 1RL

Tel: 01865 240968

Textphone: 01865 246635

Fax: 01865 792381

Contact: Hilary Grime, Unit Manager

Oxfordshire works in partnership with clients, assessing needs and providing specialist services including equipment, advice, life skills training and access to services. There is an independent interpreter service.

➢ Peterborough
See Cambridgeshire

➢ Plymouth
See Devon

➢ Poole
See Dorset

➢ Portsmouth
See Hampshire

➢ Reading
See Berkshire

➢ Redcar and Cleveland
See Cleveland

➢ Rutland
See Leicestershire

➢ Shropshire
Shropshire Social Services

St Michael's House, St Michael's Street, Shrewsbury, Shropshire, SY1 2HG

Tel: 01742 255702

Textphone: 01743 255705

Contact: Frances Lythe, Team Manager, Sensory Impairment

Shropshire can provide the following: general social work services, equipment, communication support services and services for deafblind people.

➢ Slough
See Berkshire

➢ Somerset
North Somerset Social Services

Housing and Social Services, 7 Cleveden Walk, Nailsea, Somerset, BS48 1RS

Tel: 01275 851231

Fax: 01275 810163

Contact: Joan Shaw, Social Worker with Deaf People

Somerset Social Services

Halcon Centre, Huish Close, Hamilton Road, Taunton, Somerset, TA1 4DY

Tel: 01823 338781

Fax: 01823 325410

Website: www.somerset.gov.uk

Contact: Nyree Bevan, Head Manager, Sensory Loss Services

Somerset can provide the following: general social work services, equipment, communication support services, services for deafblind people, and residential and rehabilitation services following assessment.

➢ South Gloucestershire
See Avon

> ### South Humberside

North East Lincolnshire Social Services

William Molson Centre, Kent Street, Grimsby, South Humberside, DN32 7DJ

Tel: 01472 325222

Textphone: 01472 325234

Fax: 01472 325310

Contact: Janet Atkinson, Technical Officer with Deaf People, Rehabilitation and Occupational Therapy

Services available from North East Lincolnshire are: general social work provision, equipment, rehabilitation services and services for deafblind people. There is no specialist social worker with deaf people in North East Lincolnshire. Social work is carried out by generic social workers who use independent sign language interpreters.

North Lincolnshire Social Services

Monarch House, Arkwright Way, Queensway Industrial Estate, Scunthorpe, South Humberside, DN16 1AL

Tel: 01724 296414

Contact: Mike Poulton, Senior Practitioner, Physical Disability

Units 1/2 Ashley Estate, Exmoor Avenue, Skippingdale Industrial Estate, Scunthorpe, South Humberside, DN15 8NJ

Tel: 01724 280331

Textphone: 01724 279787

Fax: 01724 840564

The North Lincolnshire Social Services Disability Team aims to provide equipment, advice, information and rehabilitation services for deaf and hard of hearing people.

> ### South Yorkshire

Barnsley Social Services

Health, Home and Care Services, Moorland Avenue, Barnsley, South Yorkshire, S70 6PH

Tel: 01226 282025

Textphone: 01226 290043

Fax: 01226 730935

Contact: R Daley, Prinicipal Social Worker with Deaf People

Tel: 01226 299932

Barnsley can provide the following: general social work services, equipment, communication support services, services for deafblind people, residential services, hostel and other accommodation, specialist services for deaf people from ethnic minorities and rehabilitation services.

Doncaster Social Services

The Council House, P O Box 251, Doncaster, South Yorkshire, DN1 3DA

Tel: 01302 737784

Textphone: 01302 737784

Fax: 01302 737778

Contact: Sandra Conway, Care Manager, Sensory Team

Doncaster can provide general social work services and communication support services.

Rotherham Social Services

Crinoline House, Effingham Square, Rotherham, South Yorkshire, S65 1AW

Tel: 01709 382121

Textphone: 01709 822354

Fax: 01709 822325

Contact: Jill Jones, Care Manager, Sensory Disability Team

Rotherham can provide general social work services, equipment, communication support services (via agency agreement with the RNID), services for deafblind people, and residential and rehabilitation services. They also support Rotherham Deaf Advice Centre (managed by Rotherham Deaf Club Committee) and a Deaf Youth Club (in conjunction with the Youth Service).

Sheffield Social Services

Redvers House, Union Street, Sheffield, South Yorkshire, S1 2JQ

Tel: 0114 273 4977

Textphone: 0114 273 4977

Contact: Norman Creighton, Team Manager, Sensory Impairment

The following services are available: social work, equipment, services for deafblind people, and residential and rehabilitation services.

> ### Southampton
See Hampshire

> ### Southend
See Essex

➢ Staffordshire

Cannock Social Services
Ivy House, 202 Wolverhampton Road, Cannock, Staffordshire, WS11 1AT
Tel: 01543 510300
Videotel: 01543 503728

Codsall Social Services
Histons Hill, Codsall, Staffordshire, WV8 1AA
Tel: 01902 434000
Videotel: 01902 842119

Leek Social Services
County Buildings, Fountain Street, Leek, Staffordshire, ST13 6JR
Tel: 01538 483112
Videotel: 01538 371228

Lichfield Social Services
County Buildings, Lombard Court, Lichfield, Staffordshire, WS13 6DP
Tel: 01543 510800
Videotel: 01543 420715

Newcastle Social Services
The Holborn, Castle Hill Road, Newcastle Under Lyme, Staffordshire, ST5 2SX
Tel: 01782 296005
Videotel: 01782 710416

Staffordshire Social Services
Lombard Court, Lombard Street, Lichfield, Staffordshire, WS13 6DP
Tel: 01543 510800
Textphone: 01543 510849
Videotel: 01543 420715
Fax: 01543 510817
Contact: Eleanor Unwin, Assistant Team Manager, Sensory Impairment Team St Chads Place, Stafford, ST16 2LR

Staffordshire can provide the following: general social work services, equipment, sign language interpreting services and services for deafblind people. It can also provide details of lipreading classes available in Staffordshire. Video-conferencing equipment is available in various social services area offices throughout Staffordshire.

Stoke-on-Trent Social Services
Regent Centre, Regent Road, Hanley, Stoke-on-Trent, Staffordshire, ST1 3TD
Tel: 01782 235234
Contact: John Dennerly, Head of Sensory Impairment Team

Tamworth Social Services
21-22 Church Street, Tamworth, Staffordshire, B79 7BX
Tel: 01827 475506
Videotel: 01827 475506

➢ Stockton-on-Tees
See Cleveland

➢ Stoke-on-Trent
See Staffordshire

➢ Suffolk
Suffolk Social Services
49 Fonnereau Road, Ipswich, Suffolk, IP1 3JN
Tel: 01473 583545
Textphone: 01473 583560
Fax: 01473 583559
Contact: Mark Witcomb, County Team Manager, Services to Deaf People
Tel: 01473 288484
Textphone: 01473 216829

Suffolk can provide the following: general social work services, equipment, sign language interpreting services and services for deafblind people.

➢ Surrey
Carshalton Social Services
The Lodge, Honeywood Walk, Carshalton, Surrey, SM5 3PB
Tel: 020 8770 4799/ 8770 4337
Contact: Janet Decianti, Child and Family Services

Croydon Social Services

Taberner House, Park Lane, Croydon, Surrey, CR9 2BA

Tel:	020 8686 4433
Fax:	020 8681 6519
E-mail:	simon_wadsworth@croydon.gov.uk
Contact:	Simon Wadsworth, Team Manager, Sensory Impairment Team

The Sensory Impairment Team provide assessment, equipment, adaptations, social work and rehabilitation for profoundly deaf, hard of hearing, visually impaired and deafblind people.

Kingston-upon-Thames Social Services

Crescent Resource Centre, Cocks Crescent, off Blagdon Road, New Malden, Surrey, KT3 4TA

Tel:	020 8949 1955
Textphone:	020 8949 0573
Fax:	020 8949 6331
Contact:	Carol Barnshaw, Sensory Impairment Team Manager

The Sensory Impairment Team provides a service to people of all ages with a hearing loss, sight loss or dual sensory loss. Provision includes assessments for equipment, social work support, and assistance with welfare benefits. A duty officer is available Monday, Wednesday and Friday mornings.

Merton Social Services

Civic Centre, London Road, Morden, Surrey, SM4 5DX

Tel:	020 8543 4490
Textphone:	020 8543 3212
Fax:	020 8545 4555
Contact:	Jane Platts, Social Worker for Deaf and Hard of Hearing People
Tel:	020 8545 4490

Merton can provide the following: general social work services, equipment and services for deafblind people.

Reigate and Banstead Social Services

Noke Drive, Redhill, Surrey, RH1 4AX

Tel:	01737 778675
Fax:	01737 778676
Contact:	Kelly Hayes

Surrey Social Services

Rentwood Resource Centre, School Lane, Fetcham, Leatherhead, Surrey, KT22 9JX

Tel:	01372 376558
Textphone:	01372 376558
Videotel:	01372 363981
Fax:	01372 360224
Contact:	Chris Pyatt, Senior Practioner, Deaf Services Team

Textphone: 01372 362509

The following services are available from Surrey: general social work services, equipment, communication support services and rehabilitation services. All communication support is provided by the Surrey Interpreting Agency located at the same address. Chris Pyatt's textphone is also an out-of-hours answering machine.

Sutton Social Services

Civic Offices, St Nicholas Way, Sutton, Surrey, SM1 1EA

Tel:	020 8770 5000
Fax:	020 8770 5450

The following services are available directly or by referral: social work, equipment, interpreter support using freelancers, lipspeakers, services for deafblind people, residential services, and specialist services for deaf people from ethnic minorities. SHARP is a voluntary organisation set up by social, health and voluntary services to help people with their NHS hearing aids. They have a network of volunteers who will visit people in their own home, to help people who are having problems with their aid and show them how to keep it in good working order. For further details write to: SHARP, Freepost CN2417, Carshalton, Surrey SM5 3BZ or telephone: 020-8770 4860 (voice).

> ## Thamesdown
See Wiltshire

> ## Thurrock
See Essex

> ## Torbay
See Devon

> ## Tyne and Wear

Gateshead Social Services
Civic Buildings, Prince Consort Road, Gateshead, Tyne and Wear, NE8 4HJ

Tel: 0191 490 1616

Textphone: 0191 478 5981

Fax: 0191 477 8343

Contact: Angela Todd, Team Leader, Sensory Loss Team

The following services are available: general social work services, equipment, communication support services, services for deafblind people and residential services.

Newcastle upon Tyne Social Services
Shieldfield Centre, 4-8 Clarence Walk, Shieldfield, Newcastle Upon Tyne, Tyne and Wear, NE2 1AL

Tel: 0191 222 0377

Textphone: 0191 232 0722

Fax: 0191 222 0599

Contact: Pamela Satterthwaite, Team Manager, Sensory Support Team

Newcastle provides general social work services for adults, equipment and services for deafblind people. Duty social workers are available Monday and Thursday from 9.30am to 12 noon. The Technical officer for the hearing impaired is available on Tuesdays from 9.30am till 12 noon. The social worker for deaf children is part of social services children and families section, but based at Shieldfield Centre attached to the Sensory Support Unit.

North Tyneside Social Services
Care in the Community, 126 Great Lime Road, West Moor, Newcastle, Tyne and Wear, NE12 0RQ

Tel: 0191 200 8181

Textphone: 0191 200 8414

Fax: 0191 200 6079

Contact: Andy Weeks, Social Worker with Deaf People

North Tyneside's Sensory Support Team provides a wide range of services for people who are deaf, deafened, deafblind, hard of hearing, blind and partially sighted. Services include assessments of need and the provision of advice, information, equipment, communication support, rehabilitation, home care, day care, residential care and respite care.

South Tyneside Social Services
South Tyneside House, Westoe Road, South Shields, Tyne and Wear, NE33 2RL

Tel: 0191 427 1717

Textphone: 0191 456 5692

Fax: 0191 427 9704

Contact: Carol Taylor, Social Worker, Deaf Adults

South Tyneside can provide the following: general social work services, equipment, communication support services, services for deafblind people, residential services, hostel and other accommodation, specialist services for deaf people from ethnic minorities and rehabilitation services.

Sunderland Social Services
50 Fawcett Street, Sunderland, Tyne and Wear, SR1 1RF

Tel: 0191 553 7254

Fax: 0191 553 7208

Contact: Mike Gilchrist, Team Manager, Sensory Disability Team

Independent Living Centre, Dock Street, Monkwearmouth, Sunderland, Tyne and Wear, SR6 0EA

Tel: 0191 553 2905

Textphone: 0191 553 2902

Fax: 0191 553 2911

Sunderland can provide the following services: social work support, equipment, services for deafblind people and rehabilitation services.

> ## Warwickshire
Warwickshire Social Services
Hollybush House, Bond Gate, Nuneaton, Warwickshire, CV11 4AR

Tel: 01926 344406

Textphone: 01926 351166

Fax: 01926 327110

Contact: Albert Thomson, Team Manager, Services to Deaf People

Warwick House, Wheat Street, Nuneaton, Warwickshire, CV11 4AQ

Provision of general social work services, information and advice about regional and national resources, equipment and working with service users to improve services.

➤ West Midlands

Birmingham Social Services

Louise Ryland House, 44 Newhall Street,
Birmingham, West Midlands, B3 3PL

Tel: 0121 303 9944

Fax: 0121 303 2769

Contact: Eileen McCabe, Planning Officer,
Physical and Sensory Services

Tel: 0121 303 3546

Birmingham Social Services runs an NVQ assistance for BSL learning, and provides a wide range of services for deaf and hard of hearing people as well as as adult community services such as welfare benefits, advice and information. Provides grants for equipment servicing, also has a mobile service for home visits and social services to the community.

Coventry Social Services

Centre for Independent Living, Faseman Avenue, Tile Hill North, Coventry, West Midlands, CV4 9RB

Tel: 024 7669 4766

Textphone: 024 7669 4766

Fax: 024 7642 2583

Website: www.coventry.gov.uk

Coventry can provide the following services: social work support, equipment, communication support services and services for deafblind people.

Dudley Social Services

Queens Cross Centre, Wellington Road, Dudley, West Midlands, DY1 1RB

Tel: 01384 813462

Textphone: 01384 241411

Fax: 01384 813464

Contact: Janice Spiller, Social Worker, Deaf and Hearing Impaired People

Textphone: 01384 230025

Please note that both of the above telephone numbers are also 24-hour answering machines. The following services are available directly or by referral from Queens Cross Centre: social work, equipment, interpreter support, services for deafblind people, and people with additional disabilities, and rehabilitation services provided by agency agreement. We also have our own information room in the Hearing Impaired Unit, which displays a wide range of aids and adaptations available to hearing impaired people. Our aids will help you with the television, telephone, doorbell, etc. We also have a video library, and information to take away on all aspects of hearing impairment.

Sandwell Social Services

Resource Centre, Dagger Lane, West Bromwich, West Midlands, B71 4BB

Tel: 0121 525 5347

Contact: Lynn Taylor, Community Welfare Worker

Disability Living Centre, Stoney Lane, West Bromwich, West Midlands, B71 7FA

Tel: 0121 553 4343

Sandwell can provide the following: general social work services, equipment, and services for deafblind people.

Solihull Social Services

P O Box 32, Council House, Solihull, West Midlands, B91 3QY

Tel: 0121 704 6000

Contact: Steve Jones, Disability Development Worker

Physical Disability Team, Lowbrook Centre, Chichester Grove, Chelmsley Wood, Solihull, West Midlands, B37 5RZ

Tel: 0121 788 4464

All social services for deaf people in Solihull are provided under an agency agreement by the Birmingham Institute for the Deaf. Details of the availability and location of services are available from the Centre for the Deaf. The Institute is also a centre for a deaf club.

Walsall Social Services

Civic Centre, Darwall Street, Walsall, West Midlands, WS1 1RG

Tel: 01922 652700

Fax: 01922 646350

Contact: Jane Barnett, Team Manager

The following services are available directly or by referral: general social work services, equipment, interpreter support (including freelance), lipspeaking, rehabilitation, residential services (not specifically for deaf people) and services for deafblind people.

Wolverhampton Social Services

Neville Garrett Centre, Bell Street,
Wolverhampton, West Midlands, WV1 3PR

Tel:	01902 553666
Textphone:	01902 553677
Fax:	01902 556643
Contact:	Dorothy Jones, Principal Social Worker Sensory Disabilities Team

Social work advice and support for deaf and hard of hearing people (children and adults) and their families. Assessment for equipment for use within the home. Assessment for services through care in the community provisions. Maintaining registers of people who are hearing and/or visually impaired.

➤ West Sussex

West Sussex Social Services

County Hall, The Grange, Tower Street, Chichester, West Sussex, PO19 1QT

Tel:	01243 777100
Fax:	01243 777324
Contact:	Sue Wood, Principal Monitoring and Development Officer, Physical and Sensory Impairment

West Sussex Social Services Department have a county team of social workers and assistant social workers specialising in working with deaf people (children and adults). Where eligible, people will receive a comprehensive assessment which may lead to the provision of equipment and/or other services.

Worthing Social Services

15 Mill Road, WORTHING, West Sussex, BN11 4JY

Tel:	01903 708100
Contact:	Chris Webber

➤ West Yorkshire

Bradford Social Services

Bradford and District Association for Deaf People, 25 Hallifield Road, Bradford, West Yorkshire, BD1 3RP

Tel:	01274 729280
Textphone:	01274 722752
Fax:	01274 370482
E-mail:	deafbrad@aol.com
Contact:	Julie Ralph, Social Worker with Deaf People

Services in Bradford are provided under an agency agreement by Bradford and District Association for Deaf People. The Association can provide the following: general social work services, equipment, communication support services, and specialist services for deaf people from ethnic minorities.

Calderdale Social Services

Lawson Road, Brighouse, Halifax, West Yorkshire, HD6 1NY

Tel:	01484 710821
Fax:	01484 716790
Contact:	Vivien Travis, Social Worker with Deaf People

Calderdale can provide the following: general social work services, equipment, communication support services, services for deafblind people and rehabilitation services.

Huddersfield Social Services

Services for Deaf People, Kirklees Metropolitan Council, Dewsbury Day Centre, Town Hall Way, DEWSBURY, West Yorkshire, WF12 8EQ

Tel:	01924 324346
Textphone:	01924 324354
Fax:	01924 324350
Contact:	John Parker, Team Leader, Services for Deaf People

Kirklees Social Services

Dewesbury Day Centre, Town Hall Way, Dewesbury, West Yorkshire, WF12 8EQ

Tel:	01484 223033
Textphone:	01484 420926
Fax:	01484 223049
Website:	www.kirklees.gov.uk
Contact:	John Parker, Team Leader, Services For Deaf People
Tel:	01924 324346

Kirklees can provide the following: general social work, equipment, sign language interpreting services and specialist services for deaf people from ethnic minorities.

Leeds Social Services

Centenary House, North Street, Leeds, West Yorkshire, LS2 8AY

Tel: 0113 243 8328

Fax: 0113 243 3553

Contact: John Conway, Principal Social Worker

The following services are available from the Centre for Deaf People at Centenary House: social work support, equipment,communication support, lipreading, services for deafblind people and rehabilitation. The Centre is also a centre for deaf clubs.

Wakefield Community and Social Services

Highfield House, Love Lane, Castleford, West Yorkshire, WF10 5RT

Tel: 01977 723922

Textphone: 01977 723922

Fax: 01977 723924

Contact: Carol-Ann Churm, Social Worker with Deaf People

Wakefield provide general social work services, services for deafblind people and counselling and advice. Provision of equipment is handled by Wakefield City and District Society for the Deaf.

➢ Wiltshire

Swindon Social Services

Civic Offices, Euclid Street, Swindon, Wiltshire, SN1 2JH

Tel: 01793 463000

Textphone: 01793 466973

Fax: 01793 488978

Contact: John Wilson, Social Worker with Deaf People

Wiltshire Social Services

County Hall, Bythesea Road, Trowbridge, Wiltshire, BA14 8LE

Tel: 01225 713000

Textphone: 01225 713936

Fax: 01225 713983

Contact: Margaret Nightingale, Team Manager, Hearing and Vision Team

The House, Southfield, Victoria Road, Devizes, Wiltshire, SN10 1EY

Tel: 01380 72520

Wiltshire can provide the following: general social work services, equipment, communication support services, services for deafblind people, residential services, other accommodation and rehabilitation services.

➢ Windsor and Maidenhead
See Berkshire

➢ Wokingham
See Berkshire

➢ Worcestershire

Worcestershire Social Services

County Hall, Spetchley Road, Worcester, WR5 2NT

Tel: 01905 763763

Fax: 01905 763000

Contact: Seleshe Araya, Team Manager, Sensory Impairment

31 Ombersley Street, Droitwich, Worcestershire, WR9 8QY

Tel: 01905 772288

The following services are available directly or by referral from the area specialists: social work, equipment, lipspeaking, interpreting, services for deafblind people, and residential and hostel accommodation.

➢ Wrekin
See Shropshire

➢ York
See North Yorkshire

Northern Ireland

➢ County Antrim

Down and Lisburn Health and Social Services Trust HQ

Lisburn Health Centre, Linenhall Street, Lisburn, County Antrim, BT28 1BH

Tel: 028 9266 5181

Fax: 028 9266 5179

Down and Lisburn Health and Social Services Trust, Lisburn (EHSSB)

Magheralave Road, Lisburn, County Antrim, BT28 3BP

Tel: 028 9266 5646

Contact: Christine Houston, Social Worker with Deaf People

The following services are available: social work, equipment, interpreter support, lipspeaking, services for deafblind people, residential and hostel accommodation, rehabilitation services and deaf awareness training. Communication support is available from RNID Northern Ireland.

Eastern Health and Social Services Board (HQ)

Champion House, 12-22 Linenhall Street, Belfast, County Antrim, BT2 8BS

Tel: 028 9032 1313

Fax: 028 9023 3020

Contact: Anne McGlade, Project Development and Evaluation Officer for Deaf People

Tel: 028 9055 3974

Fax: 028 9055 3620

Home First Community Trust, Ballyclare (NHSSB)

The Beeches Resource Centre, 76 Avondale Drive, Ballyclare, County Antrim, BT39 9EB

Tel: 028 9334 9797

Textphone: 028 9334 9703

Fax: 028 9335 4024

Contact: Alma Weir, Team Leader, Sensory Impairment and Physical Disabilities

Home First Trust staff who work with deaf and hard of hearing people aim to promote their independence and equality within society. Services provided include assessment of individual needs, counselling, advice, emotional support, advocacy, environmental equipment, information, liaison with local voluntary groups and access to tinnuitus support group.

Home First Community Unit, Broughshane (NHSSB)

17 Raceview Road, Broughshane, County Antrim, BT42 4JL

Tel: 028 2586 2774

Textphone: 028 2586 2774

Contact: Ann Hutchinson, Social Worker with Deaf People

Services provided are as for Ballyclare entry above.

North and West Belfast Health and Social Services Trust (EHSSB)

Everton Complex, 585-587 Crumlin Road, Belfast, County Antrim, BT14 7GB

Tel: 028 9056 6000

Textphone: 028 9039 1892

Fax: 028 9056 6066

Contact: Esther McCorry, Senior Social Worker, Social Work Physical Health, Disability Programme of Care

The team provides a wide range of services to children, adults and elderly people in the community, who experience varying degrees of hearing loss. Services provided: environmental aids, home visiting services, support and counselling for individuals and families, group work, hard of hearing clubs, contact with voluntary and statutory organisations and education services and advice on benefits and interpreting services.

North and West Belfast Health and Social Services Trust HQ (EHSSB)

Glendinning House, 6 Murray Street, Belfast, County Antrim, BT1 6DP

Tel: 028 9032 7156

Northern Health and Social Services Board (HQ)

County Hall, 182 Galgorm Road, Ballymena, County Antrim, BT42 1QB

Tel: 028 2565 3333

Textphone: 028 2566 2618

Fax: 028 2566 2237

Contact: Mary Wilmont, Director of Social Services

As purchaser, the Board is required to find out the health and social care needs of its population and plan, secure and pay for those services. The Board secures care by arranging contracts or service agreements for services with providers both within and outside its geographical area.

South and East Belfast Health and Social Services Trust (EHSSB)

Beechbank House, 11 Derryvolgie Avenue, Belfast, County Antrim, BT9 6FL

Tel: 028 9068 1735
Textphone: 028 9068 1735
Fax: 028 9066 5488
Contact: Colin Wilmont, Manager, Sensory Impaired Services

The team at Beechbank House provides a full range of social work support to hearing impaired people, covering all of South and East Belfast. This includes assessment of need, registration, social work interaction, communication, rehabilitation, mental health services, counselling, advocacy, and specialist equipment.

➢ County Armagh
Craigavon and Banbridge Community Health and Social Services Trust (SHSSB)

Cherrytrees Resource Centre, 1a Edenderry Gardens, Portadown, County Armagh, BT63 5EA

Tel: 028 3839 4088
Textphone: 028 3839 4088
Fax: 028 3839 4095
Contact: Sadie Robinson, Senior Social Worker with Deaf People

The team for deaf and hard of hearing people will promote the health and well being of people with a hearing loss by ensuring that they can access the full range of the services provided by the Craigavon and Banbridge Community Health and Social Services Trust through the provision of specialist support consistent with the individual's choice.

Southern Health and Social Services Board

Tower Hill, Armagh, County Armagh BT61 9DR

Tel: 028 3741 0041
Fax: 028 3741 4550

➢ County Down
Down and Lisburn Health and Social Services Trust, Downpatrick (EHSSB)

Ardglass Road, Downpatrick, County Down, BT30 6LZ

Tel: 028 4461 6915
Textphone: 028 4461 6915
Fax: 028 4461 7101
Contact: Roslyn Dougherty, Sensory Impairment Services Manager

Newry and Mourne Health and Social Services Trust (SHSSB)

Conifers Resource Centre, Dromalane Road, Newry, County Down, BT35 8AP

Tel: 028 3025 0800
Textphone: 028 3025 0768
Fax: 028 3025 0768
Contact: Mavis Gorman, Social Worker with Deaf People

Ulster Community and Hospitals Trust (EHSSB)

Family Resource Centre, James Street, Newtownards, County Down, BT23 4EP

Tel: 028 9181 8518
Textphone: 028 9182 2682
Fax: 028 9182 2037
Contact: Marian Breen, Deputy Programme Head, Physical/Sensory Disability

The Sight and Hearing Team provides a specialist social and rehabilitation service to people with a hearing and/or sight loss. This includes carrying out a comprehensive assessment of an individual's social, emotional, technical and communication needs. We provide counselling, advice, and information on benefits, equipment, voluntary agencies and other relevant services.

➢ County Fermanagh
Sperrin Lakeland Health and Social Care Trust (WHSSB)

Sensory Unit, Drumcoo Centre, off Cornagrade Road, Enniskillen, County Fermanagh, BT74 6AY

Tel: 028 6632 4400
Textphone: 028 6632 4400
Fax: 028 6632 7197
Contact: Dan Blake, Social Worker with Deaf People

➢ County Londonderry
Causeway Trust (NHSSB)

Brookgreen Resource Centre, Brook Street, Coleraine, County Londonderry, BT52 1QG

Tel: 028 7035 5112
Textphone: 028 7035 5112
Contact: Geraldine Fleming

Foyle Health and Social Services Trust (WHSSB)

Sensory Support Service, 16 Bishop Street, Londonderry, BT48 6PW

Tel:	028 7137 4619
Textphone:	028 7137 4619
Videotel:	028 7126 1711
Fax:	028 7137 4810
Contact:	Arlene Green, Social Worker with Deaf People

Home First Community Trust, Magherafelt (NHSSB)

60 Hospital Road, Magherafelt, Londonderry, BT45 5EG

Tel:	028 7963 2703
Fax:	028 7963 4225
Contact:	Janet Scott, Senior Social Worker, Team for Physically and Sensory Disabled

Home First can provide the following: general social work services, equipment, rehabilitation services and group work with hearing impaired people.

➢ County Tyrone

Armagh and Dungannon Health and Social Services Trust (SHSSB)

Moy Resource Centre, Dungannon Street, Moy, Dungannon, County Tyrone, BT71 7SN

Tel:	028 8778 4832
Fax:	028 8778 4669
Contact:	Kate Courtenay, Senior Social Worker
	Moy Resource Centre, Dungannon Road, Moy, Dungannon, County Tyrone, BT71 7SN

Armagh and Dungannon can provide the following: general social work services, equipment, communication support services and services for deafblind people. Other services include clubs for deaf people, hard of hearing people and people with tinnitus.

Home First Community Trust, Cookstown (NHSSB)

52 Orritor Road, Cookstown, County Tyrone, BT80 8BJ

Tel:	028 8676 2762
Fax:	028 8676 1080
Contact:	Margaret Spence, Social Worker with Deaf People

Scotland

➢ Aberdeen, City of

Aberdeen Social Services

St Nicholas House, Broad Street, Aberdeen, AB10 1BY

Tel:	01224 522253
Fax:	01224 623156
Contact:	Helen McNeill, Manager, Disabilities, Social Work Section

➢ Argyll

Argyll and Bute Social Services

Billwood Road, Lochgilphead, Argyll, PA23 7QL

Tel:	01369 701066
Textphone:	01369 702988
Fax:	01369 707739
Contact:	Simon Leach, Social Worker with Deaf/Hearing Impaired People, Cowall Resource Centre, Dunoon

➢ Ayrshire

South Ayrshire Community Services

Burns House, Burns Statue Square, AYR, KA7 1UT

Tel:	01292 616261
Textphone:	01292 616642
Fax:	01292 616622
Contact:	Bernadette Marr, Senior Social Worker with Deaf People

➤ Borders
Scottish Borders Social Services
Old School House, Newtown Street, Boswells, Borders, TD6 0SA

Tel:	01835 824000
Fax:	01835 823366
Contact:	Myra Ward, Social Worker with Deaf and Hard of Hearing People
	Social Work Department, Borders General Hospital, Huntlyburn, Melrose, Borders, TD6 9BS
Tel:	01896 745333
Textphone:	01896 662272
Fax:	01896 662299

Social work, equipment and services for deafblind people are provided directly by social services. If residential services or accommodation are required, they can be purchased from outside the area. There is no agency agreement for sign language interpreters, but 'one-off' purchases can be made as required.

➤ Clackmannanshire
Clackmannanshire Social Services
Lime Tree House, Castle Street, Alloa, Clackmannanshire, FK10 1EX

Tel:	01294 450000
Fax:	01259 452400
Contact:	Kathleen Creegan, Social Worker with Deaf People
Tel:	01259 762520

➤ Dumbartonshire
West Dumbartonshire Social Services
Council Office, Garshake Road, Dumbarton, Dumbartonshire, G82 3PU

Tel:	01389 735730
Fax:	01389 737751
Contact:	T Huntingford, Director of Social Work and Housing
	Council Office, Garshake Road, Dumbarton, G82 3PU

➤ Dumfries and Galloway

Dumfries and Galloway Social Services
Sensory Support Services, 24 Catherine Street, Dumfries, DG1 1HZ

Tel:	01387 253927
Fax:	01387 253463
Contact:	Mike Miodonski, Social Worker for the Hearing Impaired

The following services are available: social work, equipment, interpreter support and services for deafblind people.

➤ Dundee, City of
Dundee Social Services
Tayside House, 28 Crichton Street, Dundee, Angus, DD1 3RN

Tel:	01382 434000
Contact:	David MacKenzie, Manager, Physical Disabilities

Services for deafblind people in the area are provided under a joint service agreement by Tayside Association for the Deaf, 36 Roseangle, Dundee, DD1 4LY. Contact: 01382 200025 (voice) and 227052 (text). Contact: Lynn Grant, Manager. Details can be obtained direct from the Association, which provides services to Dundee, Angus and Perth and Kinross councils.

➤ East Dumbartonshire
East Dumbartonshire Social Services
2-4 West High Street, Kirkintilloch, East Dumbartonshire, G66 1AD

Tel:	0141 578 2100
Textphone:	0141 578 2153
Fax:	0141 578 2106
Contact:	Alan Brown, Team Leader, Sensory Impairment

➤ East Lothian
East Lothian Social Services
6-8 Lodge Street, Haddington, East Lothian, EH41 3DX

Tel:	01620 826600
Fax:	01620 826202
Contact:	B Walker, Director of Social Work and Housing

Assessments are handled in Edinburgh by the Deaf Society. Contact: 0131 446 3128 (voice).

➢ Edinburgh, City of
Edinburgh Social Services

Shrubhill House, 7 Shrub Place, Edinburgh, EH1 1VQ

Tel: 0131 554 4301

Fax: 0131 554 5775

➢ Falkirk
Falkirk Social Services

Brockville, Hope Street, Falkirk, FK1 5RW

Tel: 01324 506400

Fax: 01324 506401

Contact: Karen Skilling, Head of Sensory Impairment

➢ Fife
Fife Social Services

Hearing Impaired Team, 12 Station Road, Leven, Fife, KY8 4QU

Tel: 01333 592218

Textphone: 01333 592409

Fax: 01333 592215

Contact: Vivienne Brown, Team Leader

Fife can provide the following: general social work services, equipment and services for deafblind people.

➢ Glasgow, City of
Glasgow Social Services

Centre for Sensory Impaired People, 17 Gullane Street, Glasgow, G11 6AH

Tel: 0141 334 5530

Textphone: 0141 337 6784

Fax: 0141 334 5530

Glasgow City Council can provide the following: general social work services, equipment, communication support services, services for deafblind people, residential services, hostel and other accommocation, and rehabilitation services. There is also a communicator guide service for deafblind people. In addition to specialised social work services within the city, there are sign language interpreter services across the west of Scotland and beyond if appropriate.

➢ Inverclyde
Inverclyde Social Services

Dalrymple House, 195 Dalrymple Street, Greenock, Inverclyde, PA15 1UN

Tel: 01475 786811

Fax: 01475 888083

Contact: D McQuade, Director of Social Services

➢ Isle of Lewis
Western Isles Social Services

Council Offices, Sandwick Road, Stornoway, Isle of Lewis, HS1 2BW

Tel: 01851 703773

Fax: 01851 705349

The following services are available: social work and provision of equipment.

➢ Midlothian
Midlothian Social Services

Social Work Unit, Fairfield House, 8 Lothian Road, Dalkeith, Midlothian, EH22 3ZH

Tel: 0131 271 3680

Fax: 0131 271 3624

E-mail: socialw@midlothian.gov.uk

Contact: Paul Mooney, Planning and Purchasing Officer, Community Care

Midlothian Council has a contractual agreement with Edinburgh and East of Scotland Deaf Society which acts as its agent. The Society provides a comprehensive range of social work services including information and advice, assessment for and the provision of specialist equipment and support, community activities, and residential care for deaf, deafened deafblind and hard of hearing people, their families and carers. Mary Dunlop, social worker, provides a fortnightly outreach service in Dalkeith, Midlothian.

➢ Morayshire
Moray Social Services

Hearing Impaired Team, Community Services Department, Springfield House, Edgar Road, Elgin, Morayshire, IV30 6FF

Tel: 01343 557000

Fax: 01343 546367

Contact: Val Swanson, Social Worker with Deaf People

Tel: 01343 551339 (Moray Resource Centre)

➤ North Ayrshire

North Ayrshire Social Services

17 Byers Road, Kilwinning, North Ayrshire, KA13 6JY

Tel: 01294 553925

Fax: 01294 550033

Contact: Beth Stevenson, Senior Social Worker with Deaf People

➤ North Lanarkshire

North Lanarkshire Social Services

Scott House, 73-77 Merry Street, Motherwell, North Lanarkshire, ML1 1JE

Tel: 01698 332011

Fax: 01689 332095

Contact: Jim Dickie, Director of Social Services

Fax: 01698 332095

➤ Orkney

Orkney Island Social Services

School Place, Kirkwall, Orkney, KW15 1NY

Tel: 01856 873535

Fax: 01856 876159

Contact: Helen Quelch, Rehabilitation Officer Sensory Impairment, Community Social Services

               10 Laing Street, Kirkwall, Orkney, KW15 1NW

Tel: 01856 871784

Textphone: 01856 885834

Fax: 01856 870090

Orkeny provides communication, interpreting, finger-spelling, and advice and information about equipment.

➤ Perthshire

Perth and Kinross Social Services

Rosslyn House, 32 Glasgow Road, Perth, PH2 0PD

Tel: 01738 476700

Fax: 01738 476710

Contact: B Bridgeford, Director of Social Work

➤ Renfrewshire

Renfrewshire Social Services

10-12 St James Street, Paisley, Renfrewshire, PA3 2HT

Tel: 0141 889 1634

Textphone: 0141 848 7232

Fax: 0141 842 1052

Contact: Lizann O'Hare, Senior Social Worker, Unit for the Deaf

➤ Ross-Shire

Highland Social Services

Slioch, Castle Street, Dingwall, Ross-Shire, IV15 9HU

Tel: 01349 865262

Textphone: 0345 023398

Fax: 01349 863456

Contact: John Gill, Manager, Deaf Services and Hearing Support Team

Fax: 01349 864438

Highland Social Services provides specialist assessment, advice, support and information where appropriate to people who are deaf, hard of hearing, deafblind and their families or carers.

➤ Shetland Islands

Shetland Social Services

92 St Olaf Street, Lerwick, Shetland Islands, ZE1 0ES

Tel: 01595 744405

Textphone: 01595 522739

Contact: John Wilson, Social Worker

Fax: 01595 744436

The following services are available from St Olaf Street: social work, equipment, lipspeaking services and limited services for deafblind people. Specialist services may be provided by contacting the Aberdeen and North East Society for the Deaf.

➤ South Lanarkshire

South Lanarkshire Social Services

154 Montrose Crescent, Hamilton, South Lanarkshire, ML3 6LL

Contact: Sandy Cameron, Director of Social Work

Tel: 01698 454444

➢ Stirlingshire
Stirling Social Services
Drummond House, Wellgreen Place, Stirling, FK8 2DY
Tel: 01786 471177
Contact: Anne Wright

➢ Tayside
Angus Social Services
County Buildings, Market Street, Forfar, Tayside, DD8 3WS
Tel: 01307 461460
Fax: 01307 473366
Contact: George Meechan, Senior Welfare Rights Officer, Disabilities

➢ West Lothian
West Lothian Social Services
Bathgate Social Work Centre, 69 Whitburn Road, Bathgate, West Lothian, EH48 1HE
Tel: 01506 776700
Fax: 01506 776735
Contact: Pamela Main, Manager, Community Care North Group

Wales

➢ Anglesey
See Gwynedd

➢ Blaenau Gwent
See Gwent

➢ Bridgend
See Mid Glamorgan

➢ Caerphilly
See Mid Glamorgan

➢ Cardiff
See South Glamorgan

➢ Carmarthenshire
See Dyfed

➢ Ceredigion
See Dyfed

➢ Clwyd
Denbighshire Social Services
Station Road, Ruthin, Clwyd, LL15 1EJ
Tel: 01824 703551
Textphone: 01824 704811
Videotel: 01824 704046
Fax: 01824 705662
Contact: Hugh Taylor, Social Worker with Deaf People

Denbighshire provides social work, advocacy, counselling, information, assessment for equipment and a resource centre (based in Rhyl).

Flintshire Social Services
Terrig House, Chester Street, Mold, Clwyd, CH7 1HB
Tel: 01352 701300
Textphone: 01352 754943
Videotel: 01352 758050/ 01352 754055
Fax: 01352 701499
Contact: Paul Harper, Social Worker with Deaf People

Flintshire can provide the following: general social work services, equipment, services for deafblind people. Videophone for Paul Harper is available on Wednesdays from 9.30 to 11.30am only, on 01352 758050, as he is often out of the office. Melanie Major (office based) is on 01352 745055.

Wrexham Social Services

Guildhall, P O Box 1284, Wrexham, Clwyd, LL11 1WF

Tel: 01987 292000

Fax: 01987 292106

Contact: Julie Roberts, Social Worker with Deaf People

            3-5 Grosvenor Street, Wrexham, Clwyd, CH7 1EJ

Tel: 01987 267234

Textphone: 01987 261173

Fax: 01987 290619

➢ Conwy

See Clwyd

➢ Denbighshire

See Clwyd

➢ Dyfed

Carmarthenshire Social Services

County Hall, Carmarthen, Dyfed, SA31 1UP

Tel: 01267 234567

Fax: 01267 230848

Contact: Sarah Hope, Social Worker with Deaf People, Adult Team

            Cambrian Place, Carmarthen, Dyfed, SA31 1QG

Tel: 01267 224414

Fax: 01267 223950

Carmarthenshire Social Services can provide the following: general social work, equipment, communication support services and services for deafblind people. Lipreading classes are provided by social services; sign language classes are out of county and provided by the Education Department.

Ceredigion Social Services

Carningli, Priory Street, Cardigan, Dyfed, SA43 1BT

Tel: 01239 614121

Fax: 01239 614708

Contact: Sian Davies, Social Worker with Deaf People

Textphone: 01239 615287

Ceredigion provides social work support and counselling to deaf and hard of hearing people and their families and provides an assessment of needs and services to people within their own homes. It offers assessment, demonstration and provision of specialised equipment and registration of deafness.

Pembrokeshire Social Services

Meadow Park Resource Centre, Stokes Avenue, Haverfordwest, Dyfed, SA61 2RB

Tel: 01437 764551

Fax: 01437 760703

Contact: Rose Barker, Disabilities Manager

Pembrokeshire can offer the following services: general social work services, provision of equipment, communication support services and services for deafblind people. Residential care is provided through an agency. Lipreading and sign language tuition is provided through an agency. There is also a voluntary support group network, a local National Deaf Children's Society group and a tinnitus support group.

➢ Flintshire

See Clywd

➢ Gwent

Blaenau Gwent Social Services

Municipal Offices, Civic Centre, Ebbw Vale, Gwent, NP3 6XB

Tel: 01495 350555

Textphone: 01495 322792

Fax: 01495 301255

Contact: Pat Hughes, Social Worker with Deaf People

            Civic Offices, Angel Street, Bridgend, Mid Glamorgan, CF31 1LX

Tel: 01495 322770

Fax: 01495 322790

Monmouthshire Social Services

County Hall Civic Centre, Croesyceiliog, Cwmbran, Torfaen, NP44 2XH

Tel: 01633 644644

Fax: 01633 644045

Contact: Julie Boothroyd, Community Care Team Manager

            Regent House, Regent Way, Chepstow, Monmouthshire, NP6 5BY

Tel: 01291 629436

Textphone: 01291 620311

Fax: 01291 628337

Monmouthshire can provide the following: general social work services, equipment, and rehabilitation services. Sign language interpreters, lipspeakers, services for deafblind people, and residential and other forms of accommodation services for deaf people are all provided by social services in conjunction with other agencies.

Newport Social Services
Civic Centre, Newport, Gwent, NP9 4UR

Tel:	01633 246571/ 246724
Fax:	01633 251727
Contact:	Steven Williams, Social Worker with Deaf People
Tel:	01633 244721 ext 5369

Torfaen Social Services
Civic Hall, Pontypool, Torfaen, NP4 6YB

Tel:	01495 762200
Fax:	01495 755513
Contact:	Helen Jackson, Social Worker with Deaf People
	Mill House, Coed Eva, Cwmbran, Gwent, NP44 7AE
Tel:	01633 648744
Fax:	01633 648797

➢ Gwynedd
Conwy Social Services
Builder Street, Llandudno, Gwynedd, LL30 1DA

Tel:	01492 574000
Fax:	01492 592116
Contact:	Sue Lonergan, Social Worker with Deaf People
	19 Rosemary Avenue, Colwyn Bay, Clwyd, LL29 7RA
Tel:	01492 533274
Textphone:	01492 535435
Fax:	01492 535569

Gwynedd Social Services
Council Offices, Shirehall Street, Caernarfon, Gwynedd, LL55 1BH

Tel:	01286 672255
Fax:	01286 673993
Contact:	Judith Easter, Social Worker with Deaf
Tel:	01286 677726

Services are provided under an agency agreement by North Wales Deaf Association, The Bungalow, Plas Tre Marl, Broad Street, Llandudno Junction Conwy LL31 9HL. Contact: 01492 580016

(Textphone) and 573998 (Voice and Fax). The contact is Mrs Jane Priestley who is the administrator. They can provide deaf awareness training, communication support and advice and information. Equipment is on display and there are clubs and lipreading classes. Services provided directly by Gwynedd are social work services, equipment and services for deafblind people.

Isle of Anglesey Social Services
Council Offices, Llangefni, Gwynedd, LL77 7TW

Tel:	01248 750057
Fax:	01248 750032
Contact:	Judith Easter, Social Worker with Deaf People
Tel:	01248 752771
Fax:	01248 750107

Services provided are as for Gwynedd, above.

➢ Merthyr Tydfil
See Mid Glamorgan

➢ Mid Glamorgan
Bridgend Social Services
Physical Disabilities Team 1, Brigend County Council, Sunnyside, Bridgend, Mid Glamorgan, CF31 4AR

Tel:	01656 642200
Fax:	01656 648689
Contact:	Jane Hewitt, Social Worker with Deaf People
Tel:	01656 643643
Textphone:	01656 642285

Bridgend provides individual assessment of needs to access rights, daily requirements and equipment for deaf and hard of hearing people.

Caerphilly Social Services
Social Services and Housing Directorate, Hawtin Park, Gellihas, Pontllanfraith, Blackwood, NP2 2PZ

Tel:	01443 864557
Textphone:	01443 864537
Fax:	01443 864523
Contact:	Jenny Beaton, Principal Advisor, Physical Disability and Sensory Impairment

Merthyr Tydfil Social Services

Civic Centre, Castle Street, Merthyr Tydfil, Mid
Glamorgan, CF47 8AN

Tel:	01685 725000
Fax:	01685 722146
Contact:	Bernardette Maynard, Social Worker with Deaf People
	Taff Fechan Buildings, Castle Street, Merthyr Tydfil, Mid Glamorgan, CF47 8UJ
Tel:	01685 383723
Textphone:	01685 387368
Fax:	01685 850526

Rhondda Cynon Taff Social Services

The Pavilions, Cambrian Industrial Park, Clydach
Vale, Tonypandy, Rhondda, Cynon,Taff, CF40 2XX

Tel:	01443 431513
Contact:	David Coombes, Social Worker with Deaf People
	District Office, Llewellyn Street, Aberdare, Mid Glamorgan, CF44 8HT
Tel:	01685 875481
Fax:	01685 881741

➢ Monmouthshire
See Gwent

➢ Neath Port Talbot
See West Glamorgan

➢ Newport
See Gwent

➢ Pembrokeshire
See Dyfed

➢ Powys

Powys Social Services

County Hall, Spa Road East, Llandrindod Wells,
Powys, LD1 5LG

Tel:	01597 826000
Fax:	01597 826210
E-mail:	sheilacl@powys.gov.uk
Contact:	Sheila Clarke, Senior Social Work Practitioner
	The Gwalia, Ithon Road, Llandrindod Wells, Powys, LD1 6AA
Tel:	01597 827102
Textphone:	01597 827115
Fax:	01597 827101

Powys can provide the following services for deaf
and hard of hearing people: assessment, general
social work services, specialist equipment, and
sign language interpreting.

➢ Rhondda, Cynon,Taff
See Mid Glamorgan

➢ South Glamorgan
Cardiff Social Services

County Hall, Atlantic Wharf, Cardiff, South
Glamorgan, CF1 5UW

Tel:	029 2087 2000
Fax:	029 2087 2597
Contact:	Maria Wilkinson, Social Worker with Deaf People
	34 The Parade, City Road, Roath, Cardiff, South Glamorgan, CF2 3AD
Tel:	029 2045 6525
Textphone:	029 2045 6525
Fax:	029 2045 5308

Basic provision to help and aid deaf and hard of
hearing people of the community.

Vale of Glamorgan Social Services

Civic Offices, Holton Road, Barry, Cardiff, South
Glamorgan, CF63 4RU

Tel:	01446 700111
Fax:	01446 745566
E-mail:	pr@valeofglamorgan.co.uk
Contact:	Susan Hockridge, Social Worker with Deaf People
	Vale Resources Centre, Hen Goleg, College Fields Close, Barry, South Glamorgan, CF6 6LF
Tel:	01446 730462
Fax:	01446 721980

44

➤ Swansea
See West Glamorgan

➤ Vale of Glamorgan, The
See South Glamorgan

➤ West Glamorgan
Neath Port Talbot Social Services

Area 2 Social Services, 8 Wind Street, Neath, West Glamorgan, SA11 3EH

Tel: 01639 765300

Textphone: 01639 765300

Fax: 01639 765321

Contact: Anthony Troy, Senior Social Work Practioner

Neath can provide the following: general social work services, equipment, communication support services, services for deafblind people, residential services, hostel and other accommodation and rehabilitation services.

Swansea Social Services

County Hall, Oystermouth Road, Swansea, West Glamorgan, SA1 3SN

Tel: 01792 63600

Fax: 01792 636700

Contact: Pam Bolam, Social Worker with Deaf People

Tel: 01792 636177

Mental Health

Specialist mental health services are an essential part of the services offered to deaf people. There are inherent dangers brought about by poor communication in the areas of diagnosis and treatment of deaf people. It is therefore important that they should receive help from professional people with sign language skills and in-depth knowledge of the psychological, sociological and psychiatric aspects of deafness.

Organisations are listed alphabetically by name.

Brent Adolescent Centre

Johnstone House, 51 Winchester Avenue, London, NW6 7TT

Tel: 020 7328 0918
Fax: 020 7328 0918
E-mail: msauma@easynet.co.uk
Contact: Maria Lancaster

Brent Adolescent Centre is a preventative mental health service for young people aged between 14 and 21. We offer consultations, assessment and confidential treatment to young people in distress or with more serious emotional problems. We also offer consultations, supervision and courses to professionals who deal with young people.

British Society for Mental Health and Deafness

High Trees, Springfield Hospital, 61 Glenburnie Road, London, SW17 7DJ

Tel: 020 8682 6925
Fax: 020 8682 6950
Contact: Peter Hindley, Secretary
Textphone: 020 8682 6950
Fax: 020 8682 6461

A multi-disciplinary team providing an outpatient and consultation service to deaf children and adolescents with emotional, behavioural and mental problems, and to their familes. We have agreement to open an inpatient unit for deaf children and adolescents in the year 2000. In the interim we have established an outreach service to support deaf children and adolescents who need admission to psychiatric inpatient units.

Buckinghamshire Association for Mental Health

Tindal Centre, Bierton Road, Aylesbury, Buckinghamshire, HP20 1HU

Tel: 01296 437328

European Network of Users and Ex-Users in Mental Health

P O Box 40066, 1009 BB Amsterdam, The Netherlands

Tel: 0031 20 694 1512

Falcon House Club House

Falcon House, 46 Oakmead Road, London, SW12 9SJ

Tel: 020 8673 9922
Textphone: 020 8673 9944
Fax: 020 8673 9955

Falcon House Club House is an active club with over one hundred members. For further details, contact Falcon House direct. Falcon House is part of Sign (The Anastasia Trust) providing services in mental health and deafness...and campaigning for more!

Horton Lane Health Centre

West Park, Horton Lane, Epsom, Surrey, KT19 8PB

Tel: 01372 202020
Contact: Christina Elliott, Head Speech and
              Language Therapist
Tel: 01737 202020 ext 3371
Fax: 01372 203103

Services are offered to people who are deaf and have learning difficulties or a mental illness.

National Centre for Mental Health and Deafness

John Denmark Unit, Mental Health Services, Bury New Road, Prestwich, Manchester, Lancashire, M25 3BL

Tel: 0161 772 3400
Textphone: 0161 772 3407
Fax: 0161 798 5853
Contact: Susan McAteer-Brown, Unit
              Administrator

The Centre has recently developed a counselling service run by and for deaf people. It is currently in the process of developing a business case to consider the viability of developing specialist forensic services for deaf people. More information will be provided when available. For further details, contact either Dr B Montiero or Sally Cook on 0161 772 3400.

National Deaf Mental Health Services

Queen Elizabeth Psychiatric Hospital, Mindelsohn Way, off Vincent Drive, Edgbaston, Birmingham, West Midlands, B15 2QZ

Tel:	0121 627 2930
Fax:	0121 697 8286
Contact:	Pauline Waldron, Administration Manager
Fax:	0121 627 2934

The service provides multi-disciplinary assessment, treatment and rehabilitation of patients aged over 16 and under 65. It offers advice and consultation to general psychiatric services and other services for deaf people in Britain. The 10-bedded unit is fully equipped with environmental living aids suitable for the needs of deaf people. All staff use British Sign Language. Psychiatric illness is treated by appropriate physical and/or psychotherapeutic regimes. A day-patient/inpatient activity programme is also offered. Community psychiatric nurses carry out substantial community support. At present, a number of outpatient clinics are provided at Denmark House, Addenbrooke Hospital in Cambridge, RNID Poolemead in Bath, RNID Court Grange in Devon and at Nottingham Social Services for the deaf. Referrals are taken from GPs and consultant psychiatrists together with other services such as social workers, probation services and educational establishments.

NI Association for Mental Health (Central Office)

80 University Street, Belfast, County Antrim, BT7 1HE

Tel:	028 9032 8474
Fax:	028 9023 4940
E-mail:	anne@niamh.co.uk
Contact:	Judith Lee, Information Manager

Pathfinder Mental Health Services NHS Trust - Deaf Child and Family Services

High Trees, Springfield Hospital, 61 Glenburnie Road, London, SW17 7DJ

Tel:	020 8682 6925
Fax:	020 8784 6461
Contact:	Karen Kitson

Pathfinder Mental Health Services NHS Trust - National Deaf Services

Old Church, 146a Bedford Hill, London, SW12 9HW

Tel:	020 8675 2100
Textphone:	020 8675 2200
Videotel:	020 8675 9707
Fax:	020 8675 2266
Contact:	Herbert Klein, Service Support Manager, Adult Team

People's Voices

66 Church Street, Chesham, Buckinghamshire, HP5 1HY

Tel:	01494 793143

Provides advocacy services to people with mental health problems.

RNID Richardson House

Billinge End Road, Blackburn, Lancashire, BB2 6PT

Tel:	01254 677119
Textphone:	01254 682942
Fax:	01254 696623
Contact:	John Arnold, Principal

Richardson House is a national high-quality rehabilitation and training centre for deaf people aged between 16 and 40 who have additional mental health or behavioural problems. It provides small group units with eight or nine residents sharing a lounge, dining room, kitchen and bathroom and having single bedrooms. In addition there are two self-contained houses and seven outreach flats. Altogether this comprises accommodation for 35 residents. Provision is made for deafblind people. Richardson House is based around four distinctive services. The aim is to develop daily living skills so that residents can reach their full potential, and eventually move to semi- or independent living in the community. Training courses include life skills, daily living skills, money management, personal skills, personal awareness, sex education, English, British Sign Language, maths and functional literacy, computers, art and craft, sewing and woodwork. Rehabilitation courses consist of group and individual-based programmes designed to develop and enhance independent living skills. Courses include such areas as cookery, health and hygiene, personal care and money management. There is also a professional counselling service. Holidays are arranged on a group and individual basis for all residents and respite care and assessment are also available.

SIGN

The Anastasia Society, 13 Station Road,
Beaconsfield, Buckinghamshire, HP9 1YP

Tel: 01494 816777
Textphone: 01494 816777
Fax: 01494 812555
Contact: Stephen Powell, Chief Executive

Sign is a national voluntary organisation offering a range of support to deaf people who have experienced mental health difficulties and who are striving to live independently. Its aim is to provide long-term supportive accommodation and continuing care in the community and to aid the move from institutionalised care to independent living. Projects are being developed nationwide. Referrals are usually via social services departments.

Speech and Language Therapists

Speech and language therapy is the process of enabling people to communicate to the best of their ability. Speech and language therapists assess the nature of the client's problems and provide treatment, advice and support. They also work closely with families, carers and members of other professions including doctors, physiotherapists and teachers.

Some speech and language therapists also work with people who have eating and swallowing difficulties as well as communication problems.

Most speech and language therapists work in NHS hospitals or clinics but some work in independent practice, in research or in schools.

This section is listed alphabetically by hospital within country and county sections.

England

➢ Avon

Blackberry Hill Hospital

The Speech and Hearing Department, Manor Road, Bristol, Avon, BS16 2EW

Tel: 0117 975 4834

Textphone: 0117 9753835 Frenchay Hospital

Fax: 0117 965 6061

Contact: Helen Merry, Hearing Therapist

Frenchay Hospital

Frenchay, Bristol, B16 1LE

Tel: 0117 975 3946

Fax: 0117 970 1070

Contact: Eileen Grist, Communication Aid Centre Manager

A resource centre for people who might benefit from using a communication aid, ranging from pointing charts to computer-based speech output devices. Provides opportunity for trial of a wide variety of the most up-to-date systems available. Objective advice given without obligation to any particular manufacturer.

Southmead Hospital

The Audiology Department, Westbury-on-Trym, Bristol, Avon, BS10 5NB

Tel: 0117 959 5680

Fax: 0117 959 5671

Contact: Dawn Webster, Coordinator

Tel: 0117 959 5161

A specialist speech and language therapy service is available for deaf children and adults. The following services are available for children from pre-school age to 18 and for adults: assessment and treatment, counselling and advice. A peripatetic service is available for schools; children are seen in groups and individually. All adults are seen individually. A service is provided for deafened children and adults. Two of the three therapists at Middlesex Hospital are part of the Cochlear Implant Research Team who will also take referrals.

➢ Berkshire

Prospect Park Hospital

Reading University, London Road, Reading, Berkshire, RG1 5BU

Tel: 0118 958 6161

Contact: Angela Hughes, Manager, Speech and Language Therapy Service

             Speech and Language Therapy Admin, Wokingham Hospital, Barkham Road, Wokingham, Berkshire, RG41 2RE

Tel: 0118 949 5092

Fax: 0118 949 5001

This service provides support for all children up to age 16 identified as having a degree of hearing impairment requiring amplification and where hearing loss is educationally or socially significant. An open referral system exists, and an initial appointment will take place within two months of the referral. Following assessment, the therapist will plan a programme of intervention to improve those communication skills identified in assessment. This will be discussed fully with family and professionals involved. The speech and language therapist's role may be advisory or direct in the form of regular therapy (individual or small group). Liaison with and training of other professionals is an essential part of team work. Advice and support to parents is available.

➤ **Bournemouth**
See Dorset

➤ **Brighton and Hove**
See East Sussex

➤ **Bristol, City of**
See Avon

➤ **Buckinghamshire**

Aylesbury Vale Healthcare NHS Trust

Cambridge Place House, Cambridge Place, Aylesbury, Buckinghamshire, HP20 2LQ

Tel: 01296 394388

Fax: 01296 485878

Contact: Elizabeth Eastburn, Therapy Services Manager

Assessment and treatment are available for pre-school children and a peripatetic service covers children in the local hearing impaired department. Children in mainstream schools or nursery provision are not covered by the service which cannot be developed further at this stage due to financial constraints.

➤ **Cambridgeshire**

Chesterton Hospital

Union Lane, Cambridge, CB4 1BT

Tel: 01223 216792

Fax: 01223 365645

Contact: Pamela Hinds, Speech Therapist

A specialist service is available for deaf children from pre-school age to 18. The following services are available: assessment and treatment and advice. A peripatetic service is available to schools. Work is done in groups and in individual sessions. A service is provided for deafened children.

Hinchingbrooke Healthcare Trust

Primrose Lane, Huntingdon, Cambridgeshire, PE18 6SE

Tel: 01480 415204

Fax: 01480 415212

Contact: Philippa Fenton, Speech and Language Therapist

A specialist speech therapy service is provided for deaf children from pre-school to 18. The following services are available: assessment, treatment, advice and peripatetic services to schools. All work is done on an individual basis. The following services are available for deaf adults: assessment, treatment and advice. Work is done in group and individual sessions. A service is also provided for deafened children and adults. The department is awaiting news regarding the Trust's disinvestment plans. This is likely to result in cuts to the service affecting all areas of the work. The therapists do not know what the speech and language therapy service will be able to offer in the future.

Janet O'Keefe Speech and Language Therapy Services

The Warren, 82 Cannon Street, Little Downham, Ely, Cambridgeshire, CB6 2SS

Tel: 01353 698156

Fax: 01353 698156

Contact: Janet O'Keefe

Assessments and therapy can be arranged within two weeks of initial contact. Charges are set at the level recommended by the Association of Speech and Language Therapists in Independent Practice and the Royal College of Speech and Language Therapists.

Werrington Health Centre

Skaters Way, Peterborough, Cambridgeshire, PE4 6NB

Tel: 01733 578962

Fax: 01733 325659

➤ **Cheshire**

Garven Place Clinic

Sankey Street, Warrington, Cheshire, WA1 1GP

Tel: 01925 651188

Fax: 01925 234791

Contact: Ann Barlow, Head Speech and Language Therapist

No specialist service is provided for deaf children or adults. The general service can provide the following to children from pre-school age: assessment, treatment (including home programmes) and advice. Work is done in groups and on an individual basis.

Kingsway Health Centre

Kingsway, Widnes, Cheshire, WA8 7QE

Tel: 0151 424 3055
Fax: 0151 424 3055
Contact: Philip Turner, Speech Therapist Manager

No specialist service is available for deaf children and adults. The general service can provide counselling and advice for children from pre-school to 11, subject to referral. Attempts are being made to change the service. A joint finance submission has been made and negotiations are taking place.

Macclesfield District General Hospital

Victoria Road, Macclesfield, Cheshire, SK10 3BL

Tel: 01625 661716
Fax: 01625 663770
Contact: L A Batchelor, Consultant Community Paediatrician-Audiology
Tel: 01625 612197

Diagnostic and management service for hearing impaired children from birth. 'At risk' screening in place. Intergrated adult and paediatric service.

Timperley Health Centre

169 Grove Lane, Timperley, Altrincham, Cheshire, WA15 6PH

Tel: 0161 980 8041
Fax: 0161 903 9030
Contact: Susan Younghouse, Head of Speech and Language Therapy, Professions Allied to Medicine

There is no specialist service provided for deaf children or adults. The speech and language therapy service is working with peripatetic teachers to improve links; however, the service is patchy. The therapists feel they are not being fully used to advise on language and very few children are referred to the service. Those children who are referred are seen individually.

➢ Cleveland

General Hospital

Holdforth Road, Hartlepool, Cleveland, TS24 9AH

Tel: 01429 266654
Textphone: 01429 860103
Fax: 01429 261744
Contact: Shirley Norris, Head of Audiology Services
Tel: 01429 267901 ext 4140

There is no specialist service for deaf children or adults. The general service can see both deaf children and adults in individual sessions. A peripatetic service to schools is run by the local education authority.

North Tees General Hospital

Hardwick, Stockton-on-Tees, Cleveland, TS19 8PE

Tel: 01642 624705
Fax: 01642 624379
Contact: Jenny Wright, Family Health Special Needs Manager

There is no specialist service for deaf children and adults. The general service can provide the following for deaf children from pre-school age onwards: assessment, treatment, and advice. A peripatetic service to schools is available. Work is done in groups and individually. Deaf adults can receive assessment, treatment and advice in individual and group sessions.

➢ Cornwall

St Lawrence's Hospital

Bodmin, Cornwall, PL31 2QT

Tel: 01208 251372
Fax: 01208 251517
Contact: Sue Newman, Speech and Language Therapy Adviser

There is no specialist service for deaf children and adults. The general service provides assessment and treatment in individual sessions for children from pre-school to 18. The service works alongside the teachers of the deaf/audiology department. Generally, the speech and language therapy service only becomes involved when a co-existing communication disorder is identified alongside deafness. The general service can provide assessment, treatment and advice in individual sessions for deaf adults.

Treliske Hospital

Truro, Cornwall, TR1 3LJ

Tel: 01872 274242
Fax: 01872 252603
Contact: Julie Bradford, Communication Aid Centre
Tel: 01872 252470 ext 2470

To provide first time line assessment of children and adults presenting with communication difficulties which require alternative or augmentative communication. Where an assessment is deemed highly complex and beyond the scope of the communication aids resource, onward referrals to other centres such as access centres or Frenchay Hospital are undertaken following permission from the designated fundholder.

➢ County Durham
Darlington Memorial Hospital
Hollyhurst Road, Darlington, County Durham, DL3 6HX
Tel: 01325 743001
Fax: 01325 743605
Contact: Joanne Shotbolt, Chief Audiologist

South Durham Health Care Speech and Language Therapy Department aims to provide a specialist service which encompasses the assessment, evaluation and appropriate management of disorders of human communication and associated difficulties, through parent/carer training as well as individual and group programmes of care.

Stanley Health Centre
Clifford Road, Stanley, County Durham, DH9 0XE
Tel: 01207 214878
Fax: 01207 214878
Contact: Sue Hood, Head of Service, Child Speech and Language Therapy Manager

➢ Cumbria
Carlisle Central Clinic
50 Victoria Place, Carlisle, Cumbria, CA1 1ET
Tel: 01228 603220
Fax: 01228 603201
Contact: Ana Harrison, Speech and Language Therapy Manager

No specialist service is available for deaf children or adults. The general service can provide the following for children from pre-school age to 18: assessment and treatment in individual sessions. Any referrals are made to community therapists and are part of the general caseload. It is hoped that one of the therapists will be able to develop a specialist interest in the field.

➢ Derby
See Derbyshire

➢ Derbyshire
Community Health Services NHS Trust
Southern Derbyshire
121 Osmaston Road, Derby, DE1 2GA
Tel: 01332 363371
Fax: 01332 293217
Contact: Trish Thompson, Head of Speech and Language Therapy Services

No specialist service is available for deaf children. The general service can provide assessment, treatment, counselling and advice, mostly in individual sessions although groups are used as appropriate. Advice and support are also given to the Early Years Centre. A service can only be provided for deaf adults with significant learning disabilities who can receive assessment, treatment and advice.

➢ Devon
Barnstaple Health Centre
Vicarage Street, Barnstaple, Devon EX32 7BT
Tel: 01271 371761
Fax: 01271 321586
Contact: Jennie Godden, Speech and Language Therapy Services Manager
            Vicarage Street, Barnstaple, Devon, EX32 7BT

Speech and language therapy is a service for children and adults across all of North Devon. Currently there is no specific input for the deaf community but it is hoped that a service for children will be started during 1999.

Bull Meadow Clinic
Bull Meadow Road, Exeter, Devon, EX2 4JF
Tel: 01392 208545
Fax: 01392 413624
Contact: Fiona Halstead, Director, Speech and Language Therapy

No specialist service is provided for deaf children or adults.

> Dorset

Dorset Healthcare NHS Trust

11 Shelley Road, Boscombe, Bournemouth, Dorset, BH1 4JQ

Tel: 01202 443209

Contact: Tony Corcoran, Clinical Audiologist Victoria Road, Bournemouth, Dorset, BH1 4RS

Tel: 01202 303400

There is no specialist speech and language therapy service in Dorset, with the exception of limited provision for children attending the units for children with a hearing impairment. There is no service for deaf adults.

> East Riding of Yorkshire

See Humberside

> East Sussex

Brighton General Hospital

Elm Grove, Brighton, East Sussex, BN2 3EW

Tel: 01273 693600

Contact: Isobel Bassett, Manager, Speech and Language Therapy Services

Tel: 01273 242074

South Downs Health NHS Trust provides community and mental health services to 300,000 people in the Brighton, Hove and Lewes areas of East Sussex, and gets its income principally from the East Sussex, Brighton and Hove Health Authority. Our aim is to look after the local population to the best of our ability whether at home, in hospital or visiting one of our clinics or health centres.

Eastbourne and County NHS Health Trust

Sturton Place, Station Road, Hailsham, East Sussex, BN27 2AU

Tel: 01323 847619

Fax: 01323 841606

Contact: Elizabeth Innes, Head of Speech and Language Therapy Services

Tel: 01323 847619 ext 215

This is the general speech and language therapy department. The specialist service is supplied by the Eastbourne and Seaford Paediatric Team at Langney, Eastbourne.

Hastings and Rother NHS Trust

Furness Mount, 4 Holmesdale Gardens, Hastings, East Sussex, TN34 1LY

Tel: 01424 437082

Contact: Rosemary Hunt, Speech and Language Therapy Department Manager

There is currently no specialist provision for deaf children and adults.

Ian Gow Health Centre

Milfoil Drive, Eastbourne, East Sussex, BN23 8ED

Tel: 01323 760111

Contact: Mary Bell, Team Leader, Speech and Language Therapist, Paediatric Team

We aim to provide an integrated service in conjuction with all other relevant agencies to clients referred to speech and language therapy. Our service is for pre-school and school-aged children.

> Essex

Barbara Tingey Speech and Language Therapy Centre

61 Abbey Road, Newbury Park, Ilford, Essex, IG2 7LZ

Tel: 020 8518 3131

Fax: 020 8518 3131

Contact: Jenny Cole, Speech and Language Therapy Services Manager

The following services are available for deaf children from pre-school to 16: assessment, treatment, advice and a peripatetic service to schools. Work is done either in groups or individually. Adults can obtain assessment, treatment and advice in individual sessions. A service is also provided for deafened children and adults.

Child Development Centre

Hamstel House, Hamstel Road, Harlow, Essex, CM20 1RB

Tel: 01279 827194

Fax: 01279 444298

Contact: Inyang Adegbola, Specialist Speech and Language Therapist for the Hearing Impaired

Tel: 01279 827194

Fax: 01279 444298

A specialist service is provided for deaf children from pre-school age to 16. This service was established in 1997 and work is done in collaboration with peripatetic teachers from the special needs support service. Services include assessment and treatment, counselling and advice. All work is done in individual sessions. There is no specialist service for deaf adults.

Essex County Hospital

Lexden Road, Colchester, Essex, CO3 3NB

Tel: 01206 834549
Textphone: 01206 834549
Fax: 01206 834603
Contact: Lesley Chapman, Hearing Therapy Manager

The hearing therapy and audiology departments work closely together providing diagnostic, hearing aid and rehabilitation services. The hearing therapy department offers assessment and rehabilitation including tinnitus management and counselling, hearing aid orientation, communication training, and deaf awareness training. The speech therapy department at Central Clinic provides a service to deaf children.

Speech and Language Therapy Services

8-10 Tye Common Road, Billericay, Essex, CM12 9ND

Tel: 01277 632913
Fax: 01277 633299
Contact: Elspeth Clayton, Head of Speech and Language Therapy Services

There is no specialist service available for deaf children or adults. The general service can provide the following for deaf children from pre-school to 18: assessment, treatment, counselling, advice and a peripatetic service to schools. Work is done in groups. All individual sessions are held in schools. A service is also provided for deafened children only. The speech therapy service maintains very close links with the hearing therapy service.

➢ Gillingham and Rochester
See Kent

➢ Hampshire

Central Health Clinic, Southampton

East Park Terrace, Southampton, Hampshire, SO14 0YL

Tel: 023 8090 2525
Fax: 023 8090 2602
Contact: Sarah Worsfold, Chief Speech Therapist

ENT Department, Royal South Hants Hospital, Southampton, Hampshire, SO14 0YG

Tel: 023 8063 4288 ext 2794

A specialist speech and language therapy service is available for deaf children from pre-school age to 18. The following services are available for children: assessment and treatment, counselling, advice and peripatetic services to schools. Work is done in groups and on an individual basis. The following services are available for deaf adults: assessment, treatment and advice. Work is done in groups and individual sessions. A service is provided for deafened adults and children.

Parklands Hospital

Fairway House, Aldermaston Road, Basingstoke, Hampshire, RG24 9RH

Tel: 01256 376476
Contact: Louise Allen, Speech and Language Therapist

A specialist service for deaf children from pre-school to 11 years is being developed. The service consists of assessment, treatment and advice to carers and schools, and liaison with teachers of the deaf is a priority. A limited assessment and advice service is available to adults.

Portsmouth Healthcare NHS Trust

151 Locksway Road, Southsea, Portsmouth, Hampshire, PO4 8LD

Tel: 023 9289 4410
Fax: 023 9229 3790
Contact: Margaret Meikle, Speech and Language Therapist

Royal Hampshire County Hospital

Romsey Road, Winchester, Hampshire, SO22 5DG

Tel: 01962 824437
Fax: 01962 824860
Contact: Helen Martin, Audiology Services Manager
E-mail: Helen.Martin@weht.swest.nhs.uk

We aim to provide an up-to-date, high quality and comprehensive service for the local community. Liaising closely with colleagues and other professionals we will endeavour to provide a friendly and efficient approach tailored to patient needs. The all age service is provided by a team of audiological scientists, technicians and assistants.

Southampton General Hospital

Tremona Road, Shirley, Southampton, Hampshire, SO16 6YD

Tel: 023 8085 2288

Fax: 023 8079 4756

Contact: Alison Proudman, Speech and Language Therapist

Tel: 023 8079 6455

A centre for people of any age living within the Southampton and South West Hampshire Health District who are severely speech impaired. Maintains a supply of specialised communication aids for demonstration and assessment purposes. Referrals through health care professionals, speech and language therapists, GPs, consultants. Clients seen on appointment basis only.

➢ Hartlepool
See Cleveland

➢ Herefordshire
Herefordshire Community Health Trust

Belmont Abbey, Belmont, Hereford, HR2 9RP

Tel: 01432 344344

Fax: 01432 363900

Contact: Trisha Collier, Professional Advisor, Speech and Language Therapy

Tel: 01432 344344 ext 3733

A specialist service is provided for deaf adults and children. Children from pre-school to 18 can receive assessment and treatment in individual sessions. Adults also receive assessment and treatment in individual sessions in short blocks of specific work. Only one session per week is dedicated to this client group. The service works very closely with audiology and teachers of the deaf.

The Speech and Language Centre

Franche Clinic, Marpool Place, Kidderminster, Herefordshire, DY11 5BB

Tel: 01562 752749

Fax: 01562 862695

Contact: Christine Green, Head of Speech and Language Therapy Services

No specialist service is provided for deaf children or adults. The general service can provide the following for children from pre-school age to 18 and for adults: assessment and treatment in individual sessions. A service is also provided for deafened children and adults.

➢ Hertfordshire
Lister Hospital

Coreys Mill Lane, Stevenage, Hertfordshire, SG1 4AB

Tel: 01438 314333

Fax: 01438 781145

Contact: Celia Panter, Audiologist

A specialist service is provided for deaf children from pre-school to 11 and deaf adults. Deaf children can receive assessment, treatment, counselling and advice in either group or individual sessions. There is also a peripatetic service to schools and two weekly sessions at a local unit/resource base. Deaf adults can obtain assessment, treatment and counselling in individual sessions.

The Avenue Health Centre

The Avenue, Watford, Hertfordshire, WD1 3NU

Tel: 01923 226436

Contact: Julia Bertolotti, Clinical Head of Speech and Language Therapy
            Knutsford House, Peace Prospect, Watford, Hertfordshire, WD1 3HA

An advisory speech/language therapy service is available to pre-school children presenting with a diagnosed bilateral sensorineural hearing loss requiring aids. This consultative service provides assessment, advice and information in collaboration with the advisory teacher for hearing impairment. Direct therapy is not provided.

> ## Isle of Wight
St Mary's Hospital
Parkhurst Road, Newport, Isle of Wight, PO30 5TG

Tel: 01983 521948

Contact: Joan Crosley, Speech and Language Therapy Services Manager

There is no specialist service available for deaf children or adults. The general service can provide the following to children from pre-school age to nine: assessment, treatment, counselling, advice and a peripatetic service available to schools and clinics. Work with children is on an individual basis. From 9 to 16 years of age, children are seen by teachers of the hearing impaired, and advice is given by speech and language therapy in conjunction with teachers.

> ## Kent
Foster Street Clinic
Foster Street, Maidstone, Kent, ME15 6NH

Tel: 01622 226075

Fax: 01622 226077

Contact: Flowie Lowe, Therapy Services for Children

There is no specialist service for deaf children or adults as this service is not funded by the health authority.

Kent and Canterbury Hospital
Ethelbert Road, Canterbury, Kent, CT1 3NG

Tel: 01227 766877

Textphone: 01227 783087

Fax: 01227 783018

Contact: Diana Rodda, Senior Hearing Therapist

Tel: 01227 766877 ext 4483

Services provided for adults with an acquired hearing loss include: assessment and treatment, counselling, advice on provision of equipment, vestibular rehabilitation, liaison with social services and other professionals, group services, individual therapy or rehabilitation, tinnitus counselling and fitting maskers, individual sessions, obscure auditory dysfunction rehabilitation, provision of information via lectures and work with special needs groups. Selective neonatal screening is performed. There is assessment and treatment of children although this may be complementary to Kent Paediatric Audiology Service provision.

Livingstone Hospital
East Hill, Dartford, Kent, DA1 1SA

Tel: 01322 622370

Fax: 01322 622315

Contact: Jane Poupart, Head of Speech and Language Therapy

No specialist service is available for deaf children or adults.

Medway Hospital
Windmill Road, Gillingham, Kent, ME7 5NY

Tel: 01634 830000

Fax: 01634 815811

Contact: Julia Ritchie, Speech and Language Therapy Manager

Children's services are developing, but no specialist service is available for deaf adults. The general service can provide the following to children from pre-school age to 18 and adults: assessment, treatment and advice. All work is done in individual sessions. There is input in the Total Communication Centre. They receive occasional referrals for adults but will normally contact the hearing therapists in the neighbouring Maidstone District, where there is also a Hearing Impaired Centre.

Oxleas NHS Trust
Speech and Language Therapy Department, Pinewood House, Old Bexley Lane, Bexley, Kent, DA5 2BW

Tel: 01322 526282

Fax: 01322 555491

Contact: Liz Clark, Director of Therapies

No service. Resumption contingent on health authority/education authority funding at levels to enable recruitment and development of a viable service.

Queen Mary's Hospital
Frognal Avenue, Sidcup, Kent, DA14 6LT

Tel: 020 8302 2678

Fax: 020 8308 3052

Contact: Elisabeth Clark, Director of Therapies Medical Unit Occupational Therapy

Tel: 020 8302 2678 ext 4159/ 3052

Some assessment and advice to pre-school deaf children through community clinic service. There is no service for deaf adults. Previous service non-viable due to funding and recruitment difficulties.

Tonbridge Cottage Hospital

Vauxhall Lane, Tonbridge, Kent, TN11 0NE

Tel: 01732 368928

Fax: 01732 368000

Contact: Sue Browne, Children's Clinical Team Leader, Speech and Language Therapy Service

There is no specialist service for deaf children or adults. The general service can provide the following for children from pre-school age to 18 and adults: assessment, treatment, counselling and advice. Work is done in groups and in individual sessions. Parent workshops are also organised.

Willows Clinic

Redhill, Chislehurst, Kent, BR7 6DA

Tel: 020 8467 1631

Contact: Jane McGregor, Speech and Language Therapist

Speech and Language Therapy, Hawes Down Clinic, Hawes Lane, West Wickham, Kent, BR4 9AE

Tel: 020 8777 4521

A specialist service is available for severely and profoundly deaf children from 2 to 16 years attending a primary and secondary hearing impaired unit. An advisory service is available for pre-school children and children attending mainstream schools.

➢ Lancashire

Birch Hill Hospital

Union Road, Rochdale, Lancashire, OL12 9QB

Tel: 01706 755880

Contact: Lesley Culling, Speech and Language Therapy Services Manager

There is no specialist speech and language therapy service run for deaf children. Few deaf children are referred to the service as most are seen by teachers of the deaf. However, all who are referred can obtain assessment, treatment and advice in individual sessions.

Bolton Community Health Care NHS Trust

St Peter's House, Silverwell Street, Bolton, Lancashire, BL1 1PP

Tel: 01204 371331

Contact: Nancy Darrall, Speech and Language Therapist

Thomason Memorial School, Devonshire Road, Bolton, Lancashire, BL1 4JP

Tel: 01204 360091

Provision of speech and language therapy for children and young people with hearing impairment to develop their spoken communication skills to their full potential, writing through either spoken English or sign language as a teaching medium.

Bury Health Authority

Fairfield Hospital, Rochdale Old Road, Bury, Lancashire, BL9 7TD

Tel: 0161 764 6081

Fax: 0161 705 3028

Contact: Ros Walker, Manager of Speech and Language Therapy

No specialist service is provided for deaf children or adults. The general service can provide services for children from pre-school age to 18 and adults. All work is done in individual sessions. A service is also provided for deafened children and adults.

Cannon Street Clinic

Cannon Street, Oldham, Lancashire, OL9 6EP

Tel: 0161 652 0414

Fax: 0161 627 4579

Contact: F Renzulli, Manager of Audiology Services

Tel: 0161 652 0414 ext 225

A specialist service offers assessment, treatment and advice to deaf children from pre-school age to 18, in the home, nurseries or clinics as appropiate. A peripatetic service is available to mainstream primary schools. Assessment, treatment and advice is offered to deaf adults. All work is done in individual sessions.

Chorley and South Ribble NHS Trust

73 Tunley Holme, Bamber Bridge, Preston, Lancashire, PR5 8ES

Tel: 01772 628586

Contact: Jo Cooper, Speech and Language Therapy Manager

There is no specialist service for deaf children and adults. The general service provides the following services from pre-school age to 16 and through adulthood: assessment, treatment, counselling and advice. A peripatetic service is available (to schools only for children who are statemented). Work is done either in groups or on an individual basis. A service is provided for deafened children and adults.

Longsight Health Centre

256-258 Stockport Road, Manchester, Lancashire, M13 ORR

Tel: 0161 248 1208

Fax: 0161 224 0694

Contact: Nora Crawford, Principal Speech and Language Therapist

Tel: 0161 248 1208 ext 235

A base for special needs therapists. Children of all ages will be referred onwards to the most appropriate speech and language therapy centre to deal with their requirements.

Ormskirk and District General Hospital

Wigan Road, Ormskirk, Lancashire, L39 2AZ

Tel: 01695 577111

West Lancashire NHS Trust provides a comprehensive range of health services across acute and community settings.

Salford Community Healthcare NHS Trust

Sandringham House, Castle Courts, Windsor Street, Salford, Manchester, M5 4DG

Tel: 0161 212 4015

Fax: 0161 212 4051

Contact: Kim Williams, Specialist Speech and Language Therapist, Mental Health and Deafness

            John Denmark Unit, National Centre for Mental Health & Deafness, Bury New Road, Prestwich, Greater Manchester, M25 3BL

Tel: 0161 772 3400

No specialist service is routinely available. However, because of a specialist tertiary service for deaf adults with mental illness there is access to advice. The general service provides assessment, treatment and advice to children aged up to 18 years. Children are seen individually or in groups in liaison with teachers of the deaf. A service is also provided for deafened children and adults.

Southport Speech and Language Therapy Service

52 Hoghton Street, Southport, Lancashire, PR9 0QU

Tel: 01704 530940

Contact: Lynn Gosling, Coordinator, Children's Speech and Language Therapy Service

The Speech and Language Therapy Service provides an assessment and management service for communication and swallowing disorders, provided in the community and offered to children; adults with acquired neurological disorders and adults with learning difficulties. We have no specialist service for deaf children or adults but frequently liaise with the Birkdale School for the Partially Hearing and the Local Education Authority's Hearing Impaired Advisory Team.

Wigan Children's Hearing Services

Jack Ashley Centre, Park Road, Hindley, Wigan, Lancashire, WN2 3RY

Tel: 01942 526312

➤ Lincolnshire
Lincoln District Healthcare NHS Trust

92 Newland, Lincoln, LN1 1YA

Tel: 01522 514814

Contact: Virginia Blackoe, Chief Speech & Language Therapist

To enable people with speech and language difficulties to fulfil their individual potential by: early detection of problems with early assesment and management of the problem by; recognition, minimisation and, where possible, elimination of difficulties; and increased knowledge/awareness of communication problems among professionals and public.

➤ London

Camden and Islington Speech and Language Therapy Services

1st Floor, East Wing, St Pancras Hospital, 4 St Pancras Way, London, NW1 OPE

Tel:	020 7530 3190
Fax:	020 7530 3180
Contact:	Anne O'Sullivan, Principal Speech and Language Therapist for Deaf People
	330-332 Gray's Inn Road, London, WC1X 8DA
Tel:	020 7915 1633
Textphone:	020 7915 1633
Fax:	020 7915 1623

Community Service: a specialist service is available to deaf children in the Camden area. Children must be either: pre-school Camden and Islington residents to qualify for domiciliary visits; schoolchildren attending special schools or units such as Frank Barnes, Laycock, Hargrave Park, Penn or Heathlands schools; or any deaf child referred to the Nuffield Centre at the Royal National Throat Nose and Ear Hospital. These children can receive assessment, treatment, counselling and advice in either individual sessions or in groups. Hospital Services: deaf and deafened adults can obtain assessment, treatment, counselling and advice in either individual sessions or groups. A service is provided to deafened children and adults. There is also a cochlear implant service at the RNTNE hospital for both adults and children.

Elizabeth Blackwell House

Elizabeth Blackwell House, Wardalls Grove, Avonley Road, London, SE14 5ER

Tel:	020 7771 5134
Fax:	020 7771 5115
Contact:	Laura Threadgill, Specialist Speech and Language Therapist
	Priory Manor Child Development Centre, 1 Blagdon Road, Lewisham, London, SE13 7HL
Tel:	020 7690 3838
Fax:	020 7771 4540

A specialist service for deaf children from pre-school to 18 is available from the Priory Manor Child Development Centre, providing assessment, treatment, counselling, advice and peripatetic services to schools. Work is done in groups and in individual sessions. There is also training available for nursery keyworkers, individual support workers and other involved professionals. Domiciliary and nursery visits are also arranged. The specialist adult service is available from Guy's Hospital.

Guy's Hospital

Ground Floor, Thomas Guy's House, St Thomas' Street, London, SE1 9RT

Tel:	020 7955 4081
Textphone:	020 7955 4081
Fax:	020 7955 8849
Contact:	Karen Archer, Hearing Therapist and Cochlear Implant Coordinator
Textphone:	020 8922 8034

The specialist service for deaf adults for Optimum Health Services is available from Guy's, consisting of assessment, treatment, counselling (at a basic level) and advice. Work is done in groups and individually.

Hammersmith Hospital

Du Cane Road, London, W12 0HS

Tel:	020 8383 3076
Fax:	020 8383 3076
E-mail:	SPLangHAM@hhnt.org

There is no specialist service available for deaf children or adults. Advice is offered to deaf adults if hearing problems are present in conjunction with other difficulties.

Hurst Road Health Centre

Hurst Road, London, E17 3BL

Tel:	020 8520 8513
Contact:	Andrea Lillystone, Speech and Language Therapist
	Hawkswood School, Antlers Hill, Chingford, London, E4 7RT
Tel:	020 8529 2561
Textphone:	020 8524 8230
Fax:	020 8524 8230

A specialist service is provided for children who are deaf or who have a significant/permanent hearing impairment. Children from pre-school age up to 18 can obtain assessment, treatment and advice in group or individual sessions. The pre-school service is currently being developed in conjunction with the peripatetic service to schools. Therapy continues in summer holidays and in term-time there is regular therapy both in the school for deaf children and also specific provision within four mainstream schools. A service is also provided for deafened children.

Memorial Hospital

Shooters Hill, London, SE18 3RZ

Tel: 020 8312 6374

Fax: 020 8319 3336

Contact: Jane Thomas, Specialist Speech and
           Language Therapist

A specialist service is provided to deaf children from pre-school age to 16. However, the service is not available to children above year 1 in mainstream schools who do not have a statement of special needs. The following services are available: assessment and treatment, advice and some peripatetic work in schools. Work is done in groups and on an individual basis. An advice only service is available to adults. Therapists also provide a service for deafened children and, additionally, have experience with children who have had a cochlear implant.

National Hospital for Neurology and Neuro Surgery

Queen Square, London, WC1N 3BG

Tel: 020 7837 3611

Fax: 020 7829 8720

Contact: Renata Whurr, Head of Speech and
           Language Therapy Department

There is no specialist service for deaf children or adults.

Newham Speech and Language Therapy

84 West Ham Lane, London, E15 4PT

Tel: 020 8250 7340

Fax: 020 8250 7340

Contact: Helena Jenkins, Specialist Speech and
           Language Therapist, Deaf and Partially
           Hearing People

Speech and language therapy for deaf and partially-hearing children is provided in schools by the health trust. Newham operates an inclusive education policy and is working towards bi-lingualism for deaf students. We aim to give skills to access the educational curriculum and enable the development of confident communicators.

SEN Centre

85 Harford Street, London, E1 4PY

Tel: 020 7423 9655

Fax: 020 7423 9655

Contact: Rachel Chadwick, Senior Speech and
           Language Therapist

A specialist speech and language therapy service is provided for deaf children from pre-school to 16 who must be attending school in Tower Hamlets or be resident in the borough at pre-school age. Those attending school outside the borough receive therapy in school. The following services are available: assessment, treatment, advice and peripatetic services to schools. Work is done in groups and on an individual basis. There is no specialist service for deaf adults. A service is provided for deafened children.

Speech, Language and Hearing Centre

1-5 Christopher Place, Chalton Street, London, NW1 1JF

Tel: 020 7383 3834

Textphone: 020 7380 0350

Fax: 020 7383 3099

E-mail: info@speech-lang.org.uk

Website: www.speech-lang.org.uk

The Speech, Language and Hearing Centre is for babies and children under five years of age who have hearing impairment or delay in speech, language or communication. It offers assessment, a morning nursery school and afternoon therapy clinic.

St Ann's Hospital

St Ann's Road, London, N15 3TH

Tel: 020 8442 6000

Fax: 020 8442 6769

Contact: Jane Elias, Head of Speech and
           Language Therapy

Tel: 020 8444 9007

A specialist speech and language therapy service is provided for deaf children. The following services are provided for deaf children from pre-school age to 18: assessment and treatment, counselling and advice. Work is done in group sessions and on an individual basis. A service is also provided for deafened children. Services include general hearing aid work, tinnitus counselling and balance work. Domiciliary visits can be arranged.

St Thomas' Hospital

Lambeth Palace Road, London, SE1 7EH

Tel: 020 7922 8034

Textphone: 020 7922 8241

Fax: 020 7922 8088

Contact: Karen Archer, Hearing Therapist and
           Cochlear Implant Coordinator

Full audiological service. Implantable and bone anchored hearing aids. Full hearing therapy service including domiciliary visits and vestibular and tinnitus therapy. Adult and paediatric cochlear implant programme.

The City Lit Centre for Deaf People

Tel: 020 7405 5118
Videotel: 020 7831 0736
Fax: 020 7831 6121
E-mail: CFDP@citylit.ac.uk
Contact: Karen Considine, Head of Centre
Textphone: 020 7405 5118

See entry under Further Education.

The Medical Centre

7e Woodfield Road, London, W9 3XZ
Tel: 020 7286 5111
Fax: 020 7451 8177
Contact: Sara Bowcott, Speech and Language Therapist
            Neasden Clinic, London, NW10 1TH
Tel: 020 7450 7844
Fax: 020 7452 1607

A specialist speech and language therapy service is available for deaf children from pre-school age to 18. The following services are available: assessment, treatment, peripatetic sessions and advice to schools. Work is done either in groups or in individual sessions. There is no service for deaf or deafened adults. A specialist service is provided for deafened children.

➢ Merseyside

Netherfield Road Family Clinic

123 Netherfield Road, Liverpool, Merseyside, L5 5ET
Tel: 0151 207 3263
Fax: 0151 298 2192
Contact: Maggie Gunn, Speech and Language Therapy Manager

No specialist service is provided for deaf children or adults. The general service can provide assessment, treatment, advice and a peripatetic service to schools. All work is done in individual sessions. The service provides support for children from 5 to 7 years old. Deaf adults can receive assessment, treatment and advice in individual sessions. There is no service for deafened children or adults.

The Elms Clinic

50 Cowley Hill Lane, St Helens, Merseyside, WA10 2AW
Tel: 01744 454372
Fax: 01744 620172
Contact: Helen Jones, Senior Speech and Language Therapist

There is no specialist service for deaf children or adults. The general service can provide the following services to children from pre-school age to 16 and adults: assessment, treatment and advice. A peripatetic service to schools is only available for statemented children from reception to 16. All services for children are provided in community clinics.

➢ Middlesex

Laurel Lodge Clinic

Harlington Road, Uxbridge, Middlesex, UB8 3HD
Tel: 01895 231221
Fax: 01895 236018
Contact: Lesley Johnson, District Speech and Language Therapist

A specialist service is provided for deaf children from pre-school age to 18. The following services are provided: assessment and treatment, counselling and advice, peripatetic sessions (to four mainstream schools as well as special units). Work is done in groups and in individual sessions. The therapist also attends a parents' group in the evenings. A service is also provided for deafened children.

Northwick Park Hospital

Watford Road, Harrow, Middlesex, HA1 3UJ
Tel: 020 8864 3232
Fax: 020 8869 2174
Contact: Peter Savundra, Consultant Audiological Physician

Thelma Golding Health Centre

92 Bath Road, Hounslow, Middlesex, TW3 3EL
Tel: 020 8321 2451
Fax: 020 8321 2260
Contact: Jill Rose, Hearing Impairment Service Coordinator, Speech and Language Therapy Department

A specialist speech and language therapy service provided to the paediatric caseload. The service is provided pre-school to children in mainstream schools, and those in centres for the deaf attached to mainstream schools. The service provides

4

assessment and management of hearing impaired children.

➤ Norfolk

James Paget Hospital

Lowestoft Road, Gorleston, Great Yarmouth, Norfolk, NR31 6LA

Tel: 01493 452343/ 452287

Fax: 01493 452778

Contact: Lisa Dickson, Manager

A specialist speech therapy service is provided for deaf children and adults consisting of assessment, treatment and advice given in either group or individual sessions. There is also a peripatetic service for schools. A service is provided for deafened children and adults. Hearing therapy services include general hearing aid work and tinnitus counselling. Domiciliary visits can be arranged.

St James Clinic

Extons Road, King's Lynn, Norfolk, PE30 5NU

Tel: 01553 773951

Fax: 01553 774753

Contact: Hilary Watson, Manager of Speech Therapy Services

Tel: 01733 762911

There is a specialist service available for deaf children in Peterborough. The specialist service can provide the following for children from pre-school age to 11: assessment and treatment, counselling, advice and peripatetic services to schools. All work is done in individual sessions. A hearing assessment clinic with an ENT consultant and a teacher of hearing impaired children is available in Peterborough.

➤ North East Lincolnshire

See Humberside

➤ North Humberside

Westwood Hospital

Woodlands, Beverley, North Humberside, HU17 8BU

Tel: 01482 886634

Fax: 01482 886541

Contact: Zoe Wood, Specialist Speech and Language Therapist

Tel: 01482 675758

A specialist speech therapy service is available for deaf children from pre-school age to 18. The following services are available: assessment, treatment, counselling, advice and peripatetic sessions in schools. Work is done in groups and individual sessions. Deaf adults are seen as required.

➤ North Lincolnshire

Doncaster Road Clinic

6 Haldenby House, Berkley Business Centre, Doncaster Road, Scunthorpe, North Lincolnshire, DN15 7DQ

Tel: 01724 860770

Contact: Karen Griffiths, Coordinator, Paediatric Speech and Language Therapy Department

A specialised speech and language therapy service is available for deaf children from pre-school to 18 providing assessment, treatment, counselling, advice and a peripatetic service to schools. Work is done in groups and on an individual basis. There are few referrals for deaf adults. However, as required, adults can obtain assessment, treatment, counselling and advice in either groups or individual sessions. A peripatetic service is also available.

➤ North Yorkshire

Harrogate Speech and Language Therapy Service

2 Dragon Parade, Harrogate, North Yorkshire, HG1 2BY

Tel: 01423 523076

Contact: Sandra Woods, Speech and Language Therapy Deputy Manager

No specialist services are available for deaf children or adults. The general service can provide the following for deaf children from pre-school age to 18: assessment, treatment, counselling, advice and a peripatetic service to schools. Work is done in individual sessions. Adults can be seen by the service and obtain assessment, treatment, counselling and advice in individual sessions. There is also a peripatetic service.

Monkgate Health Centre

31 Monkgate, York, YO3 7PB

Tel: 01904 630351

Contact: Robin Hull, Manager, Speech and Language Therapy Services

➤ Northamptonshire

Northamptonshire Speech and Language Therapy

Sunnyside, Cliftonville, Northampton, NN1 5BE

Tel:	01604 232337
Fax:	01604 583795
Contact:	Breda Avil, Speech and Language Therapy Manager
Tel:	01604 235834

A specialist service is available for deaf children only, from 5 to 11 years of age, providing assessment, treatment, advice and a peripatetic service to schools. Work is done in groups and on an individual basis as appropriate. The service offered is mainly based within educational settings, especially within units for hearing impaired children, which means that the service offered can be truly multi-disciplinary. The general service can provide assessment, treatment and advice in individual sessions for deaf adults. A service is also provided for deafened children and adults.

➤ Northumberland

St George's Hospital

Morpeth, Northumberland, NE61 2NH

Tel:	01670 517006
Fax:	01670 510902/ 510416

Northumberland Community Health has merged with North Tyneside Healthcare. The speech and language therapy services have also merged. At present, due to different purchasers, the services to people with hearing impairments remain different.

➤ Oxfordshire

Radcliffe Infirmary

Woodstock Road, Oxford, OX2 6HE

Tel:	01865 224559
Fax:	01865 224566
Contact:	Jane Schofield, Speech and Language Therapy Clinical Coordinator

A specialist service is provided for deaf children from pre-school to 18, providing assessment, treatment, counselling, advice and a peripatetic service to schools. Work is done in groups and on an individual basis. Adults are also seen in either groups or individual sessions for assessment, treatment, counselling and advice. There is also a service for deafened children and adults.

➤ Peterborough
See Cambridgeshire

➤ Portsmouth
See Hampshire

➤ Reading
See Berkshire

➤ South Yorkshire

Doncaster Gate Hospital

Doncaster Gate, Rotherham, South Yorkshire, S65 1DW

Tel:	01709 820000 ext 3234
Contact:	Gillian Slater, Service Manager, Speech and Language Therapy Department

Rotherham Speech and Language Therapy Department provides the following service to clients with hearing impairment as follows: children attending the three hearing impaired units (on site); children who have a statement of Special Educational Need in mainstream schools; and a clinic-based service for clients whose hearing impairment forms part of their communication difficulties.

➤ Southampton
See Hampshire

➤ Staffordshire

Stoke-on-Trent Speech and Language Therapy Service

Residency III, Hilton Road, Stoke-on-Trent, Staffordshire, ST4 6SD

Tel:	01782 552485
Fax:	01782 552491

The speech/language therapy service is an integrated, comprehensive service for North Staffordshire. Services to children and adults who are hearing impaired or deaf are provided as part of a general clinic caseload with support from a specialist speech/language therapist. This therapist also provides services to the local school for the deaf and units for the hearing impaired, and has skills in British Sign Language and specific training in cochlear implants. We are in the process of developing our approach to pre-school hearing impaired children.

> ## Stockton-on-Tees
See Cleveland

> ## Stoke-on-Trent
See Staffordshire

> ## Suffolk
Allington NHS Trust
571 Foxhall Road, Ipswich, Suffolk, IP3 8LX

Tel:	01473 703118
Fax:	01473 703400
Contact:	Sally O'Neill, Head of Adults Section, Speech and Language Therapy

A specialist service is provided for deaf children from pre-school age to 16: assessment and treatment, and advice including pre-school advice and therapy as part of a multi-disciplinary team. A peripatetic service is available to schools. Work is done in groups and individually. No specialist service is available for deaf adults or deafened children. They attend hospital clinics and see therapists with the adult caseload.

Child Health Centre
Hospital Road, Bury St Edmunds, Suffolk, IP33 3LH

Tel:	01284 775081
Fax:	01284 750282
Contact:	Keri Morrow, Specialist Speech and Language Therapist in Hearing Impairment

A specialist speech and language therapy service is available for deaf school-aged children educated within a hearing impaired unit. An advisory service is available for pre-school children. The specialist service includes assessment, therapy on an individual or small group basis, advice, support for carers, liaison and joint working with other agencies.

> ## Surrey
Epsom General Hospital
Dorking Road, Epsom, Surrey, KT18 7EG

Tel:	01372 735277
Textphone:	01372 735313
Fax:	01372 735159
Contact:	Judith Hunt, Hearing Therapy Department

The Hearing Therapy Department provides a rehabilitation programme to adults who have an acquired hearing loss. This includes counselling, hearing aid management and auditory rehabilitation. There is also a tinnitus and vertigo clinic. Community Hearing Health in conjunction with a RAD support worker provides a service to people in their own homes.

Frimley Children's Centre
Church Road, Frimley, Camberley, Surrey, GU16 5AD

Tel:	01483 782932
Fax:	01483 782998
Contact:	Briony Cooper, Chief Speech and Language Therapist

A specialist speech and language therapy service is available for deaf children from pre-school to secondary age. It includes assessment, treatment, monitoring and advice. Children are seen either at home, in mainstream school or in hearing impaired units. There is close liaison with parents and other professionals.

Surrey Oaklands NHS Trust
West Park, Horton Lane, Epsom, Surrey, KT19 8PB

Tel:	01372 202020
Contact:	Christina Elliott, Head Speech and Language Therapist
Tel:	01737 202020 ext 3371
Fax:	01372 203103

Services are offered to people who are deaf and have learning difficulties or a mental illness.

> ## Tyne and Wear
Bensham Hospital
Saltwell Road, Gateshead, Tyne and Wear, NE8 4YL

Tel:	0191 402 6667
Fax:	0191 402 6650
Contact:	Hilary Newman, Manager, Speech and Language Services

We aim to help those who have communication difficulties to achieve their maximum potential by offering assessment, advice and treatment as appropriate.

Freeman Hospital

High Heaton, Newcastle-upon-Tyne, Tyne and Wear, NE7 7DN

Tel:	0191 284 3111
Fax:	0191 213 1968
Contact:	Liz Hole, Specialist Speech and Language Therapist
Tel:	0191 284 3111 ext 26646

A specialist speech therapy service is available for deaf children from pre-school age to 16. A limited service is provided for adults. The following services are available: assessment and treatment, advice, and peripatetic services to schools. Individual or group work is offered as appropriate. A service is also provided for deafened children and adults.

Northumbria Healthcare Trust

Health Department, Albion Road, North Shields, Tyne and Wear, NE29 0HG

Tel:	0191 219 6685
Fax:	0191 219 6650
Contact:	Gill Close, Senior Specialist Speech and Language Therapist
	Monkhouse Deaf Support Centre, Wallington Avenue, North Shields, Tyne and Wear
Tel:	0191 258 4462

A specialist speech therapy service is available for deaf children from pre-school age to 18. The following services are available: assessment, treatment, counselling, advice and a peripatetic service to schools. Profoundly deaf children with hearing aids and cochlear implants receive intensive therapy.

➢ Warwickshire

Cape Road Clinic

Cape Road, Warwick, CV34 4JP

Tel:	01926 400001
Contact:	Elizabeth Roche, Specialist Speech and Language Therapist

A specialist service is available for deaf children from pre-school age upwards. Children can obtain assessment, treatment, counselling and advice either in group or individual sessions. A peripatetic service to schools is also run by the service. Deaf adults can receive assessment and treatment only if hearing loss is part of some additional difficulty.

➢ West Midlands

Birmingham Heartlands Hospital

Bordesley Green East, Bordesley Green, Birmingham, West Midlands, B9 5SS

Tel:	0121 766 6611
Fax:	0121 776 6935
Contact:	M Waddell, Speech and Language Therapy Service Manager
Tel:	0121 766 6611 ext 4856

Carnegie Centre

Hunters Road, Hockley, Birmingham, West Midlands, B19 1DR

Tel:	0121 554 3899
Fax:	0121 554 2040
Contact:	Miriam Somerville, General Manager, Primary Care

We provide a speech and language therapy service to people living in the northern half of Birmingham.

Child Health Clinic

Red Hill Street, Wolverhampton, West Midlands, WV1 1NR

Tel:	01902 312123
Contact:	Rowena Samuels, Senior Speech and Language Therapist
Tel:	01902 444363

Our provision for the deaf and hearing impaired children and adults in Wolverhampton is currently under review. At present we provide a service to children from 2 to 10 years of age. The aim is to re-evaluate the need and probably expand the range of clients seen.

Coleshill Road Clinic

Brooklands, Coleshill Road, Marston Green, Birmingham, West Midlands, B37 7HL

Tel:	0121 779 6981
Textphone:	0121 329 4972
Fax:	0121 779 4348
Contact:	Kate Richards, Head of Speech and Language Therapy for Hearing Impairment
Tel:	0121 779 6981 ext 4924

There is a specialist service for deaf children from pre-school age to 18, providing assessment, treatment, counselling, advice and a peripatetic service to schools. Work is done in groups and in individual sessions. Deaf adults also receive this level of service and there is also a service for deafened children and adults.

Dudley Central Clinic

Hall Street, Dudley, West Midlands, DY2 7BX

Tel:	01384 459530
Fax:	01384 237525
Contact:	Sue Dobson, Speech and Language Therapist

Specialist service for deaf and hearing impaired clients offering information, advice, support and training in communication and individual/group therapy in home, integrated unit, mainstream school and clinic settings. Caseload includes deaf, deafened and cochlear implanted clients, and therapists work in spoken and signed English and British Sign Language as appropiate.

Gulson Hospital

Gulson Road, Coventry, West Midlands, CV1 2HR

Tel:	024 7684 4058
Fax:	024 7684 4058
Contact:	Jillian Kelly, Manager, Speech and Language Therapy

The speech and language therapy service provides assessment and intervention for people of all ages with communication and swallowing difficulties. There is no specialist service for either deaf children or adults. Children are seen for assessment, treatment and advice in liaison with specialist teachers. Adults are offered assessment of communication and advice, or referral to other agencies.

Queen Elizabeth Hospital

Edgbaston, Birmingham, West Midlands, B15 2TH

Tel:	0121 627 2360
Fax:	0121 627 2361

The following services are available for pre-lingually deaf and deafened adults: assessment, treatment, counselling and advice. Work is done in groups and in individual sessions. The therapist also has input into the Cochlear Implant Programme and the bone-anchored hearing aid programme. Specialist paediatric speech and language therapy is provided for deaf children at Longwill School for the Deaf and Birmingham Children's Hospital.

Queslett Road Clinic

5 Lakeview Close, Queslett Road, Great Barr, Birmingham, West Midlands, B43 7EZ

Tel:	0121 480 5947
Fax:	0121 480 5966
Contact:	Rebecca Hewitt, Specialist Speech and Language Therapist

A specialist service is provided for deaf children from pre-school up to 18 and adults. The service consists of assessment, treatment and advice in individual sessions. Peripatetic sessions are also available and children are also seen in groups. There is a service for deafened children and adults.

Rehabilitation Services For Deafened People

Tel:	0121 627 8930
Textphone:	0121 627 8932
Fax:	0121 627 8931
Contact:	Christine Mann, Coordinator/Administrator

See entry under Resource Centres.

Selly Oak Hospital

Raddlebarn Road, Birmingham, West Midlands, B29 6JD

Tel:	0121 627 8106
Textphone:	0121 627 8915
Fax:	0121 627 8914
E-mail:	juliethomas@university-b.wmids.nhs.uk
Contact:	Stuart Burrell, Hearing Assessment and Rehabilitation Centre (HARC)

The specialist service provided here is specifically for adults providing assessment, treatment, counselling and advice. Work is done in groups and on an individual basis. Assessment for suitability for a cochlear implant or a bone anchored hearing aid is available. In addition to conventional air conduction or bone conduction hearing aids, there is also rehabilitation and training in the use of aids and also of vibro-tactile aids.

The Cottage Hospital

27a Birmingham Road, Sutton Coldfield, West Midlands, B72 1QH

Tel:	0121 355 6031
Fax:	0121 321 1299
Contact:	Paula Boxall, Occupational Therapist

No specialist service is available for deaf children or adults. The general service provides the following for children from pre-school age to 18 and adults: assessment, treatment and advice.

➤ West Sussex
Graylingwell Hospital
9 College Lane, Chichester, West Sussex, PO19 4FX

Tel: 01243 787970

Fax: 01243 815263

Contact: Julia Rob, Speech and Language
            Therapy Manager

Tel: 01243 787970 ext 4260

No specialist service is provided for deaf children or adults. The general service can provide the following for children from pre-school age to 18: assessment and treatment, and advice. A peripatetic service is available to schools. All work is done in individual sessions. A limited service of assessment, treatment and advice is available for deaf adults, and for deafened adults and children based on communication need.

➤ West Yorkshire
Bradford Royal Infirmary
Duckworth Lane, Bradford, West Yorkshire, BD9 6RJ

Tel: 01274 542200

Fax: 01274 364026

Contact: Sue Falkingham, Audiology, ENT and
            Eye Unit

Tel: 01274 364071

Princess Royal Community Health Centre
Greenhead Road, Huddersfield, West Yorkshire, HD1 4EW

Tel: 01484 301400

Fax: 01484 482901

Contact: Christine Carter, Specialist Speech
            and Language Therapist for Hearing
            Impaired

Tel: 01484 301400 ext 4329

Speech and language therapy service for deaf children.

Royal Halifax Infirmary, Clover Hill Annexe
Clover Hill Road, Halifax, West Yorkshire, HX1 2YP

Tel: 01422 345911

Contact: Judy Lennon, Speech and Language
            Therapy Services Manager

There is no specialist service for deaf children or adults. The general service can provide assessment and treatment as part of a multi-disciplinary team providing a peripatetic service to schools for children from pre-school to 18. A

service is provided for deafened children only if there is another primary communication difficulty.

St Mary's Hospital
Greenhill Road, Leeds, West Yorkshire, LS12 3QE

Tel: 0113 279 0121

Contact: Lynne Silvester, Speech and Language
            Therapist, Deaf and Hearing Impaired
            Resourced Schools

Specialist speech therapy service available from diagnosis to 18 years of age. Assessment, treatment, counselling and advice available mainly as peripatetic sessions to resourced schools following the bilingual approach but also to non-resourced mainstream schools. Treatment in group or individual sessions as appropriate. No specific specialised service for adults.

Wakefield Health Authority
White Rose House, West Parade, Wakefield, West Yorkshire, WF1 1LT

Tel: 01924 814400

Fax: 01924 814401

Speech and Language Therapy Service is at Pinderfields Hospital - Telephone 01924 201688.

➤ Wiltshire
Swindon Health Centre
Carfax Street, Swindon, Wiltshire, SN1 1ED

Tel: 01793 428506

Fax: 01793 408500

Contact: Bridget Guy, Speech and Language
            Therapist

A specialist service for deaf children and adults is being developed. Services available for children from pre-school to 18 are: assessment, treatment and advice. Work is done individually and in groups. Deaf adults can also obtain assessment and treatment.

> Worcestershire
Catshill Clinic
The Dock, Catshill, Bromsgrove, Worcestershire, B61 0NJ

Tel: 01527 488326

Contact: Claire Albutt, Speech and Language Therapist

Isaac Maddox House, Shrub Hill Road, Worcester, Herefordshire, WR4 9RW

Tel: 01905 681592

Worcestershire Community Healthcare NHS Trust provides a speech and language therapy service for deaf children and for children who have cochlear implants. Assessment, treatment, advice and support is available to the children, their parents and other carers.

> York
See North Yorkshire

Northern Ireland

> County Antrim
Ballymoney Health Centre
21 Newal Road, Ballymoney, County Antrim, BT53 6HB

Tel: 028 7066 0301

Textphone: 028 2766 0301

Fax: 028 7066 0321

E-mail: je.johnston@p345.gp.n-1.nrls.uk

Communication Aid Centre - Musgrave Park Hospital
Stockman's Lane, Belfast, County Antrim, BT9 7JB

Tel: 028 9066 9501 ext 2917

Fax: 028 9068 3662

Contact: Hilary Robinson

The role of the centre is to: advise and assess disabled people for communication aids and recommend purchase by community trusts where appropriate; maintain a loan bank of current communication technology; provide a telephone advice service; educate speech and language therapists (and others on request) in communication technology.

Northern Health and Social Services Board
County Hall, 182 Galgorm Road, Ballymena, County Antrim, BT42 1QB

Tel: 028 2565 3333

Textphone: 028 2566 2618

Fax: 028 2566 2237

Contact: George McGuigan, Area Information Officer

A specialist service is available to deaf children, from pre-school age to 18, from Jordanstown School, 85 Jordanstown Road, Newtownabbey, County Antrim BT37 0QE. Tel: 028 9086 3541 (voice/text). The following services are available: assessment and treatment, counselling and advice. Work is done in groups and also in individual sessions. A service is also provided for deafened children.

Shankill Health Centre
136-138 Shankill Road, Belfast, County Antrim, BT13 2BD

Tel: 028 9031 6960

Fax: 028 9031 6969

Contact: Valerie Heron, Eastern Health and Social Services Board

Thornfield House School
8-12 Jordanstown Road, Newtownabbey, County Antrim, BT37 0QF

Tel: 028 9085 1089

Fax: 028 9086 5543

Contact: Ursula Gates, Northern Health and Social Services Board

> County Down
Bannvale House
10 Moyallon Road, Gilford, County Down, BT63 5JX

Tel: 028 3883 1983

Fax: 028 3883 1993

E-mail: roseline.moore@bannvale.cbct.n-i.hsh.uk

Contact: Roseline Moore, Speech and Language Therapist, Child Development Clinic

A specialist service is provided for hearing impaired children from pre-school age to 18, providing assessment, treatment and advice in individual sessions. The current service provides only for children. The hearing therapist provides a service for deafened adults.

Market Street Clinic

Market Street, Downpatrick, County Down, BT30 6LZ

Tel: 028 4461 3511

Fax: 028 4461 5994

Contact: Heather Crawford, Manager

➢ County Londonderry

Altnagelvin Hospital

Glenshane Road, Londonderry, BT47 1SD

Tel: 028 7131 1972

Textphone: 028 7134 2998

Fax: 028 7161 1218

Contact: Alison Kelly, Speech Therapist

Tel: 028 7134 5171 ext 3433

The Audiology Department at Altnagelvin Hospital offers a comprehensive service to the hearing impaired which includes a walk-in repair service. It provides a full audiological service to the ENT consultants in the main hospital, and also provides a limited service at outlying centres. A 'direct access' type clinic for the over 65s referred for possible hearing aid provision is also offered.

Mid Ulster Hospital

59 Hospital Road, Magherafelt, County Londonderry, BT45 5EX

Tel: 028 7963 1031

Fax: 028 7963 2464

Contact: Teresa Bradley, Speech and Language Therapist

Tel: 028 7963 1031 ext 3223

Western Health and Social Services Board

15 Gransha Park, Clooney Road, Londonderry, BT47 1TG

Tel: 028 7186 0086

Fax: 028 7186 0311

A specialist speech and language therapy service is available for deaf children from pre-school age to 18 (over 16s seen only if still in full-time education). The following services are available: assessment, treatment, advice, counselling and peripatetic services to schools. Work is done in groups and on an individual basis. A service is provided for deafened children.

➢ County Tyrone

Tyrone and County Hospital

1 Donaghanie Road, Omagh, County Tyrone, BT79 0NS

Tel: 028 8224 5211

Contact: Jill Caulfield, Speech Therapist

Scotland

➢ Aberdeenshire

Grampian Healthcare NHS Trust

Speech and Language Therapy, Springfield Road, Aberdeen, AB15 7RF

Tel: 01224 310582

Fax: 01224 310515

Contact: Margaret Jamieson, Speech and Language Therapy Manager

Grampian Healthcare speech and language therapy services aim to promote and enhance the communication skills of clients who present with a hearing impairment, either within the recently introduced bilingual policy at Aberdeen School for the Deaf or through the oral approach used in the specialist unit and mainstream education. A specialist service is also available for adult hearing impaired clients. A specialist speech and language therapy service is provided for deaf children from pre-school upwards. The service is oriented towards the provision of assessment, individual and group therapy, and advice/support to parents. We are also developing a pre-school hearing impaired club targeting early language and communication skills and support to parents. A service for deaf adults is also available.

➢ Angus

Dundee Centre for Child Health

19 Dudhope Terrace, Dundee, Angus, DD3 6HH

Tel: 01382 346626

Contact: Susan Howden, Specialist Speech and Language Therapist

Tel: 01382 346550

The speech and language therapy department offers a specialist service for deaf people in Dundee, Perth and Angus. Children are seen for therapy in their own homes, nurseries, schools and health centres. Adults born deaf or with acquired hearing loss are seen as outpatients in Ryehill Health Centre, Dundee.

Ninewells Hospital

Dundee, Angus, DD1 9SY

Tel: 01382 660111

Fax: 01382 633918

Contact: Jan Brodie, Chief Therapist

A specialist service is available for deaf children from pre-school to 18. The service provides assessment, treatment, counselling, advice and a peripatetic service to schools. Work is done in groups and in individual sessions. There is no specialist service for deaf adults and only very limited resources for deafened adults. A service is provided for deafened children.

➤ Ayrshire

Kilmarnock Central Clinic

16 Old Irvine Road, Kilmarnock, Ayrshire, KA1 2BD

Tel: 01563 545725

Contact: Louise Steel, Speech and Language Therapist

Deaf children from pre-school age upwards can obtain assessment, treatment, counselling and advice. Work is done in groups and in individual sessions. There is also a peripatetic service to schools. A service is also provided for deafened children.

North Ayr Health Centre

Glenmuir Place, Whiteletts, Ayr, KA8 9RW

Tel: 01292 885500

Fax: 01292 885555

Contact: Diane McLarty, Speech and Language Therapist

Tel: 01292 571236

Deaf children from pre-school age upwards can obtain assessment, treatment, counselling and advice. Work is done in groups and in individual sessions. There is also a peripatetic service to schools. A service is also provided for deafened children.

➤ Dumfries and Galloway

Nithbank Hospital

Nithbank, Dumfries, DG1 2SD

Tel: 01387 244000

Fax: 01387 244531

Contact: Alyson Hogg, Chief Clinical Specialist, Hearing Impairment, Speech and Language Therapy

Tel: 01387 244530

A specialist speech therapy service is available for deaf children from pre-school age to 18. The following services are available: assessment, treatment, counselling, advice and a peripatetic service to schools. All children diagnosed as requiring speech therapy are immediately included in this service. Work is done in group sessions and on an individual basis. Cochlear implant rehabilitation is also provided for both adults and children. The following services are available for deaf adults: assessment, treatment, counselling and advice. Work is done in individual sessions. A service is also provided for deafened children and adults.

➤ Inverness-Shire

Highland Communities NHS Trust

Moorfield Ferry Road, Dingwall, Inverness-Shire, IV15 9QS

Tel: 01349 863313 ext 146

Fax: 01349 865852

Contact: Elizabeth Kraft, Speech and Language Therapy Specialist for Hearing Impaired

A specialist speech and language therapy service is available for deaf children from pre-school age to 18. The following services are available: assessment, treatment, counselling, advice and peripatetic services to schools. Work is done in groups and in individual sessions. Pre-school visits are made in close liaison with the local teacher of the deaf. A six-weekly pre-school group is run jointly with Highland Deaf Education Service. The following services are available for deaf adults: assessment, treatment, counselling and advice. Work is done in groups and in individual sessions. A peripatetic service is also available. Adults are seen mainly by either self referrals or referral from social workers. One speech therapist is a qualified lipreading teacher and another is currently training for the same.

➤ Isle of Lewis
Western Isles Hospital
Macaulay Road, Stornoway, Isle of Lewis, HS1 2AF
Tel: 01851 704704

Contact: Thelma Bevis, Area Speech and
            Language Therapist
Tel: 01851 704704 ext 2282

No specialist service is available to deaf children or adults. The general service can provide the following for children from pre-school age to 18: assessment, treatment, and advice in individual sessions. Deaf adults can obtain assessment, treatment, counselling and advice in individual sessions. There is a service for deafened children and adults. The service is for communication difficulties associated with deafness and works with other professionals in the field such as teachers of the deaf and audiologists.

➤ Lanarkshire
Road Meetings Hospital
Goremire Road, Carluke, Lanarkshire, ML8 4PS
Tel: 01555 752242

Fax: 01555 752328

Contact: Irene Miller, Head of Service, Speech
            and Language Therapy Department

Our service is now available to all deaf people living within the Trust's catchment area. We assess, treat and counsel within education, health centres and domestic situations. Our aim is to maximise communication skills from as early a stage as possible.

➤ Midlothian
Royal Infirmary Edinburgh
39 Lauriston Place, Edinburgh, Midlothian, EH3 9EN
Tel: 0131 317 3688

Fax: 0131 317 3689

E-mail: h.mcleish@qmced.ac.uk

Website: www.sls.qmced.ac.uk

Contact: Alison McDonald, Specialist Speech
            and Language Therapist
            Sighthill Health Centre, 380 Calder
            Road, Edinburgh, Midlothian, EH11
            4AU
Tel: 0131 537 7118

Fax: 0131 536 3417

A specialist speech therapy service is available in Lothian from the Edinburgh Sick Children's NHS Trust. It is based at Douglas House. A specialist speech therapy clinic for hearing impaired children from pre-school age to 18 years is held at Sighthill Health Centre, where the peripatetic speech and language therapy service is based.

Scottish Centre for Research into Speech Disability
Clerwood Terrace, Edinburgh, Midlothian, EH12 8TS
Tel: 0131 317 3688

E-mail: h.mcleish@qmced.ac.uk

Website: www.sls.qmced.ac.uk

The SCRSD is a new centre equipped with state of the art instrumentation for recording and analysing both normal and disordered speech and for providing visual feedback as an aid to therapy. The Centre houses a clinic where much of the research is carried out and which provides clinical training for speech and language therapy undergraduates. As the clinic has an interest in therapy for deaf adults it provides therapy for a limited number of adult deaf people (pre- and post- lingual) and also undertakes the post-cochlear implant rehabilitation for adults with acquired hearing loss. This is on a consultancy basis as part of the Cochlear Implant Team based at the Edinburgh Royal Infirmary.

➤ Peeblesshire
St Ronan's Health Centre
Angle Park, Innerleithen, Peeblesshire, EH44 6QE
Tel: 01896 830203

Fax: 01896 831202

Contact: Ruth Isherwood, Speech and
            Language Therapist for Deaf People

A specialist service is provided for deaf children and adults. Therapy is available within a designated unit for deaf children from pre-school age upwards. Assessment, treatment and advice are available. Work is done in groups and on an individual basis. A more limited service is available for deaf adults, who can also receive assessment, treatment and advice in individual sessions and groups.

4

➢ Stirlingshire

Falkirk and District Royal Infirmary

1 Majors Loan, Falkirk, Stirlingshire, FK1 5QE

Tel: 01324 616154

Contact: Frances McMenemy, Speech and
                   Language Therapist

A specialist speech and language therapy service is available for both prelingual and deafened children and adults. This consists of assessment, treatment, counselling and advice on all aspects of speech and language and communication skills. The therapists providing this service all have some additional training in working with deaf people.

Wales

➢ Clwyd

Mold Community Hospital

Ash Grove, Mold, Clwyd, CH7 1XG

Tel: 01352 758893

E-mail: diane.lott@ccc-tr.wales.nhs.uk

Contact: Sarah Ellis, Specialist Speech and
                   Language Therapist

Tel: 01978 356551

Fax: 01352 750469

A specialist service is available for deaf children from pre-school age to 18, from 16 Grosvenor Road, Wrexham LL11 1BU (Tel: 01978 356551), and Royal Alexandra Hospital, Marine Drive, Rhyl, Denbighshire, LL18 3AS (Tel: 01745 343188/ 344574 (voice/fax)). The following services are available: assessment and treatment, counselling and advice. Work is done in groups and on an individual basis. Deaf adults are seen by the general service. A service is also available for deafened children and adults.

➢ Dyfed

Prince Philip Hospital

Bryngwyn Mawr, Dafen, Llanelli, Carmarthenshire, SA15 8QF

Tel: 01554 756567

Fax: 01554 772271

➢ Gwent

Royal Gwent Hospital

Cardiff Road, Newport, Gwent, NP9 2UB

Tel: 01633 234234

➢ Mid Glamorgan

Princess of Wales Hospital

Coity Road, Bridgend, Mid Glamorgan, CF31 1RQ

Tel: 01656 752192

Textphone: 01656 752192

Fax: 01656 752107

E-mail: audiology.pwh@bridgend-
                   tr.wales.nhs.uk

Contact: Marion Beard, Specialist Speech and
                   Language Therapist

The hospital supports deaf and hearing impaired people through its Audiology Department, including joint clinics serving children. There are excellent links with education, and suitable children and adults can benefit from the Cochlear Implant Programme, established in 1993. Audiology, hearing therapy and specialist speech and language therapy are available.

Ystrad Mynach Hospital

Caerphilly Road, Ystrad Mynach, Mid Glamorgan, CF82 7XU

Tel: 01443 812201

Contact: Christine Smith, Speech and Language
                   Therapist

Tel: 01633 234141

To provide assessment and advice on a peripatetic basis to children with hearing impairment as a primary difficulty, and to provide specialist support/advice to community therapists who manage children where hearing impairment is secondary to other difficulties.

➢ Powys

Brecon War Memorial Hospital

Community Health Office, The Annexe, Temple Street, Llandridod Wells, Powys, LD1 5HF

Tel: 01874 622443

Fax: 01874 711828

Contact: Liz Rolt, Head of Speech and
                   Language Therapy

Tel: 01597 824280

Fax: 01597 824280

E-mail: liz.rolt@powys_tr.wales.nhs.uk

No specialist service is provided for deaf children or adults. The general service can provide the following for children from pre-school age to 18: assessment, treatment, counselling, advice and a peripatetic service to schools. Work is done in individual sessions.

➢ South Glamorgan

Communication Aid Centre - Rookwood Hospital

Fairwater Road, Cardiff, South Glamorgan, CF5 2YN

Tel: 029 2056 6281

Fax: 029 2056 4065

Contact: Margaret Desmond, Communication
            Aid Centre

Tel: 029 2055 5677

We aim to provide a service to both adults and children who are experiencing severe communication impairment and who require assessment regarding augmentative communication support.

➢ West Glamorgan

Swansea Speech and Language Therapy Services

Trinity Buildings, Orchard Street, Swansea, West Glamorgan, SA1 5AT

Tel: 01792 651501

Fax: 01792 517018

Contact: Samantha Dales, Speech and
            Language Therapist

Tel: 01792 517863

A specialist service is provided for deaf children. The following services are available for children from pre-school age to 18: assessment and treatment, counselling and advice. A peripatetic service is available, provided by the education service. Work with children is in groups and on an individual basis. The service also organises parent support groups which provide parents with an opportunity to learn and develop communication skills and strategies to help their child's language development. There is currently no specific service for deaf adults.

Hearing Therapists

The primary role of a hearing therapist is to provide aural rehabilitation to adults with an acquired hearing loss. The core elements of aural rehabilitation include lipreading skills, auditory training, communication training and relaxation therapy.

Many hearing therapists also undertake more specialised services. These include management of tinnitus, obscure auditory dysfunction, hyperacusis and dizziness.

It should be noted that most hearing therapists will willingly accept direct enquiries about their services. However the majority will only accept referrals from a professional source, for example audiological centres, which include Ear, Nose and Throat and Hearing Aid Centres.

This section is listed alphabetically by hospital within country and county sections.

England

➤ Avon

Blackberry Hill Hospital

The Speech and Hearing Department, Manor Road, Bristol, Avon, BS16 2EW

Tel: 0117 975 4834

Textphone: 0117 9753835 Frenchay Hospital

Fax: 0117 965 6061

Contact: Helen Merry, Hearing Therapist

Monday to Thursday 9am to 4.30pm. Friday 9am to 3.30pm.

Brentry Hospital

Charlton Road, Westbury-on-Trym, Bristol, Avon, BS10 6JH

Tel: 0117 908 8589

Fax: 0117 959 2308

Phoenix NHS Trust provides health and social care to people with learning disabilities across Avon, including a specialist hearing therapy service. The specialist hearing therapists provide full aural assessment and rehabilitation interventions including hearing tests, hearing aid fittings and follow-ups, communication programmes, advice and staff-training nationally.

St Martins Hospital

Midford Road, Bath, Avon, BA2 5RP

Tel: 01225 836097

Fax: 01225 837934

Contact: Jane Milligan, Head of Hearing Therapy Services

Services provided for adults with an acquired hearing loss include: assessment and treatment, counselling, advice on provision of equipment, vestibular rehabilitation, liaison with social services and other professionals, group work, individual therapy or rehabilitation, tinnitus counselling and fitting maskers, individual sessions, obscure auditory dysfunction rehabilitation, provision of information via lectures, and work with special needs groups (including work with people with learning disabilities).

Weston-Super-Mare General Hospital

Grange Road, Uphill, Weston-Super-Mare, Avon, BS23 4TQ

Tel: 01934 647038

Contact: Norma Kaufman, Hearing Therapist

We are a NHS hospital department whose aim is to provide a high quality service for all our patients. Services provided for adults with an acquired hearing loss include: assessment and treatment, counselling, advice on provision of equipment, vestibular rehabilitation, liaison with social services and other professionals, group work, individual therapy or rehabilitation, tinnitus counselling and fitting maskers, individual sessions, obscure auditory dysfunction rehabilitation and provision of information via lectures.

➤ Bath & NE Somerset
See Avon

Bedfordshire
Bedford General Hospital
Kempston Road, Bedford, MK42 9DJ
Tel: 01234 792191
Textphone: 01234 795888
Fax: 01234 218106
E-mail: KATIEBROWN@bedhos.anglox.nhs.uk
Contact: Rob Richens, Hearing Therapist

Services provided for adults with an acquired hearing loss include: assessment and treatment, counselling, advice on provision of equipment, liaison with social services and other professionals, individual therapy or rehabilitation, tinnitus counselling and fitting maskers, individual sessions, and provision of information via lectures.

Luton and Dunstable Hospital
Lewsey Road, Luton, Bedfordshire, LU4 0DZ
Tel: 01582 497154
Fax: 01582 598990
Contact: Tracy Carroll, Hearing Therapist
Hearing Services

Provides audiological support for ear, nose and throat department. This includes providing hearing tests, issuing hearing aids and offering rehabilitation. Hearing aid repairs and issuing of batteries. The hearing therapist works within the department, offering counselling, practical advice and support and assessing and issuing environmental aids. Also offers auditory training and lipreading tuition. The hearing aid department also a offers direct referral system.

Berkshire
King Edward VII Hospital
St Leonards Road, Windsor, Berkshire, SL4 3DP
Tel: 01753 636224
Textphone: 01753 636229
Fax: 01753 636229
Contact: Debbie King, Hearing Therapist
Audiology Unit

The following services are available: assessment and treatment, counselling, advice on provision of equipment, vestibular rehabilitation, liaison with social services and other professionals, group work, individual therapy or rehabilitation, tinnitus counselling, retraining therapy and relaxation, individual sesssions, provision of information via lectures, and work with special needs groups. Also provided is deaf awareness training for professionals and friends/family.

Royal Berkshire Hospital
London Road, Reading, Berkshire, RG1 5AN
Tel: 0118 987 7231
Textphone: 0118 987 7085
Fax: 0118 987 7075
Contact: Lisa Waite, Senior Hearing Therapist
Hearing Therapy, Audiology II
Tel: 0118 987 7085

Adults with an acquired hearing loss can obtain assessment, treatment, counselling, advice on provision of equipment, vestibular rehabilitation, liaison with social services and other professionals, group work, individual therapy or rehabilitation, tinnitus counselling and the fitting of maskers, individual sessions, obscure auditory dysfunction rehabilitation, provision of information via lectures, work with special needs and cochlear implant rehabilitation.

Blackpool
See Lancashire

Bristol, City of
See Avon

Buckinghamshire
Amersham Health Centre
Chiltern Avenue, Amersham, Buckinghamshire, HP5 6AY
Tel: 01494 722111 ext 262
Fax: 01494 727693
Contact: Jenny Burton, Hearing Therapy
Services Manager

Our aim is the provision of a rehabilitation service suffiently soon after diagnosis to prevent an acquired hearing loss, or related condition, from becoming a serious handicap to the patient. Therapy includes: advice and support to hearing aid users; teaching communications skills; assessing patients' needs for equipment at work; counselling; tinnitus retraining therapy; and vestibular rehabilitation exercises. We also refer to other agencies where appropriate.

5

Stoke Mandeville Hospital

Mandeville Road, Aylesbury, Buckinghamshire, HP21 8AL

Tel: 01296 315755

Textphone: 01296 315725

Contact: Chris Poole, Hearing Therapist Audiology

Services provided include: assessment and treatment, counselling, advice on provision of equipment, liaison with social services and other professionals, group work, individual therapy or rehabilitation, tinnitus counselling and fitting maskers, individual sessions, obscure auditory dysfunction rehabilitation and provision of information via lectures. Lipreading classes are also held here.

Wycombe General Hospital

Queen Alexandra Road, High Wycombe, Buckinghamshire, HP11 2TT

Tel: 01494 734214

Contact: Jenny Burton, Hearing Therapy Services Manager

Tel: 01494 722111

Hearing Therapy and Audiology clinics are held in tandem on certain days. Group reviews for new hearing aid users are also held jointly.

> Cambridgeshire

Addenbrooks Hospital

Hills Road, Cambridge, CB2 2QQ

Tel: 01223 217797

Textphone: 01223 274494

Fax: 01223 217559

E-mail: cat.hodgson@msexc.addenbrooks.anglox.nhs.uk

Contact: Catriona Hodgson, Hearing Therapist, Audiology Department

Provides an audiology service to Cambridge and the surrounding area. Follow-ups, individual rehabilitation programmes, communication courses, lipreading, auditory training, assistive listening devices. A comprehensive care package is offered to all patients as needed.

Edith Cavell Hospital

Bretton Gate, Peterborough, Cambridgeshire, PE3 9GZ

Tel: 01733 874000

Fax: 01733 874001

Contact: Pauline Barnes, Senior Audiological Scientist, Audiology Department

Hinchingbrooke Hospital

Hinchingbrooke Park, Huntingdon, Cambridgeshire, PE18 8NT

Tel: 01480 416416

Contact: Shona McIntosh, Chief Audiologist

Provides a complete service to both adults and children who are needing support, advice or guidance to cope with their deafness. Also provides a full diagnostic service, and tinnitus retraining. Willingness to help or advise anyone needing information and help with any problems relating to deafness.

> Cheshire

Warrington General Hospital

Lovely Lane, Warrington, Cheshire, WA5 1QG

Tel: 01925 662420

Fax: 01925 662048

NHS hearing aid fitting, maintenance, batteries. Full audiometric assessment. Paediatric audiology (including hearing aids). Tinnitus clinic.

> Cleveland

North Riding Infirmary

Newport Road, Middlesbrough, Cleveland, TS1 5JE

Tel: 01642 854051

Textphone: 01642 854072

Fax: 01642 854073

E-mail: audiology@audionri.enterprise_plc.com

Website: homepages.enterprise.net/audionri

Contact: Sandra Murphy, Hearing Therapist Audiology

Tel: 01642 854051 ext 4072

Services provided for adults with an acquired hearing loss includes: assessment and treatment, counselling, advice on provision of equipment, liaison with social services and other professionals, group work, individual therapy or rehabilitation, tinnitus counselling and fitting maskers, individual sessions and provision of information via lectures. The regional Cochlear Implant Programme is also based here.

➢ Cornwall
St Michael's Hospital
Trelissick Road, Hayle, Cornwall, TR27 4JA

Tel: 01736 753234

Fax: 01736 753344

Contact: Lynn Tregenna

Tel: 01736 753234 ext 2268

The Audiology department provides the following services for deaf and hard of hearing people: hearing tests, hearing aid fitting and maintenance, referral to hearing therapy for tinnitus counselling, help with Menieres disease, cochlear implants, environmental equipment at home and at work, referral to social services.

Treliske Hospital
Treliske, Truro, Cornwall, TR1 3LJ

Tel: 01872 274242

Fax: 01872 252603

Contact: Veronica Lavers, Senior Hearing Therapist

Tel: 01872 253744

Textphone: 01872 240892

Fax: 01872 254919

➢ County Durham
Dryburn Hospital
North Road, Durham City, Durham, DH1 5TW

Tel: 0191 333 2166

Textphone: 0191 333 2741

Fax: 0191 333 2724

Contact: Andrea Hall, Hearing Therapist

Provides a complete rehabilitation service to adults with an acquired hearing loss and/or tinnitus.

➢ Derbyshire
Saltergate Health Centre
Saltergate, Chesterfield, Derbyshire, S41 1SX

Tel: 01246 552950

Textphone: 01246 552950

Fax: 01246 552950

Contact: Claire Wootton, Hearing Therapist Audiology Department

Services provided for adults with an acquired hearing loss include: assessment and treatment, counselling, advice on provision of equipment, liaison with social services and other professionals, group work, individual therapy or rehabilitation, tinnitus counselling and fitting maskers, individual sessions, provision of information via lectures, and work with special needs groups.

➢ Devon
Derriford Hospital
Plymouth, Devon, PL6 8DH

Tel: 01752 777111

Textphone: 01752 763180

Contact: Daniel Donovan, Audiology Manager Audiology Department, Level 07

Tel: 01752 763176

Fax: 01752 763185 (Audiology)

Services provided for adults with an acquired hearing loss include: assessment and treatment, counselling, advice on provision of equipment, liaison with social services and other professionals, individual therapy or rehabilitation, tinnitus counselling, provision of information via lectures. All work is done in individual sessions.

➢ Dorset
Dorset County Hospital
Audiology and Hearing Therapy Department, South Wing, Williams Avenue, Dorchester, Dorset, DT1 2JY

Tel: 01305 254262

Textphone: 01305 254444

Fax: 01305 254155

Contact: Edna Laker, Hearing Therapist Audiology and Hearing Therapy Services

Services provided for adults with an acquired hearing loss include: assessment and treatment, counselling, advice on provision of equipment, liaison with social services and other professionals, group work, individual therapy or rehabilitation, tinnitus counselling and fitting maskers, obscure auditory dysfunction rehabilitation and provision of information via lectures.

West Dorset Hospital
Damers Road, Dorchester, Dorset, DT1 2JY

Tel: 01305 254262

Services provided for adults with an acquired hearing loss include: assessment and treatment, counselling, advice on provisions of equipment, liaison with social services and other professionals, group work, individual therapy or rehabilitation, tinnitus counselling and fitting maskers, obscure auditory dysfunction rehabilitation and provision of information via lectures.

Yeatman Hospital

Hospital Lane, Sherborne, Dorset, DT9 3JF

Tel: 01935 813991

Contact: Eleanor Haillay, Casualty Outpatients Department

The Outpatients department at the Yeatman Hospital has a weekly outpatient clinic for ear, nose and throat patients, by appointment. The clinic is led by a consultant from the local district general hospital (Dorchester). Audiology and hearing and technicians attend on the same day (Tuesday), hearing therapist attends on alternate Mondays.

➤ Essex

Corringham Health Centre

Giffords Cross Road, Corringham, Stanford-Le-Hope, Essex, SS17 7QQ

Tel: 01375 674436

Textphone: 01375 361481

Fax: 01375 645313

Contact: Meryl Robinson, Hearing Therapist

To provide rehabilitation and counselling services to adults with acquired hearing loss and/or tinnitus. Issue of tinnitus white noise generators and management of tinnitus. Deaf awareness training. Special interest in adults with profound acquired hearing loss. New equipment loan library.

Essex County Hospital

Lexden Road, Colchester, Essex, CO3 3NB

Tel: 01206 834549

Textphone: 01206 834549

Fax: 01206 834603

Contact: Anna Biggins, Audiology and Hearing Aid Department

Hearing therapy services provided include: assessment and treatment, counselling, advice on provision of equipment, liaison with social services and other professionals, individual therapy or rehabilitation, tinnitus counselling and fitting maskers, individual sessions, obscure auditory dysfunction rehabilitation, provision of information via lectures, work with special needs groups and communication training/lipreading short courses.

Southend Hospital

Prittlewell Chase, Westcliff-on-Sea, Essex, SS0 0RY

Tel: 01702 435555

Fax: 01702 221300

The Hearing Therapy department provides support for all adults with an acquired hearing loss or tinnitus. A joint service is provided for vestibular rehabilitation and learning difficulties.

➤ Gloucestershire

Gloucester Royal Hospital

Occupational Therapy, Gloucester Hospital, Great Western Road, Gloucester, GL1 3NN

Tel: 01452 394258

Textphone: 01452 394258

Fax: 01452 394432

Services provided for adults with an acquired hearing loss include: assessment and treatment, counselling, advice on provision of equipment, liaison with social services and other professionals, group work, individual therapy or rehabilitation, tinnitus counselling and the fitting of maskers, individual sessions, obscure auditory dysfunction rehabilitation and provision of information via lectures.

➤ Hampshire

Ashvale Health Clinic

Wharf Road, Ashvale, Aldershot, Hampshire, GU12 5BA

Tel: 01252 317551

Fax: 01252 334352

Contact: Jacqueline Hocking, Hearing Therapist ENT Department

The Hearing Therapy Service provides adults (aged 16 plus) with an acquired hearing loss, information on equipment and advice on a variety of services within the Surrey and Hampshire Borders NHS Trust. Lipreading classes, a tinnitus group and hard of hearing club and tinnitus clinics are all up and running in the area.

Royal South Hampshire Hospital

Brintons Terrace, Southampton, Hampshire, SO14 0YG

Tel: 023 8082 5436

Textphone: 023 8082 5436

Fax: 023 8082 5085

Contact: Alison Downie, Principal Hearing Therapist
Audiology and Hearing Therapy Department

Services include: assessment and treatment, hearing aid work and tinnitus counselling. The department comprises: audiology, hearing aid clinic, hearing therapy, and undertakes hearing and balance tests on adults and children as a service to the Ear, Nose and Throat department, and hearing tests for patients referred directly by GPs, and it issues, maintains and reviews hearing aid provision. Hearing Therapy provides counselling for adults with an acquired hearing loss.

➢ Hertfordshire

Hertfordshire Hearing Advisory Service

Tel: 01707 324582

Textphone: 01707 375486

Fax: 01707 390644

E-mail: info@hhas.demon.co.uk

Contact: S Grant, Secretary

See entry under Resource Centres.

➢ Kent

Kent and Canterbury Hospital

Ethelbert Road, Canterbury, Kent, CT1 3NG

Tel: 01227 766877

Textphone: 01227 783087

Fax: 01227 783018

Services provided for adults with an acquired hearing loss include: assessment and treatment, counselling, advice on provision of equipment, vestibular rehabilitation, liaison with social services and other professionals, group services, individual therapy or rehabilitation, tinnitus counselling and fitting maskers, individual sessions, obscure auditory dysfunction rehabilitation, provision of information via lectures and work with special needs groups. Selective neo-natal screening is performed. There is assessment and treatment of children although this may be complementary to Kent Paediatric Audiology Service provision.

Kent and Sussex Hospital

Mount Ephraim, Tunbridge Wells, Kent, TN4 8AT

Tel: 01892 526111 ext 2701

Fax: 01892 528381

E-mail: mary-thomas@hearing-therapy.freeserve.co.uk

Contact: Mary Thomas, Senior Hearing Therapist

A comprehensive hearing therapy service provided within an ear, nose and throat department, offering rehabilitation for adults with an acquired hearing loss. Services include tinnitus retraining therapy and fitting of tinnitus instruments, counselling, advice in specialist equipment, teaching of lipreading, auditory skills and communication tactics.

Kent County Ophthalmic and Aural Hospital

Church Street, Maidstone, Kent, ME14 1DT

Tel: 01622 673444 ext 6244

Fax: 01622 226197

Contact: Mary Thomas, Senior Hearing Therapist

A hearing therapy service is provided within the Ear, Nose and Throat department, for adults with acquired hearing loss. Younger patients are seen following consultants' referral. The service includes assessment and treatment, counselling, tinnitus retraining therapy, auditory retraining and lipreading and provision of information via lectures and training. Note: This service is also provided at Medway Hospital, Gillingham, Kent (contact as above).

Royal Victoria Hospital Folkestone

Radnor Park Avenue, Folkestone, Kent, CT19 5HN

Tel: 01303 850202

The Royal Hospitals Trust provides a full audiological diagnostic, assessment and rehabilitiation service for children and adults with hearing vestibular dysfunction, tinnitus and hyperacusis. The team includes otolaryngologists, an audiological scientist, a hearing therapist and a full complement of audiology technical staff. One of the consultant otolaryngologists specialises in paediatric audiology and another has a special interest in deaf and hearing impaired adults and people with tinnitus.

➢ Lancashire

Centre for Human Communication and Deafness

Oxford Road, Manchester, Lancashire, M13 9PL

Tel:	0161 275 3363
Textphone:	0161 275 3361
Fax:	0161 275 3373
E-mail:	deborah.mowman@man.ac.uk
Website:	www.man.ac.uk/education/caedsp.htm#top
Contact:	Deborah Mawman, Hearing Therapist

The Centre for Audiology provides the following services: assessment and treatment, counselling, advice on the provision of equipment, liaison with social services and other professionals, individual therapy or rehabilitation, individual sessions, provision of information via lectures and cochlear implant rehabilitation.

Hope Hospital

Stott Lane, Salford, Lancashire, M6 8HD

Tel:	0161 787 4702
Fax:	0161 787 4237
Contact:	Sheila Fidler, Hearing Therapist Audiology

Services provided for adults with an acquired hearing loss include: auditory training, lipreading one-to-one, employment advice for the hearing impaired, hearing and orientation and support, assessment and treatment, counselling, advice on provision of equipment, liaison with social services and other professionals, group work, lipreading classes, individual therapy or rehabilitation, tinnitus counselling and fitting maskers, individual sessions, obscure auditory dysfunction rehabilitation, provision of information via lectures and work with special needs groups. Heather Bamforth is a senior audiologist at Hope Hospital. She is also qualified as a registered hearing aid dispenser and is able to sell commercial hearing aids on behalf of Salford Community Trust.

Nelson Health Centre

Leeds Road, Nelson, Lancashire, BB9 9TG

Tel:	01282 690138
Textphone:	01282 690138
Fax:	01282 601544
Contact:	Shirley Godfrey, Manager, Hearing Therapy Services

A domiciliary service is available to those unable to attend the hearing therapy clinic. The service values the support of families, carers and staff of other agencies and voluntary organisations in facilitating adaption to hearing loss and reducing the effects of sensory disability. Advice and training are offered as required.

Victoria Hospital

Whinney Heys Road, Blackpool, Lancashire, FY3 8NR

Tel:	01253 303500
Textphone:	01253 306735
Fax:	01253 306709
Contact:	Rebecca Dobson, Hearing Therapist
Fax:	01253 837934

Services include assessment and treatment, general hearing aid work, cochlear implant rehabilitation and balance work. Domiciliary visits can be arranged. A hearing support group meets here.

Withington Hospital

Nell Lane, Manchester, Lancashire, M20 2LR

Tel:	0161 291 3195
Textphone:	0161 291 3195
Fax:	0161 291 3154
Contact:	Dr Graham Day, Head of Audiological Services, Consultant Audiological Scientist
Tel:	0161 291 3150

South Manchester NHS Trust provides a full diagnostic service for adults and children with hearing loss, tinnitus or balance disorders. In addition, services provided for adults with an acquired hearing loss include: assessment and treatment, counselling, advice on provision of equipment, liaison with social services and other professionals, group work, individual sessions, individual therapy or rehabilitation, tinnitus counselling and fitting maskers, and provision of information via lectures. Lipreading classes at this centre are held on Mondays from 1 to 3pm. Dr Day and Patricia Mellor are registered hearing aid dispensers and are available for consultation by appointment. Please telephone for further information.

➢ Leicester

See Leicestershire

➢ Leicestershire

Leicester Royal Infirmary

Infirmary Square, Leicester, LE1 5WW

Tel: 0116 254 1414

Fax: 0116 258 5631

Contact: Ena Martin, Hearing Therapist

Tel: 0116 258 5578

Services provided for adults with an acquired hearing loss include: counselling, advice on provision of equipment, liaison with social services and other professionals, group work, individual therapy or rehabilitation, tinnitus counselling and fitting maskers, individual sessions, provision of information via lectures, individual and group lipreading.

➢ London

Central Middlesex Hospital

Acton Lane, London, NW10 7NS

Tel: 020 8453 2374

Textphone: 020 8453 2350

Fax: 020 8453 2630

The services provided for adults with an acquired hearing loss include: assessment and treatment, counselling, advice on provision of equipment, liaison with social services and other professionals, individual therapy or rehabilitation, tinnitus counselling and fitting maskers, obscure auditory dysfunction, rehabilitation and provision of information via lectures.

Charing Cross Hospital

1st Floor, South Wing, Fulham Palace Road, London, W6 8RF

Tel: 020 8846 1023

Fax: 020 8846 1022

Contact: Jayne Evans, Hearing Therapist

We offer a range of rehabilitation for adults with obscure auditory dysfunction, acquired hearing loss, tinnitus or dizziness on an individual basis, including a referral system for obtaining assistive devices from the Local Authority. We also hold regular seminars and lectures to train and promote better understanding of hearing impairment.

Guy's Hospital

St Thomas Street, London, SE1 9RT

Tel: 020 7955 4081

Textphone: 020 7955 4081

Fax: 020 7955 8849

Contact: Karen Archer, Hearing Therapist and Cochlear Implant Coordinator

Textphone: 020 8922 8034

The following services are available: assessment and treatment, counselling, advice on provision of equipment, vestibular rehabilitation, liaison with social services and other professionals, individual therapy or rehabilitation, tinnitus counselling and the fitting of maskers, individual sessions, obscure auditory dysfunction, rehabilitation and provision of information via lectures. Also available is advice on cochlear implants, bone anchored hearing aids and implantable hearing aids. Lipreading tuition to individuals is also available.

Royal National Throat Nose and Ear Hospital

330-332 Grays Inn Road, London, WC1X 8DA

Tel: 020 7915 1521

Videotel: 020 7713 5031

Fax: 020 7915 1511

Services provided for adults being fitted with a cochlear implant include: assessment, treatment, counselling, advice on provision of equipment, vestibular rehabilitation, liaison with social services and other professionals, group work, individual therapy or rehabilitation, tinnitus counselling and fitting maskers, individual sessions, obscure auditory dysfunction rehabilitation, provision of information via lectures and work with special needs groups. The UCL Cochlear Impant Programme is based here and can also be accessed via the e-mail address above. The direct phone numbers are 020 7915 1301/2 and Fax: 020 7915 1303.

St Ann's Hospital

St Ann's Road, London, N15 3TH

Tel: 020 8442 6000

Fax: 020 8442 6769

Contact: Mark Sleigh, Hearing Therapist

Tel: 020 8442 6524

Textphone: 020 8442 6387

Services include: general hearing aid evaluation and fitting, tinnitus counselling and hearing therapy. In addition to this we provide neuro-otology assessments, school screening, and domiciliary visits.

St Bartholomew's Hospital

West Smithfield, London, EC1A 7BE

Tel: 020 7601 7434

Contact: Helen Pitman, Hearing Therapist

We aim to provide an assessment and rehabilitation service that includes: testing, fitting and management of hearing aids; communication training; enviromental aid advice and demonstration; counselling; support group for deafened adults; tinnitus management (TRT); relaxation therapy; vestibular testing and rehabilitation.

St George's Hospital

Department of Audiological Medicine, Lanesborough Wing Level O, London, SW17 0QT

Tel: 020 8725 1880

Textphone: 020 8725 3019

Fax: 020 8725 1874

Contact: Janet Woodcock, Chief Hearing
            Therapist
            Hearing Therapy, ENT Outpatients

Tel: 020 8725 1882

Textphone: 020 8725 3020

The deaprtment of Audiological Medicine provides an outpatient service for people of all ages having problems with hearing, balance, tinnitus or communication. The Hearing Therapy department aims to continue assessment, management and rehabilitation of the above. We aim to expand so that habituation rehabilitation for balance, tinnitus and hearing is brought in line with demand. Continuing education will be prioritised.

St Mary Abbots Hospital

2 Beatrice Place, London, W8 5LP

Tel: 020 8846 6011

Fax: 020 8846 6012

Contact: Jayne Evans, Hearing Therapist,
            Hearing Aid Clinic

We offer a range of rehabilitation for adults with obscure auditory dysfunction, acquired hearing loss, tinnitus or dizziness on an individual basis, including a referral system for obtaining assistive devices from the Local Authority. We also hold regular seminars and lectures to train and promote better understanding of hearing impairment.

St Thomas' Hospital

Lambeth Palace Road, London, SE1 7EH

Tel: 020 7922 8034

Textphone: 020 7922 8241

Fax: 020 7922 8088

Contact: Karen Archer, Hearing Therapist and
            Cochlear Implant Coordinator

We provide a major cochlear implant programme in the region for adults and PALDS. We also offer a comprehensive service for bone anchored hearing aids and Vibrant Soundbridge Implantable hearing aids. St Thomas' and Guy's offer a full audiological service, including hearing therapy, tinnitus and vestibular rehabilitation and counselling and day service.

The City Lit Centre for Deaf People

Tel: 020 7405 5118

Videotel: 020 7831 0736

Fax: 020 7831 6121

E-mail: CFDP@citylit.ac.uk

Contact: Bunty Levene, Hearing Therapist

Tel: 020 7242 3078

Textphone: 020 7430 0548

See entry under Further Education.

The Royal London Hospital

Whitechapel, London, E1 1BB

Tel: 020 7377 7673

Contact: Helen Pitman, Hearing Therapist,
            Audiology and Hearing Service

We aim to provide an assessment and rehabilitation service that includes: testing, fitting and management of hearing aids, communication training, environmental aid service and demonstration, counselling, support group for deafened adults, tinnitus management (TRT), relaxation therapy, vestibular testing and rehabilitation.

➢ Luton
See Bedfordshire

➢ Merseyside

Arrowe Park Hospital
Arrowe Park Road, Wirral, Merseyside, L49 5PE
Tel: 0151 604 7113
Textphone: 0151 604 7448
Fax: 0151 604 1682
Contact: Ann Bennoch, Chief Technician

Services provided for adults with an acquired hearing loss include: assessment and treatment, counselling, advice on provision of equipment, individual therapy or rehabilitation, tinnitus counselling and fitting maskers. Lipreading classes are also held here.

Hearing Care Liverpool
Darwin Cottage, 71 Sefton Road, Litherland, Liverpool, Merseyside, L21 9HG
Tel: 0151 920 9420
Fax: 0151 920 9420
Contact: Dee Davies, Hearing Therapist

Services include: general hearing aid work, tinnitus counselling and balance work. Domiciliary visits can be arranged.

Royal Liverpool University Hospital
Prescot Street, Liverpool, Merseyside, L7 8XP
Tel: 0151 706 2000
Fax: 0151 706 5976

Services provided include: assessment and treatment, vestibular rehabilitation, tinnitus counselling or fitting maskers, individual sessions, provision of information via lectures.

Victoria Central Hospital
Mill Lane, Wallasey, Merseyside, L44 5UF
Tel: 0151 678 5111
Fax: 0151 639 2478
Contact: Ann Bennett, Chief Technician, Audiology
Tel: 0151 604 7113
Hearing aid support service on Friday mornings only.

➢ Middlesex

Ashford Hospital
London Road, Ashford, Middlesex, TW15 3AA
Tel: 01784 884126
Fax: 01784 884107
Contact: Tanya Morgan, Hearing Therapist

The following services are available: hearing aid provision and follow-up, counselling on hearing loss, tinnitus and obscure auditory dysfunction, liaison with social services and other professionals.

Chase Farm Hospital
The Ridgeway, Enfield, Middlesex, EN2 8JL
Tel: 020 8366 9117
Textphone: 020 8967 5923
Fax: 020 8967 5923 (ring first)
Contact: Valerie Tait, Hearing Therapist, The Hearing Aid Centre

Services include: general hearing aid work and rehabilitation, tinnitus management, balance work, environmental aids advice and assessment, deaf awareness training, communication training.

Hillingdon Hospital
Pield Heath Road, Uxbridge, Middlesex, UB8 3NN
Tel: 01895 279343
Fax: 01895 279669
Contact: Pauline Dorrian, Hearing Therapist
Tel: 01895 279817

Hearing therapy services provided include: assessment and treatment, counselling, advice on provision of equipment, vestibular rehabilitation, liaison with social services and other professionals, individual therapy or rehabilitation, tinnitus counselling and fitting white noise generators, and individual sessions.

West Middlesex University Hospital
Twickenham Road, Isleworth, Middlesex, TW7 6AF
Tel: 020 8560 2121
Textphone: 020 8565 5677
Fax: 020 8565 5333
Contact: Eleni Kirkbride, Hearing Therapist

The purpose of the Hearing Therapy Unit is to provide an efficient and comprehensive service to people with auditory disorders. The aim is to help individuals to overcome some of their problems, thereby improving their quality of life.

➤ Norfolk

Colman Hospital

Unthank Road, Norwich, Norfolk, NR2 2PJ

Tel: 01603 288917

Textphone: 01603 288993

Fax: 01603 288946

Contact: Michael Horwood, Chief Hearing
            Therapist

James Paget Hospital

Lowestoft Road, Gorleston, Great Yarmouth,
Norfolk, NR31 6LA

Tel: 01493 452343/ 452287

Fax: 01493 452778

Contact: Michael Horwood, Hearing Therapist
            Audiology Department

Tel: 01493 452343/ 452287/ 452287

A specialist speech therapy service is provided for
deaf children and adults consisting of assessment,
treatment and advice given in either group or
individual sessions. There is also a peripatetic
service for schools. A service is provided for
deafened children and adults. Hearing therapy
services include general hearing aid work and
tinnitus counselling. Domiciliary visits can be
arranged.

Queen Elizabeth Hospital

Gayton Road, King's Lynn, Norfolk, PE30 4ET

Tel: 01553 613805

Textphone: 01533 613888

Fax: 01553 613700

Services include general hearing aid work and
tinnitus counselling. Domiciliary visits can be
arranged.

➤ North Yorkshire

Friarage Hospital

Northallerton, North Yorkshire, DL6 1JG

Tel: 01609 763212

Fax: 01609 764638

Contact: Christine Welsh, Audiologist/ Hearing
            Therapist
            Audiology Department

Hearing assessments, both adult and paediatric.
Hearing aid fitting and follow-up. Advice and
provision of environmental aids and liaison with
social worker for the learning impaired. Work with
adults with learning difficulties. Tinnitus
counselling, fitting of retraining devices. Some
individual therapy or rehabilitation.

➤ Nottinghamshire

Hearing Services Centre Nottingham

Ropewalk House, 113 The Ropewalk, Nottingham,
NG1 6HA

Tel: 0115 948 5525

Fax: 0115 948 5515

The Hearing Services Centre provides a wide range
of high quality services to people of all ages.
These include comprehensive testing of hearing
and balance disorders; rehabilition of hearing
problems using modern technology and
techniques from hearing aids to cochlear implants;
tinnitus management; and services for adults with
learning disabilities.

➤ Oxfordshire

Radcliffe Infirmary

Woodstock Road, Oxford, OX2 6HE

Tel: 01865 224559

Fax: 01865 224566

Contact: Richard Gledhill, Audiology
            Department

A specialist service is provided for deaf children
from pre-school to the age of 18, providing
assessment, treatment, counselling, advice and a
peripatetic service to schools. Work is done in
groups and on an individual basis. Adults are also
seen in either groups or individual sessions for
assessment, treatment, counselling and advice.
There is also a service for deafened children and
adults. Services provided for adults with an
acquired hearing loss include: assessment and
treatment, counselling, advice on provision of
equipment, liaison with social services and other
professionals, individual therapy or rehabilitation,
tinnitus counselling and fitting maskers, individual
sessions and obscure auditory dysfunction
rehabilitation. The Regional Cochlear Implant
Programme is based here.

➤ Peterborough

See Cambridgeshire

➤ Plymouth

See Devon

➤ Reading
See Berkshire

➤ Shropshire
Princess Royal Hospital

Apley Castle, Grainger Drive, Telford, Shropshire, TF6 6TF

Tel: 01952 641222
Textphone: 01952 222901
Fax: 01952 243405
Contact: Vicky Fieldhouse, Hearing Therapist
            Audiology Department

Services include general hearing aid work and balance work. Domiciliary visits can be arranged.

Royal Shrewsbury Hospital (North)

Mytton Oak Road, Shrewsbury, Shropshire, SY3 8XQ

Tel: 01743 261482
Textphone: 01743 261484
Fax: 01743 261483

Mainstream hospital Audiology department within a district general hospital, offering hearing aid services, tinnitus support and hearing therapy. Many clinics are held in local premises throughout Shropshire. There are close working relations with the Sensory Impairment Team, Sensory Resource Service (offering hearing aid support workers and communication courses) and the education services. Beginners' lipreading courses are provided free of charge throughout the county.

➤ Somerset
Musgrove Park Hospital

Musgrove Park, Taunton, Somerset, TA1 5DA

Tel: 01823 342188
Textphone: 01823 342188
Fax: 01823 336877
Contact: Lisa Richards, Hearing Therapist

Hearing therapy service provided for adults with a hearing loss. Service include: assessment and treatment, counselling, advise on provisions of equipment, liasion with social services and other professionals, Tinnitus retraining, vestibular rehabilitation, lipreading, deaf awareness lectures. Rehabilitation for all deafened adults.

➤ South Yorkshire
Doncaster Royal Infirmary

Armthorpe Road, Doncaster, South Yorkshire, DN2 5LY

Tel: 01302 553115
Textphone: 01302 553115
Fax: 01302 738308

Services include: tinnitus counselling and balance work, general assessment, hearing aid work, counselling skills. Domiciliary visits can be arranged. Classes in lipreading are also available.

➤ Southampton
See Hampshire

➤ Southend
See Essex

➤ Staffordshire
North Staffordshire Hospital

Hartshill Road, Stoke-On-Trent, Staffordshire, ST4 7PA

Tel: 01782 716095
Textphone: 01782 715444
Fax: 01782 716591
Contact: Jane Clarke, Hearing Therapist
            Audiology Department
Tel: 01782 554095

Services include: hearing tests, hearing aid provision and maintenance, satellite clinics, bone-anchored hearing aid work, domiciliary visits by arrangement. Hearing therapy services include: tinnitus counselling, hearing tactics, follow-ups, relaxation, some lipreading (one-to-one) and vertigo rehabilitation.

Stafford District General Hospital

Weston Road, Stafford, ST16 3SA

Tel: 01785 257731
Videotel: 01785 230538
Contact: Louise Storrow, Hearing Therapist
Tel: 01785 257731 ext 4183

The hearing therapist is employed part-time and cannot offer a full service. The service offers assessment, treatment, advice on provision of equipment, liaison with social services and other professionals, individual therapy and rehabilitation, tinnitus counselling and the fitting of maskers, individual sessions and lipreading skills.

Stoke-on-Trent
See Staffordshire

Suffolk
Ipswich and Suffolk Hospital
Heath Road, Ipswich, Suffolk, IP4 5PD
Tel: 01473 703873
Textphone: 01473 703112
Fax: 01473 703111
Contact: Tricia Black, Hearing Therapist

Provides an aural rehabilitation service to adults with hearing loss and offers counselling and support for tinnitus, hyperacusis and balance problems. Domiciliary visits can be arranged.

Surrey
Epsom General Hospital
Dorking Road, Epsom, Surrey, KT18 7EG
Tel: 01372 735277
Textphone: 01372 735313
Fax: 01372 735159
Contact: Judith Hunt, Hearing Therapy Department

The Hearing Therapy department provides adults with an acquired hearing loss who have a rehabilitation programme, including counselling, hearing aid management and auditory rehabilitation. There is also provision of a tinnitus and vertigo clinic. Community Hearing Health, in conjunction with RAD Support Worker provides a service to people in their own homes.

Frimley Park Hospital
ENT Department, Portsmouth Road, Frimley, Camberley, Surrey, GU16 5UJ
Tel: 01276 604604
Textphone: 01276 604604 ext 4620
Fax: 01276 604148
Contact: Jacqueline Hocking, Hearing Therapist

Tinnitus self-help group meets locally on the second Wednesday of each month. Tinnitus cllinic twice per month. Hearing aid work, balancer course. Domiciliary visits, counselling, environmental aid work. Lipreading classes.

Mayday University Hospital
London Road, Thornton Heath, Surrey, CR7 7YE
Tel: 020 8401 3063

The aim of the Hearing Therapy department is to promote good communication between people with normal hearing and those who are hard of hearing. We deal with tinnitus and cochlear implants, teach lipreading, and rehabilitate people with all levels of hearing loss.

Royal Surrey County Hospital
Egerton Road, Guildford, Surrey, GU2 5XX
Tel: 01483 464108
Textphone: 01483 571122
Fax: 01483 464108
Contact: Tanya Morgan, Hearing Therapist, Audiology Department

The following services are available: assessment and treatment including hearing aid provision and follow-ups, counselling, advice on provision of equipment, liaison with social services and other professionals, group work, individual therapy or rehabilitation, tinnitus counselling, obscure auditory dysfunction and provision of information via lectures.

St Helier Hospital
Wrythe Lane, Carshalton, Surrey, SM5 1AA
Tel: 020 8296 2911
Textphone: 020 8644 1968
Fax: 020 8641 4546
Contact: Pauline Tarrant, Hearing Aid Dispenser, Audiology Department
Tel: 020 8296 2565

Provides a comprehensive diagnostic and rehabilitative audiological service for both adults and children, supported by a full range of hearing therapy services. This includes aural rehabilitation with a range of NHS hearing aids. A private dispensing service is also available.

➢ Tyne and Wear
Sunderland General Hospital
Woodford Williams Wing, Chester Road
Outpatients, Sunderland, Tyne and Wear, SR4 7TU

Tel: 0191 569 9001

Fax: 0191 569 9213

E-mail: audiology.rmpd@sunderland.ac.uk

Website: www.fe-inf.demon.co.uk/sei/chs

The Audiology department is located at
Sunderland Royal Hospital providing a service to a
population of approximately 700,000 and covering
the main population centres of Sunderland, South
Shields and Washington. There are a total of 21
staff in the department including two audiological
scientists, 12 audiology technicians, a hearing
therapist, three earmould lab technicians, two
ATOs and clerical support. The department
provides a comprehensive range of audiological
services including adult and paediatric aural
rehabilitation, adult and paediatric hearing
assessment, ERA and vestibulacity and hearing
therapy. The hospital has excellent audiological
facilities. Satellite services are provided at
Palmers Community Hospital in South Tyneside
and Washington Health Centre.

➢ Warrington
See Cheshire

➢ West Midlands
Cottage Street Hearing Centre
Cottage Street, Brierley Hill, Dudley, West
Midlands, DY5 1RE

Tel: 01384 480011

Textphone: 01384 75372

Fax: 01384 485387

Contact: Rachel Byng, Audiology Services
                Manager

The Audiology Service offers a comprehensive
range of hearing assessments. Neonatal hearing
screening on 'targeted' babies. Children's hearing
tests up until leaving education. Paediatric
hearing aid fittings. Adult hearing assessment via
GPs or Ear, Nose and Throat referral. NHS hearing
aid fittings and tinnitus counselling via Ear, Nose
and Throat referral. 'Drop in' service for advice
and hearing aid maintenance: open Monday to
Friday until 7pm.

Hearing Services Centre Birmingham
Western Road, Birmingham, West Midlands, B18
7QQ

Tel: 0121 507 4875

Contact: Gemma Stevens, Hearing Therapist

Services provided include: assessment and
treatment, counselling, advice on provision of
equipment, vestibular rehabilitation, liaison with
social services and other professionals, group
work, individual therapy or rehabilitation,
individual sessions, provision of information via
lectures, and work with special needs group.
There is also a branch of David Ormerod Hospital
Hearing Centre here. Opening times are from 9am
to 4.30pm Monday to Friday. Service includes five
years' guaranteed aftercare service and a free six-
monthly hearing healthcheck.

Rehabilitation Services For Deafened People

Tel: 0121 627 8930

Textphone: 0121 627 8932

Fax: 0121 627 8931

Contact: Christine Mann,
                Coordinator/Administrator

See entry under Resource Centres.

West Park Hospital
Park Road West, Wolverhampton, West Midlands,
WV1 4PW

Tel: 01902 444055

Textphone: 01902 444057

Fax: 01902 444056

Contact: Paul Holiday, Professional Head of
                Audiology

The Hearing Services department provides an
audiological service to hearing impaired children
and adults. Technical services include a range of
hearing and balance tests plus provision of
hearing aids, instruction in their use, and repair
and maintenance. Hearing Therapy services
include advice on communication tactics,
individual and group lipreading sessions, advice
on environmental aid provision and tinnitus
retraining therapy. Relaxation training for tinnitus
patients is also provided on a group or individual
basis. Services are provided at West Park Hospital
plus additional locations throughout
Wolverhampton. Outreach clinics are provided at
out-of-town locations on a regular basis.

Yardley Green Hospital

Yardley Green Road, Birmingham, West Midlands, B9 5PX

Tel: 0121 766 6611

Fax: 0121 766 6935

Contact: Amanda Casey, Hearing Aid Centre

Hearing therapy service for adults with acquired hearing loss. Rehabilitation and management of associated disorders such as tinnitus, vestibular dysfunction, obscure auditory dysfunction and hyperacusis.

➤ West Yorkshire

Bradford Royal Infirmary

Duckworth Lane, Bradford, West Yorkshire, BD9 6RJ

Tel: 01274 542200

Fax: 01274 364026

Contact: Pauline Beesley, Audiologist

Tel: 01274 542200 ext 4311

Services provided for adults with an acquired hearing loss include: assessment and treatment, counselling, advice on provision of equipment, liaison with social services and other professionals, individual therapy or rehabilitation, tinnitus counselling and tinnitus retraining therapy, individual sessions, provision of information via lectures, assessment of adults (regarding suitability for a cochlear implant), counselling the person with hearing loss and family members, providing rehabilitation for the adult implantee.

➤ Wiltshire

Salisbury District Hospital

Odstock Road, Salisbury, Wiltshire, SP2 8BJ

Tel: 01722 429335

Textphone: 0800 435543

Fax: 01722 322871

Contact: Karen Dewhurst, Audiology
            Department Manager

Department of Audiology and Hearing Therapy serving the Ear, Nose and Throat department at Salisbury District Hospital for Salisbury Health Care NHS Trust. Private consultations for commercial hearing aids are also available.

➤ Windsor and Maidenhead

See Berkshire

Northern Ireland

➤ County Antrim

Royal Victoria Hospital Belfast

Grosvenor Road, Belfast, County Antrim, BT12 6BA

Tel: 028 9024 0503

Textphone: 028 9089 4622

Fax: 028 9043 8471

Contact: Mary Mitchell, Senior Hearing
            Therapist
            Hearing Therapy

Tel: 028 9089 4622

The following services are provided: assessment and treatment, counselling, advice on provision of equipment, vestibular rehabilitation, liaison with social services and other professionals, group work, individual therapy or rehabilitation, tinnitus counselling and the fitting of maskers, individual sessions, obscure auditory dysfunction rehabilitation, provision of information via lectures, and work with special needs groups. Repair clinic for hearing aids is held from 9.30am till 12 noon on Mondays, Wednesdays and Thursdays and from 2 till 4pm on Fridays.

Ulster Hospital

Upper Newtownards Road, Dundonald, Belfast, County Antrim, BT16 0RH

Tel: 028 9048 4511

Fax: 028 9048 1166

Hearing aid repair clinic is open on Tuesdays and Thursdays from 2 to 4pm.

⟩ County Armagh
Craigavon Area Hospital

68 Lurgan Road, Portadown, Craigavon, County Armagh, BT63 5QQ

Tel: 028 3833 4444

Textphone: 028 3861 2632

Fax: 028 3835 0068

Contact: Geraldine Bankhead, Hearing Therapist

Tel: 028 3861 2632

Services provided for adults with an acquired hearing loss include: assessment and treatment, counselling, advice on provision of equipment, liaison with social services and other professionals, group work, individual therapy or rehabilitation, tinnitus counselling and fitting maskers, individual sessions, obscure auditory dysfunction rehabilitation, provision of information via lectures, work with special needs groups, and assertiveness classes for hard of hearing people.

Eire

⟩

Beaumont Hospital

Beaumont Road, Dublin 9, Eire

Tel: 00 353 1 837 7755

Fax: 00 353 1 837 6982

Contact: Kay Walsh, Hearing Therapist Coordinator

Tel: 00 353 1 809 2191

The Cochlear Implant Programme at Beaumont Hospital in Dublin is the national centre for assessment and implantation for children and deafened adults. The centre only accepts referrals from ear professionals in the medical field. Children and adults who attend and who are not suitable for implantation also receive ongoing support.

Scotland

⟩ Fife
Victoria Hospital

Hayfield Road, Kirkcaldy, Fife, KY1 2HP

Contact: Christine Placido, Audiology Department

To provide assessment and rehabilitation for children and adults who have hearing and balance problems and tinnitus.

⟩ Midlothian
Royal Infirmary Edinburgh

Clerwood Terrace, Edinburgh, Midlothian, EH12 8TS

Tel: 0131 317 3688

Fax: 0131 317 3689

E-mail: h.mcleish@qmced.ac.uk

The hearing therapist's role is to provide rehabilitation for adults with hearing problems and for associated disorders. The service also includes: counselling, relaxation, communication training, lipreading, environmental aids display, tinnitus retraining and cochlear implant rehabilitation. Also helps with hearing aid follow-up and works closely with Audiology, social services and voluntary workers.

Wales

⟩ Bridgend
See Mid Glamorgan

⟩ Cardiff
See South Glamorgan

⟩ Clwyd
Glan Clwyd Hospital

Rhuddlan Road, Bodelwyddan, Rhyl, Clwyd, LL18 5UJ

Tel: 01745 534524

Textphone: 01745 534342

Fax: 01745 534932

Website: www.glanclwyd.demon.co.uk/audiology/index.html

Contact: Christine Wynne, Chief Medical Technical Officer (Audiology)

Services provided include: assessment, treatment, counselling, advice on provision of equipment, vestibular rehabilitation, liaison with social services and other professionals, group work, individual therapy or rehabilitation, tinnitus counselling and fitting maskers, individual sessions, provision of information via lectures, and cochlear implants. There is also a branch of David Ormerod Hospital Hearing Centre here. Opening times are 9am to 4.15pm Monday to Friday. Service includes five years' guaranteed aftercare service and a free six-monthly hearing health check.

5

➢ Gwynedd
Llandudno Hospital

Ffordd Ysbyty, Llandudno, Gwynedd, LL30 1LB

Tel: 01492 860066

Fax: 01492 871668

Contact: Jenny Buels, Hearing Therapist

Tel: 01248 384384

Hearing therapy aims to maximise communicative ability and involves advice/information on hearing aids and environmental aids, plus tinnitus counselling, auditory training, lipreading tuition, cochlear implant rehabilitation, relaxation therapy and balance rehabilitation. Regular clinics are held in several parts of the country. Domiciliary visits can be arranged.

Ysbyty Gwynedd

Penrhosgarnedd, Bangor, Gwynedd, LL57 2PW

Tel: 01248 384384

Fax: 01248 370629

Contact: Jenny Buels, Hearing Therapist

Hearing therapy aims to maximise communicative ability and involves advice/information on hearing aids and environmental aids, plus tinnitus counselling, auditory training, lipreading tuition, cochlear implant rehabilitation, relaxation therapy and balance rehabilitation. Regular clinics are held in several parts of the country. Domiciliary visits can be arranged if necessary.

➢ Mid Glamorgan
Princess of Wales Hospital

Coity Road, Bridgend, Mid Glamorgan, CF31 1RQ

Tel: 01656 752192

Textphone: 01656 752192

Fax: 01656 752107

E-mail: audiology.pwh@bridgend-tr.wales.nhs.uk

Contact: Jonathan Joseph, Principal Audiological Scientist

Tel: 01656 752189

The Cochlear Implant Programme in Brigend offers assessment, surgery and rehabilitation services for adults and children. Audiology services include: general hearing aid work, tinnitus counselling, environmental aid work and vestibular rehabilitation.

➢ South Glamorgan
University Hospital of Wales

Heath Park, Cardiff, South Glamorgan, CF4 4XW

Tel: 029 2074 7747

Textphone: 029 2074 3179

Fax: 029 2074 3288

Contact: Jonathan Arthur, Chief Audiologist, Adult Unit

Tel: 029 2074 3179

The following services are provided: assessment and treatment, counselling, advice on the provision of equipment, vestibular rehabilitation, liaison with social services and other professionals, group work, individual therapy or rehabilitation, tinnitus counselling and fitting maskers, individual sessions, obscure auditory dysfunction rehabilitation, provision of information via lectures, work with special needs groups, and rehabilitation of profoundly deaf people with vibro tactile aids and cochlear implants.

➢ Swansea
See West Glamorgan

➢ West Glamorgan
Singleton Hospital

Sketty, Swansea, West Glamorgan, SA2 8GA

Tel: 01792 285861

Textphone: 01792 285861

Fax: 01792 208647

Comprehensive NHS hearing aid service. Advice for hearing impaired people. Tinnitus counselling and provision of noise generators.

Audiology Clinics

This section is a list of hospitals and clinics providing audiological services. Further details should be obtained from the departments themselves.

This section is listed alphabetically by hospital within country and county sections.

England

➢ Avon

Bristol Royal Hospital for Sick Children

St. Michaels Hill, Bristol, Avon, BS2 8BJ

Tel: 0117 928 5350

We offer a comprehensive paediatric audiology service including diagnosis of hearing loss, confirmation of normal hearing, management of hearing loss (both sensorineural and conductive), fitting and ongoing monitoring of hearing aids, liaison with education service. We aim to diagnose and treat appropriately, any child with congenital permanent deafness within the first year of life.

Bristol Royal Infirmary

Marlborough Street, Bristol, Avon, BS2 8HW

Tel: 0117 923 0000

Textphone: 0117 934 9869

Fax: 0117 928 5859

Royal United Hospital

Combe Park, Bath, Avon, BA1 3NG

Southmead Hospital

Westbury-on-Trym, Bristol, Avon, BS9 1LP

Tel: 0117 959 5680

St Michael's Hospital

Southwell Street, Bristol, Avon, BS2 8EG

Tel: 0117 928 5854

Weston-Super-Mare General Hospital

Grange Road, Uphill, Weston-Super-Mare, Avon, BS23 4TQ

Tel: 01934 647038

➢ Bath & NE Somerset

See Avon

➢ Bedfordshire

Bedford General Hospital

Kempston Road, Bedford, MK42 9DJ

Tel: 01234 792191

Textphone: 01234 795888

Fax: 01234 218106

E-mail: KATIEBROWN@bedhos.anglox.nhs.uk

Covers Ear, Nose and Throat clinics on site and outreach clinics in Bedfordshire. Issues and repairs hearing aids for all age groups. Performs auditory brain-stem response testing on babies and people with learning disabilities. They have facilities to perform caloric tests and other balance function tests. A domiciliary service is available.

Luton and Dunstable Hospital

Lewsey Road, Luton, Bedfordshire, LU4 0DZ

Tel: 01582 497154

Fax: 01582 598990

➢ Berkshire

King Edward VII Hospital

St Leonards Road, Windsor, Berkshire, SL4 3DP

Tel: 01753 636224

Textphone: 01753 636229

Fax: 01753 636229

Royal Berkshire Hospital

London Road, Reading, Berkshire, RG1 5AN

Tel: 0118 987 7231

Textphone: 0118 987 7085

Fax: 0118 987 7075

Wexham Park Hospital

Wexham Street, Wexham, Slough, Berkshire, SL2 4HL

Tel: 01753 633000

Fax: 01753 634848

6

> ## Bournemouth
See Dorset

> ## Brighton and Hove
See East Sussex

> ## Buckinghamshire
Milton Keynes General Hospital
Standing Way, Eaglestone, Milton Keynes,
Buckinghamshire, MK6 5LD
Tel: 01908 660033
Fax: 01908 669348

Stoke Mandeville Hospital
Mandeville Road, Aylesbury, Buckinghamshire,
HP21 8AL
Tel: 01296 315755
Textphone: 01296 315725

Wycombe General Hospital
Queen Alexandra Road, High Wycombe,
Buckinghamshire, HP11 2TT
Tel: 01494 734214

Full audiology service provided between
Amersham and Wycombe Hospitals, including
open repair-times, appointments and home visits.
Full range of audiological tests including electro-
nystagmography, brain-stem response testing,
otoacoustic emissions and visual response
audiometry. A service for all ages is provided.

> ## Cambridgeshire
Addenbrooks Hospital
Hills Road, Cambridge, CB2 2QQ
Tel: 01223 217797
Textphone: 01223 274494
Fax: 01223 217559

The regional Cochlear Implant Programme is
based here.

Edith Cavell Hospital
Bretton Gate, Peterborough, Cambridgeshire, PE3
9GZ
Tel: 01733 874000
Fax: 01733 874001

Hinchingbrooke Hospital
Hinchingbrooke Park, Huntingdon,
Cambridgeshire, PE18 8NT
Tel: 01480 416416

Services provided for adults with an acquired
hearing loss include: assessment and treatment,
counselling, advice on provision of equipment,
vestibular rehabilitation, liaison with social
services and other professionals, group work,
individual therapy or rehabilitation, tinnitus
counselling and fitting noise generators, individual
sessions, obscure auditory dysfunction
rehabilitation, and provision of information via
lectures.

> ## Channel Islands
Overdale Hospital
Westmount Road, Jersey, Channel Islands, JE1 3UH
Tel: 01534 623000

> ## Cheshire
Countess of Chester Hospital
Liverpool Road, Chester, Cheshire, CH2 1DP
Tel: 01244 364838

Leighton Hospital
Middlewich Road, Crewe, Cheshire, CW1 4QJ
Tel: 01270 612197

Macclesfield District General Hospital
Victoria Road, Macclesfield, Cheshire, SK10 3BL
Tel: 01625 661716
Fax: 01625 663770

Stockport Infirmary
Wellington Road South, Stockport, Cheshire, SK1
3UA

Warrington Hospital
Lovely Lane, Warrington, Cheshire, WA5 1QG
Tel: 01925 662420
Fax: 01925 662048

➢ Cleveland
General Hospital
Holdforth Road, Hartlepool, Cleveland, TS24 9AH
Tel: 01429 266654
Textphone: 01429 860103
Fax: 01429 261744

North Riding Infirmary
Newport Road, Middlesbrough, Cleveland, TS1 5JE
Tel: 01642 854051
Textphone: 01642 854072
Fax: 01642 854073
E-mail: audiology@audionri.enterprise_plc.com
Website: homepages.enterprise.net/audionri
Full all-age audiology service, including vestibular rehabilitation, cochlear implants, bone anchored hearing aids, in-the-ear hearing aids and earmould manufacture.

➢ Cornwall
Cornwall County Audiology Service
Educational Audiology Centre, Priory Road, St Austell, Cornwall, PL25 5AB
Tel: 01726 61004
Textphone: 01726 61004
Fax: 01726 63803

The County Audiology Service provides assessment, teaching, advisory and equipment services for infants, pupils and students with all types and degrees of hearing loss. Principal aims of the Service are to enhance pupils' linguistic abilities and educational opportunities, and to provide advice and support for families, schools and colleges.

➢ County Durham
Dryburn Hospital
North Road, Durham City, Durham, DH1 5TW
Tel: 0191 333 2166
Textphone: 0191 333 2741
Fax: 0191 333 2724

Services provided for adults with an acquired hearing loss include: assessment and treatment, counselling, advice on provision of equipment, liaison with social services and other professionals, individual therapy or rehabilitation, group work, tinnitus counselling and fitting maskers, and cochlear implant rehabilitation. Lipreading, relaxation and communication classes are also held here.

➢ Cumbria
Cumberland Hospital
Carlisle, Cumbria, CA2 7HY
Tel: 01228 523444

Cumberland Infirmary
Newtown Road, Carlisle, Cumbria, CA2 7HY
Tel: 01228 814422
Fax: 01228 591889

Furness General Hospital
Dalton Lane, Barrow-In-Furness, Cumbria, LA14 4LB

Westmorland General Hospital
Burton Road, Kendal, Cumbria, LA9 7RG
Tel: 01539 795369

➢ Derbyshire
Chesterfield Royal Infirmary
Calow, Chesterfield, Derbyshire, S44 5BL
Tel: 01246 277271

Diagnostic investigation department in support of acute services with limited technical staff and limited hearing aid supplies. Rehabilitative/ hearing aid therapy services are located in Chesterfield at Saltergate Health Centre, telephone 01246 552950. Saltergate is the contact point for all satellite clinics.

Derby Royal Infirmary
London Road, Derby, DE1 2QY
Tel: 01332 254711

Saltergate Health Centre
Saltergate, Chesterfield, Derbyshire, S41 1SX
Tel: 01246 552950
Textphone: 01246 552950
Fax: 01246 552950

Scarsdale Hospital
Newbold Road, Chesterfield, Derbyshire, S41 7PF

➢ Devon

Derriford Hospital

Plymouth, Devon, PL6 8DH
Tel: 01752 777111
Textphone: 01752 763180

North Devon District Hospital

Raleigh Park, Barnstaple, Devon, EX31 4JB
Tel: 01271 322476
Textphone: 01271 322746
Fax: 01271 311541

The Audiology Department covers adult and child rehabilitation in the North Devon area. Also supports the ENT services in diagnostic testing. The service includes tinnitus retraining therapy, vestibular rehabilitation and general audiology assessing and rehabilitation with support from social services.

Plymouth General Hospital

Freedom Fields, Plymouth, Devon, PL4 7JJ

Royal Devon and Exeter Hospital

Barrack Road, Exeter, Devon, EX2 5DW
Tel: 01392 402071
Textphone: 01392 402080
Fax: 01392 402067

Torbay Hospital

Lawes Bridge, Torquay, Devon, TQ2 7AA
Tel: 01803 655132
Fax: 01803 655011

The Audiology Department provides a service for the population of South Devon which includes diagnosis and rehabilitation. The fitting of hearing aids, counselling and follow-up for adults and children is undertaken by the department.

➢ Dorset

Bridport Community Hospital

Hospital Lane, North Allington, Bridport, Dorset, DT6 5DR

Dorset County Hospital

Williams Avenue, Dorchester, Dorset, DT1 2JY
Tel: 01305 254262
Textphone: 01305 254444
Fax: 01305 254155

Full range of diagnostic and rehabilitation services in hearing and balance, including: consultant ENT surgeons, staff grade surgeons, audiology scientists, audiology technicians and hearing therapists. Good liaison with local self-help group in hearing impairment and tinnitus.

Royal Victoria Hospital Bourenmouth

17 Poole Road, Bournemouth, Dorset, BH4 9DG

Weymouth and District Hospital

Melcombe Avenue, Weymouth, Dorset, DT4 7BB
Tel: 01305 772211

➢ East Sussex

All Saints Hospital

The Meads, Eastbourne, East Sussex, BN21 3PQ
Tel: 01323 417400

Conquest Hospital

The Ridge, St Leonards-On-Sea, East Sussex, TN37 7RD
Tel: 01424 755255

Princess Alice Hospital

Carew Road, Eastbourne, East Sussex, BN21 2AX
Tel: 01323 413783

Royal East Sussex Hospital

Cambridge Road, Hastings, East Sussex, TN34 1EP

Royal Sussex County Hospital

Eastern Road, Brighton, East Sussex, BN2 5BE
Tel: 01273 664809

➢ Essex

Clacton and District Hospital
Tower Road, Clacton-on-Sea, Essex, CO15 1LH
Tel: 01255 421145

Essex County Hospital
Lexden Road, Colchester, Essex, CO3 3NB
Tel: 01206 834549
Textphone: 01206 834549
Fax: 01206 834603

Harold Wood Community Clinic
24 Gubbins Lane, Romford, Essex, RM3 0BE
Tel: 01708 340022
Fax: 01708 465158

Paediatric audiology clinic - involving neonatal screening, auditory rehabilitation.

King George Hospital
Barley Lane, Goodmayes, Essex
Tel: 020 8970 8345

We are a small MRSA isolation unit dealing with acute medical/surgical orthopaedic problems. We have facilities to repair and maintain hearing aids as well as providing hearing tests for our patients.

Oldchurch Hospital
Queen Mary Block, Waterloo Road, Romford, Essex, RM7 0BE

Orsett Hospital
Rowley Road, Orsett, Grays, Essex, RM16 3EU
Tel: 01268 592324
Fax: 01268 592343

Full ENT testing and diagnosis. All aspects of hearing aid rehabilitation, bone anchored hearing aids, tinnitus retraining therapy via hearing therapist, paediatric hearing tests and fitting and maintenance of aids.

Southend Hospital
Prittlewell Chase, Westcliff-on-Sea, Essex, SS0 0RY
Tel: 01702 435555
Fax: 01702 221300

St George's Hospital
117 Suttons Lane, Hornchurch, Essex, RM12 6RS
Tel: 01708 465462
E-mail: ivanniasegaram@compuserve.com

St John's Hospital
Wood Street, Chelmsford, Essex, CM2 9BG
Tel: 01245 513304
Fax: 01245 513695

We are an NHS hearing aid department working closely with the ENT consultants and clinicians. We provide the full range of diagnostic hearing and vestibular tests. We issue NHS hearing aids and maskers. A hearing therapist is available once a month for tinnitus retraining and counselling.

St Margaret's Hospital
The Plain, Epping, Essex, CM16 6TN
Tel: 01279 827126

Vicarage Fields Health Centre
Vicarage Drive, Barking, Essex, IG11 7NR

➢ Gloucestershire

Cheltenham General Hospital
Sandford Road, Cheltenham, Gloucestershire, GL53 7AN
Tel: 01242 274119

Winchcombe Hospital
Cheltenham Road, Winchcombe, Cheltenham, Gloucestershire, GL54 5NQ

➢ Halton
See Cheshire

➢ Hampshire

North Hampshire Hospital
Aldermaston Road, Basingstoke, Hampshire, RG24 9NA
Tel: 01256 473202
Fax: 01256 313064

Queen Alexandra Hospital

Southwick Hill Road, Cosham, Portsmouth, Hampshire, PO6 3LY

Tel: 023 9228 6755

Royal Hampshire County Hospital

Romsey Road, Winchester, Hampshire, SO22 5DG

Tel: 01962 824437

Fax: 01962 824860

Royal Hospital Haslar

Haslar Road, Gosport, Hampshire, PO12 2AA

Royal South Hampshire Hospital

Brintons Terrace, Southampton, Hampshire, SO14 0YG

Tel: 023 8082 5436

Textphone: 023 8082 5436

Fax: 023 8082 5085

Services include: assessment and treatment, hearing aid work and tinnitus counselling. The department comprises Audiology, Hearing Aid Clinic, Hearing Therapy. It undertakes hearing and balance tests on adults and children as a service to ENT. Hearing tests for patients referred direct by GPs. Issues, maintains and reviews hearing aids and their provision. Hearing Therapy provides counselling for adults with an acquired hearing loss.

> **Herefordshire**

Hereford County Hospital

Union Walk, Hereford, HR1 2ER

Tel: 01432 355444 ext 4258

Fax: 01432 264840

Hereford General Hospital

Nelson Street, Hereford, HR1 2PA

Tel: 01432 355444

> **Hertfordshire**

Hertford County Hospital

North Road, Hertford, SG14 1LP

Lister Hospital

Coreys Mill Lane, Stevenage, Hertfordshire, SG1 4AB

Tel: 01438 314333

Fax: 01438 781145

Queen Elizabeth II Hospital

Howlands, Welwyn Garden City, Hertfordshire, AL7 4HQ

St Albans City Hospital

Waverley Road, St Albans, Hertfordshire, AL3 5PN

Tel: 01727 897835

The Audiology Department of St Albans and Hemel Hempstead NHS Trust covers audiology and hearing aid work at St Albans City Hospital. We have repair sessions at St Albans on Tuesdays and Thursdays 11am to 12 noon, and at Hemel Hempstead General Hospital on Wednesdays 11am to 12 noon.

Watford General Hospital

Vicarage Road, Watford, Hertfordshire, WD1 8HB

Tel: 01923 244366

Fax: 01923 217440

> **Isle of Man**

Nobles Hospital

Westmoreland Road, Douglas, Isle of Man, IM1 4QA

Tel: 01624 642142

Fax: 01624 642544

> **Isle of Wight**

St Mary's Hospital

Parkhurst Road, Newport, Isle of Wight, PO30 5TG

Tel: 01983 521948

> **Kent**

Bromley Hospital

Cromwell Avenue, Bromley, Kent, BR2 9AJ

Tel: 020 8289 7000

Fax: 020 8289 7127

Supply and repair of all NHS aids. Direct GP referrals.

Buckland Hospital
Coombe Valley Road, Dover, Kent, CT17 0HD
Tel: 01304 201624

Kent and Canterbury Hospital
Ethelbert Road, Canterbury, Kent, CT1 3NG
Tel: 01227 766877
Textphone: 01227 783087
Fax: 01227 783018

Assessment, hearing aid provision, therapy and advice on other services are available as appropriate to children (in some cases, complementary to any provision made by the Kent Paediatric Audiology Service) and adults who present with hearing aid difficulties, tinnitus or disorders of the vestibular system.

Queen Mary's Hospital
Frognal Avenue, Sidcup, Kent, DA14 6LT
Tel: 020 8302 2678
Fax: 020 8308 3052

Some assessment and advice to pre-school deaf children through community clinic service. There is no service for deaf adults.

Royal Victoria Hospital Folkestone
Radnor Park Avenue, Folkestone, Kent, CT19 5HN
Tel: 01303 850202

William Harvey Hospital
Kennington Road, Willesborough, Ashford, Kent, TN24 0LZ

➤ **Lancashire**
Ballie Street Health Centre
Ballie Street, Rochdale, Lancashire, OL16 1XS
Tel: 01706 755072

Beaumont Hospital
Slyne Road, Lancaster, Lancashire, LA1 2HX

Birch Hill Hospital
Union Road, Rochdale, Lancashire, OL12 9QB
Tel: 01706 755880

Rochdale Healthcare Trust aims to diagnose and aid the hearing impaired population within the district of Rochdale. Provides an extensive

paediatric and school age diagnostic service, whilst also giving 'back up' to ENT for hearing tests, evoked reponse audiometry and electro-nystagmography. Hearing aids are provided both through a direct referral system and through ENT.

Blackburn Royal Infirmary
Bolton Road, Blackburn, Lancashire, BB2 3QG
Tel: 01254 294504

Blackpool Victoria Hospital
Whinney Heys Road, Blackpool, Lancashire, FY3 8NR
Tel: 01253 303500
Textphone: 01253 306735

Burnley General Hospital
Casterton Avenue, Burnley, Lancashire, BB10 2PQ

Cannon Street Clinic
Cannon Street, Oldham, Lancashire, OL9 6EP
Tel: 0161 652 0414
Fax: 0161 627 4579

The Audiology Department performs hearing tests in order to measure hearing acuity and to aid in the diagnosis of hearing function. The unit fits hearing aids, provides aural rehabilitation and a support service for hearing impaired patients. The department provides specialist children's services, tinnitus services and a school entry screening service.

Chorley and South Ribble District and General Hospital
Preston Road, Chorley, Lancashire, PR7 1PP
Tel: 01257 261222 ext 5165

Fairfield General Hospital
Rochdale Old Road, Bury, Lancashire, BL9 7RG
Tel: 0161 764 6081
Fax: 0161 705 3028

Hearing aid fittings and follow-ups. Repairs to hearing aids. Hearing tests and tests of middle ear function. Paediatric hearing testing, school age clinics, school screening. ABR testing, ENG and ERA testing. Insertion gain and visual re-inforcement audiometry.

6

Halliwell Health Centre

Aylesford Walk, Bolton, Lancashire, BL1 3SQ
Tel: 01204 371707
Fax: 01204 365760

Hope Hospital

Stott Lane, Salford, Lancashire, M6 8HD
Tel: 0161 787 4702
Fax: 0161 787 4237

The Community Audiology Department delivers a comprehensive service to adults and children. Areas of expertise include: direct referral service, hearing aid provision, diagnostic assessment, paediatric audiology service, tinnitus retraining clinics and support group, bone-anchored hearing aids, learning disability programme, hearing therapy, dispensing of commercial hearing aids to adults.

Manchester Northern Hospital

Cheetham Hill Road, Manchester, Lancashire, M8 9PA

Manchester Royal Infirmary

Oxford Road, Manchester, Lancashire, M13 9WL
Tel: 0161 276 4417
Fax: 0161 276 8511

North Manchester General Hospital

Delaunays Road, Manchester, Lancashire, M8 5RJ
Tel: 0161 720 2678

Consultation is by appointment only and appointments are available between 9.15am and 4.30pm. The centre deals with all private aids, environmental aids and NHS hearing aids.

Ormskirk and District General Hospital

Wigan Road, Ormskirk, Lancashire, L39 2AZ
Tel: 01695 577111

Our department at Ormskirk aims to provide friendly and professional advice on all aspects of the audiology care of our patients. Activities: advice, counselling, supply, rehabilitation for hearing aids and tinnitus, full range of hearing and diagnostic testing, domiciliary service, open access for hearing aid repairs and batteries, postal service.

Park Hospital

Moorside Road, Urmston, Manchester, Lancashire, M41 5SL

Queen Victoria Hospital

Thornton Road, Morecambe, Lancashire, LA4 5NN
Tel: 01524 411661ext 300

The department provides a wide range of investigative and rehabilitative services for hearing impaired people. Included are targeted neonatal screening, tinnitus counselling and support as well as the usual adult audiology services. The department will transfer to Lancaster in late 1999.

Rossendale General Hospital

Rawtenstall, Rossendale, Lancashire, BB4 6NE
Tel: 01706 215151
Fax: 01706 233210

Royal Albert Edward Infirmary

Wigan Lane, Wigan, Lancashire, WN1 2NN
Tel: 01942 244000
Textphone: 01942 244000

Royal Bolton Hospital

Minerva Road, Farnworth, Bolton, Lancashire, BL4 0JR
Tel: 01204 390390
Fax: 01204 390330

The Audiology Department provides and maintains hearing aids and gives communcation advice. We also provide tinnitus retraining therapy. A full range of hearing tests is also available.

Royal Preston Hospital

Sharoe Green Lane, Fulwood, Preston, Lancashire, PR2 9HT
Tel: 01772 710751

Tameside General Hospital

Darnton Road, Ashton-under-Lyne, Lancashire, OL6 9RW
Tel: 0161 331 6381
Textphone: 0161 331 6700
Fax: 0161 331 6650

Full audiological service including hearing assessments (adults and children), hearing aid provision, vestibular assessments. Tinnitus retraining therapy, ABR hearing aid repair clinics at local health centres. Aims to provide a fully comprehensive audiology service. We have close links with community, social services and education services.

Trafford General Hospital

Moorside Road, Davyhulme, Manchester, Lancashire, M41 5SL

Tel: 0161 746 2304

We provide: diagnostic audiology, free NHS hearing aid provision, open access hearing aid repair/advice clinics, direct GP referral for the over 60s, domiciliary service for the housebound, tinnitus rehabilitation and counselling service, access to a registered hearing aid dispenser for those wishing to purchase a hearing aid.

Withington Hospital

Nell Lane, Manchester, Lancashire, M20 2LR

Tel: 0161 291 3195

Textphone: 0161 291 3195

Fax: 0161 291 3154

South Manchester NHS Trust provides a full diagnostic service for adults and children with hearing loss, tinnitus or balance disorders. In addition, services provided for adults with an acquired hearing loss include: assessment and treatment, counselling, advice on provision of equipment, liaison with social services and other professionals, group work, individual sessions, individual therapy or rehabilitation, tinnitus counselling and fitting maskers, and provision of information via lectures. Lipreading classes at this centre are held on Mondays at 1pm to 3pm.

Wythenshaw Hospital

Southmoor Road, Manchester, Lancashire, M23 9LT

➢ Leicester
See Leicestershire

➢ Leicestershire
Leicester Royal Infirmary

Infirmary Square, Leicester, LE1 5WW

Tel: 0116 254 1414

Fax: 0116 258 5631

➢ Lincolnshire
Lincoln County Hospital

Greetwell Road, Lincoln, LN2 5QY

Tel: 01522 573254

Fax: 01522 573253

Pilgrim Hospital

Sibsey Road, Boston, Lincolnshire, PE21 9QS

Tel: 01205 364801

Fax: 01205 354395

➢ London
Braidwood Audiology Clinic

20 Elmcourt Road, London, SE27 9BZ

Tel: 020 8670 8131

Fax: 020 8761 8840

Central Middlesex Hospital

Acton Lane, London, NW10 7NS

Tel: 020 8453 2374

Textphone: 020 8453 2350

Fax: 020 8453 2630

Charing Cross Hospital

1st Floor South Wing, Fulham Palace Road, London, W6 8RF

Tel: 020 8846 1023

Fax: 020 8846 1022

Dulwich Hospital

East Dulwich Grove, London, SE22 8PT

Great Ormond Street Hospital for Sick Children

Great Ormond Street, London, WC1N 3JH

Tel: 020 7813 8316

Fax: 020 7813 8261

Guy's Hospital

Thomas Guy's House, St Thomas' Street, London, SE1 9RT

Tel: 020 7955 4081

Textphone: 020 7955 4081

Fax: 020 7955 8849

Full audiological service with range of hearing aids including bone anchored and implantable. Full hearing therapy service including domiciliary visits, vestibular and tinnitus therapy. Adult and paediatric cochlear implant programme based at St Thomas' Hospital.

King's College Hospital
Mapother House, De Crespigny Park, London, SE5 9RS

Tel: 020 7346 5343

Fax: 020 7346 5336

The Audiology Department provides a full audiological and vestibular investigative service and a comprehensive service for patients of all ages, using NHS and commercial hearing aids. Direct referrals are accepted for all patients.

Memorial Hospital
Shooters Hill, London, SE18 3RZ

Tel: 020 8312 6374

Fax: 020 8319 3336

Optimum Health Services NHS Trust
Newcomen Centre, Guy's Hospital, St Thomas Street, London, SE1 9RT

Tel: 020 7955 4637

Fax: 020 7955 4950

Provides a local service for the assessment of hearing of children in Lewisham and Southwark and a sub-regional specialised tertiary referral service for the assessment and management of hearing impaired children in south-east London and adjacent counties. Based in one of the foremost UK centres for child development and paediatric neurology.

Queen Mary's University Hospital
Roehampton Lane, London, SW15 5PN

Tel: 020 8780 3274

Fax: 020 8355 2862

Royal Free Hospital
Pond Street, London, NW3 2QG

Tel: 020 7830 2055

Audiology Department provides clinical support for ENT, hearing aid provision and support for adults and relevant referrals.

Royal London Hospital
Whitechapel, London, E1 1BB

Tel: 020 7837 8833

Textphone: 020 7377 7673

The Audiology Service offers two main services as follows: Diagnostic: audiology testing of hearing; advanced testing to aid differential diagnosis; paedaetric service - school screening, etc. Rehabilitation: fitting, follow up and management of hearing aids; repair sessions; community service and home visits; hearing therapy services. Committed to providing a quality service within the Royal Hospital Trust.

St Ann's Hospital
St Ann's Road, London, N15 3TH

Tel: 020 8442 6000

St Bartholomew's Hospital
West Smithfield, London, EC1A 7BE

Tel: 020 7601 7434

St George's Hospital
Department of Audiological Medicine, Lanesborough Wing Level O, London, SW17 0QT

Tel: 020 8725 1880

Textphone: 020 8725 3019

Fax: 020 8725 1874

St Mary Abbots Hospital
2 Beatrice Place, London, W8 5LP

Tel: 020 8846 6011

Fax: 020 8846 6012

St Mary's Hospital
Praed Street, Paddington, London, W2 1NY

Tel: 020 7886 1015

St Thomas' Hospital
Lambeth Palace Road, London, SE1 7EH

Tel: 020 7922 8034

Textphone: 020 7922 8241

Fax: 020 7922 8088

The Portland Hospital

234 Great Portland Street, London, W1N 5PH

Tel: 0800 393709 Freephone

Fax: 020 7390 8053

E-mail: audiology@portlandchc.demon.co.uk

The organisation aims to provide high quality health care services in the private sector. These aim to meet the needs of a wide cross-section of the public, through diverse and comprehensive services and facilities. They include diagnostic and rehabilitative audiology for children and adults. The service offers cochlear implant programmes, hearing aid dispensing, tinnitus therapies and physician consultations.

West Ham Lane Health Centre

84 West Ham Lane, London, E15 4PT

Tel: 020 8250 7340

Fax: 020 8250 7340

Whipps Cross Hospital

Whipps Cross Road, London, E11 1NR

Whittington Hospital

Highgate Hill, London, N19 5NF

Tel: 020 7288 5220

We provide a full hearing aid service along with a full audiological and tinnitus service.

➢ Merseyside

Arrowe Park Hospital

Arrowe Park Road, Wirral, Merseyside, L49 5PE

Tel: 0151 604 7113

Textphone: 0151 604 7448

Fax: 0151 604 1682

Services provided for adults with an acquired hearing loss aged 60 and over, direct referral service, for those under 60, via ENT, which includes: assessment, provision of appropriate hearing aids, counselling service on provision of environmental aids, individual therapy or rehabilitation, tinnitus counselling, desensitisation therapy, maskers etc,; also hearin aid support service at seven locality clinics on the Wirral.

Royal Liverpool University Hospital

Prescot Street, Liverpool, Merseyside, L7 8XP

Tel: 0151 706 2000

Fax: 0151 706 5976

Services provided include: assessment and treatment, vestibular rehabilitation, tinnitus counselling or fitting maskers, individual sessions, provision of information via lectures.

Southport General Infirmary

Scarisbrick New Road, Southport, Merseyside, PR8 6PH

Tel: 01704 547471

St Helens Hospital

Marshalls Cross Road, St Helens, Merseyside, WA9 3DA

Tel: 01744 458291

Victoria Central Hospital

Mill Lane, Wallasey, Merseyside, L44 5UF

Tel: 0151 678 5111

Hearing Aid support service on Friday mornings only.

Walton Hospital

107 Rice Lane, Liverpool, Merseyside, L9 1AE

Tel: 0151 529 4697

Whiston Hospital

Warrington Road, Prescot, Merseyside, L35 5DR

➢ Middlesbrough
See Cleveland

➢ Middlesex
Ashford Hospital

London Road, Ashford, Middlesex, TW15 3AA

Tel: 01784 884126

Fax: 01784 884107

The following services are available: hearing aid provision and follow-up, counselling on hearing loss, tinnitus and obscure auditory dysfunction, liaison with social services and other professionals.

Chase Farm Hospital
The Ridgeway, Enfield, Middlesex, EN2 8JL
Tel: 020 8366 9117
Textphone: 020 8967 5923
Fax: 020 8967 5923 (ring first)

Services include general hearing aid work, tinnitus counselling, balance work, environmental aids advice and assessment, deaf awareness training, communication training.

Ealing Hospital
Uxbridge Road, Southall, Middlesex, UB1 3EU
Tel: 020 8574 2244
Textphone: 020 8574 2244

Edgware General Hospital
Burnt Oak Broadway, Edgware, Middlesex, HA8 0AD
Tel: 020 8732 0740
Fax: 020 8213 4676

Hearing aid issues within three months, most within six weeks. Domiciliary visits, and all other duties within an Audiology Hearing Aid Clinic.

Hillingdon Hospital
Pield Heath Road, Uxbridge, Middlesex, UB8 3NN
Tel: 01895 279343
Fax: 01895 279669

The Audiology Department provides the following: assessment of individual hearing loss via GP or ENT consultant. Provision of the full range of NHS hearing instruments, their maintanance and replacement. Home visiting services for those not physically able to attend the centre.

Mount Vernon Hospital
Rickmansworth Road, Northwood, Middlesex, HA6 2RN

Northwick Park Hospital
Watford Road, Harrow, Middlesex, HA1 3UJ
Tel: 020 8864 3232
Fax: 020 8869 2174

West Middlesex University Hospital
Twickenham Road, Isleworth, Middlesex, TW7 6AF
Tel: 020 8560 2121
Textphone: 020 8565 5677
Fax: 020 8565 5333

➤ Norfolk
Colman Hospital
Unthank Road, Norwich, Norfolk, NR2 2PJ
Tel: 01603 288917
Textphone: 01603 288993
Fax: 01603 288946

James Paget Hospital
Lowestoft Road, Gorleston, Great Yarmouth, Norfolk, NR31 6LA
Tel: 01493 452343/ 452287
Fax: 01493 452778

Norfolk and Norwich Hospital
Brunswick Road, Norwich, Norfolk, NR1 3SR

Queen Elizabeth Hospital
Gayton Road, King's Lynn, Norfolk, PE30 4ET
Tel: 01553 613805
Textphone: 01533 613888
Fax: 01553 613700

The diagnosis of patients with hearing and hearing related disorders and their rehabilitation, when suitable. To provide these services to the highest standards of patient care. To maintain and wherever possible improve the services offered, to the benefit of patients.

➤ North East Lincolnshire
See Humberside

➤ North Humberside
Hull Royal Infirmary
Anlaby Road, Hull, North Humberside, HU3 2JZ

> North Lincolnshire
See Humberside

> North West Somerset
See Avon

> North Yorkshire
Friarage Hospital

Northallerton, North Yorkshire, DL6 1JG

Tel: 01609 763212

Fax: 01609 764638

Harrogate District Hospital

Lancaster Park Road, Harrogate, North Yorkshire, HG2 7SX

Tel: 01423 885959

Selby War Memorial Hospital

Doncaster Road, Selby, North Yorkshire, YO8 9BX

Tel: 01757 702664

Fax: 01757 213783

St Mary's Hospital

Dean Road, Scarborough, North Yorkshire, YO12 7SW

Tel: 01723 342821

York District Hospital

Wigginton Road, York, YO31 8HE

Tel: 01904 453913

> Northamptonshire
Isebrook Hospital

Irthlingborough Road, Wellingborough, Northamptonshire, NN8 1LP

Kettering General Hospital

Rothwell Road, Kettering, Northamptonshire, NN16 8UZ

Tel: 01536 492328

Northampton General Hospital

Cliftonville, Northampton, NN1 5BD

Tel: 01604 545964

Textphone: 01604 634700 ext 5912

Nuffield Diagnostic Clinic

Cottingham Road, Corby, Northamptonshire, NN17 2UW

> Northumberland
Blyth Community Hospital

Thoroton Street, Blyth, Northumberland, NE24 1DX

Tel: 01670 396400

Fax: 01670 396492

Audiology - Wednesdays.

> Nottinghamshire
Kings Mill Hospital

Mansfield Road, Sutton-in-Ashfield, Nottinghamshire, NG17 4JL

Nottingham General Hospital

Park Row, Nottingham, NG1 6HA

Queens Medical Centre

Derby Road, Nottingham, NG7 2UH

Tel: 0115 924 9924 ext 43739

Retford Hospital

North Road, Retford, Nottinghamshire, DN22 7XF

Tel: 01777 705261

Bassetlaw Hearing Services provides a range of community and hospital services to the local population including direct referral services for children, and adults over 60 years, for hearing aid provision. We aim to improve the quality of life for the hearing impaired and to provide a quality, individual service, delivering in a caring manner.

> Oxfordshire
Horton General Hospital

Oxford Road, Banbury, Oxfordshire, OX16 9AL

6

Radcliffe Infirmary
Woodstock Road, Oxford, OX2 6HE
Tel: 01865 224559

> **Peterborough**
See Cambridgeshire

> **Plymouth**
See Devon

> **Portsmouth**
See Hampshire

> **Redcar and Cleveland**
See Cleveland

> **Shropshire**
Princess Royal Hospital
Apley Castle, Grainger Drive, Telford, Shropshire, TF6 6TF
Tel: 01952 641222
Textphone: 01952 222901
Fax: 01952 243405

Royal Shrewsbury Hospital (North)
Mytton Oak Road, Shrewsbury, Shropshire, SY3 8XQ
Tel: 01743 261482
Textphone: 01743 261484
Fax: 01743 261483

> **Slough**
See Berkshire

> **Somerset**
Yeovil District Hospital
Higher Kingston, Yeovil, Somerset, BA21 4AT

> **South Gloucestershire**
See Avon

> **South Humberside**
Grimsby District General Hospital
Scartho Road, Grimsby, South Humberside, DN33 2BA

> **South Yorkshire**
Barnsley District General Hospital
Gawber Road, Barnsley, South Yorkshire, S75 2AP

Doncaster Royal Infirmary
Armthorpe Road, Doncaster, South Yorkshire, DN2 5LT
Tel: 01302 553115
Textphone: 01302 553115
Fax: 01302 738308

Royal Hallamshire Hospital
Glossop Road, Sheffield, South Yorkshire, S10 2JF
Tel: 0114 2713058

Five repair sessions a week. Direct referral system. Reassessment of hearing aid provision. Tinnitus clinics. Vestibular rehabilitation clinics. ENGs. Review clinics. New moulds. Exchange of hearing aids.

> **Southampton**
See Hampshire

> **Staffordshire**
Burton District Hospital
Belvedere Road, Burton-On-Trent, Staffordshire, DE13 0RB
Tel: 01283 566333
Fax: 01283 593005

Cannock Chase Hospital
Brunswick Road, Cannock, Staffordshire, WS11 2XY

North Staffordshire Hospital
Hartshill Road, Stoke-on-Trent, Staffordshire, ST4 7PA
Tel: 01782 716095
Textphone: 01782 715444
Fax: 01782 716591

Sir Robert Peel Hospital
Plantation Lane, Mile Oak, Tamworth, Staffordshire, B78 3NG
Tel: 01827 263800
Fax: 01827 263803

Stafford District General Hospital
Weston Road, Stafford, ST16 3SA
Tel: 01785 257731
Videotel: 01785 230538

➢ Suffolk
Ipswich and Suffolk Hospital
Heath Road, Ipswich, Suffolk, IP4 5PD
Tel: 01473 703873
Textphone: 01473 703112
Fax: 01473 703111

West Suffolk Hospital
Hardwick Lane, Bury St Edmunds, Suffolk, IP33 2QZ

Full ENT audiological service including auditory brain-stem response and otoacoustic emissions. Full hearing aid service with three outreach clinics. Targets paediatric otoacoustic emissions. Tinnitus help.

➢ Surrey
East Surrey Hospital
Three Arch Road, Redhill, Surrey, RH1 5RH

Farnham Road Hospital
Farnham Road, Guildford, Surrey, GU2 5LX

Frimley Park Hospital
Portsmouth Road, Frimley, Camberley, Surrey, GU16 5UJ
Tel: 01276 604604
Textphone: 01276 604604 ext 4620
Fax: 01276 604148
Tinnitus self-help group meets locally twice a month, tinnitus clinic twice a month, hearing aid work, balance course, domiciliary visits, counselling, environmental aid work, lipreading classes.

Kingston Hospital
Galsworthy Road, Kingston Upon Thames, Surrey, KT2 7QU
Tel: 020 8546 7711 ext 2144

Royal Surrey County Hospital
Egerton Road, Guildford, Surrey, GU2 5XX
Tel: 01483 464108
Textphone: 01483 571122
Fax: 01483 464108

The following services are available: assessment and treatment including hearing aid provision and follow-up, counselling, advice on provision of equipment, liaison with social services and other professionals, group work, individual therapy or rehabilitation, tinnitus counselling, obscure auditory dysfunction, and provision of information via lectures.

St Helier Hospital
Wrythe Lane, Carshalton, Surrey, SM5 1AA
Tel: 020 8296 2911
Textphone: 020 8644 1968
Fax: 020 8641 4546

➢ Torbay
See Devon

➢ Tyne and Wear
Sunderland General Hospital
Kayll Road, Sunderland, Tyne and Wear, SR4 7TP
Tel: 0191 569 9001
Fax: 0191 569 9213
E-mail: audiology.rmpd@sunderland.ac.uk
Website: www.fe-inf.demon.co.uk/sei/chs

6

> Warwickshire
Community Audiology Unit
Pool Bank Street, Nuneaton, Warwickshire, CV11 5DB

Tel: 024 7635 1333
Textphone: 024 7635 1333
Fax: 024 7635 0509

George Elliot Hospital
College Street, Nuneaton, Warwickshire, CV10 7DJ

Riversley Park Hospital
Coton Road, Nuneaton, Warwickshire, CV11 5TP

South Warwickshire Hospital
Lakin Road, Warwick, CV34 5BW

> West Midlands
Birmingham Children's Hospital
Steelhouse Lane, Birmingham, West Midlands, B4 6NL

Birmingham Heartlands Hospital
Bordesley Green East, Bordesley Green, Birmingham, West Midlands, B9 5SS

Tel: 0121 766 6611
Fax: 0121 776 6935

Cottage Street Hearing Centre
Cottage Street, Brierley Hill, Dudley, West Midlands, DY5 1RE

Tel: 01384 480011
Textphone: 01384 75372
Fax: 01384 485387

The Audiology Service offers a comprehensive range of hearing assessments: neonatal hearing screening on 'targeted babies', children's hearing tests up until leaving education, paediatric hearing aid fittings, adult hearing assessment via GPs or ENT referral, NHS hearing aid fittings via ENT referral and tinnitus counselling. 'Drop in' service for advice and hearing aid maintenance is open Monday to Friday inclusive, Thursday until 7pm.

Coventry and Warwickshire Hospital
Stoney Stanton Road, Coventry, West Midlands, CV1 4FH

Tel: 024 7684 4094

Sandwell General Hospital
Lyndon, West Bromwich, West Midlands, B71 4HJ

Tel: 0121 607 3443
Fax: 0121 607 3443

Hearing aid repair/battery service. Tinnitus counselling. Hearing therapy. Lipreading. Direct access hearing aid clinics. Paediatric service (community based). Specialist hearing aid selection. Domiciliary service.

Selly Oak Hospital
Raddlebarn Road, Birmingham, West Midlands, B29 6JD

Tel: 0121 627 8106
Textphone: 0121 627 8915
Fax: 0121 627 8914
E-mail: juliethomas@university-b.wmids.nhs.uk

The specialist service provided here is specifically for adults, providing assessment, treatment, counselling and advice. Work is done in groups and on an individual basis. Assessment for suitability for a cochlear implant or a bone anchored hearing aid is available. In addition to conventional air conduction or bone conduction hearing aids, there is also rehabilitation and training in the use of aids and also of vibro-tactile aids.

Walsall Manor Hospital
Moad Road, Walsall, West Midlands, WS1 2PS

Tel: 01922 721172
Fax: 01922 656312

Yardley Green Hospital
Yardley Green Road, Birmingham, West Midlands, B9 5PX

Tel: 0121 766 6611
Fax: 0121 766 6935

➤ West Sussex
Crawley Hospital
West Green Drive, Crawley, West Sussex, RH11
7DH

Tel: 01293 600300
Fax: 01293 600360

Royal West Sussex Hospital
Spitalfield Lane, Chichester, West Sussex, PO19
4SE

Worthing Hospital
Lyndhurst Road, Worthing, West Sussex, BN11
2DH

Tel: 01903 205111

➤ West Yorkshire
Airedale General Hospital
Skipton Road, Steeton, Keighley, West Yorkshire,
BD20 6TD

Tel: 01535 651190
Textphone: 01535 651360
Fax: 01535 655129

Bradford Royal Infirmary
Duckworth Lane, Bradford, West Yorkshire, BD9
6RJ

Tel: 01274 542200
Fax: 01274 364026

Clayton Hospital
Northgate, Wakefield, West Yorkshire, WF1 3LG
Tel: 01924 214324

Dewsbury and District Hospital
Healds Road, Dewsbury, West Yorkshire, WF13
4HS

Tel: 01924 816070

Audiology provide an aural diagnostic and
rehabilitation service to adults and children. They
aim to enable clients to achieve and maintain
optimum independence through informed
decisions. They work closely with other health
professionals, education and social services to
provide a client-centred service.

Halifax General Hospital
Huddersfield Road, Halifax, West Yorkshire, HX3
0PW

Huddersfield Royal Infirmary
Acre Street, Huddersfield, West Yorkshire, HD3 3EA
Tel: 01484 422191 ext 2541

Leeds General Infirmary
Great George Street, Leeds, West Yorkshire, LS1
3EX

Tel: 0113 243 2799
Textphone: 0113 392 2484
Fax: 0113 392 6088

Pontefract General Infirmary
Southgate, Pontefract, West Yorkshire, WF8 1PL

Royal Halifax Infirmary
Free School Lane, Halifax, West Yorkshire, HX1 2PS

St James' University Hospital
Beckett Street, Leeds, West Yorkshire, LS9 7TF
Tel: 0113 206 4336
Fax: 0113 206 5480

➤ Wiltshire
Princess Margaret Hospital
Okus Road, Swindon, Wiltshire, SN1 4JU
Tel: 01793 426447

ENT audiology, hearing aid service, direct referral
assessment, open access paediatric service,
paediatric hearing aid service, vestibular
assessment, tinnitus counselling, at-risk neonatal
assessments. Education service to any interested
groups. After-dinner talks.

Salisbury Central Health Clinic
Avon Approach, Salisbury, Wiltshire, SP1 3SL

Salisbury District Hospital
Salisbury, Wiltshire, SP2 8BJ
Tel: 01722 429335
Textphone: 0800 435543
Fax: 01722 322871

> Windsor and Maidenhead
See Berkshire

> Worcestershire
Worcester Royal Infirmary
Castle Street, Worcester, WR1 3AS
Tel: 01905 763333

> York
See North Yorkshire

Northern Ireland

> County Antrim
Antrim Area Hospital
Bush Road, Antrim, BT41 2RL
Tel: 028 9442 4511

Belfast City Hospital
Out Patients Department, Wing F, Lisburn Road, Belfast, County Antrim, BT9 7AD
Tel: 028 9032 9241 ext 2961

Hearing aid repair clinics are held on Tuesdays and Fridays 2 to 4.30pm. Lipreading classes held in Chest Clinic, Belfast City Hospital, by Mrs Wilma McCreary. Saturdays 10.30am to 12.30pm. Access by referral from either GP, ENT consultant, audiology service or social services.

Dalriada Hospital
Coleraine Road, Ballycastle, County Antrim, BT54 6BA
Tel: 028 2076 2666
Fax: 028 2076 9891

Hearing aid repair clinic is open from 10am to 12 noon, on the second and fourth Wednesday of the month.

Moyle Hospital
Old Glenarm Road, Larne, County Antrim, BT40 1RP
Tel: 028 2563 5483

Daignostic audiology, hearing aid fitting and hearing rehabilitation.

Ulster Hospital
Upper Newtownards Road, Dundonald, Belfast, County Antrim, BT16 0RH
Tel: 028 9048 4511
Fax: 028 9048 1166

Waveney Hospital
Cushendall Road, Ballymena, County Antrim, BT43 6HH
Tel: 028 2565 3377

Diagnostic Centre and rehabilitation.

Whiteabbey Hospital
Doagh Road, Newtownabbey, County Antrim, BT37 9RH
Tel: 028 9086 5181

Hearing aid repair clinic is open on Wednesday from 9.30am to 12.30pm. Diagnostic audiology. Hearing aid fitting. Hearing rehabilitation.

> County Armagh
Armagh Community Hospital
Tower Hill, Armagh, BT61 9DR
Tel: 028 3752 2281 ext 4201
Fax: 028 3741 4522

Hearing aid repair clinic is open on Thursday from 10.30am till 12 noon.

Craigavon Area Hospital
68 Lurgan Road, Portadown, Craigavon, County Armagh, BT63 5QQ
Tel: 028 3833 4444
Textphone: 028 3861 2632
Fax: 028 3835 0068

> County Down
Banbridge Polyclinic
Linenhall Street, Banbridge, County Down, BT32 3EH
Tel: 028 4062 2222
Fax: 028 4062 2622

Hearing aid repair clinic is by appointment only. Please contact the Audiology Department at Craigavon Area Hospital on 028 3861 2168 (direct line).

Bangor Hospital

Castle Street, Bangor, County Down, BT20 4TA

Tel: 028 9147 5115

Fax: 028 9127 4332

Hearing aid repair clinic is open on Wednesdays and Thursdays from 9.30am to 12 noon.

Daisy Hill Hospital

5 Hospital Road, Newry, County Down, BT35 8DR

Tel: 028 3752 2281 ext 7281

Hearing aid repair clinic is open Mondays and Wednesdays from 2.30 to 4pm and on Fridays from 9.30am to 12 noon.

Downe Hospital

9a Pound Lane, Downpatrick, County Down, BT30 6JA

Tel: 028 4461 3311 ext 3705

Fax: 028 4461 5699

Hearing aid repair clinic is open on Monday from 9.30am to 12 noon.

➢ County Fermanagh

Erne Hospital

Cornagrade Road, Enniskillen, County Fermanagh, BT74 6AY

Tel: 028 6632 4711

Textphone: 028 6624 5211 ext 2185

The hearing aid repair clinic is open on Friday from 10am to 12 noon. The 324711 number is used only during repair clinics and 245211 is for use at all other times.

➢ County Londonderry

Altnagelvin Hospital

Glenshane Road, Londonderry, BT47 1SD

Tel: 028 7131 1972

Textphone: 028 7134 2998

Fax: 028 7161 1218

Coleraine Hospital

28a Mountsandel Road, Coleraine, County Londonderry, BT52 1JA

Tel: 028 7034 4177 ext 2147

Fax: 028 7035 0000

Hearing aid repair clinic open on Friday from 9.30am to 12.30pm. Audiology clinic all day Wednesday and Friday.

Mid-Ulster Hospital

59 Hospital Road, Magherafelt, County Londonderry, BT45 5EX

Tel: 028 7963 1031

Fax: 028 7963 3050

Hearing aid clinic is open on Thursday from 9.30am to 12.30pm.

➢ County Tyrone

South Tyrone Hospital

Carland Road, Dungannon, County Tyrone, BT71 4AU

Tel: 028 8772 2821 ext 3507

Fax: 028 8772 7332

An audiometric and hearing aid service is provided at SouthTyrone Hospital to patients of all ages. Patients are referred via their GP to an ENT clinic where the necessary audiometric tests and arrangements for hearing aids or tinnitus tests are carried out. A domiciliary service is also available for housebound patients.

Tyrone County Hospital

Hospital Road, Omagh, County Tyrone, BT79 0AP

Tel: 028 8224 5211 ext 2185

Hearing aid repair clinic is open on Monday from 9 to 11am and on Wednesday from 2pm to 4pm.

Scotland

➢ Aberdeenshire

Aberdeen Royal Hospital

Woolmanhill, Aberdeen, AB25 1LD

Tel: 01224 840764

Textphone: 01224 840764

Fax: 01224 840980

The Audiology Department aims to provide a comprehensive audiology and NHS hearing aid service throughout Grampian, Orkney and Shetland.

➢ Angus

Montrose Royal Infirmary

66 Bridge Street, Montrose, Angus, DD10 8AJ

Tel: 01674 830361

Fax: 01674 830361

Every first, third and fifth Monday afternoon of the month we have a two-lane ENT clinic and a two-lane audiology clinic.

➤ Argyll

Lorn and Islands District General Hospital

Glengallan Road, Oban, Argyll, PA34 4HH

Tel: 01631 567500

Fax: 01631 567134

Audiology service: diagnostic audiology, direct referral hearing aid service and tinnitus management for adults and children. Areas covered: Argyll, based in Oban plus satellite clinics in Lochgilphead, Campeltown, Mull, Coll, Tiree, Colonsay. This is a single-handed post.

➤ Ayrshire

Ayr Hospital

Dalmellington Road, Ayr, KA6 6DX

Tel: 01292 610555 ext 4173

Crosshouse Hospital

Crosshouse, Kilmarnock, Ayrshire, KA2 0BE

Tel: 01563 521133 ext 2080

Fax: 01563 572009

The Cochlear Implant Programme at Crosshouse Hospital provides a national cochlear implant service for the whole of Scotland. It provides a range of specialist skills in asessment, implantation and rehabilitation for people with a profound sensorineural deafness. It is the only centre in Scotland undertaking paediatric implantation.

➤ Dumbartonshire

Dumbarton Health Centre

Station Road, Dumbarton, Dunbartonshire, G82 1PW

Tel: 01389 602601

Assessment and management of hearing loss - adults and paediatrics. Tinnitus management: can provide only limited counselling due to pressure of workload. Screening of all Primary 1 school children.

➤ Dumfries and Galloway

Dumfries and Galloway Royal Infirmary

Bankend Road, Dumfries, DG1 4AP

Tel: 01387 246246

➤ Fife

Dunfermline and West Fife District and General Hospital

Reid Street, Dunfermline, Fife, KY12 7DX

Queen Margaret Hospital

Whitefield Road, Dunfermline, Fife, KY12 0SU

➤ Inverness-Shire

Raigmore Hospital

Perth Road, Inverness, IV2 3UJ

Tel: 01463 704406

➤ Lanarkshire

Gartnavel General Hospital

1053 Great Western Road, Glasgow, Lanarkshire, G12 0YN

Tel: 0141 2113054

Glasgow Royal Infirmary

Alexandra Parade, Glasgow, Lanarkshire, G31 2ER

Tel: 0141 211 4000

Services/clinics provided by Glasgow Royal Infirmary (Audiology) include: direct referral clinic, hearing aid reassessment clinic, severe hearing impaired clinic, paediatric audiology clinic, tinnitus assessment clinic, hearing aid service and repair clinic, postal repair/battery issue service.

Law Hospital

Carluke, Lanarkshire, ML8 5ER

Tel: 01698 351100

Royal Hospital for Sick Children

Dalnair Street, Yorkhill, Glasgow, Lanarkshire, G3 8SJ

Tel: 0141 201 0000

Our philosophy is to provide a comprehensive audiological service which includes a full range of diagnostic age-related hearing assessments as well as an extensive hearing aid provision and rehabilitation service. We aim to provide this service in a child-friendly environment, involving parents and professionals in each child's management.

Southern General Hospital

1345 Govan Road, Glasgow, Lanarkshire, G51 4TF

Tel: 0141 201 1438

In our small department we carry out standard hearing tests, on all age groups. If required, a suitable hearing aid will be tried and issued. The hearing aid recipient will be reviewed for rehabilitation at a later date.

Stobhill General Hospital

Balornock Road, Glasgow, Lanarkshire, G21 3UW

Tel: 0141 201 3000

Fax: 0141 201 3887

Strathclyde Hospital

Airbles Road, Motherwell, Lanarkshire, ML1 3BW

Tel: 01698 361100

Carry out hearing tests for ENT consultants, take impressions and issue hearing aids. There is no repair clinic at this hospital.

Victoria Infirmary

Langside Road, Glasgow, Lanarkshire, G42 9TY

Tel: 0141 201 5570

➢ Midlothian

Edinburgh Royal Infirmary

Level Four, Lauriston Building, 39 Lauriston Place, Edinburgh, Midlothian, EH3 9EN

Tel: 0131 536 3682

Western General Hospital

Crewe Road, Edinburgh, Midlothian, EH4 2XU

➢ Morayshire

Spynie Hospital

Elgin, Morayshire, IV30 2PW

Tel: 01343 558387

Fax: 01343 552185

Contact: V Tierney, Audiology Department

This is a one-person department working as part of the Aberdeen NHS.

➢ Perthshire

Perth Royal Infirmary

Taymount Terrace, Perth, PH1 1NX

Tel: 01738 623311

We aim to provide a prompt and caring service for the patients of Perth and Kinross Healthcare Trust. Our activities include vestibular function testing, evoked response audiometry, audiological services for ENT Clinics, hearing aid issues and repairs.

➢ Renfrewshire

Inverclyde Royal Hospital

Larkfield Road, Greenock, Renfrewshire, PA16 0XN

Tel: 01475 633777

Royal Alexandra Hospital

Coresbar Road, Paisley, Renfrewshire, PA2 9PN

Tel: 0141-887 9111

Textphone: 0141-887 9111

Fax: 0141-887 6701

➢ Scottish Borders, The

Borders General Hospital

Melrose, Scottish Borders, The, TD6 9BS

Tel: 01896 754333

Fax: 01896 823476

Provision of NHS hearing instruments, maintenance of hearing instruments, diagnostic audiological testing of children and adults.

➢ Stirlingshire

Stirling Royal Infirmary

Livilands Gate, Stirling, FK8 2AU

Tel: 01786 434000

Fax: 01786 450558

➢ West Lothian

Bangour General Hospital

Broxburn, West Lothian, EH52 6ZE

St John's Hospital at Howden

Howden West, Livingston, West Lothian, EH54 6PP

Tel: 01506 419666

Fax: 01506 416484

6

➢ Clwyd

Bryn y Neuadd

Aber Road, Llanfairfechan, Conwy, Clwyd, LL33 0HH
Tel: 01248 682682
Fax: 01248 681832

Glan Clwyd Hospital

Rhuddlan Road, Bodelwyddan, Rhyl, Clwyd, LL18 5UJ
Tel: 01745 534524
Textphone: 01745 534342
Fax: 01745 534932
Website: www.glanclwyd.demon.co.uk/audiology/index.html

Wrexham Maelor Hospital

Croesnewydd Road, Wrexham Technology Park, Wrexham, Clwyd, LL13 7TD
Tel: 01978 291100
Fax: 01978 290951

An audiology service for all ages is provided. Services include assessment and rehabilitation for hearing impairment and balance disorders.

➢ Dyfed

Bronglais Hospital

Caradoc Road, Aberystwyth, Dyfed, SY23 1ER
Tel: 01970 623131
Textphone: 01970 635943
Fax: 01970 635923

Prince Philip Hospital

Bryngwyn Mawr, Dafen, Llanelli, Carmarthenshire, SA15 8QF
Tel: 01554 756567
Fax: 01554 772271

West Wales General Hospital

Dolgwili Road, Carmarthen, Dyfed, SA31 2AF
Tel: 01267 235151

Withybush General Hospital

Fishguard Road, Haverfordwest, Dyfed, SA61 2PZ
Tel: 01437 774000
Fax: 01437 773115

Full audiometric/audiology and hearing aid rehabilitation services. Commercial hearing aid fittings to children and war pensioners (if non-NHS is suitable). School and pre-school audiology testing. Tinnitus retraining therapy and basic counselling. Tinnitus management, Electro-nystagmography. Some direct referrals and home visits. Community/satellite clinics. District audiology services. British Sign Language (basic) services. Our aims are to make our services accessible to everybody, provide a quality healthcare service, provide a better hearing healthcare for our patients, and work towards keeping waiting lists down.

➢ Gwent

Nevill Hall Hospital

Brecon Road, Abergavenny, Monmouthshire, NP7 7EG
Tel: 01873 852091
Fax: 01873 859168

Royal Gwent Hospital

Cardiff Road, Newport, Gwent, NP9 2UB
Tel: 01633 234234

➢ Gwynedd

Llandudno Hospital

Ffordd Ysbyty, Llandudno, Gwynedd, LL30 1LB
Tel: 01492 860066
Fax: 01492 871668

Ysbyty Gwynedd

Penrhosgarnedd, Bangor, Gwynedd, LL57 2PW
Tel: 01248 384384
Fax: 01248 370629

To provide a locally based comprehensive audiology service to determine the nature and extent of hearing loss of any person suspected of having a handicap due to hearing impairment. The aims are to assist people with hearing impairment and their families to minimise the consequent impact on their lives.

➢ Merthyr Tydfil
See Mid Glamorgan

➢ Mid Glamorgan
Bridgend General Hospital
Quarella Road, Bridgend, Mid Glamorgan, CF31 1JP
Tel: 01656 752752

Dewi Sant Hospital
Albert Road, Pontypridd, Mid Glamorgan, CF37 1LB

East Glamorgan General Hospital
Church Village, Pontypridd, Mid Glamorgan, CF38 1AB
Tel: 01443 216850
Fax: 01443 217213

To provide a comprehensive audiology and hearing aid service. We are the only hospital in South Wales for tinnitus retraining therapy. We provide a foundation for education and adult life for hard of hearing and profoundly deaf children. We aim to educate patients and professionals regarding the RNID.

Llwynypia Hospital
Llwynypia, Tonypandy, Mid Glamorgan, CF40 2LX
Tel: 01443 440440
Fax: 01443 431611

Full audiology and hearing aid service for adults and children, tinnitus retraining therapy.

Prince Charles Hospital
Gurnorns Estate, Merthyr Tydfil, Mid Glamorgan, CF47 9DT
Tel: 01685 721721
Fax: 01685 388001

Princess of Wales Hospital
Coity Road, Bridgend, Mid Glamorgan, CF31 1RQ
Tel: 01656 752192
Textphone: 01656 752192
Fax: 01656 752107
E-mail: audiology.pwh@bridgend-
            tr.wales.nhs.uk

The Department of Audiology provides a full range of audiological and vestibular assessments for both adults and children. Adult and paediatric auditory rehabilitation is available. There are services for tinnitus counselling and associated management. Hearing therapy services are available in addition to an environmental aid clinic.

Ystrad Mynach Hospital
Caerphilly Road, Ystrad Mynach, Mid Glamorgan, CF82 7XU
Tel: 01443 812201

There is a specialist service for deaf children from pre-school to 18, providing advice in a peripatetic service to schools. If the primary difficulty is hearing impairment then these children are seen by the service. Other children will be seen in the community clinics with specialist support and advice available to community therapists. Advice is given to deaf adults as part of the general adult acute/community caseload.

➢ Neath Port Talbot
See West Glamorgan

➢ Newport
See Gwent

➢ Powys
Brecon War Memorial Hospital
Cerrigcochion Road, Brecon, Powys, LD3 7NS
Tel: 01874 622443
Fax: 01874 711828

To provide a basic service for deaf people in the community.

Bronllys Hospital
Bronllys, Brecon, Powys, LD3 0LU

➢ Rhondda, Cynon,Taff
See Mid Glamorgan

➢ South Glamorgan
University Hospital of Wales
Heath Park, Cardiff, South Glamorgan, CF4 4XW
Tel: 029 2074 7747
Textphone: 029 2074 3179
Fax: 029 2074 3288

6

➤ West Glamorgan

Neath General Hospital

Pant-yr-Heol, Neath, West Glamorgan, SA11 2LQ

Tel: 01639 641161

Fax: 01639 633081

Port Talbot Hospital

Hospital Road, Port Talbot, West Glamorgan, SA12 6PD

Tel: 01639 641161

The department also has facilities at Neath Hospital. We are also responsible for the school screening programme for Swansea, Neath and Port Talbot. Community support clinics are covered. We carry out full audiological diagnostic testing, a full hearing aid service, and a GP referral system which has been running for five years.

Singleton Hospital

Sketty, Swansea, West Glamorgan, SA2 8QA

Tel: 01792 285861

Textphone: 01792 285861

Fax: 01792 208647

The aim of the department is to promote a high-quality hearing assessment, hearing aid and tinnitus service to the area.

Cochlear Implant Centres

This is a list of centres providing cochlear implant treatment and follow-up.

This section is listed alphabetically by hospital within country and county sections.

England

➤ Avon

West of England Cochlear Implant Programme

Southmead Hospital, Monks Park Road, Southmead, Bristol, Avon, BS10 5NB

Tel: 0117 959 5151

Fax: 0117 959 5168

Adults and children.

➤ Cambridgeshire

East of England Cochlear Implant Centre

Audiology Department, Addenbrooks NHS Trust, Hills Road, Cambridge, CB2 2QQ

Tel: 01223 217589

Fax: 01223 217559

Adults and children.

➤ Cleveland

North East Cochlear Implant Programme

North Riding Infirmary, Newport Road, Middlesbrough, Cleveland, TS1 5JE

Tel: 01642 854068

Fax: 01642 854064

➤ East Sussex

Brighton Cochlear Implant Programme

Royal Susex County Hospital, Eastern Road, Brighton, BN2 5BE

Tel: 01273 696955

Fax: 01273 602730

➤ Hampshire

South of England Cochlear Implant Programme

Audiology Clinic, Institute of Sound and Vibration Research, University of Southampton, Highfield, Southampton, SO17 1BJ

Tel: 023 8059 3522

Fax: 023 8059 4981

➤ Lancashire

Manchester Cochlear Implant Programme

Centre of Audiology, University of Manchester, Oxford Road, Manchester, M13 9PL

Tel: 0161 275 3361

Fax: 0161 276 8511

➤ London

Great Ormond Street Cochlear Implant Programme

Department of Audiology, Hospital for Sick Children, Great Ormond Street, London, WC1N 3JH

Tel: 020 7405 9200

Fax: 020 7813 8261

Guy's and St Thomas Cochlear Implant Service

Guy's and St Thomas Hospital Trust, St Thomas Hospital, Lambeth Palace Road, London, SE1 7EH

Tel: 020 7928 9292

Textphone: 020 7922 8241

Fax: 020 7922 8088

Portland Hospital Cochlear Implant Programme

Portland Private Hospital, 234 Great Portland Street, London, W1N 5PH

Tel: 020 7390 8060

Fax: 020 7890 8053

Royal National Throat, Nose and Ear Cochlear Implant Programme

The Royal National Throat Nose and Ear Hospital, 330-332 Gray's Inn Road, London, WC1X 8EE

Tel: 020 7915 1301

Fax: 020 7915 1303

➤ Nottinghamshire

Nottingham Adult Cochlear Implant Programme

Hearing Services Centre, Directorate of ENT/Audiology, Ropewalk House, 113 The Ropewalk, Nottingham, NG1 6HA

Tel: 0115 948 5565

Fax: 0115 948 5515

7

Nottingham Paediatric Cochlear Implant Programme
University Hospital NHS Trust, Ropewalk House, 113 The Ropewalk, Nottingham, NG1 6HA

Tel: 0115 948 5549

Fax: 0115 948 5560

➤ Oxfordshire
Oxford Cochlear Implant Programme
Radcliffe Infirmary NHS Trust, Department of Otolaryngology, Woodstock Road, Oxford, OX2 6HE

Tel: 01865 311188

Fax: 01865 224544

➤ South Yorkshire
Sheffield Cochlear Implant Programme
North Trent Dept of Medical Audiology, The Central Sheffield University Hospitals, Glossop Road, Sheffield, S10 2JF

Tel: 0114 271 1900 ext 1285/ 1281

➤ West Midlands
Birmingham Adult Cochlear Implant Programme
Selly Oak Hospital, Raddlebarn Road, Birmingham, West Midlands, B29 6JD

Tel: 0121 627 8106

Fax: 0121 456 4697

Hearing assessment rehabilitation centre.

Birmingham Paediatric Cochlear Implant Programme
Birmingham Children's Hospital, The Jack Ashley Centre, 4 Church Road, Edgbaston, Birmingham, West Midlands, B15 3TD

Tel: 0121 454 8084

Fax: 0121 454 3028

➤ West Yorkshire
Yorkshire Cochlear Implant Programme
Audiology Department, Bradford Royal Infirmary, Duckworth Lane, Bradford, West Yorkshire, BD9 6RJ

Tel: 01274 364853

Fax: 01274 364853

Adults and children.

Northern Ireland

➤ County Antrim
Belfast Regional Cochlear Implant Programme
Belfast City Hospital, Middle Dufferin, Lisburn Road, Belfast, County Antrim, BT9 7AB

Tel: 028 9026 3603

Fax: 028 9026 3549

Adults and children.

Eire

➤ Co Dublin
Dublin Cochlear Implant Programme
Beaumont Hospital, P O Box 1297, Beaumont Road, Dublin 9, Co Dublin, Eire

Tel: 00 353 183 777 55

Fax: 00 353 180 927 53

Adults and children.

Scotland

➤ Ayrshire
Kilmarnock Cochlear Implant Programme
Department of Otolaryngology, Crosshouse Hospital, Crosshouse, Kilmarnock, Ayrshire, KA2 0BE

Tel: 01563 521133 ext 2080

Fax: 01563 572009

➤ Midlothian
Edinburgh Cochlear Implant Programme
Royal Infirmary, Lauriston Building, ENT Level 4, 39 Lauriston Place, Edinburgh, Midlothian, EH3 9EN

Tel: 0131 536 1000

Fax: 0131 536 1001

The regional adult cochlear implant programme is based here.

Wales

➤ Clwyd
North Wales Cochlear Implant Programme
H M Stanley Hospital, Upper Denbigh Road, St Asaph, Clwyd, LL17 0RS

Tel: 01745 589773 ext 4526

Fax: 01745 583143

➢ Mid Glamorgan

Bridgend Cochlear Implant Programme

Bridgend Hospital, Audiology Department,
Quarella Road, Bridgend, Mid Glamorgan, CR31 1JP

Tel: 01656 752752 ext 2795

Fax: 01656 752737

Adults and children.

➢ South Glamorgan

Cardiff Cochlear Implant Programme

Welsh Hearing Institute, University Hospital of
Wales, Heath Park, Cardiff, South Glamorgan, CF4
4XW

Tel: 029 2074 3472

Fax: 029 2074 3838

Adults and children.

7

Tinnitus

Tinnitus is the word for noises that some people hear 'in the ears' or 'in the head'. Nearly all of us have experienced tinnitus temporarily - for a few hours after going to a disco, for example, or when listening carefully in a very quiet room. We are not usually troubled by occasional tinnitus, but tinnitus noises may become a problem if they persist. Some people find tinnitus difficult to live with.

People with troublesome tinnitus are often referred by their GP to the tinnitus service of a hospital's ENT, audiology or hearing therapy department, for examination, treatment and therapy. For details of these services please contact the RNID Tinnitus Helpline (see details below).

This section lists a variety of national and international organisations and local groups able to support and advise people in managing their tinnitus. For an up to date list of these groups please contact the RNID Tinnitus Helpline.

All groups listed here have been contacted to ensure details are correct. However, old groups cease to exist and new groups open their doors with incredible speed and it is sometimes difficult to ensure that every group listed is still in business, or to guarantee that every group in existence is listed. If you spot incorrect details or know that your group is not here, then please phone, fax or write to the RNID Tinnitus Helpline and we will ensure that your group details are added/ amended.

National Organisations

➢ England

Tinnitus Action

P O Box 14904, London, SE18 3ZX
Tel: 020 8316 6116
Fax: 020 8317 8934
E-mail: Tinnitus@btinternet.com
Website: www.tinnitus.co.uk

Offers general advice and support for tinnitus sufferers. Quarterly magazine: 'Sound Sense'.

RNID Tinnitus Helpline

Castle Cavendish Works, Norton Street, Nottingham, NG7 5PN
Tel: 0345 090210 Helpline
Textphone: 0845 601 0821
Fax: 0115 978 5012
E-mail: tinnitushelpline@btinternet.com
Website: www.rnid.org.uk
Contact: Kathie Price, Manager
Tel: 0115 942 1525
Textphone: 0115 942 1525

Funded and administered by RNID, the Tinnitus Helpline gives information, advice and support on tinnitus and its management. A free information pack is available to helpline callers. The Helpline also produces a range of factsheets and a helpline newsletter is produced three times a year. All calls are charged at local rate on the helpline number which is open Monday to Friday, 10am to 3pm.

British Tinnitus Association

4th Floor, White Building, Fitzalan Square, Sheffield, South Yorkshire, S1 2AZ
Tel: 0800 018 0527 Freephone
            0114 273 0122
Fax: 0114 279 6222
E-mail: tinnitus@dial.pipex.com
Contact: Val Rose, Operations/ Publications
            Manager

The BTA exists to provide help and support to people with tinnitus. The association provides information, advice, training and an information exchange. It also organises conferences, undertakes research, campaigns to improve services for people with tinnitus, organises self-help groups and produces a quarterly journal for its members. Its services are also available to other organisations, professionals and the general public. Quarterly magazine: 'Quiet'.

International Organisations

➢ Australia

New South Wales Tinnitus Support Group

P O Box 600, Woollahra 2025, New South Wales, Australia
Tel: 0061 2 93617331
Textphone: 0061 2 93617338
Fax: 0061 2 93617333

Quarterly newsletter 'Tinnitus Talk'. Branches in Canberra, Coffs Harbour, Epping, North Gosford, Parramatta, and Pensinsular (Manly Vale). This is part of the Australian Tinnitus Association.

8

Tinnitus Association of Western Australia

29 West Parade, Perth 6000, Western Australia
Tel: 0061 8 9328 3283
Fax: 00618 9328 3885
Quarterly newsletter: 'WA Tinnitus News'.

Tinnitus Association Victoria Inc

c/o Better Hearing Australia, 5 High Street,
Prahran, Victoria 3181, Australia
Tel: 0061 3 9510 1577
Fax: 0061 3 9510 6076

➤ Austria

Österreichischer Schwerhörigenbund Referat Tinnitus

Radegundstrasse 10, A-8045 Graz, Austria
Tel: 0043 316 67 13 27
Fax: 0043 316 68 10 93

➤ Belgium

Belgique Acouphènes

Avenue H de Brouckère 22, B-1160 Bruxelles,
Belgium
Tel: 0032 2 660 3142
Fax: 0032 2 672 8855

➤ Canada

Tinnitus Association of Canada

23 Ellis Park Road, Toronto, Ontario, M6S 2V4,
Canada
Tel: 001 416 762 1490
Fax: 001 416 769 1109
E-mail: chasm@pathcom.com
Website: www.kadis.com/ta/tinnitus.htm

➤ Czech Republic

Cesky Tinnitus Klub

Habova 1571, CZ-15500 Praha 5, Czech Republic

➤ Denmark

Ménière og Tinnitus Foreningen (MTF)

Høstvej 5, DK-8600 Silkeborg, Denmark
Tel: 0045 86 827 860

➤ Eire

Cork Tinnitus Support Group

c/o Phyllis Higgins, Crestlands, Westbourne Park,
Magazine Road, Cork, Eire
This local self help group is part of the Irish
Tinnitus Association (ITA).

Irish Tinnitus Association

35 North Frederick Street, Dublin 1, Eire
Tel: 00353 1 872 3800
Fax: 00353 1 872 3816
E-mail: nad@iol.ie

North East Dublin Tinnitus Support Group

Irish Tinnitus Association, 35 North Frederick
Street, Dublin 1, Eire
Tel: 00 353 1 872 3800
Fax: 00 353 1 872 3816
This is a local self help group of the Irish Tinnitus
Association (ITA). It holds meetings to provide
information, help and support for all who live in
the area.

South Dublin Tinnitus Support Group

c/o 8 Woodlands Avenue, Dun Laoghaire, Eire
Contact: Clare Jennings

West of Ireland Tinnitus Support Group

The Magnet, Market Street, Clifden, County
Galway, Eire
Contact: Tom Connolly

➤ Finland

Finnish Tinnitus Association

Ulappasaarentie 3C 34, SF-00980 Helsinki, Finland
Tel: 0035 8 03 44 19 26
Fax: 0035 8 03 44 19 27

➤ France

France Acouphènes

BP 547, 75667 Paris Cedex 14, France
Tel: 00 33 1 43 95 03 99
Fax: 00 33 1 43 95 03 99
E-mail: france.acouphenes@francemel.com
Website: www.chez.com/acouphenes
French Tinnitus Organisation. Quarterly
newsletter: 'Tinnitussimo'.

➤ Germany
Deutsche Tinnitus-Liga e.V.
Postfach 349, Am Lohsiepen 18, D-42353
Wuppertal, Germany
Tel: 00 49 202 24 65 20
Fax: 00 49 202 24 65 220
Website: www.tinnitus-liga.de
Quarterly magazine: 'Tinnitus Forum'.

➤ India
Indian Tinnitus Association
H 3-12-33 H1 Ganesh Nagar, Ramanthapur,
Hyderabad 500-013, India
Tel: 00 91 40 703 8035

➤ Israel
Tinnton Society
P O Box 23223, Tel Aviv 61231, Israel
Tel: 00972 3 629 9389

➤ Netherlands
Commissie Tinnitus
Nederlandse Vereniging voor Slechthorenden,
Postbus 9505, NL-3506 GM Utrecht, The
Netherlands
Tel: 0031 30 2 617 616
Fax: 0031 30 2 616 869
Website: www.tinnitus.nvvs.nl

➤ New Zealand
New Zealand Tinnitus Association
P O Box 100734, North Shore Mail Centre,
Glenfield, Auckland 10, New Zealand
Tel: 0064 9 478 6992
Branches in Ashburton, Auckland, Christchurch,
Lower Hutt, New Plymouth and Tauranga.

➤ Norway
Norwegian Tinnitus Committee
Hørselshemmedes Landsforbund, Lilleakerveien
31a, 0283 Oslo, Norway
Tel: 0047 22 52 32 00
Fax: 0047 22 52 55 20
E-mail: santonse@sn.no.

➤ Spain
**Asociacion de Personas Afectadas por Tinitus
(APAT)**
Apdo Correos 57, 08320 El Masnou, Barcelona,
Spain
Tel: 0034 93 555 4955

➤ Sweden
Tinnitusføreningen I Göteborg
Bangatan 39, S-41464 Gothenburg, Sweden
Tel: 0046 31 122007
Fax: 0046 31 122307

➤ Switzerland
Schweizerische Tinnitus-Liga
Sekretariat Maja Hammer, Ländliweg 12, CH 5400
Baden, Switzerland
Tel: 0041 56 222 81 40

Local Groups
➤ England
Avon
Bristol Tinnitus Support Group
43 Ridgehill, Bristol, Avon, BS9 4SB
Tel: 01275 838128
Contact: Gordon Brand
Tel: 0117 962 4803

Offers support, information, loans, meetings,
relaxation courses. Meets at the Bristol Centre for
the Deaf, 16-18 King Square, Bristol, on the first
Thursday of each month, from 2.15 to 4pm.

Berkshire
Chiltern Tinnitus Support Group
7 Southview, High Road, Cookham, Maidenhead,
Berkshire, SL6 9BN
Tel: 01628 484318
Contact: N Darling
Tel: 01628 523072

The group's aim is to offer support to those who
are distressed by their tinnitus problem. We have
interesting speakers at each meeting and try to
balance the year with some light-hearted subjects
as well as information on tinnitus management
and relaxation techniques. We offer refreshments
and a raffle and good company.

The Group meets at the Community Centre,
Stratton Rd, Princes Risborough on the last
Thursday in the month between 2pm - 4pm.

8

Reading Tinnitus Support Group

17 Pitts Lane, Earley, Reading, Berkshire, RG6 1BX
Tel: 0118 926 4043
Contact: June Curnow

Contact: phone after 6pm or send a letter. Meets at the Pathology Department, Royal Berks Hospital, London Road, Reading, on the first Saturday of each month at 2.30pm (except January and August).

Cambridgeshire
Cambridge Tinnitus Support Group

30 Horseheath Road, Linton, Cambridge, CB1 6LU
Contact: John Cammann
Tel: 01223 891 198

The group meets at CAMTAD Cambridge, Buchan House, Buchan Street, Cambridge on the 1st and 2nd Saturday in February, April, June, September and November.

Channel Islands
Jersey Tinnitus Support Group

Wyvern, 11 La Rue de Podetre, St Helier, Jersey, Channel Islands, JE2 3HE
Tel: 01534 721927 Helpline
Contact: Marian Pitt

The Jersey Tinnitus Association offers support. We meet each second Tuesday of the month at George V Homes Hall, St Aubins Road, St Helier, with speakers or social events.

Cheshire
Runcorn Tinnitus Support Group

2 Stonebarn Lane, Palace Fields, Runcorn, Cheshire, WA7 2QE
Tel: 01928 714879
Contact: R Hampson

Offers advice, support, fundraising. Meets Halton CHC, 75 High Street, Runcorn, on the second Monday in month, 7.30 to 9.30pm.

Cornwall
Cornwall Tinnitus Group

Moorgron, Tolgullow St Day, Redruth, Cornwall, TR16 5PD
Contact: Lena Thomas
             Saranor, School Hill, Burnwithian, St Day, Redruth, Cornwall, TR16 5LG

Truro Tinnitus Support Group

Saranor, School Hill, Burnwithian, St Day, Redruth, Cornwall, TR16 5LG
Tel: 01209 820873 24hr answerphone
Contact: Jacqueline Doré
             Torpoint Tinnitus Support Group, Bramley Cottage, Wilcove, Torpoint, Cornwall, PL11 2PH
Tel: 01752 813722

Offers counselling, speakers, loans, meetings. Branches in Liskeard, Bude (Hazell Maguire: 01288 353695) and Torpoint (Jacqueline Doré: 01752 813722). Meets at Postgraduate Centre, Treliske Hospital, Truro, quarterly - see press.

County Durham
Durham Tinnitus Support Group

Dryburn Hospital, North Road, Durham, DH1 5TW
Tel: 0191 386 4911 ext 2166
Contact: Simon Milligan, Hearing Therapist

Offers support and advice. Meets in the Commitee Room, Dryburn Hospital, on the last Monday of each month 1.30 to 3.30pm

Sunderland Tinnitus Support Group

151 Eden Lane, Peterlee, County Durham, SR8 5DS
Tel: 0191 586 0467
Contact: Roy Telfer

We provide help, advice and social contact for people having difficulty in coping with tinnitus. We maintain contact with local audiology departments. We raise funds to enable us to donate to research and to run our group, especially as there is no funding from central office.

Derbyshire
Chesterfield Tinnitus Support Group

Newbold Road, Chesterfield, Derbyshire, S41 7PF
Tel: 01246 552950

Contact during office hours by phone. Offers support, information and fundraising. Meets at the Audiology Department, Scarsdale Hospital 2nd Friday each month at 7.30 pm.

Derby Tinnitus Support Group

23 Woodminton Drive, Chellaston, Derby, DE73 1RZ
Tel: 01332 702423
Contact: J Wain

Covers a 10-mile radius of Derby. Telephone after 6pm or on weekends. Offers meetings, information, fundraising and support. The group meets at the Central Library Meeting Room, The Strand, Derby on the 4th Monday of January, March, May, July, September between 2pm-4pm.

Ilkeston Tinnitus Support Group

148 Oliver Road, Kirk Hallam, Ilkeston, Derbyshire, DE7 4JU

Tel: 0115 930 7953

Contact: E Bamford

Covers Ilkestone, Heanor, Trowell, Spondon and Stapleford. Offers support and meetings. Meets at the Ilkeston Medical Centre on the last Wednesday of every month, 7 to 8.30pm.

Swadlincote Tinnitus Support Group

c/o Lincote Resource Centre, Off Hall Farm Road, Widge Shaft, Swadlincote, Derbyshire, DE11 8LH

Contact: Norma Tyson

Devon
Exeter Tinnitus Support Group

63d Rosebery Road, Exmouth, Devon, EX8 1SQ

Tel: 01395 278166

Contact: Peter Stockhill

The group meets at the Monford House, Wonford Road, Exeter on the 1st Thursday, bi-monthly at 7pm.

Plymouth Tinnitus Support Group

Hearing & Sight Centre, Pounds House, Outlands Road, Peverell, Plymouth, Devon, PL2 3PX

Tel: 01752 788999

Textphone: 01752 768573

Fax: 01752 780470

Contact: Dawn Clarke

The aims of the support group at the Hearing & Sight Centre is to provide mutual support to people with tinnitus. The objectives are to support each other, to share experiences of tinnitus with others, to gain access to information and to decide on future group activities. The Tinnitus Support Group will meet monthly.

Torquay Tinnitus Support Group

28 Westhill Road, Paignton, Devon, TQ3 2ND

Tel: 01803 664272

Contact: Jackie Walker

Contact by letter or phone after 8pm. Meets at Torbay Hospital Social Club, Lawes Bridge, Torquay on the 3rd Thrusday each month at 7.30pm.

Dorset
Blandford Tinnitus Support Group

Hill View, Blandford Road, Tarrant Rawston, Blandford Forum, Dorset, DT11 8SH

Tel: 01258 452406

Meets at Blandford Hospital on the fourth Friday of each month at 4pm.

Bournemouth and District Tinnitus Group

102 Recreation Road, Poole, Dorset, BH12 2AL

Tel: 01202 747951

Contact: Joan Loosemore

Aims: to supply help, information and support to anyone with tinnitus, by telephone and leaflets. Monthly meetings with speaker (usually health-based), open discussion on ways of coping. Equipment such as maskers, under-pillow speakers, tapes and books on tinnitus available on loan to members.

Dorset Hearing and Tinnitus Association

17 East Street, Blandford Forum, Dorset, DT11 7DU

Tel: 01305 255563

Contact: Edna Laker, Hearing Therapist

Tel: 01305 255562

Previously the Weymouth Tinnitus Support Group (now defunct). Contact Edna Laker for help and advice only. Patients now referred to Dorset Hearing and Tinnitus Association in Blandford Forum.

East Sussex
Sussex Tinnitus Association

13 Cownwy Court, Park Crescent, Rottingdean, Brighton, East Sussex, BN2 7JB

Tel: 01273 308736

The Sussex Tinnitus Association is a Registered Charity catering for people suffering from tinnitus in Sussex. The Association has close contact with all hospitals, ENT specialists and audiologists who refer patients to us. Six groups hold quarterly meetings and members receive a bi-monthly newsletter. Counselling is available. The group has meetings in Brighton, Worthing, Eastbourne, Bexhill on Sea, Haywards Heath and Hastings.

Essex

Chelmsford Tinnitus Support Group

12 Essex Avenue, Chelmsford, Essex, CM1 4AQ

Tel: 01245 265015

The aims of the Chelmsford Tinnitus Group is to provide support to tinnitus sufferers in the local area. We do not supply equipment such as hearing aids or noise generators as these are provided by the local NHS hospital. Helpful advice is given, together with literature about tinnitus in general, and information about where these devices are available. The group meets at the OAP Centre, Cottage Place, Chelmsford on the 1st Tuesday of each month between 7.30 - 9.30pm.

Harlow Tinnitus Support Group

90 Bishopsfield, Harlow, Essex, CM18 6UN

Tel: 01279 442594 Helpline

Contact: Mike Jackson

Offers support, newsletter, meetings. Meets at Latton Centre, Southern Way, Harlow, on the first Wednesday of each month.

Redbridge and District Tinnitus Group

345 Fullwell Avenue, Clayhall, Ilford, Essex, IG5 0RR

Tel: 020 8550 3510 Helpline/ 020 8556 6350 evenings

Fax: 020 8550 3510

Contact: Harry Hartle

Aims: to give help and support to anyone who experiences tinnitus regardless of their affiliation. Information booklet sent to all who make a request. Equipment available to try out at the Walk-in service. Temporary loan of equipment when available.

Whistle Stop Basildon Tinnitus Support Group

14 Dukes Road, Billericay, Essex, CM11 1BP

Tel: 01268 524985 Helpline

Contact: Pat Davie

Tel: 01268 524985 Helpline

Offers helpline, meetings, newsletter, fundraising. Meets at the Reading Rooms, Billericay High Street, on the third Friday of each month at 7.30pm except January and August.

Gloucestershire

Gloucester Tinnitus Support Group

19 The Avenue, Charlton Kings, Cheltenham, Gloucestershire, GL53 9BL

Tel: 01242 513734

Contact: Don Bennett

Offers support and meetings. Meets at the Gloucester Centre for the Deaf, Colin Road, Barnwood, Gloucester, on the second Monday of the month in November, January and March at 2pm, and May, July and September at 7pm.

Hampshire

Portsmouth Tinnitus Support Group

279 Arundel Street, Fratton, Portsmouth, Hampshire, PO1 1LX

Tel: 023 9238 8627

Contact: N Clark
                    72 Carlton Road, Fareham, Hampshire, PO16 8JH

Contact by letter or phone after 6pm. Offers support, talks, newsletter. Meets at The Deaf Centre, 279 Arundel Street, Portsmouth on the second Saturday of every moth from 2pm to 4pm. One workshop a year.

Southampton Tinnitus Support Group

15 Belton Road, Sholing, Southampton, Hampshire, SO19 1DS

Tel: 023 8044 2492

Contact: D Mercer

Contact by letter or phone. Meets at Fairbairn Centre, Augustine Road, Southampton on the fourth Thursday, every other month, May, July, September, November, January.

Herefordshire

Hereford Tinnitus Self Help Group

WHAD Hereford Centre, Penn House, 9-10 Broad Street, Hereford, HR4 9AP

Tel: 01989 566214

Contact: Rachael Thompson

Our group helps sufferers to cope with tinnitus in everyday life by offering sympathetic discussion, sharing experiences, the use of soothing tapes, methods of relaxation, booklets and information. Also, to hear talks given by speakers from fields of work allied to health including tinnitus. We are also supported by a local audiologist. The group meets on the third Wednesday of every month from 2pm to 4pm at Penn House.

8

Hertfordshire

Cheshunt Tinnitus and Ménières Support Group

30 Allard Close, Rosedale, Cheshunt, Waltham Cross, Hertfordshire, EN7 6JW

Tel: 01992 630230
Contact: Carolyne King

Offers support and meetings. Meets at the Octagonal Room, Bishops College, Cheshunt on the second Monday of each month at 7.30pm.

Isle of Wight

Isle of Wight Tinnitus Self Help Group

The Riverside Centre, Newport, Isle of Wight, PO30 5WD

Tel: 01983 855845
Contact: Jack Richards, Chairman
              74 Mill Hill Road, Cowes, Isle of Wight, PO31 7EE

Self help group supporting those with tinnitus. Meets at 6.30pm on the second Wednesday, every 3 months with speakers, information and social contact.

Kent

Bexley Tinnitus Support Group

15 Holmsdale Grove, Bexleyheath, Kent, DA7 6NZ

Tel: 01322 669347
Contact: M O'Sullivan

We offer advice and support to tinnitus sufferers and their families. We have a library of books, videos, cassettes which can be borrowed free of charge. We also provide a domicillary service for anyone who wants to discuss their particular problem in their own home. We invite speakers to our meetings, such as ENT consultants, audiologists, alternative medicine practioners, etc. We publish a bi-monthly news sheet. Annual subscriptions: £5.

Canterbury Tinnitus Support Group

10 Cherry Avenue, Canterbury, Kent, CT2 8EN

Tel: 01227 463385
Contact: Dorothy Hutchinson

The group meets at the Speech and Language Therapy Department at Kent and Canterbury Hospital on the second Wednesday of every other month (January, March, May, July, September, November) from 2pm until 4pm. There is also a drop-in clinic at the same location at the same times. The group is affiliated to National BTB and exists to provide help and support for all experiencing the disturbing effects of tinnitus. The

group takes telephone enquiries and a member of the group, a trained nurse, will receive training (January 1999) to become the official group counsellor. Each year a representative is sent to the National Conference of British Tinnitus Association in order to keep abreast of new developments and treatments for tinnitus.

Tonbridge Tinnitus Support Group

30 Edward Street, Southborough, Tunbridge Wells, Kent, TN4 0HA

Tel: 01892 544425
Contact: Rita Scales

Contact by phone or letter. The group offers support, advice and socials. The group meets at the Old Fire Station, Castle St, Tonbridge on the 3rd Tuesday each month at 2pm.

Lancashire

Burnley Tinnitus Support Group

63 Lower Manor Lane, Burnley, Lancashire, BB12 0EF

Tel: 01282 453164
Contact: J Danby

Offers counselling, talks, meetings. Meets in the Ex-Elderly Day Care Centre at Burnley General Hospital last Tuesday in the month (excluding July and December) from 7.30pm.

Bury Tinnitus Support Group

Fairfield General Hospital, Bury, Lancashire, BL9 7TD

Tel: 0161 705 3664
Contact: J Lord
              185 Market Street, Tottington, Bury, Lancashire, BL8 3LT

Meets at the Postgraduate Centre, Bury, on the second Monday of each month at 10am.

Manchester Tinnitus Support Group

18 Gorseyfields, Droylsden, Manchester, Lancashire, M43 6DZ

Tel: 0161 370 8362 after 6pm
Contact: Frances Wharton

Offers counselling, speakers, self-help, discussions, meetings. Meets at Manchester Deaf Club, Crawford House, Booth Street, East Manchester (0161 273 3415) on the first Wednesday of each month, 1.30 to 3.30pm (not January).

Wigan Tinnitus Support Group

297 Bolton Road, Westhoughton, Wigan,
Lancashire, BL5 3EL
Tel: 01942 818374
Contact: R Swannick

Meets at Astley Labour Club, Manchester Rd,
Astley, on the first Thursday of each month at
7.30pm.

Leicestershire
Leicester Tinnitus Support Group

35 Grosvenor Close, Glen Parva, Leicester, LE2 9UG
Tel: 0116 277 6508
Contact: A Randle

Offers counselling, speakers. Meets at the Centre
for Deaf People, 135 Welford Rd, Leicester (0116
255 6776). Quarterly publication and 'Buzz Group'
held on the first and third Wednesday of each
month at 2pm.

London
North West London Branch, British Tinnitus Association

5 Spencer Court, 14-16 Granville Road, London,
N12 0HJ
Tel: 020 8349 9353
Contact: B Aronsohn

Covers north west London - the boroughs of
Barnet and Brent. Contact can be made by phone
or letter. Offers advice, support, talks. Meets every
second month at the Parish Centre on the corner
of Heriot Road and Brent Street NW4 2DG at 2pm
on the second Saturday of every month.

Streatham Tinnitus Group

14 Elizabeth Cooper Lodge, 91 Thurleigh Road,
London, SW12 8TY
Tel: 020 8673 3915
Contact: J Gould

The group meets on the first Monday of each
month from 1pm to 2.30pm excluding Bank
Holidays at the Whittingham Centre, Rutford Road,
Streatham SW16 2DQ. Provides mutual support
for people experiencing tinnitus and helping those
newly diagnosed to cope with with associated
stress. Members share helpful advice; we have no
medical qualifications. Friendship and support
have helped many. Quite a small group, mainly
retired. Social activities include annual outings as
well as having talks likely to help.

West London Tinnitus Group

86 Cedar Grove, Ealing, London, W5 4AR
Tel: 020 8932 0896
Fax: 020 8932 0896
Contact: Vic Wooster

Offers support and information. Meetings at the
Michael Flanders Centre, Church Road, London,
W3, on the last Saturday of each month at 2.30pm.

Merseyside
Bebington, Wirral Tinnitus Support Group

4 Meadway, Lower Village, Heswall, Wirral,
Merseyside, L60 8PH
Tel: 0151 342 4594

Contact by phone or letter. The group offers
couselling, newsletter and social events and
meets at St Barnabas Village Hall, The Cross,
Bromborough, Wirral.

Liverpool Tinnitus Support Group

16 Bradfield Street, Liverpool, Merseyside, L7 0EP
Tel: 0151 263 9771
Contact: Brenda Doherty

Offers support, advice, talks and meetings. Meets
at the Centre for the Deaf, Queens Drive, Liverpool
(Telephone: 0151 228 0888) on the first
Wednesday of the month at 1pm.

Southport Tinnitus Support Group

22 Beach Priory Gardens, Southport, Merseyside,
PR8 1RT
Contact: M Linsley

The Southport Tinnitus Support Group provides
support and advice to people with tinnitus and
their families. At our meetings, in addition to ear,
nose and throat speakers, we have others from all
walks of life. The group meets at Southport
General Infirmary, Scarisbrick New Road,
Southport on the fourth Wednesday at 7pm each
month except August and December.

Middlesex
Hounslow Tinnitus Support Group

2 Viscount Road, Stanwell, Staines, Middlesex,
TW19 7RD
Tel: 01784 255485
Contact: J Hazelby

Offers support, lectures and loans. Meets at the
Voluntary Centre, 51 Grove Road, Hounslow, on
the third Saturday of the month, 2 to 4pm.

8

Norfolk
North Walsham Tinnitus Support Group

Woodwinds, Davey Hill, Cromer, Norfolk, NR27 9JL

Tel: 01263 512773 24-hour Helpline
Fax: 01263 512773
Contact: Doreen Sharp, Coordinator

To extend support, help and comfort to members with tinnitus. To provide and discuss the latest information on tinnitus. Meetings are held monthly at North Walsham Community Centre, Norfolk on the first Tuesday of the month at 7pm except January.

North Humberside
Hull Tinnitus Support Group

109 Southella Way, Kirkella, Hull, North Humberside, HU10 7LZ

Tel: 01482 656033
Contact: Bill Howard

Offers counselling and a newsletter. Meets at the New Graduate Centre, Hull Royal Infirmary, Anlaby Road, Hull.

North Yorkshire
Scarborough Tinnitus Support Group

8 Woodland Ravine, Scarborough, North Yorkshire, YO12 6TA

Tel: 01723 352517

Contact by letter or phone after 5pm. Offers meetings, speakers.The group meets at Westborough Methodist Church on the 2nd Thrusday each month at 6.30pm.

York Tinnitus Support Group

14 Calf Close, Haxby, York, YO32 3NS

Tel: 01904 764090
Contact: Gerald Orchard

The York Tinnitus Support Group no longer holds meetings and is in effect 'in moth balls' until local demand increases. Currently the former committee members are acting as 'helpers' for tinnitus sufferers in the area by discussing issues and sending out literature.

Northamptonshire
Nene Valey Tinnitus Group

Berryfield, Oundle Road, Polebrook, Peterborough, Cambridgeshire, PE8 5LQ

Tel: 01832 274906
Contact: David Lamburn

Meetings held quarterly: 6 January, 7 April, 7 July and 6 October 1999. Held at Old People's Welfare Centre, Irthlingborough, at 2.30pm. Telephone support; contact David Lamburn for details.

Nottinghamshire
Mansfield Tinnitus and Ménières Group

123 Dale Close, Langwith, Mansfield, Nottinghamshire, NG20 9EG

Tel: 01623 742110
Contact: K Bishop

To help each other and any other person who has a problem and seeks advice and understanding. Counselling via phone and personal contact. Literature forwarded following telephone counselling. Literature, videos and cassettes available on loan. We have speakers on varied topics including tinnitus and Ménières, relaxation, and social evenings. Meetings held at Society for Deaf People, 1 Wood Street, Mansfield on the fourth Tuesday of every month at 7.30pm except January and February.

Nottingham Tinnitus Support Group

168 Moor Road, Papplewick, Nottingham, NG15 8EQ

Tel: 0115 963 2154
Contact: Barrie Fisher

A self-help group working for the relief and cure of tinnitus. Our experiences and knowledge of this problem can be of great help to fellow sufferers. There is a membership fee of £5 which includes affiliation to the British Tinnitus Association. Members have free access to information packs and literature, the quarterly 'Quiet' magazine, speakers at meetings and practical help such as pillow speakers and relaxation tapes on loan. meetings held at YMCA, Shakespeare Street, Nottingham every Wednesday at 2pm (except those Wednesdays following a Bank Holiday).

Somerset

Somerset Tinnitus and Hard of Hearing Support Group

13 Laxton Close, Taunton, Somerset, TA1 2UL
Tel: 01823 274496
Contact: Charles Spiller, Chairman/Coordinator

Members exchange experiences and suggestions for coping with tinnitus. Most months there are informative talks related to the subject. Provides the much-needed emotional support, therapy techniques, in some cases counselling, and the chance to try new electronic equipment. Meetings held at Halcon Day Centre, Huish Close, Hamilton Road, Taunton on the fourth Wednesday of each month at 7pm.

Yeovil Tinnitus Self-Help Group

13 St Margarets Road, Tintinhull, Yeovil, Somerset, BA22 8PL
Tel: 01935 822320
Contact: Jill Harris

Annual subscription includes affiliation to British Tinnitus Association and 'Quiet' journal, group newsletters and other relevant information. An opportunity for sufferers to exchange useful ways of coping and to know that life can be lived to the full despite tinnitus. Meetings are held at Penn House, Penn Hill in Yeovil on the fourth Monday of every other month (January, March etc.) at 7pm.

South Yorkshire

Barnsley Tinnitus Support Group

c/o Audiology Department, Barnsley District General Hospital NHS Trust, Gawber Road, Barnsley, South Yorkshire, S75 2EP
Tel: 01226 777937
Contact: Liza Smeeton, Head of Audiology Department

The Barnsley Tinnitus Support Group meets on the second Tuesday of the month at 2pm at Barnsley District General Hospital. Meetings are varied and informal and there is always a member of the audiology staff present to talk to.

Doncaster Tinnitus Support Group

Doncaster Royal Infirmary, Thorne Road, Doncaster, South Yorkshire, DN2 5LT
Tel: 01302 553115
Textphone: 01302 553115
Fax: 01302 792334
Contact: Sandy Grimes, Audiology

Offers: meetings, support, lay counselling, telephone support. Library of books and tapes for loan (deposit required). Attended by tinnitus therapist. Speakers on tinnitus and related subjects. Meets at the Deaf Centre, Stirling Street, Doncaster, on the fourth Wednesday of each month at 2.30pm. Sandy Grimes can be reached by phone between 8.30am and 4.30pm Monday to Friday.

Rotherham Tinnitus Support Group

48 The Oval, Anston, Sheffield, South Yorkshire, S25 4BY
Tel: 01909 563374
Contact: Harlan Senior

The aims of the group are to bring together people with tinnitus and other interested parties and persons within the Rotherham area to give the opportunity to share information and advice on tinnitus; and the opportunity to engage in activities which meet their needs and interests. Meetings are held at SAlvation Army Citadel, Effingham Street, Rotherham on the third Thursday of the month at 2pm.

Sheffield Tinnitus Support Group

47 Charnock Dale Road, Gleadless, Sheffield, South Yorkshire, S12 3HQ
Tel: 0114 239 6708
Contact: S Hawthorn

We aim to help all those with tinnitus in the Sheffield district by holding monthly social meetings, and invite speakers who can talk about tinnitus and its problems, or speakers who can give insights into relaxing hobbies. We have three telephone helplines, and publish a quarterly newsletter. Meetings are held at St matthews Rooms, Carver Street, Sheffield on the second Wednesday of each month from 1.30pm to 3.30pm

Staffordshire

North Staffordshire Hard of Hearing and Tinnitus Group

Tel: 01782 393879
Contact: A Davies, Secretary

See entry under Deaf Clubs.

Stafford Tinnitus Support Group

'Home', 26 Whitgreave Lane, Great Bridgeford, Stafford, ST18 9SJ
Tel: 01785 282655
Contact: Keith Storr

Self-help group giving support, advice and information about tinnitus including tinnitus retraining therapy. Meetings are held at the Post Graduate Medical centre, District Hospital, Weston Road, Stafford on the third Tuesday of each month from 7pm to 9pm.

Stoke-on-Trent Hard of Hearing and Tinnitus Support Group

19 Friars Walk, Westlands, Newcastle under Lyme, Staffordshire, ST5 2HA

Tel: 01782 639955
Contact: David Clarke

Meets Staffs Society for the Deaf, Wellesley Street, Shelton, Stoke (01782 219161), on Tuesdays, 7pm to 10pm.

Suffolk
Bury St Edmunds Tinnitus Support Group

34 Highwood Crescent, Gazeley, Newmarket, Suffolk, CB8 8RU

Tel: 01638 750867
Contact: Trevor Jones

Meets at the Centre for the Deaf, Northgate Street, Bury St Edmonds, on the second Wednesday every other month at 7.30pm.

Surrey
Croydon Tinnitus Support Group

Mayday Hospital, Mayday Road, Thornton Heath, Surrey, CR7 7YE

Tel: 020 8401 3063 (see below)
Fax: 020 8401 3423
Contact: Chris Wood, Hearing Therapist

Provides ongoing support for tinnitus sufferers living in the Croydon area who have attended the Croydon Hearing Therapy Department for tinnitus counselling. The group is also open to non-Croydon residents wishing to meet other tinnitus sufferers for support and information. Partners are also welcome. The telephone number shown above is for information about group meetings only - it is not a Helpline.

Epsom Tinnitus Support Group

82 Elgar Avenue, Surbiton, Surrey, KT5 9JN

Tel: 020 8643 2537
Contact: T Siddall

Offers support with ear/head noises. Meets the last Monday of every month at 7.30pm (except May), sometimes with speakers. There are socials occasionally. The group has books/magazines on tinnitus available on loan to members. Meets at Social Services Department, Ashley Road, Epsom, Surrey.

Guildford Tinnitus Support Group

5 Windy Wood, Godalming, Surrey, GU7 1XX

Tel: 01483 429927
E-mail: jim.elsa@aol.com
Contact: Jim Mitchell

Areas covered: southwest Surrey and nearby areas. Information and guidance sent to all enquiries. Meetings: about six times a year in St Nicholas parish church hall, Bury Street, Guildford. Subjects: relevant to those who experience tinnitus.

Warwickshire
Nuneaton Tinnitus Support Group

42 Gadsby Street, Nuneaton, Warwickshire, CV11 4NY

Tel: 024 7632 6866
Contact: Irene Fall

Meets CVS, 72 High Street, Nuneaton, on the second Tuesday of each month 2pm.

Warwick Tinnitus Support Group

The Bungalow, Manor Hall, Sandy Lane, Lillington, Warwickshire

Tel: 01926 413706 after 7pm
Contact: Sandra Howkins
Tel: 01926 413706 after 7pm after 7pm

Contact: by post. Meets at Warwick Arms, High Street, Warwick on the third Thursday of the month at 7.30pm. Meetings - some with speakers on topics relating to tinnitus or general subjects. Some meetings just comprise chatting amongst members.

West Midlands
Birmingham Tinnitus Group
Birmingham Institute for Deaf People, Ladywood Road, Birmingham, West Midlands, B16 8SZ
Tel: 0121 455 0601
Textphone: 0121 246 0601
Fax: 0121 455 0601
Contact: Eileen Hewitson, Chair
            60 Croftdown Road, Birmingham, West Midlands, B17 8RD
Tel: 0121 681 2826

The group meets from 7.30 to 9pm on the first Thursday of alternate months and offers mutual support, activities and counselling for tinnitus sufferers. The group aims to help, support and advise anyone in the West Midlands area with tinnitus. We have a monthly drop-in session in the city centre. We produce six newsletters a year, and this is our main point of contact, along with the telephone. In addition the group meets at Carrs Lane Church Centre, Birmingham City Centre on the 3rd Thrusday each month at 10am.

Coventry Tinnitus Support Group
64 Jobs Lane, Coventry, West Midlands, CV4 9EE
Tel: 024 7646 4979
Contact: K Randall

Offers counselling and meetings. The group meets at the Walsall Deaf Centre, 59a Lichfield Road (01922 29177) on the second Tuesday of each month, 10.30am to 12 noon and at the Henry Fry Centre, Hertford Place, Queens Road, Coventry on the 3rd Tuesday each month at 1.30pm.

Walsall Tinnitus Support Group
49 Littlewood Road, Cheslyn Hay, Walsall, West Midlands, WS6 7EU
Tel: 01922 418809
Contact: Brenda Taylor

Offers support, meetings and speakers. Meets Walsall Deaf Centre, 59a Lichfield Road (01922 29177) on the second Tuesday of each month 10.30am to 12 noon.

Wolverhampton Tinnitus Support Group
West Park Hospital, Park Road West, Wolverhampton, West Midlands, WV1 4PW
Tel: 01902 444055

West Yorkshire

Bradford Tinnitus Group
Bradford Royal Infirmary, Audiology Department, Duckworth Lane, Bradford, West Yorkshire, BD9 6RJ
Tel: 01274 364071 (Helpline)
Contact: Sue Falkingham, Hearing Therapist
Tel: 01274 591601

Meets on the 1st Wednesday of each month at the ENT Department, Bradford Royal Infirmary.

Keighley Tinnitus Support Group
28 Hillcrest Avenue, Silsden, Keighley, West Yorkshire, BD20 9NH
Tel: 01535 652479
Contact: R Binns

Meets at 147 Skipton Road, Keighley, on the third Friday of each month (except February, July and August) at 6pm.

Leeds Tinnitus Support Group
25 Grove Farm Crescent, Cookridge, Leeds, West Yorkshire, LS16 6B2
Tel: 01274 591601/ 0113 240 8683
Contact: Dorothy Skidmore
            7 St. Matthias Street, Leeds, West Yorkshire, LS4 2DZ
Tel: 0113 278 0948

Offers help, advice, loans, home visits. Meets at the Civic Hall, Portland Crescent entrance, Leeds on Tuesdays at 6.30pm.

Wiltshire
Bradford upon Avon Tinnitus Support Group
18 Woodmanhead, Warminster, Wiltshire, SP12 8TE
Tel: 01985 214197
Fax: 01985 214197
Contact: J Coles

Meets on the first Tuesday of the month at 7.30 pm at Fitzmaurice Place Lounge, Junction Road, Bradford upon Avon.

Salisbury Tinnitus Support Group
Salisbury District Hospital, Odstock Road, Salisbury, Wiltshire, SP2 8BJ
Tel: 01722 429337
Contact: Celia Whiteside

Meetings with speakers are held at the Deaf Centre, Love Lane, Salisbury on the first Wednesday of each month at 7.30pm except January and August. Anyone requiring help is

8

referred, through their doctor, to the hearing therapist at the Salisbury and District Hospital, Odstock.

Swindon Tinnitus Support Group

23 Tavistock Road, Park North, Swindon, Wiltshire, SN3 2QD

Contact: Charles Jackson

The group meets at the Thistle Hotel on the second and fourth Mondays in the month at 8.30pm.

Worcestershire
Worcester Tinnitus Support Group

56 Fruitlands, Malvern, Worcestershire, WR14 4XA

Tel: 01684 567496

Contact: Ivan Spencer

Contact by letter or phone. The Group meet at the Ground Floor Lecture Room, Worcester Royal Infirmary on the 2nd Wednesday of each month at 2pm and at the Lyttleton Rooms, Church Street, Malvern on the 1st Wednesday of each month at 2pm.

➢ Northern Ireland
County Antrim
Ulster Tinnitus Association

58 Madigan Park, Carrickfergus, County Antrim, BT38 7JW

Contact: Tom Orr, Secretary

Our first duty is to tinnitus sufferers in Northern Ireland where we have at present six tinnitus support groups. Such groups afford tinnitus sufferers the opportunity to come together for discussion on problems, experiences and any matters of mutual interest that might help and relieve suffering in day-to-day living with tinnitus. There are groups at Ballymena, Craigavon, Belfast, Moy, Newry and Londonderry. Belfast group meets at the Audiology Department, Level 7D, Royal Victoria Hospital, Belfast on the third Thursday of each month at 2pm.

County Armagh

Craigavon Tinnitus Self-Help Group

c/o Cherrytrees Resource Centre, 1a Edenberry Gardens, Portadown, Craigavon, County Armagh, BT63 5EA

Tel: 028 3839 4088
Textphone: 028 3839 4088
Fax: 028 3839 4095
Contact: J Cameron
                    17 Annesborough Road, Lurgan, Craigavon, County Armagh, BT67 9JD

Provides a meeting place for tinnitus sufferers. Provides up-to-date information. Invites selected speakers. Provides monthly newsletter. Raises funds. Liaises with hearing therapists and senior social workers. Meets on the third Monday of the month from 7.30pm.

County Down
Newry Tinnitus Support Group

Conifers Resource Centre, Dromalane Road, Newry, County Down, BT35 8AP

Tel: 028 3025 0800

The group meets at the Conifers Resource Centre, Dromalane Road, Newry, Co Down on the 1st Wednesday of each month at 10.30am.

County Londonderry
Derry Tinnitus Support Group

Sensory Support Service, 16 Bishop Street, Londonderry, BT48 6PW

Tel: 028 7137 4619

Contact the Sensory Support Service for further details. The Group meets at MEDC, Altnaglevin Hospital, Derry on the 3rd Thursday of each month at 7.30pm.

County Tyrone
Moy Tinnitus Support Group

Moy Resource Centre, Dungannon Road, Moy, Dungannon, County Tyrone, BT71 7SN

Tel: 028 8778 4832
Fax: 028 8778 4669
Contact: L Nesbitt

Meets on the second Wednesday of each month (except July and August) at 2.30pm. Part of the Ulster Tinnitus Association (Belfast Group).

➢ Scotland
Aberdeenshire
Aberdeen Tinnitus Support Group
2 Deeside Gardens, Aberdeen, AB15 7PN
Tel: 01224 495675/ 494566
Textphone: 01224 494566
Fax: 01224 483894
Contact: John Askey, Society for the Deaf
                13 Smithfield Road, Aberdeen, AB24
                4NR

Aims: to help each other to live with tinnitus; to collect and disseminate knowledge on the subject of tinnitus with interested parties; to work with, and in support of, the medical profession in their research and treatment of tinnitus and related conditions; to support other groups and associations with similar aims in the education and relief of all who suffer from tinnitus.

Angus
Dundee Tinnitus Support Group
50 Peebles Drive, Dundee, Angus, DD4 0TZ
Tel: 01382 480287 (after 6pm)
Contact: Margaret McGill

Offers support and understanding. Meets at the Centre for the Deaf, 36 Roseangle, Dundee, monthly at 7pm.

Dumbartonshire
West of Scotland Tinnitus Group
Kingarth, 22 Silverton Avenue, Dumbarton, G82 1BX
Tel: 01389 762299 (evenings)
Fax: 01389 879042
Contact: Peter Stewart

The group meets at the Harvest Clinic, 201 St George's Road, Glasgow on the first Saturday bi-monthly at 10.30am.

Fife
Dunfermline Tinnitus Support Group
4 Craig Street, Rosyth, Dunfermline, Fife, KY12 0BT
Contact: H Russell

Offers discussion, speakers, and demonstrations. Meets at Tower House East Port, Dunfermline on the third Monday of each month at 2pm.

Grampian

Aberdeen and North East Deaf Society
Tel: 01224 494566
Textphone: 01224 495675
Fax: 01224 494661
Contact: Rosemary Burt, Principal Officer
Textphone: 01224 495676
Fax: 01224 483894
See entry under Regional Organisations.

Lanarkshire
Hamilton Tinnitus Support Group
Voluntary Resource Centre, 57 Argyle Drive, Hamilton, Lanarkshire, ML3 9EG
Tel: 01698 891755
Contact: Mary Fitzpatrick

Contact by letter, telephone or visit. Meetings to be decided (Oct 1998).

Midlothian
Edinburgh Tinnitus Support Group
5 Longstone Terrace, Edinburgh, Midlothian, EH14 2AL
Tel: 0131 443 7926
Contact: G Johnstone

Offers support, newsletter, talks and loans. Meets at 49 Albany Street, Edinburgh, quarterly at 2.30pm.

➢ Wales
Clwyd
North Wales Ménières and Tinnitus Group
19 Llys Alafowlia, Denbigh, Clwyd, LL16 3HX
Tel: 01745 812466
Contact: M Pike
                Waen y Brodlas, Brynford, Holywell, Clwyd, CH8 8LS

Offers talks and social gatherings. Meets at Glan Clwyd Hospital, Bodelwyddan, near Rhyl, on the third Thursday of the month at 6.30pm.

Wrexham Tinnitus Support Group
Clwydian Community Care Trust, 16 Grosvenor Road, Wrexham, Clwyd, LL11 1DU
Tel: 01978 356551

Contact by letter or phone. The Group offers advice, support and counselling. It meets fortnightly at 16 Grosvenor Road on Wednesdays at 1.30pm.

8

Dyfed
Tinnitus Support Group
39 Brooke Avenue, Milford Haven, Dyfed, SA73 2LS
Contact: Michael Green

Gwynedd
Holyhead Tinnitus Support Group
Cartref, 5 Cae Braenar, Caergybi, Holyhead,
Gwynedd, LL65 2PN
Tel: 01407 764233/ 763734 (after 6pm,
              weekdays only)
Contact: M Williams

Offers talks and discussions. Meets at St David's
Priory, Richmond Hill, Holyhead at 7pm on
Wednesdays, irregularly.

Mid Glamorgan
Caerphilly HIT Squad (Hearing Impairment and Tinnitus)
c/o 22 Greenwood Court, Lansbury Park,
Caerphilly, Mid Glamorgan, CF83 1QJ
Tel: 029 2086 4622 (evenings)
E-mail: research.wcva@pop3.poptel.org.uk
Contact: Martin Griffiths, Chairman

The Caerphilly HIT (Hearing Impairment and
Tinnitus) Squad is run by people with hearing
problems and seeks to gather national and local
information and disseminate it to local members
as well as aiming to promote awareness on a local
level. The group also campaigns for better local
services and would be interested in taking part in
national campaigns to strengthen our case for
social inclusion and also to increase access to
television and film productions by pressing for
more and better-quality subtitled programmes.
The group is aimed at hard of hearing and those
with tinnitus. This is not done to exclude deaf
people but rather to include hard of hearing
people who may otherwise be reluctant to join
deaf clubs due to their inability to sign. Meets at
the Wesley Methodist Hall, Crescent Road,
Caerphilly on the first Monday of each month.
Contact M Griffiths to confirm dates.

East Glamorgan Self Help Group
East Glamorgan General Hospital, Audiology
Department, Church Village, Pontypridd, Mid
Glamorgan, CF38 1AB
Tel: 01443 218218
Contact: Brian Spinks, Secretary
            Church Village, Pontypridd, Mid
            Glamorgan, CF38 1AB
Tel: 01443 205029

We are the only hospital practising TRT in Wales
and will take patients from the whole of Wales.
The self help group meets the first Wednesday of
the month at the Audiology Deptartment,
Llwynypia Hospital, Rhondda from 5pm-6pm. The
Secretary of the self help group is Brian Spinks
01443 205029. The group exists to promote TRT
and help support all people who have tinnitus.

West Glamorgan
Swansea Tinnitus Support Group
2 Hendrefoilan Avenue, Sketty, Swansea, West
Glamorgan, SA2 7LY
Contact: S Lloyd
              248 Middle Road, Gendros, Swansea,
              West Glamorgan, SA5 8EN
Tel: 01792 586613

Offers help, talks and loans. Meets at Singleton
Hospital, Swansea every third Thursday of the
month.

West Glamorgan Tinnitus Support Group
2 Hendrefoilan Avenue, Sketty, Swansea, West
Glamorgan, SA2 7LY
Contact: S Lloyd, Chairperson

Deafblind Resources

Deafblindness is a unique disability, much more than a combination of visual and hearing impairments. About 95% of the information people take in about the world comes through sound and vision. Without these two senses, people who are born deafblind can have enormous difficulty understanding the world around them. Deafblindness greatly affects people's mobility, access to information and communication.

Many deafblind people have some remaining hearing or vision which they can learn to use to great effect. Others have a complete loss of both.

There are more than 23,000 deafblind people living in the UK. This section lists some of the organisations both in the UK and abroad which provide services to deafblind people.

This section is divided into national organisations, international organisations, regional/ local organisations, schools, training and rehabilitation and residential services.

National Organisations

Action for Blind People

14-16 Verney Road, London, SE16 3DZ

Tel: 020 7732 8771
Fax: 020 7639 0948
E-mail: info@afbp.org
Website: www.demon.co.uk/afbp
Contact: Ida Forster, Information and Advice Centre Manager

To inspire change and create opportunities to enable blind and partially sighted people to have equal voice and equal choice.

British Retinitis Pigmentosa Society

P O Box 350, Buckingham, MK18 5EL

Tel: 01280 860363 Helpline
Fax: 01280 860515
Website: www.brps.demon.co.uk
Contact: Linda Cantor, Honorary Secretary
Tel: 01280 860195

Retinitis Pigmentosa (RP) is the name given to a group of hereditary disorders which affect the retina, the part of the eye in which the first stages of seeing take place. RP leads to deterioration of the millions of cells which make up the retina causing them to lose their ability to transmit pictures to the brain. It is now recognised as one of the most common untreatable causes of blindness in people of working age. RP is sometimes associated with other disorders, giving rise to a number of syndromes, for example Usher syndrome where deafness, usually from birth, is combined with RP. The aims of the BRPS are to raise funds for scientific research to provide a treatment or cure for RP, and to promote and extend the Welfare Support Service to cater for the special needs of RP sufferers and their families.

Deafblind UK

100 Bridge Street, Peterborough, Cambridgeshire, PE1 1DY

Tel: 01733 358100/ 0800 132320 Helpline
Textphone: 01733 358100/ 358858
Fax: 01733 358356
E-mail: jackie@deafblnd.demon.co.uk
Contact: Tracy Everitt, Information/ Advice and Advocacy Officer

             6 Rosedale Cottages, Turkey Cock Lane, Stanway, Colchester, Essex, CO3 5NA
Tel: 01206 213304
Fax: 01206 213304

Information, advice and advocacy offered to all deafblind people living in London boroughs only. Can offer advice and links to those outside London. Similar support service offered to carers, other professionals, charities and health care trusts. Work also includes family work, assessments of need - communication support, emotional support, enabling self-advocacy, training and joint working. Key aim: to enable deafblind people to access information, improve mobility and communication ability leading to the achievements of their maximum potential.

Deafblind UK (Scotland)

21 Alexandra Avenue, Lenzie, Kirkintilloch, Glasgow, Strathclyde, G66 5BG

Tel: 0141 777 6111
Textphone: 0141 777 6111
Fax: 0141 775 3311
E-mail: info@deafblindscotland.org.uk
Website: www.deafblindscotland.org.uk
Contact: Drena O'Malley, Development Manager, Scotland

Deafblind UK Scottish office provides a guide/communicator service for adults with a dual sensory impairment, usually funded by local authorities. We also provide information and support to members, families and professionals. Training is an ongoing priority, from awareness to certificate level.

Deafblind UK National Training and Rehabilitation Centre

Paston Ridings, Peterborough, Cambridgeshire, PE4 7UP

Tel:	01733 325353
Textphone:	01733 579306
Fax:	01733 323101
E-mail:	Training@deafblind.demon.co.uk
Contact:	Val Stokes, Manager, Deafblind UK National Training and Rehabilitation Centre

The Centre offers training courses for anyone working with deafblind people, run by Deafblind UK's training officer; a prospectus is available. Rehabilitation programmes, in wheelchair accessible accommodation, provide training with specially adapted equipment in an independence kitchen and a newly built computer and technology centre. Comfortable short stay accommodation is available for respite care and holidays. A brochure is available on request from Val Stokes. Independent living residential accommodation is available on site. For details of vacancies, again please contact Val Stokes. Leisure activities are also organised at Rainbow Court; details available from Val Stokes or Mike North, Social Development Officer. The whole complex looks onto a see-by-touch garden which can be visited by prior arrangement.

Sense, The National Deafblind and Rubella Association

11-13 Clifton Terrace, Finsbury Park, London, N4 3SR

Tel:	020 7272 7774
Textphone:	020 7272 9648
Fax:	020 7272 6012
E-mail:	enquiries@sense.org.uk
Website:	www.sense.org.uk
Contact:	Eileen Boothroyd, Assistant Director, Education

Sense is the national leading voluntary organisation that works and campaigns for the needs of people who are deafblind, providing advice, support, information and services for them, their families, carers and the professionals with whom they work. Sense works with people of all ages who are deafblind - including those with Usher Syndrome as well as people who have multiple disabilities including sensory impairment and learning difficulties. Sense provides a Regional Advisory Service for deafblind people, organises and runs holidays for deafblind children and multiple disabled children and young adults.

Sense provides a range of services which include residential, parents' groups, vocational training and training for teachers and other professionals working with deafblind people, advocacy, community services and communication support/guiders. Sense is also active in the international field, providing support for deafblind people in developing countries, and it publishes 'Deafblind Education', a bi-annual journal for the organisation Deafblind International, of which Sense is a member. Sense produces the journals 'Talking Sense' (4 issues per year), 'Usher UK' (3 issues per year), and 'US Families' (3 issues per year).

Sense Cymru

Shand House, 20 Newport Road, Cardiff, CF2 1DB

Tel:	029 2045 7641
Textphone:	029 2049 9644
Fax:	029 2049 9644
Contact:	Karan Jones

Sense Northern Ireland

The Manor House, 51 Mallusk Road, Mallusk, County Antrim, BT36 9RU

Tel:	028 9083 3430
Textphone:	028 9083 3430
Fax:	028 9084 4232
E-mail:	SENSNI@dial.pipex.com
Website:	www.sense.org.uk
Contact:	Meta McMullan, Divisional Services Manager

Sense provides a range of quality services across the UK including family support, children's services, residential and community services, continuing education and advocacy. It works to develop new projects and services, either as an organisation or in partnership with others, and campaigns for greater public, political and legal recognition of needs.

Sense Scotland

45 Finnieston Street, Glasgow, Lanarkshire, G3 8JU

Tel:	0141 564 2444
Textphone:	0141 564 2442
Fax:	0141 564 2443
E-mail:	kas51@dial.pipex.com
Contact:	Pat Brown

Sense Scotland works with deafblind and multiply impaired children, adults and their families. The term deafblind refers to a range of combinations of hearing and visual impairment and very rarely means total deafness and total blindness. We also work with children and adults who have impairments to both sight and hearing whether or not they have other disabilities, as well as those who have impairment to sight with other disabilities and impairment to hearing with other disabilities.

Sense Usher Services

11-13 Clifton Terrace, Finsbury Park, London, N4 3SR

Tel: 020 7272 7774
Textphone: 020 7272 9648
Fax: 020 7272 3862
E-mail: ldrescher@sense.org.uk
Website: www.sense.org.uk
Contact: Mary Guest, Head of Usher Services

Provides information and support especially after diagnosis to families and individuals with the Usher syndrome. Support involves advice, appropriate information, group activities, campaigning and help wth benefits. Two user groups, Usher UK and the Hearing Aid Users Group are maintained through the Usher Service.

International Organisations

Acquired Deafblind Network

Stichting Doof-Blinden, Professor Bronkhorstlaan, 10, 3723 MB Bilthoven, The Netherlands

The Network is part of Deafblind International. It organises conferences and provides information on acquired deafblindness to interested professionals. The committee members are professionals working in different European countries. They publish and maintain a contact list of people working in the field, detailing their activities and current interests.

American Association of the Deafblind

7202 Buchanan Street, Landover Hills, MD 20784-2236, USA

Tel: 00 1 301 588 6545
Fax: 00 1 301 588 8705
E-mail: aadb@aerols.com
Contact: Jeffrey Bohrman, President

Promotes better opportunities and services for deafblind people. Mission is to ensure that a comprehensive, coordinated system of service is accessible to all deafblind people, enabling them to achieve maximum potential through increased independence, productivity and integration into the community. The annual conventions provide a week of workshops, meetings, tours and

recreational activities.

DB-LINK

Teaching Research, 345 North Monmouth Avenue, Monmouth, OR 97361, USA

Tel: 00 1 800 438 9376/ 854 7013
Textphone: 001 800 854 7013
Fax: 00 1 503 838 8150
E-mail: dblink@tr.wou.edu
Website: www.tr.wou.edu/dblink/

DB-LINK identifies, coordinates and disseminates information related to children and young people who are deafblind. Parents, service providers, administrators and others interested in services are invited to contact DB-LINK for information. DB-LINK is a collaborative effort involving the Helen Keller National Center, Perkins School for the Blind and Teaching Research. DB-LINK is a co-sponsor of the publication 'Deafblind Perspectives'.

Deafblind International

11-13 Clifton Terrace, Finsbury Park, London, N4 3SR

Tel: 020 7272 7774
Fax: 020 7272 6012
E-mail: dbi@sense.org.uk

Formerly the International Association for the Education of the Deaf Blind, Deafblind International provides information, runs workshops and conferences and an information exchange with other organisations. It provides services to all, including academics and professionals working in the field. It publishes 'Deafblind Education' bi-annually.

Helen Keller National Center for Deaf-Blind Youths and Adults

111 Middle Neck Road, Sands Point, NY 11050, USA

Tel: 00 1 516 944 8900
Textphone: 001 516 944 8637
Fax: 00 1 516 944 7302
E-mail: abigailp@aol.com
Website: www.helenkeller.org\national
Contact: Barbara Hausman, Director of Public Relations
Tel: 00 1 516 944 8900 ext 325

HKNC's goal is to recognise the unique talents, strengths and desires of every student and to provide tailored learning opportunities and choices which parallel their future lifestyle at home or in the community. The Traditional Program emphasises vocational training and life enrichment through the efforts of many

9

departments working as a team to promote students' independence. PATH is a transdisciplinary programme focusing on communication and language development and all aspects of daily living as well as work adjustment and job skills.

Information Center for Acquired Deafblindness

Generatorvej 2a, DK-2730 Herlev, Denmark

Tel:	0045 4 485 6030
Fax:	0045 4 485 6099
E-mail:	dbcent@inet.uni2.dk
Website:	www.dbcent.dk
Contact:	Ole Mortensen, Information Manager

The Information Center for Acquired Deafblindness provides information about all aspects of acquired deafblindness, through newsletters, articles, reports, booklets and videos. Some of the materials are available in English. Furthermore, the Center initiates and participates in projects with the aim of developing new knowledge in the field of acquired deafblindness.

The Ann Sullivan Foundation for the Deafblind

Brewery Road, Stillorgan, Co Dublin, Eire

Tel:	00 353 1 289 8339
Fax:	00 353 1 289 4808
Contact:	Jim Carroll, Director

The Ann Sullivan Centre is a home for life for low functioning deafblind people. It has a specially trained staff, as people with congenital deafblindness require intensive programmes with a substantial educational element on a life-long basis.

The Deaf-Blind Association

P O Box 267, Clifton Hill, Melbourne, Victoria 3068, Australia

Tel:	00 61 3 9482 1155
Textphone:	0061 3 9489 3091
Fax:	00 61 3 9486 2092
E-mail:	dba@internex.net.au
Website:	www.internex.net.au/~dba/dba/htm

DBA provides support to deafblind people and people with other disabilities and their families. The support includes accommodation, community support, respite care, day services, general assistance and advice.

City of Sunderland Rainbow Club for the Deafblind

c/o Independent Living Centre, Dock Street, Monkwearmouth, Sunderland, Tyne and Wear, SR6 0EA

Tel:	0191 553 2901
Textphone:	0191 553 2902
Fax:	0191 553 2911
Contact:	Lynda Boland, Sensory Disability Team, Sunderland Social Services

Meets on the last Friday of each month, 2 to 4.30pm. The club provides a social outlet for deafblind people who communicate using deafblind manual. Some members, whilst not deafblind manual users, find conventional methods of communication very difficult and so we use other forms of communication suited to their dual sensory disability. The club is a regional resource and has a friendly, informal atmosphere.

Deaf-Blind Fellowship

12 Mayfair Court, Mersey Road, West Didsbury, Manchester, Lancashire, M20 2PY

Tel:	0161 434 5185

Hull and East Riding Institute for the Blind

Beech Holme, Beverley Road, Hull, Humberside, HU5 1NF

Tel:	01482 342297
Fax:	01482 443111
Contact:	M Fisher, General Manager

HERIB provides a wide range of services for blind, partially sighted and deafblind people residing in Hull and East Riding area. Services include: day centres, home visits, residential homes/flats, grants, equipment and training. Enquiries always welcome.

Liverpool Voluntary Society for the Blind

Muriel Crooke House, Youens Way, Liverpool, Merseyside, L14 2EP

Tel:	0151 221 0888
Textphone:	0151 221 0889
Fax:	0151 221 0889
Contact:	James Moran

LVSB provides services to help people who are experiencing sight problems. We work on behalf of Liverpool and Knowsley Social Services to provide assessment, training and advice. LVSB aims to contact people on the blind and partially sighted register annually, to ensure that they are receiving an appropriate service and to offer help and support. An advice line is available from 9am-5pm, Monday to Friday.

Llanelli Rainbow Deafblind Club

13 Firth Road, Llanelli, Dyfed, SA15 1PH

Tel: 01554 770770
Textphone: 01554 770770

Contact: Peter Skivington

The club meets every second and fourth Monday of each month, 7 to 9pm, at Coleshill Disabled Centre, Llanelli. It gives information and entertain members. It tries to teach deafblind manual alphabet and how to use the latest technology. It is affiliated to Deafblind UK Peterborough. It uses large print and braille whenever needed.

Sense Bristol

Woodside Road, Kingswood, Bristol, BS15 8DG

Tel: 0117 967 0008
Fax: 0117 967 0008

Contact: Cathie Kennedy, Centre Manager

Provides resources for deafblind and multi-sensory impaired children and their families in the South West.

Sense East

The Manor House, 72 Church Street, Market Deeping, Peterborough, Cambridgeshire, PE6 8AL

Tel: 01778 344921
Textphone: 01788 344921
Fax: 01778 380078

Contact: Des Roulstone, Regional Director

Provision of residential/further education, day and respite services for people aged 16 years and over with a single or dual sensory impairment and/or physical and learning disabilities, and with medical conditions. Provision of training and advice, intervenor, family and community support, and communicator wide services for the above client group.

Sense East Anglia Branch

The Lanterns, Church Lane, Playford, Ipswich, Suffolk, IP6 9DS

Tel: 01473 62243

Contact: Elizabeth Royle, Secretary

Group of parents who meet three times a year to share information and troubles.

Sense East Outreach Services

8 West Parade, Lincoln, LN1 1JT

Tel: 01522 576770
Fax: 01522 576775

Sense North

122 Westgate, Wakefield, West Yorkshire, WF1 1XP

Tel: 01924 201778
Textphone: 01924 201944
Fax: 01924 366307

Contact: Bob Snow, Head of Development

Sense South East

Hanover House, 76 Coombe Road, Norbiton, Surrey, KT2 7JE

Tel: 020 8541 1147
Textphone: 020 8541 1938
Fax: 020 8541 1132

Contact: Anna Pugh, Regional Advisory Service

Sense supports and campaigns for people who are deafblind, their families and carers. Information and advice about services in the South East, which include day and residential services, consultancy, training and family support, is available from the Advisory Service.

Sense South West

Providence Court, 37 Northernhay Street, Exeter, Devon, EX4 3ER

Tel: 01647 440887
Fax: 01647 440887

Contact: Philippa May, Regional Advisory
            Service

National charity working with people with a dual sensory loss or single sensory loss and additional disabilities. Offering advice, information, support, counselling. Access to specialist educational advice, residential care, specialist holidays, training and consultancy work. Advice on placements from age 19 and campaigning.

9

Sense West

4 Church Road, Edgbaston, Birmingham, West Midlands, B15 3TD

Tel: 0121 687 1564
Textphone: 0121 687 1564
Fax: 0121 687 1656
Website: www.sense.org.uk
Contact: Krystyna Cieslik, Regional Advisory Service

Sense provides services to deafblind people, their families and carers, and the professionals who work with them. Services include family support, assessments, residential, education and day services and outreach services for deafblind people of all ages (both congenital and acquired deafblindness).

Sense West Midlands

The Princess Royal Centre, 4 Church Road, Edgbaston, Birmingham, West Midlands, B15 3TD

Tel: 0121 456 1564

Society for Deaf and Blind People

Centenary House, North Street, Leeds, West Yorkshire, LS2 8AY

Tel: 0113 243 3250
Textphone: 0113 243 8328
Fax: 0113 243 3553
Contact: Martin Dodgson, Director

We are a voluntary organisation meeting the needs of deaf, deafblind and hard of hearing people. Our services cover social work support and advice, day centre and domiciliary support for deafblind people, interpreting services, and a communication day centre for hearing impaired people with learning difficulties. Social club, church and chaplain.

Vision Support (Cheshire and North East Wales Society for the Blind)

67 Liverpool Road, Chester, Cheshire, CH2 1AP

Tel: 01244 382222
Fax: 01244 377482
Contact: Lyn Williams

Vision Support exists to enhance the quality of life, promote the continuing independence and raise awareness of the needs of visually impaired people of all ages throughout the community.

Schools

Carnbooth School

Carmunnock, Glasgow, Lanarkshire, G76 9EG

Tel: 0141 644 2773
Fax: 0141 644 3631
Contact: Jane Eyre, Head Teacher

Carnbooth School provides education on a day or residential basis to deafblind children aged pre-5 to post-16 years. It can provide information and advice on dual sensory impairment. It can also provide speakers and written articles to promote awareness of deafblindness.

Henshaw's College

Bogs Lane, Harrogate, North Yorkshire, HG1 4ED

Tel: 01423 886451
Fax: 01423 885095
Contact: Lynne Gilland, Marketing and Liaison Officer

Our aim is to enable visually impaired young people with various additional difficulties such as hearing impairment, learning or physical disabilities, to achieve their maximum level of independence. We do so by meeting the specific needs of each student through an individually structured course programme.

Penny Field Special School

Tongue Lane, Leeds, West Yorkshire, LS6 4QE

Tel: 0113 278 3577
Fax: 0113 278 3577
Contact: Hilary Barrett

The school aims to promote: self-awareness, self-expression and self-esteem, awareness of others and of a world outside themselves, an understanding that deafblind people can affect that world, the ability to communicate with and take pleasure from others, the development of optimal independence, and an awareness of rights and self-advocacy.

Queen Alexandra College For The Blind

Court Oak Road, Harbourne, Birmingham, West Midlands, B17 9TG

Tel: 0121 428 5050
Fax: 0121 428 5047
E-mail: enquiries@qac.ac.uk
Website: www.qac.ac.uk
Contact: Sue Wright, Principal

Queen Alexandra College is a leading national residential college of further education supporting the needs of people with visual impairment both on campus and in mainstream education. Providing assessment, rehabilitation, continuing education, vocational training, guidance and placement. QAC also welcomes people with additional disabilities and learning difficulties. The college can also provide information and public speakers to talk about its work. A magazine, 'Insight', is produced three times a year.

RNIB Redhill College

Philanthropic Road, Redhill, Surrey, RH1 4DG

Tel: 01737 768935

Fax: 01737 778776

Contact: Peter Johnson, FEFC Coordinator

RNIB Redhill College is a residential further education college offering life skills, pre-vocational and vocational courses to blind and partially sighted students. The college offers flexible learning programmes to suit people with a wide range of abilities and needs, including those who are both visually and hearing impaired. New music provision is being developed in collaboration with the AMBER Trust.

Royal School for the Blind

Church Road North, Wavertree, Liverpool, Merseyside, L15 6TQ

Tel: 0151 733 1012

Fax: 0151 733 1703

Contact: J Byrne, Principal

RSB offers day and weekly places to children with visual impairments and other disabilities, mainly severe learning difficulties. We aim to offer a broad, balanced and differentiated curriculum. The school offers many excellent facilities and visits are welcome.

Sense Education and Resources and Day Centre

Meadowbank Road, Carrickfergus, County Antrim, BT38 8YF

Tel: 028 9335 5655

Textphone: 028 9335 5665

Fax: 028 9335 5873

SILD

Whitefield Schools, MacDonald Road, London, E17 4AZ

Tel: 020 8531 3426

Fax: 020 8527 3613

E-mail: whitefield_edu@msn.com

Contact: Laura Pease, Head of SILD

SILD is one of the four Whitefield schools. The primary section educates sensory impaired children with complex needs in separate classes staffed by teachers holding the mandatory qualifications. The secondary section caters for children and young people with multi-sensory impairment.

St Vincent's School for the Deafblind

30 Fullarton Avenue, Tollcross, Glasgow, Strathclyde, G32 8NJ

Tel: 0141 778 2254

Contact: Alicia Crilly, Head

A day school taking nursery pupils, primary pupils and secondary age pupils. Age range: 2 to 19 years. Total Communication philosophy is used.

Training and Rehabilitation

Elizabeth Gunn Centre

The Birmingham Royal Institute for the Blind, 49 Court Oak Road, Harborne, Birmingham, West Midlands, B17 9AY

Tel: 0121 428 5000

Contact: Carol Smith, Manager

Tel: 0121 428 5000 ext 5092

Day services for visually impaired, multi-disabled adults. Outreach. Training in sight loss awareness. Deafblind club. Physiotherapy, aromatherapy, individual assessment.

RNIB Peterborough

PO Box 173, Peterborough, Cambridgeshire, PE2 6WS

Tel: 0345 023153

Fax: 01733 371555

Provides information on products and publications for visually impaired people.

Darsdale Home for Blind People

Chelveston Road, Raunds, Wellingborough, Northamptonshire, NN9 6DA

Tel: 01933 622457

Fax: 01933 622457

Contact: Debbie Webb, Manager

Darsdale Home aims to provide quality care to people with sensory loss. All staff are trained to deal with the needs of the client group. Activities, trips and outings and accommodation are adapted and organised with advice from Deafblind UK, which has just awarded the Home accreditation.

Mary Mount Residential Home

North Mossley Hill Road, Liverpool, Merseyside, L18 8BS

Tel: 0151 724 2203

Textphone: 0151 724 2203

Fax: 0151 724 2203

Contact: Sr Louise, Sister Superior

Mary Mount can provide accommodation for up to 25 deafblind and deaf people with additional disabilities, men and women. There are no training or rehabilitation courses. Since 1998 two respite care rooms have been available.

Reardon Court

Cosgrove Close, Winchmore Hill, London, N21 3BH

Tel: 020 8447 9980

Fax: 020 8350 4802

Contact: Mark Whitbread, Manager

Reardon Court is run by the London Borough of Enfield and has three permanent units and one respite unit each taking nine residents, both men and women. It has provision for both deafblind people and deaf people with additional disabilities. The Respite Care Unit can provide care for up to two weeks per person. Day care can also be provided in a separate centre for up to 32 people. An outreach service and sheltered accommodation are also available.

RNIB Kathleen Chambers House

97 Berrow Road, Burnham-on-Sea, Somerset, TA8 2PG

Tel: 01278 782142

Fax: 01278 782673

E-mail: Helpline@rnib.org.uk
           bscott@rnib.org.uk

Contact: Barbara Scott, Manager

The aims and objectives of RNIB Kathleen Chambers House are the provison of appropriate housing, both permanent and temporary, for older people with a visual impairment, and the provision of support services to provide care, comfort and specialist assistance to realise the full potential of older people whose quality of life may have been limited by visual impairment.

RNIB Manor House

Middle Lincombe Road, Torquay, Devon, TQ1 2NG

Tel: 01803 214523

Fax: 01803 214143

E-mail: jread@rnib.org.uk

Contact: Jill Read, Centre Manager

Manor House provides residential services primarily for visually impaired people, with services for deafblind people being improved. It can provide information, advice, equipment, training, rehabilitation services, communication skills and vocational training.

RNIB Tate House

28 Wetherby Road, Harrogate, North Yorkshire HG2 7SA

Tel: 01423 886927

Fax: 01423 885192

E-mail: gsmith@rnib.org.uk

Website: www.rnib.org.uk/

Contact: Debbie Cliff, Acting Manager
            28 Wetherby Road, Harrogate, North Yorkshire, HG2 7SA

Customers at Tate House are provided with services and accommodation appropriate to their needs within an enabling environment. A wide range of activities and events are organised by our own staff including craftwork, gardening, painting, entertainment, and outings. A wide range of specialist equipment is available for use.

Sense Residential Service for Adults

41 Edenvale Avenue, Carrickfergus, County Antrim, BT38 7NP

Tel: 028 9336 3638

Fax: 028 9335 5002

St Anne's Holiday Home for Deafblind People

The Anne Lloyd Memorial Trust, 26-28 Harold Road, Clacton-on-Sea, Essex, CO15 6AJ

Tel: 01255 420595

Textphone: 01255 420595

Contact: Nigel Brown, Manager

You can enjoy a happy relaxed holiday at St Anne's, where there is accommodation for up to 13 people. Open all year round for breaks of any length. Two ground floor rooms for people with special needs. Assistance dogs welcome. Close to seafront, shops and transport.

Vision Homes Association

153 Warstone Lane, Hockley, Birmingham, West Midlands, B16 6NZ

Tel: 0121 233 2290

Fax: 0121 233 2291

Contact: Ewa Stefanowska, Chief Executive
              Oak Tree Lane Centre, 91 Oak Tree
              Lane, Selly Oak, Birmingham, West
              Midlands, B29 6JA

VHA is an organisation offering residential and other services to people (mainly young adults aged 19 years plus) who have visual impairments and multiple disabilities which may be physical or mental. This remit includes deafblind people. It manages a project for 15 clients in South Shropshire and another for six in Shrewsbury, where the emphasis is to improve the quality of life for clients by continuing education in communication and daily living skills.

9

Residential Services

There is a wide range of residential care centres that can provide residentially based services for deaf people with additional needs. Different centres cater for different needs, with some centres providing long-term care and support for elderly deaf people with additional needs and others providing rehabilitation support to young deaf children. Further details on centres and the particular type and level of care they can provide are available from centre managers.

This section is listed alphabetically by residential service within country and county sections.

England

➢ Avon

RNID Dominion Road

30 Dominion Road, Bath, Avon, BA2 1DW
Tel: 01225 462787
Textphone: 01225 462787

Contact: Christina Dunn, RNID Poolemead

Dominion Road compromises two adjoining houses in the community, each with direct provision for four deaf people with additional special needs. The home provides a stepping stone between a fully supported home and an independent flat, although some residents may choose to live there permanently. Training and development is available at the nearby Poolemead Centre and off-site workshop at Bath. It is registered as a residential care home by Bath and North East Somerset County Council.

RNID Pennard Court

Watery Lane, Twerton-on-Avon, Bath, Avon, BA2 1RN
Tel: 01225 332818
Textphone: 01225 332818
Fax: 01225 480825

Warden supervised accomodation, which forms part of the RNID Poolemead complex.

RNID Poolemead

Watery Lane, Bath, Avon, BA2 1RN
Tel: 01225 332818
Textphone: 01225 332818
Fax: 01225 480825
Contact: Mina Malpass, Head of Community Services

The Poolemead Centre is a rehabilitative and supported residential complex for deaf and deafblind people with special needs. With over 140 care staff, it caters for all ages and offers a range of educational, occupational and therapeutic opportunities, including work experience.

➢ Bath & NE Somerset
See Avon

➢ Blackburn
See Lancashire

➢ Blackpool
See Lancashire

➢ Brighton and Hove
See East Sussex

➢ Cambridgeshire
Conquest Care Home

9-10 Belmont Road, March, Cambridgeshire, PE15 8RQ
Tel: 01354 660623
Fax: 01354 660623
Contact: Michael Collinge, Manager

Belmont Road is a residential unit for people with learning disabilities. We support people with multiple disabilities including hearing loss. Many, if not all, of our residents have communication difficulties. Our aim is to provide a good quality life for the residents and a wide range of life experiences.

➤ Cheshire

Stepping Stones Residential/Day Care Unit

Weir Street, Northwich, Cheshire CW9 5HL

Tel:	01606 43261
Textphone:	01606 350226
Videotel:	01606 353905 (24 hour service)
Fax:	01606 353908
E-mail:	DSNCCrow@aol.com
Contact:	Craig Crowley, Head of Community Services

Offers short- and medium-term residential/day care placement for deaf people who have learning disabilities/difficulties as well as those with challenging behaviour, mental ill health, dementia and dual sensory disabilities. Day care facilities have been widely available since April 1999. Long-term residential care and community support are also available. Visits by appointment please.

➤ Cleveland

RNID Ransdale House

Ransdale House, 54 Caversham Road, Middlesbrough, Cleveland, TS4 3NU

Tel:	01642 320785
Textphone:	01642 320785
Fax:	01642 325437
Contact:	Tom Koegan, Manager

Ransdale House is a friendly, family-type home for six young deaf people with additional disabilities, offering life skills and other training opportunities. It has been developed in partnership with Tees Valley Housing Association and is registered as a residential care home by Middlesbrough County Council.

➤ Cornwall

RNID Pendean Court

16 Pendean Court, Barras Cross, Liskeard, Cornwall, PL14 6DZ

Tel:	01579 340201
Textphone:	01579 340450
Fax:	01579 344410
Contact:	Carole Cunliffe, Project Manager

Pendean Court offers long-term accommodation for nine deaf people aged between 18 and 60, who have mobility and learning difficulties and who may require additional support in their daily routines. The accommodation consists of seven individual bedrooms and one double, all with ensuite toilet and basin. Training is available in basic literacy, numeracy and independent living skills. Pendean Court has been developed in conjunction with Habinteg Housing Association and is registered as a residential care home by Cornwall County Council.

➤ Devon

Pines Residential Home for the Deaf

78 St Marychurch Road, Torquay, Devon, TQ1 3HG

Tel:	01803 328384
Textphone:	01803 328384
Contact:	Elsie Griffiths, Resident Proprietor

Accommodation is available for 21 deaf men and women aged 18 and over. People with diabetes and epilepsy are catered for. Facilities include double and single rooms. A short-stay service is not available but the Pines can provide respite care. The Pines works closely with Torquay Deaf Club and all the residents are members. Alarm systems using visual, audible and sensory devices are installed in all rooms and public areas.

RNIB Manor House

Tel:	01803 214523
Fax:	01803 214143
E-mail:	jread@rnib.org.uk
Contact:	Jill Read, Centre Manager

See entry under Deafblind Resources.

RNID Court Grange College

Abbotskerswell, Newton Abbot, Devon, TQ12 5NH

Tel:	01626 353401
Textphone:	01626 367677
Videotel:	01626 353616
Fax:	01626 360895

RNID have taken the decision to close the educational centre at Court Grange College. The College is due to close at the end of July 1999. Within the Court Grange complex there is a separately registered residential unit which will continue to operate until the future of the whole site is determined. For further information contact: RNID Residential and Community Services, 13b Church Farm Business Park, Corston, Bath, Avon, BA2 9AP.

➢ East Sussex
RNID Ferndale Road
32 Ferndale Road, Hove, East Sussex, BN3 6EU
Tel: 01273 220949
Textphone: 01273 777692
Fax: 01273 779743
Contact: Martin Ensom, Manager

RNID Ferndale Road offers short-term accommodation for five young deaf people with special needs, aged between 18 and 45, who require additional support and training to help them live more independently. It is situated close to local shops, amenities and bus routes. It consists of five single bedrooms, shared bath and shower rooms, communal lounge/dining room, kitchen and laundry rooms, patio and garden. Twenty-four-hour staff cover is available all year round. Developed in partnership with Hyde Housing Association, it is registered as a residential care home by Brighton and Hove Unitary Council.

RNID Wilbury Gardens
13 Wilbury Gardens, Hove, East Sussex, BN3 6HQ
Tel: 01273 205044
Textphone: 01273 205044
Fax: 01273 771891
Contact: Nigel White, Project Manager

RNID Wilbury Gardens is a detached Edwardian house which caters for eight older deaf and deafblind people with learning difficulties. The home is fully equipped to meet the personal care needs of frail older people and provides an environment in which they can have as much choice, independence and control of their own lives as possible. Facilities include: single bedrooms for all residents, lounge and dining area, passenger lift to all floors, bath/shower rooms on all floors, including a Parker Bath, conservatory and picturesque walled garden; vehicle with hydraulic hoist for wheelchairs, and 24-hour staff cover all year round. Wilbury Gardens has been developed in partnership with Hyde Housing Association and is registered as a residential care home by Brighton and Hove Unitary Council.

➢ Essex
Foley House Residential Home for Deaf/Deafblind People
Tel: 01376 326652
Fax: 01376 326652
Contact: John Bethell, Director
See entry under Deafblind Resources.

St Anne's Holiday Home for Deafblind People
Tel: 01255 420595
Textphone: 01255 420595
Contact: Nigel Brown, Manager
See entry under Deafblind Resources.

➢ Gillingham and Rochester
See Kent

➢ Gloucestershire
Butlin Home for Deaf People
2 Alexandra Road, Gloucester, GL1 3DR
Tel: 01452 522727
Textphone: 01452 381607
Contact: Sally Middleton, Residential and Day Care Manager

Butlin Home aims to provide a secure environment, where each individual is encouraged to remain independent and continue to take an active part in their life. The home has an ongoing activities plan, in which residents can take part within a group or one-to-one. Each year holidays are arranged for groups or individual needs depending on personal choice.

➢ Isle of Wight
East Hill Home For Deaf People
Ashey Road, Ryde, Isle of Wight, PO33 3EB
Tel: 01983 564068
Fax: 01983 811857
E-mail: ged@easthill.demon.co.uk
Website: www:easthill.demon.co.uk
Contact: Gerard Naggs, Officer in Charge

To work with deaf, deafened and hard of hearing people to enable them to achieve their full potential, dignity, independence and equal access to opportunities and lead the same life as anyone else.

➤ Kent

RNID Cliffe Avenue

15 Cliffe Avenue, Westbrook, Margate, Kent, CT9 5DU

Tel: 01843 232122
Textphone: 01843 230455
Fax: 01843 230455
Contact: Anna Syplywczak, Manager, Residential Services

RNID Cliffe Avenue is a home for life or a stepping stone for those who want to live independently. It caters for five deaf people, aged between 19 and 50, who have additional disabilities and need intensive support to help them reach their full potential. The accommodation consists of five single bedrooms, kitchen, lounge, dining area and garden. It is within easy access of local facilities and the beach. Respite care is available according to space and Cliffe Avenue can provide excellent facilities for residents on a short-stay basis. Developed in partnership with Hyde Housing Association, it is registered as a residential care home by Kent County Council.

RNID Roper House

St. Dunstans Street, Canterbury, Kent, CT2 8BZ

Tel: 01227 462155
Textphone: 01227 781915
Fax: 01227 452351
Contact: Steve Boggins, Head of Centre

Roper House compromises two rehabilitative and supported units which provide long- and short-stay accommodation for deaf and deafblind people of all ages and disabilities. Facilities include: 30 single bedrooms with shared bathroom facilities in the main unit, four semi-independent flats, and a supported group home for three people. There are communal lounges and dining areas, wheelchair access, a well-equipped craft and recreational centre, rehabilitation and social skills training, full range of support facilities and 24-hour staff cover, all year round. Residents who need regular care and support live in the main complex, Roper House; those needing less help live in the sheltered accomodation. Respite and day care is also available. Roper House has been developed in partnership with Hyde Housing Association and is registered as a residential care home by Kent County Council.

RNID Weatherly Close

1 Weatherly Close, John Street, Rochester, Kent, ME1 1AD

Tel: 01634 819143
Textphone: 01634 818402
Fax: 01634 819143
Contact: Fay Kirkman, Manager

RNID Weatherly Close is a modern purpose-built bungalow which provides an intimate family-type environment for five young deaf adults with additional needs and has been specially adapted for wheelchair users. It is situated within a complex of other bungalows and flats for disabled people and their families, which makes it easy for residents to mix socially. Facilities include: five single bedrooms with shared bathroom, communal lounge/dining room, modern fitted kitchen and utility room both adapted for wheelchair users, patio and garden. Weatherly Close offers training courses and work experience placements, a wide range of leisure activities, and 24-hour staff cover all year round. Weatherly Close has been developed in partnership with Habinteg Housing Association and is registered as a residential care home by Kent County Council.

➤ Lancashire

DEAFWAY

Brockholes Brow, Preston, Lancashire, PR2 5AL

Tel: 01772 796461
Textphone: 01772 652388
Videotel: 01722 705563
Fax: 01772 654439
E-mail: deafway@deafway.freeserve.co.uk
Website: www.deafway.freeserve.co.uk
Contact: David Hynes, Director

Working to achieve equality of opportunity and access for deaf people. We currently provide: residential care and rehabilitation, The Royal Cross primary school, community services, sports and social club, research and training. We also work with purchasers to create new services tailored to specific needs in all parts of the UK.

Henesy House Residential Home for Deaf People

Sudell Street, Collyhurst, Manchester, Lancashire, M40 7JF

Tel: 0161 834 8828
Textphone: 0161 834 8828
Fax: 0161 833 3674
Contact: Pauline Nolan, Matron

10

The aim of Henesy House is to provide for the emotional, material, medical and spiritual needs of deaf people who are in need of care and attention; to do that in such a way as to enable them to live as normal a life as possible within the deaf community; and to provide and maintain a standard of care as required by the Residential Care Homes Regulation of 1994 and Manchester City Council.

House Martins (Salford) Ltd

2 Rivington Road, Salford, Lancashire, M6 8GQ

Tel:	0161 736 8057
Textphone:	0161 736 8057
Fax:	0161 736 0318
Contact:	Lesley Martin
	56 Holmeswood Park, Rawtenstall, Rawtenstall, Lancashire, BB4 6HZ
Tel:	01706 221471
Textphone:	01706 221471
Fax:	01706 219646

Each house provides long-term care in a signing environment for young adults who are hearing impaired, have learning disabilities, autism, epilepsy, mental health problems and other special needs. We are committed to enhancing the quality of life and offering each individual the opportunity of reaching their potential.

RNID Richardson House

Tel:	01254 677119
Textphone:	01254 682942
Fax:	01254 696623
Contact:	John Arnold, Principal

See entry under Mental Health.

Wynfield House Home for the Deaf

115 Newton Drive, Blackpool, Lancashire, FY3 8LZ

Tel:	01253 392183
Textphone:	01253 596566
Fax:	01253 355894
Contact:	Carol Parr, Manager

Wynfield House provides residential care for elderly and infirm profoundly deaf people. There are 19 residents between the ages of 45 and 100. Short-stay, holiday and respite care services are available as and when accomodation allows.

> Leicester

See Leicestershire

> Leicestershire

RNID Leicester Project

Centre for Deaf People, 135 Welford Road, Leicester, LE2 6BE

Tel:	0116 255 6776
Textphone:	0116 254 5126
Fax:	0116 276 2373
Contact:	Carol Duddington, Community Support Worker

This project was developed in partnership with Leicester Centre for Deaf People and North British Housing Association. RNID employs a Community Support Worker to support three deaf people to live independently in their own flats.

> London

Crescent House

44 Norbury Crescent, London, SW16 4LA

Tel:	020 8679 3972
Textphone:	020 8240 1241
Contact:	Blanche Birch, Manager

A small residential home for elderly people.

Harding Housing Association

48 North Side Wandsworth Common, London, SW18 2SL

Tel:	020 8870 7577
Textphone:	020 8877 1866
Fax:	020 8874 6270
Contact:	Terry Stanley, Deaf Services Manager

Harding is a charitable foundation working in south and west London. Harding have three registered care homes for deaf people with mental health needs. Residents are given support with their emotional, physical and social needs. Residents are also encouraged to participate in a range of social and therapeutic activities both inside and outside the home.

Hyde Housing Association Southwark

285 Rye Lane, London, SE15 4UA

Tel:	020 7277 7964
Fax:	020 7277 6151

This is the area office for Southwark.

Metropolitan Housing Trust Peckham

114 Peckham Rye, London, SE15 4HA

Tel: 020 7635 1200

Fax: 020 7277 7184

Contact: Juliet McMananman

Tel: 020 7635 1208

The Trust has properties in London and the East Midlands. This office can help with supported housing in Lewisham and Southwark for single people with special needs. The office cannot take self referrals; all referrals must come through either local authority housing departments or from one of the specialised agencies working with the Trust. If people are already either council or housing association tenants they can apply to the trust to be rehoused as part of the HOMES nomination scheme.

Paddington Churches Housing Association

Canterbury House, Canterbury Road, Kilburn, London, NW6 4AL

Tel: 020 8965 7797

Textphone: 020 8965 4335

Fax: 020 8965 4428

Accommodation is at Miles House and comprises shared housing accommodation with own bedroom for 6 residents aged between 17 and 30. Both men and women are welcome and the project encourages residents to go on training courses to learn new skills. Residents are encouraged to go either to the City Lit Centre for Deaf People or any other college where communication support is available. There are no formal rehabilitation courses, but residents are encouraged to become independent, perhaps by attending a deaf club and making new friends. The minimum stay at Miles House is six months. Most residents stay on average around 18 months. Support is available for residents if they need to claim benefit or attend job clubs for example.

Reardon Court

Tel: 020 8447 9980

Fax: 020 8350 4802

Contact: Mark Whitbread, Manager

See entry under Deafblind Resources.

RNID Brondesbury Road

113 Brondesbury Road, Queens Park, London, NW6 6RY

Tel: 020 7328 8540

Textphone: 020 7328 8544

Videotel: 020 7328 6590

Fax: 020 7328 8540

Contact: Ray Hill, Project Manager

RNID Brondesbury Road is a three-storey terraced house which provides long-term support for six deaf and hard of hearing people with additional social needs. Facilities include: six single bedrooms, communal lounge, kitchen and dining area, wheelchair access on ground floor and 24-hour staff cover all year round. RNID Brondesbury Road is run in partnership with the Family Housing Association and is registered as a residential care home by the London Borough of Brent.

RNID Old Oak Road

9 Old Oak Road, London, W3 7HN

Tel: 020 8740 9531

Textphone: 020 8740 1978

Videotel: 020 8746 2800

Fax: 020 8740 9531

Contact: Ray Hill, Project Manager

Old Oak Road is a large, modern semi-detached house situated in the multicultural community of Acton, West London. It provides long-term accommodation for five deaf people with special needs who require additional support to enable them to make their own way in life. Facilities include: five single bedrooms, shared kitchen and living room, full wheelchair access on ground floor, large pleasant garden and 24-hour staff cover, all year round. It is owned by Notting Hill Housing Trust and is registered as a residential care home by the London Borough of Ealing.

Young Women's Christian Association

Helen Graham House, 57 Great Russell Street, London, WC1B 3BD

Tel: 020 7405 2177

Textphone: 020 7430 0834

Fax: 020 7242 2749

Contact: Janet Boyle, House Director

Provides affordable accommodation for those with a housing need, aged 18 to 30. Accommodation is available for 282 men and women of which seven rooms are specifically adapted for the use of deaf people. Accommodation consists of single and two bedded study bedrooms, shared kitchens, bathrooms, laundry etc. Accommodation can be short- to middle-term; generally residents stay for between six months and three years.

➢ Merseyside
Mary Mount Residential Home

Tel: 0151 724 2203
Textphone: 0151 724 2203
Fax: 0151 724 2203
Contact: Sr Louise, Sister Superior
See entry under Deafblind Resources.

➢ Middlesbrough
See Cleveland

➢ North West Somerset
See Avon

➢ North Yorkshire
RNIB Tate House

Tel: 01423 886927
Fax: 01423 885192
E-mail: gsmith@rnib.org.uk
Website: www.rnib.org.uk/
Contact: Debbie Cliff, Acting Manager
See entry under Deafblind Resources.

➢ Northamptonshire
Darsdale Home for Blind People

Tel: 01933 622457
Fax: 01933 622457
Contact: Debbie Webb, Manager
See entry under Deafblind Resources.

➢ Nottinghamshire
North British Housing Association

16 Vivian Avenue, Sherwood Rise, Nottingham, NG5 1AF
Tel: 01159 691772
Textphone: 01159 693295
Fax: 01159 692621
Contact: Sally Taylor

Vivian Avenue is housing association rented accommodation consisting of eight one-bedroomed flats and four two-bedroomed flats. Twenty men and women can be accommodated and the age range is between 18 and 45. There is

regular support from a housing support worker regarding tenancy issues.

➢ Somerset
RNIB Kathleen Chambers House

Tel: 01278 782142
Fax: 01278 782673
E-mail: Helpline@rnib.org.uk
              bscott@rnib.org.uk
Contact: Barbara Scott, Manager
See entry under Deafblind Resources.

RNID Newbridge Hill

51 Newbridge Hill, Lower Weston, Bath, Somerset, BA1 3PR
Tel: 01225 443019
Textphone: 01225 443019
Fax: 01225 443019
Contact: Ursula Forebush, Acting Manager

RNID Newbridge Hill offers long-term accommodation and short-term independence training for five deaf and deafblind people with additional disabilities. Residents need a basic level of practical and social skills as they are encouraged to take part in local community activities. Training and development is also available at the nearby Poolemead Centre and off-site workshop in Bath. Newbridge Hill is situated in a suburb of Bath, a mile from the city centre. It has good public transport links and a wide range of amenities. The home is owned by the Knightstone Housing Association and is registered as a residential care home by Bath and North East Somerset County Council.

➢ Suffolk
Bethesda Eventide Homes Ipswich

59a Henley Road, Ipswich, Suffolk, IP1 3SN
Tel: 01473 211431
Contact: Maureen Goddard, Manager

> Surrey

Netherleys Residential Care

3 Ashdown Road, Epsom, Surrey, KT17 3PL

Tel: 01372 811783

Textphone: 01372 720111

Fax: 01372 811784

Residential care for elderly deaf and deafblind people. Full support for residents. The managers and some staff are deaf and use British Sign Language and deaf-blind finger spelling to ensure good communication skills between staff and residents. Care staff are trained to help residents with daily routines like washing, bathing, toilet, dressing, eating. The home is equipped with teletext TV, Minicom, fax machine, flashing light alarm in case of fire and an emergency alarm system. Other services include chiropody, hairdressing, outings, and visits to deaf clubs. Various programmes are organised.

RNID Gibraltar Crescent

36a Gibraltar Crescent, Epsom, Surrey, KT19 9BT

Tel: 020 8393 0865

Textphone: 020 8393 7623

Videotel: 020 8786 7784

Fax: 020 8393 8649

Contact: Anne Edwards

A high standard of care is available including 24-hour staff cover. All forms of communication are used including British Sign Language, Signed Supported English and Makaton. Individual care plans are drawn up. Training is provided in home economics, personal hygiene, money management, health-care. General household activities. Activities include scouts, clubs, leisure centre, extended education classes, holidays, trips out.

> Warwickshire

Deaf-initely Independent

23 Leam Terrace, Leamington Spa, Warwickshire, CV31 1BB

Tel: 01926 886747

Textphone: 01926 886043

Fax: 01926 886747

Contact: Marie Mason, Director

Tel: 01926 337743

Textphone: 01926 337760

Fax: 01926 337743

Deaf-initely Independent provides full-time/respite placements for deaf adults with additional disabilities in two sites in Leamington

Spa. Day care (Monday-Friday) is also available. Structured, individual programmes of learning and leisure activities are offered in a friendly, family atmosphere where the philosophy is one of 'Learning Throughout Life'. Both locations offer excellent facilities.

> West Midlands

RNID Mulberry House

70 Lichfield Street, Walsall, West Midlands, WS4 2BY

Tel: 01922 615218

Textphone: 01922 722658

Fax: 01922 615218

Contact: Chris Leek, Project Manager

Mulberry House provides opportunities for deaf and deafblind people to further develop their lifeskills and personal confidence, so leading to independent living within the community, with specific and sensitive outreach support. Mulberry House has established strong links with Walsall College and Walsall Deaf Peoples Centre to further individuals' developmental opportunities. This spacious, well-converted detached property is set in its own grounds and offers: nine single bedsitting rooms with cooking facilities, communal lounge and reception room, large picturesque garden, practical training programmes, recreational facilities, rehousing assistant and 24-hour staff cover all year round. Mulberry House is owned by Caldmore Housing Association and is registered as a residential care home by Walsall Metropolitan Borough Council.

RNID Olive Lane

60 Olive Lane, Blackheath, Halesowen, West Midlands, B62 8LZ

Tel: 0121 559 0031

Textphone: 0121 559 0280

Fax: 0121 561 1288

Contact: Leanne Hickenbottom, Project Manager

RNID Olive Lane is a community-based residential care home which provides a family-type environment for eight deaf people aged 18 upwards who have additional needs or physical and learning disabilities. Facilities include: one self-contained unit on the first floor, with two bedrooms, kitchen and bathroom; five single bedrooms with vanity units and shaving points, all with wheelchair access, shared bathrooms and shower facilities, communal lounge, dining room and kitchen; emergency call system, individual doorbells and keys, textphones and 24-hour staff cover all year round. RNID Olive Lane has been

10

developed in partnership with Black Country Housing Association and is registered as a residential care home by Dudley Metropolitan Borough Council.

RNID Sandwell Community Care Project

c/o Deaf Community Social Services Centre, Dagger Lane, West Bromwich, West Midlands, B71 4BD

Tel: 0121 525 5347

Textphone: 0121 525 3092

Contact: Jenny Weir, Community Support Worker

Under a service agreement with Sandwell Council, RNID employs a Community Support Worker whose role is to work with deaf people who have been identified by Social Services as needing support to live in the community. Users of the project may have additional needs including dual sensory loss, physical or learning disabilities.

Vision Homes Association

Tel: 0121 233 2290

Fax: 0121 233 2291

Contact: Joanne Vincent, Administration Officer

See entry under Deafblind Resources.

➢ West Sussex

Hanover Housing Association

Sanford House, 5 Medwin Walk, Horsham, West Sussex, RH12 1AZ

➢ Worcestershire

Tanglewood Home For The Deaf

72 Albert Road South, Malvern, Worcestershire, WR14 3AH

Tel: 01684 574517

Contact: Gill Burns

We provide a high standard of personal care for deaf and deafblind people. We aim to make residents' lives as comfortable and interesting as possible whilst maintaining a warm and friendly atmosphere. We have a minibus fitted with wheelchair ramp, used for outings. We have a local chaplain as a regular visitor. Various social events are encouraged.

Northern Ireland

➢ County Londonderry

RNID Harkness Gardens

1-2 Harkness Gardens, Brigade Road, Londonderry, BT47 6GG

Tel: 028 7134 1005

Textphone: 028 7134 2262

Fax: 028 7134 2262

Contact: Patricia Kelly, Project Manager

RNID Harkness Gardens is a community-based supported housing project for up to six deaf and deafblind people between the ages of 18 and 50, all of whom have additional special needs and require support to help them make their own way in life. The home offers long-term care and support, although residents may move to more independent settings when they have the appropriate life skills and confidence. Harkness Gardens is about two miles from the city centre and within easy reach of local shops, transport and other amenities. It has been developed in partnership with Habinteg Housing Association and is registered as a residential care home by the Western Health and Social Services Board.

Scotland

➢ East Dumbartonshire

Deaf Connections - Craigholme

16 Roman Road, Bearsden, Glasgow, East Dumbartonshire, G61 2SL

Tel: 0141 942 3962

Fax: 0141 943 2455

Contact: Anne Roberts, Manager

Craigholme Residential Home is a specialised and unique care establishment. Our primary concern is to provide a 'home from home' where 33 profoundly deaf or deafblind elderly people can enjoy a safe, caring and loving environment in their later years. All the staff are trained in British Sign Language and the deafblind manual alphabet.

➢ Lanarkshire
Hayfield Support Services with Deaf People
268 Ballater Street, Glasgow, Lanarkshire, G5 0ND

Tel: 0141 429 1278

Textphone: 0141 429 1278

Fax: 0141 420 1990

Contact: Judy Byrne, Residential Manager

Client group: deaf people with additional disabilities. Male/female aged 16+. Community based care services. Aim: to improve quality of life via individual structured programmes. Five residential houses and day centre, sports hall, excess of 40 skilled staff. Six-week assessments undertaken.

➢ Midlothian
Castleview
65 Bruntsfield Place, Edinburgh, Midlothian, EH10 4HQ

Tel: 0131 229 4110

Fax: 0131 229 4110

Contact: Pauline Arthur, Officer-in-Charge, Residential Care

Residents lead full and active lives engaging in many activities. The older ones participate in activities such as games, arts and crafts, outings, the younger residents work towards a more independent living programme in preparation for the Millennium when all the residents will move into their own flats.

➢ Strathclyde
Deaf Connections
Tel: 0141 420 1759

Textphone: 0141 429 6682

Videotel: 0141 418 0597 (office hours)

Fax: 0141 429 6860

Contact: Gordon Chapman, Chief Executive

Videotel: 0141 418 0597

See entry under Regional Organisations.

Communication Services

Listed here are communication support units and agencies providing communication support for deaf and hard of hearing people. Communication support can be provided either through technology such as Palantype, speech-to-text operators, induction loops and radio aids, or through human aids to communication such as sign language interpreters, lipspeakers, notetakers and deafblind communicators.

This section is listed alphabetically by organisation name.

ADSI - Access for Deaf Students' Initiative

University of Bristol, Union Building, Queens Road, Clifton, Bristol, Avon, BS8 1LN

Tel: 0117 954 5727
Textphone: 0117 954 5730
Fax: 0117 954 8546
E-mail: lin.reynolds@bris.co.uk
Website: www.bris.ac.uk/Depts/ADSI
Contact: Lin Reynolds
            Union Building, Queens Road, Clifton, Bristol, Avon, BS8 1LN

All undergraduate and post graduate programmes are available to deaf students, and the Centre for Deaf Studies at the University of Bristol runs courses solely for deaf students. Technical support and equipment for individual students is funded by Disabled Students Allowance (DSA) or students' own resources. ADSI works with students to assess their needs for support and equipment, and helps them coordinate its provision. Support is available at interview, lectures, tutorials and examinations. Around 15-20 deaf or hard of hearing students are admitted each year. The university is offering a course starting in September 1998 for unemployed people over 25 years of age who communicate through lipreading or residual hearing. The course will enable participants to learn about available courses, build up confidence, meet others, and try out new ways of working. Free travel, accommodation, meals, childcare and care allowances are available. Contact Christine Chubb for futher details.

Assets Communication

c/o Deafax Trust, Technology Centre, Bulmershe Court, Reading University, Reading, Berkshire, RG6 1HY

Tel: 0118 935 1936
Textphone: 0118 935 1936
Fax: 0118 935 1936
E-mail: 101331.1044@compuserve.com
Contact: Gino Mancini, Managing Coordinator

Assets Communication (the service arm of the Deafax Trust) provides facilitators, interpreters, lipspeakers, notetakers, and other communication support for disabled students and others. It promotes positive images of deaf people through deaf and disability awareness training, provides sign communication skills training at all levels and researches communication/access issues.

Augmentative Communication Service

The Wolfson Centre, Great Ormond Street Hospital for Children, Neurodisability Service, Mecklenburgh Square, LONDON, WC1 2AP

Tel: 020 7837 7618
Fax: 020 7833 9469
Contact: Katie Price, Neurodisability Service

The ACS offers assessment and management advice to children with physical difficulties who need additional non-speech channels of communication. It can also provide a tertiary service to advise on on integrating access to assistive technology such as wheelchair use, computers and environmental controls.

Birmingham Institute for the Deaf

Tel: 0121 246 6100
Textphone: 0121 246 6101
Fax: 0121 246 6125
E-mail: bid@bid.org.uk
Website: www.bid.org.uk
Contact: Ruth Beer, Information Officer

See entry under Regional Organisations.

Calderdale Sign Language Interpreting Service

Town Hall, Halifax, West Yorkshire, HX1 1UJ

Tel: 01422 393077
Textphone: 01422 393082
Fax: 01422 393136

Provides sign language interpreting in the Calderdale area.

Co.Sign Partners in Communication Ltd

5 Chapel Street, Belmont, Bolton, Lancashire, BL7 8AU

Tel:	01204 811392
Textphone:	01204 811392
Fax:	01204 811392
E-mail:	co.sign@btinternet.com
Contact:	Cath Whitehead, Director

Co.Sign is a limited company working on a cooperative basis with a small number of freelance interpreters. For further details please contact Co.Sign.

Communication and Interpreting Services for Deaf People in North Wales (CLICS/RNID)

3 Maesgwyn Road, Wrexham, LL11 2AP

Tel:	01978 313222
Textphone:	01978 313000
Videotel:	01978 356945
Fax:	01978 313222
Website:	dspace.dial.pipex.com/town/parade/ni30/clics.htm
Contact:	Adrienne Ellis, Development Coordinator and Videophone contact

CLICS/RNID has been providing an interpreting service to agencies and individuals in north east Wales since April 1993. CLICS/RNID was set up to facilitate communication between deaf and hearing people in a wide range of settings, thereby giving deaf people access to the hearing world. CLICS/RNID provides the following services: sign language interpreters; speech-to-text reporters; lipspeakers; services for deafblind people; and notetakers.

Communication Unlimited

Upstairs Flat, Lois Ellis Home, Greenwich Drive, Derby, DE22 4AH

Tel:	01332 730537
Textphone:	01332 730493
Fax:	01332 730537

Provides sign language interpreting, notetaking, lipspeaking and deafblind communication in the Derby and Derbyshire area.

Coventry and Warwickshire Sign Language Interpreting Service

B65-69, Coventry Technical College, Butts, Coventry, West Midlands, CV1 3GD

Tel:	024 7652 0378
Textphone:	024 7622 9667
Fax:	024 7652 0378

Provides sign language interpreting, notetaking, lipspeaking and deafblind communication in the Coventry and Warwickshire area.

Croydon Communication Support Service

Selhurst High School, The Crescent, Croydon, Surrey, CR0 2HN

Tel:	020 8683 4849/ 0554
Fax:	020 8683 4922
Contact:	Jennifer Kidd, Head of Communication Support Services

This is the new office for the Communication Support Service Administration and also the Hearing Impaired Service and the Visually Impaired Service.

Deafness Support Network Communication Service

Centre for Deaf People, 13 Wilson Patten Street, Warrington, Cheshire, WA1 1PG

Tel:	01925 636866
Textphone:	01925 232551
Fax:	01925 626992

Provides sign language interpreting, speech-to-text-reporters, notetaking, lipspeaking and deafblind communication in the Cheshire, Halton and Warrington area.

Edinburgh and East of Scotland Deaf Society

Tel:	0131 556 3128
Textphone:	0131 557 4202
Fax:	0131 557 0419
E-mail:	admin@escotdeafsoc.demon.co.uk

See entry under Regional Organisations

Guildford Deaf Centre

Beverley Hall, Haydon Place, Guildford, Surrey, GU1 4LR

Tel:	01483 568598
Textphone:	01483 568598

The centre provides information for deaf people of all ages and backgrounds.

Hampshire Interpreting Service for Deaf People

Fairbairn Centre, 18 Augustine Road, Southampton, Hampshire, SO14 0PL

Tel: 023 8033 4195
Textphone: 023 8033 4195
Fax: 023 8023 2848
E-mail: hantsdeafass@compuserve.com
Website: www.info-quest.com\deafsociety

Havering Special Educational Needs Support Service

The Broxhill Centre, Broxhill Road, Harold Hill, Romford, Essex, RM4 1XN

Tel: 01708 773936
Fax: 01708 773892
Contact: Miss Harvey, Advisory Teacher for Hearing Impaired Children

Hertfordshire Communication Support Unit

Hertfordshire Hearing Advisory Service, The Woodside Centre, The Commons, Welwyn Garden City, Hertfordshire, AL7 4SE

Tel: 01707 377681
Textphone: 01707 325945
Fax: 01707 324095

Provides sign language interpreting, speech-to-text reporters, notetaking, lipspeaking and deafblind communication in the Hertfordshire area.

Hounslow Interpreting Service

41 New Heston Road, Hounslow, Middlesex, TW5 0LW

Tel: 020 8862 6639
Textphone: 020 8862 6639
Fax: 020 8862 6639

Provides sign language interpreting, notetaking and deafblind communication in the London Borough of Hounslow and surrounding area.

Kirklees Interpreting Unit

c/o Huddersfield Day Centre, Zetland Street, Huddersfield, West Yorkshire, HD1 2RA

Tel: 01484 223033
Textphone: 01484 420926
Fax: 01484 223049

Provides sign language interpreting and deafblind communication in Kirklees and the north of England.

Leeds Sign Language Interpreting Agency

Centre for Deaf People, Centenary House, North Street, Leeds, West Yorkshire, LS2 8AY

Tel: 0113 246 9990
Textphone: 0113 243 9900
Fax: 0113 246 9227

Provides sign language interpreting in the Leeds Metropolitan Borough Council area.

Leicester Centre for Deaf People

Tel: 0116 255 6776
Textphone: 0116 254 5126
Videotel: 0116 247 0626
Fax: 0116 255 6940
E-mail: knight@centrefordeafpeopleleicester. btinternet.com

See entry under Deaf Clubs

Link Centre for Deafened People

19 Hartfield Road, Eastbourne, East Sussex, BN21 2AR

Tel: 01323 638230
Textphone: 01323 638230
Fax: 01323 642968
Contact: Lorraine Gailey, Director

LINK provides week-long rehabilitation courses for people who have lost most or all of their hearing as adults, together with their families. The aim is to assist adjustment to deafness by providing intensive psychological support (such as communication skills, and confidence building) and giving practical help and advice.

Multimedia Information Unit

1-3 Worship Street, London, EC2A 2AB

Tel: 020 7588 3522
Textphone: 020 7588 3528
Fax: 020 7588 3526
E-mail: ldap@ndirect.co.uk
Website: www.tomd.demon.co.uk/ldap/page2. html
Contact: Lucy Franklin, Administrator

Produces information videos in British Sign Language (with subtitling and voice over) for the UK deaf community. It can also provide consultancy services to organisations wishing to make their information accessible to deaf people. The London Deaf Access Project produces information videos in BSL for the deaf community. It also runs media workshops for deaf people and has a library of signed videos.

Norfolk Deaf Communication Services

The Deaf Centre, Johnson Place, Vauxhall Street, Norwich, Norfolk, NR2 2SA

Tel: 01603 660889
Textphone: 01603 661113
Fax: 01603 660889
E-mail: suemoore@ndcs.demon.co.uk
Website: www.ndcs.demon.co.uk
Contact: Sue Moore

Provides sign language interpreter service and a range of communication support to deaf people and hearing families with deaf children in Norfolk.

North Nottinghamshire Sign Language Interpreting Service

1 Wood Street, Mansfield, Nottinghamshire, NG18 1QB

Tel: 01623 429260
Textphone: 01623 652029

Provides sign language interpreting and deafblind communication in North Nottinghamshire.

Nottinghamshire Sign Language Interpreting Service

22 Forest Road West, Nottingham, NG7 4EQ

Tel: 0115 978 6984/ 6881
Textphone: 0115 978 6984/ 6881
Fax: 0115 942 3729
Contact: Catherine Martland, Interpreting
                 Service Coordinator

Provides sign language interpreting throughout the county of Nottinghamshire.

Open College of Sign Language

Council Offices, Dragon Lane, Whiston, Prescot, Merseyside, L35 3QU

Tel: 0151 426 1471

The Open College provides training in sign language. It also runs the Golden Hands Scheme, which trains hearing people to communicate with deaf people in four days. The Open College also runs Tiny Talking Hands, a project designed to enable very young children from infant school age and upwards to communicate with profoundly deaf children through sign language. For further details of Tiny Talking Hands please contact Emily Mason or Lorraine Cooke on: 01905 612505.

Oxford Sign Language Interpreting Service

The Deaf and Hard of Hearing Centre, St Ebbe's, Littlegate Street, Oxford, OX1 1RL

Tel: 01865 243447
Textphone: 01865 246054
Fax: 01865 249823

Provides sign language interpreting, notetaking, lipspeaking and deafblind communication in the Oxfordshire area.

Race, Equality and Communication Services

Woodside Centre, Highgate Road, Holly Hall, Dudley, West Midlands, DY2 0TH

Tel: 01384 813400
Textphone: 01384 74667

Provides sign language interpreters for people in the Dudley area for various situations, for example welfare issues, access to social services, GP and hospital appointments and employment.

RNID Communication Services Unit Bristol

ADSI, 4th Floor, Student's Union, Bristol University, Queens Road, Clifton, Bristol, BS8 1LN

Tel: 0117 954 5729
Textphone: 0117 954 5730
Fax: 0117 954 5731
Contact: Wena Jackson

The service provides a full range of communication support plus SpeedText/Hi-Linc training. Communication support is available to staff and students at the university. Training services are available to all. The unit was established specifically to meet the communication needs of deaf and hard of hearing students at Bristol University. The focus of communication work is speech-to-text, but sign language interpreting and lipspeaking are also provided.

RNID Communication Services Unit Central

Walton House, Walton Street, Aylesbury, Buckinghamshire, HP21 7QQ

Tel: 01296 392294
Textphone: 01296 392295
Fax: 01296 392294
Contact: Sandra Jones, Unit Coordinator

Central CSU offers a professional, independent, confidential and comprehensive service to promote equal access for all deaf people. The unit provides sign language interpreters, notetakers, lipspeakers, deafblind communicators and speech-to-text transcription. Anyone who wants to communicate with a deaf or hard of hearing person, or who wants to provide equal access, or anyone who is deaf themselves, is encouraged to use the service. The area covers all of East Anglia, Buckinghamshire and Northamptonshire.

RNID Communication Services Unit Merseyside

Merseyside Society for Deaf People, Queen's Drive, West Derby, Liverpool, Merseyside, L13 0DJ
Tel: 0151 709 3663
Textphone: 0151 709 3833
Fax: 0151 228 4872
Contact: Julie McCulloch, Coordinator

RNID Merseyside CSU aims to provide the following services: sign language interpreters, lipspeakers, notetakers, deafblind communicators, Palantype, speech-to-text transcription, loop systems.

RNID Communication Services Unit North

National Computing Centre, Armstrong House, Oxford Road, Manchester, M1 7ED
Tel: 0161 242 2368
Textphone: 0161 242 2371
Fax: 0161 242 2317
Contact: Christian Leyland, Coordinator
             National Computing Centre, Armstrong House, Oxford Road, Manchester, Lancashire, M1 7ED

RNID North East CSU provides sign language interpreters, lipspeakers, notetakers, deafblind communicators, Palantype and speech-to-text transcription. It covers Greater Manchester.

RNID Communication Services Unit North East

National Computing Centre, Armstrong House, Oxford Road, Manchester, M1 7ED
Tel: 0161 242 2263
Textphone: 01642 312355
Videotel: 0161 236 2871
Fax: 0161 242 2317
Contact: Hilary Wharton, Administrator and Coordinator

The Unit provides sign language interpreters, lipspeakers, notetakers, deafblind communicators, Palantype and speech-to-text transcription services. It can also provide loop systems. Areas covered are: Northumberland, Tyne & Wear, County Durham, Cleveland and North Yorkshire.

RNID Communication Services Unit Northern Ireland

Wilton House, 5 College Square North, Belfast, County Antrim, BT1 6AR
Tel: 028 9023 9619
Textphone: 028 9031 2033 Text answerphone
Fax: 028 9031 2032
Contact: Geraldine Dornan, CSU Coordinator

RNID Northern Ireland CSU seeks to offer the following services: sign language interpreters (British Sign Language and Irish Sign Language), lipspeakers, notetakers, deafblind communicators, speech-to-text transcription and loop systems. Catchment area is Northern Ireland.

RNID Communication Services Unit Scotland

9 Clairmont Gardens, Glasgow, Lanarkshire, G3 7LW
Tel: 0141 332 0343
Textphone: 0141 332 4767
Fax: 0141 332 4768
Contact: Margaret Nesbitt, Coordinator

Scotland CSU provides sign language interpreters, lipspeakers, deafblind communicators, speech-to-text operators and notetakers. The unit also provides a communication training programme, and is starting a videotelephony service in the near future.

RNID Communication Services Unit South East

19-23 Featherstone Street, London, EC1Y 8SL
Tel: 020 7296 8064/ 8066
Textphone: 020 7296 8065
Fax: 020 7296 8083
E-mail: se-csu@rnid.org.uk
Contact: Jaz Azam, Coordinator

RNID South East CSU provides a service for all counties covered by RNID South East region. It has standing contracts with East Sussex, Brighton and Hove, West Sussex, Kent, Essex, London Borough of Redbridge and Camden and Islington Health Authority and therefore funding for assignments is assured. Surrey, Hampshire and the rest of Greater London are not covered contractually, but the CSU will try to work with the client to find some form of funding.

RNID Communication Services Unit South West

13b Church Farm Business Park, Corston, Bath, Avon, BA2 9AP

Tel: 01225 873590
Textphone: 0800 622401 Freephone
Videotel: 01225 874804
Fax: 01225 874246
E-mail: sw-csu@rnid.org.uk
Contact: Ena Caddy, Coordinator
Contact: Margaret Freke, Coordinator

The unit provides sign language interpreters, lipspeakers, notetakers, deafblind communicators and SpeedText operators. Catchment areas: Cornwall, Devon, Dorset, Berkshire, Wiltshire, Somerset, Former Avon, Gloucestershire.

RNID Communication Services Unit Cymru

Room 4, Norton Lodge, Norton Avenue, Mumbles, Swansea, West Glamorgan, SA3 5TP

Tel: 01792 402154
Textphone: 0800 622401
Fax: 01792 406090
Contact: Tracy Conway, Coordinator
Contact: Jayne Thomas, Coordinator

RNID Communication Services Unit Wolverhampton

The Methodist Centre, 24 School Street, Wolverhampton, West Midlands, WV1 4LF

Tel: 01902 423717
Textphone: 01902 423716
Videotel: 01902 310116
Fax: 01902 714456
Contact: Karen Lowe, CSU Coordinator
Contact: Julie Markall, CSU Coordinator

RNID Wolverhampton CSU provides the following services: sign language interpreters, lipspeakers, notetakers, deafblind communicators, Palantype, speech-to-text transcription. The CSU also provides communication services for Rampton Hospital in Retford, Nottinghamshire.

RNID Communication Services Unit Yorkshire

Kirk House, Browning Road, Herringthorpe, Rotherham, South Yorkshire, S65 2LG

Tel: 01709 372163
Textphone: 01709 372182
Fax: 01709 372163
Contact: Liz Woolston, Coordinator
Contact: Jayne Briggs, Coordinator

RNID South Yorkshire CSU aims to provide the following services: sign language interpreters, lipspeakers, notetakers, deafblind communicators, Palantype, speech-to-text transcription and loop systems.

RNID East Anglia Project Cambridge

Centre for Deaf People, 8 Romsey Terrace, Cambridge, CB1 3NH

Tel: 01223 411010
Textphone: 01223 411030 (and answerphone)
Contact: Sandra Johns
Textphone: 01223 411030

RNID Cambridge CSU aims to provide the following services: sign language interpreters, lipspeakers, notetakers, deafblind communicators, Palantype, speech-to-text transcription, loop systems. Catchment areas are: Cambridge and East Anglia Local Authorities.

RNID Typetalk - The National Telephone Relay Service

John Wood House, Glacier Building, Harrington Road, Brunswick Business Park, LIVERPOOL, Merseyside, L3 4DF

Tel: 0151 709 9494 (admin)
            0800 7 311 888 (Helpline)
Textphone: 0800 500 888 (Helpline)
Fax: 0151 709 8119
Website: www.rnid.org.uk
Contact: Phil Jennings, Director
Tel: 0151 709 9494 (switchboard)

Typetalk, the RNID service funded by BT, runs two important services for textphone users - the National Telephone Relay Service and the Text Users' Rebate Scheme (TURS). The 24-hour Telephone Relay Service operates all year round. It provides a communications link between deaf, deafened, hard of hearing, deafblind or speech-impaired people with textphones (textphone users) and hearing people worldwide, over the public telephone network. There is no registration fee and calls are charged as though dialled direct. Typetalk also provides text users with a direct link to the emergency services. Textphone users needing fire, police, ambulance or coastguard services can dial 0800 112999. The Text Users' Rebate Scheme provides substantial rebates on both BT and Typetalk bills as typed calls are generally longer and therefore more expensive than standard voice calls. To join you must be over eight years old, deaf, deafblind, hard of hearing, deafened or speech-impaired and only able to use a textphone. Those who are eligible receive a rebate of 60 per cent off their phone bills to a limit of £160 each year. Deafblind registered users can receive a limit of up to £600 each year. For more information, help or advice contact Typetalk on the following numbers: 0151 709 9494 (voice), 0151 709 8119 (fax); registration 0800 500 888 (textphone); billing/rebate 0800 592 593 (textphone); technical help 0800 592 600 (textphone). Information and bills are available in large print and braille.

Royal Association in Aid of Deaf People - Head Office

Tel: 01206 509509
Textphone: 01206 577090
Fax: 01206 769755
E-mail: info@royaldeaf.org.uk
Website: www.royaldeaf.org.uk
Contact: Tracey Barlow, Administrator

See entries under Regional Organisations.

SASU

Coventry Technical College, Winfray Building, Queens Road, Coventry, West Midlands, CV1 3GD
Tel: 024 7652 6730
Textphone: 024 7652 6947
Fax: 024 7652 0378
E-mail: c.fenton@covcollege.ac.uk
Contact: Jenny Tinsley, Coordinator of FE Support Services for Deaf Students
Tel: 024 7652 6730 ext 6529

Provides communication support for deaf and hard of hearing students attending seven colleges in Coventry and Warwickshire, Coventry University and Warwick University. Provides in-class communication support, notetaking and lipspeaking; additional tutorials and language modification; also advice about equipment and environmental aids. SASU is a National Association of Tertiary Education for Deafened People recognised assessor.

Sign Language Bureau

Middlesex University, Queensway, Enfield, Middlesex, EN3 4SF
Tel: 020 8292 1091
Textphone: 020 8292 1501
Fax: 020 8362 5360
E-mail: slb.@mdx.ac.uk

The Sign Language Bureau is London's oldest booking agency providing sign language interpreters. It provides interpreters for all types of assignment including legal, social services, medical, employment, education and entertainment.

Sign Solutions - Legal Sign Language Solutions

Beacon Hill, Rednal, Birmingham, West Midlands, B45 9QW

Provides sign language interpreting nationwide.

Sign Teach

11 Packwood Close, Bentley Heath, Solihull, West Midlands, B93 8AN
Tel: 01564 770490
Textphone: 01564 770490
Fax: 01564 770490
Contact: Janet Beech-McCoy

Sign Teach is made up of a group of teachers of sign language who offer weekend courses leading to the CACDP Stage II exam, and CACDP New Stage III exam.

SignAway

31 Fernhurst Road, Croydon, Surrey, CR0 7DJ
Tel: 020 8406 9061
Textphone: 020 8655 4161
Fax: 020 8654 9282

Provides sign language interpreting, notetaking, lipspeaking and deafblind communication in Greater London, Kent, Surrey, Sussex and nationwide.

Speech-To-Text Reporting Services

61 Carey Street, London, WC2A 2JG
Tel: 020 7831 8472
Fax: 020 7831 2526
Contact: Sue Lennie

Providers of high quality speech-to-text reporters (Palantype and stenograph) for deaf and hard of hearing people with nationwide coverage. They specialise in major conference work with either scrolling subtitles superimposed at the base of an image of the speaker's face, or a full screen display of the text.

Staffordshire Society for the Deaf Lichfield

Lombard Court, Lombard Street, Lichfield, Staffordshire, WS13 6DP
Tel: 01543 415308
Textphone: 01543 415308
Contact: Margaret Bunting, Senior Social Worker
             7 Market Street, Lichfield, Staffordshire, WS13 6LE

Sign language interpreting agency.

Stoke-on-Trent and Staffordshire Deaf Society

Tel:	01782 219161
Textphone:	01782 281125
Videotel:	01782 206575
Fax:	01782 281125
E-mail:	christopher.harrison@dial.pipex.com
Contact:	Tom Wordley, Chief Executive

See entry under Regional Organisations.

Surrey Interpreting Agency

Rentwood Resource Centre, School Lane, Fetcham, Leatherhead, Surrey, KT22 9JX

Tel:	01372 360718
Textphone:	01372 362471
Fax:	01372 363239

Provides sign language interpreting, speech-to-text reporters, notetaking, lipspeaking and deafblind communication in the Surrey area.

Sutton Service for the Hearing Impaired

Glastonbury Centre, Glastonbury Road, Morden, Surrey, SM4 6NZ

Tel:	020 8770 6741
Textphone:	020 8770 6741
Fax:	020 8770 6743
Contact:	Helen Joseph, Service Coordinator

SWITCHED

c/o Centre For The Deaf, 16-18 King Square, Bristol, Avon, BS2 8JL

Tel:	0117 924 9868
Textphone:	0117 944 1344
Fax:	0117 924 4884
Contact:	Mary Gutfreund, Secretary
	103 Hill Street, Kingswood, Bristol, Avon, BS15 4ST

SWITCHED provides sign language training, workshops and information exchange to its members and also to the public. They produce a quarterly newsletter called SWITCHED.

The Sign Language Bureau Enfield

Middlesex University, Queensway, Enfield, Middlesex, EN3 4SF

Tel:	020 8292 1091
Textphone:	020 8292 1501
Fax:	020 8362 5360
E-mail:	LB@mdx.ac.uk
Contact:	Marion Jamison, Administrator

An independent interpreting agency which arranges the provision of sign language interpreters to public and private sector organisations and individuals.

University of Middlesex

Queensway, Enfield, Middlesex, EN3 4SF

Tel:	020 8292 1501
Contact:	Alan Muller, Special Needs Coordinator, Able Centre

University of Northumbria Special Needs Research Unit

Coach Lane, Newcastle Upon Tyne, Tyne and Wear, NE7 7XA

Tel:	0191 227 4211
Fax:	0191 266 4061
Contact:	Jim Sandhu
E-mail:	Jim@snru-unn.demon.co.uk.

University of Wolverhampton Communication Support Unit

Stafford Street, Wolverhampton, West Midlands, WV1 1SB

Tel:	01902 322325
Fax:	01902 322739

Provides sign language interpreting and notetaking nationwide.

Visual Interpreting and Communication Service in Shropshire

The Disability Resource Centre, Lancaster Road, Shrewsbury, Shropshire, SY1 3NJ

Tel:	01743 440060
Textphone:	01743 440050
Fax:	01743 461349

Provides sign language interpreting, notetaking, lipspeaking and deafblind communication in the Shropshire, Telford and Wrekin area.

Waltham Forest Interpreting Service

Alpha Business Centre, 60 South Grove, London, E17 7NX

Tel:	020 8521 7835
Textphone:	020 8521 3777
Fax:	020 8521 8552

Provides sign language interpreting, notetaking and deafblind communication in Greater London. Community languages interpreting and translations also undertaken.

11

Worcester and Hereford Interpreting Service
13 Castle Street, Worcester, WR1 3AD
Tel: 01905 723351
Contact: Sarah Bown

Equipment Suppliers and Manufacturers

This section aims to provide information on manufacturers and suppliers of equipment and what each company can provide. A series of numbers follow each entry and relate to the key given below. A further list at the end of this section lists companies by the type of products they can provide. Companies are listed alphabetically by name.

Please note that inclusion in this list does not imply RNID recommendation of any company or product.

RNID Sound Advantage sells a wide range of products for deaf and hard of hearing people through their 'Solutions' catalogue. All products are tested by RNID to make sure they are safe and of a high quality. For contact details see entry for RNID Sound Advantage.

Key:

Alerting devices

1 - Doorbells
2 - Smoke alarms
3 - Alarm clocks
4 - Baby alarms/monitors
5 - Telephone call indicators/Flashing lights
6 - Multi-function alerting systems
7 - Vibrating pads
8 - Paging systems
9 - Fire alarms
10 - Bed wetting alarms
11 - Tactile acoustic monitors

Telecommunications

12 - Text telephones
13 - Voice telephones
14 - Video telephones
15 - PC-based textphones
16 - Mobile telephones/textphones
17 - Internet/E-mail
18 - Telephone adaptations
19 - Text pagers

Listening devices
TV/Conversation aids

20 - Radio aids
21 - Infra-red aids

22 - Personal loops
23 - Other personal conversation aids

Loop systems

24 - Domestic loop systems
25 - Public loop systems
26 - Portable loop systems
27 - Loop installation
28 - Loop hire
29 - Loop adaptations - eg microphones

Infra-red installations

30 - Domestic infra-red installations
31 - Public infra-red installations

Television

32 - Closed captions (video decoders)
33 - Teletext adapters
34 - VCRs (capable of recording subtitles)
35 - Teletext televisions
36 - Subtitling

Hearing aids

37 - Body worn
38 - Behind the ear
39 - In the ear
40 - Canal aids
41 - FM systems
42 - Ear moulds
43 - Accessories (batteries etc.)

Implanted devices

44 - Cochlear implants
45 - Implanted/semi-implanted hearing aids

Audiological equipment

46 - Noise generators
47 - Speech/auditory trainers
48 - Sound level meters
49 - Admittance meters
50 - Ear protectors
51 - Audiometers
52 - Real ear measuring systems
53 - Hearing aid test systems

12

3M Occupational Health & Environmental Safety Group

3M House, P O Box 1, Market Place, Bracknell, RG12 1JU

Tel: 0870 60 800 60 Helpline
Fax: 01334 858000

Manufacturer of hearing protection equipment including disposable, reusable and banded ear plugs, and a range of ear muffs including helmet-mounted and electronic versions.

Equipment

50.

A and M Hearing

Faraday Road, Crawley, West Sussex, RH10 2LS

Tel: 01293 423700
Fax: 01293 403080
Contact: Ms al-Bahrani, Customer Services Manager

Equipment

3, 5, 18, 22, 23, 37, 38, 39, 40, 41, 42, 43, 46, 47, 49, 51, 52, 53.

AJ Sound and Vision Ltd

181-183 Warwick Road, London, W14 8PU

Tel: 020 7373 4639
Fax: 020 7370 2823

Professional installation of loop systems and video/CCTV systems and public address. Hire available. Clients include the Cabinet Office, Inland Revenue, St Paul's Cathedral, Corporation of London.

Equipment

5, 8, 13, 18, 19, 20, 21, 22, 24, 25, 26, 27, 28, 29, 32, 34, 35, 36, 48, 50.

AB Transistor

P O Box 49093, 100 28 Stockholm, Sweden

Tel: 0046 8 654 1820/ 654 8480

UK distributor: Gordon Morris Ltd.

Acoustic Consultants Ltd

Raleigh House, 9a Wellsway, Keynsham, Bristol, BS18 1HS

Tel: 0117 986 2956
Fax: 0117 986 0554
Contact: S Peliza, Director

Provides cost-effective designs in noise and acoustics. Testing of auditorium acoustics and environmental noise surveys using the latest digital real time equipment. Planning and environmental impact assessments - for transportation systems (aircraft, road and rail), mineral workings, utilities, power generation, industry and leisure activities. Legal aspects - trained and qualified expert witness. Includes planning appeals and Legal Aid cases. Architectural acoustics - auditoria for speech, drama and musical performances, recording studios. Building noise control - internal and external control HVAC services for venues such as hotels, offices and airports etc. Acoustic Consultants is a member of the Association of Noise Consultants.

Acoustical Investigation and Research Organisation Ltd

Duxons Turn, Maylands Avenue, Hemel Hempstead, Hertfordshire, HP2 4SB

Tel: 01442 247146
Fax: 01442 256749
E-mail: AIRO@bcs.org.uk
Website: www.airo.co.uk
Contact: W Stevens, Principal Consultant

AIRO offers a comprehensive measurement and consultancy service in acoustics, noise control, vibration studies and electro-acoustic system design for any scale of project, whether design or remedial. With experienced staff and substantial laboratory facilities, AIRO provides a complete service which is independent, impartial and confidential. AIRO's expertise encompasses many areas, including environmental noise appraisals, acoustic design and noise control in buildings, industrial noise, measurement and appraisal of sound insulation, transportation noise and expert testimony at public enquiries and legal hearings. AIRO has also been accredited as a NAMAS TESTING laboratory number 0483. AIRO is a member of the Association of Noise Consultants.

Equipment

25.

Acoustics and Noise Partnership

P O Box 91, Newport, NP9 1YP

Tel: 01633 252957
Fax: 01633 252958
E-mail: paultrew@mcmail.com

Acoustics and Noise Partnership offers a complete service in consultancy and design in building, environmental, industrial and electro acoustics. Its particular field of interest lies in building acoustics and sound systems. However, Acoustics and Noise Partnership is happy to tackle most noise and acoustic-related problems, with particular attention paid to current and proposed standards. Preparation of land surveys and acoustic designs for planning applications, liaision with local authorities to provide mutually acceptable solutions to noise problems, and expert assistance in the preparation of legal briefs, form a significant part of the day-to-day workload of the company. Acoustics and Noise Partnership is a member of the Association of Noise Consultants.

Advanced Bionics UK Ltd

Grain House, Mill Court, Great Shelford, Cambridgeshire, CB2 5LD

Tel: 01223 847888
Fax: 01223 847898
E-mail: info@abionics.fr
Website: www.cochlearimplant.com
Contact: Fiona Robinson

Clarion Multi-Strategy.

Equipment

44.

Advanced Hearing Systems

68 High Matlock Road, Stannington, Sheffield, South Yorkshire, S6 6AT

Tel: 0114 234 3666
E-mail: advan.hear@virgin.net
Website: www.advancedhearing.co.uk
Contact: Dennis Coath, Hearing Aid Dispenser

Loop installation. Areas covered: UK-wide. Mr Coath is also a qualified hearing aid dispenser and is available for home visits which are free of charge, as are hearing tests. A two-week free trial period is offered on aids and no deposit is required.

Equipment

1, 2, 3, 4, 5, 6, 7, 8, 9, 12, 14, 20, 21, 22, 23, 24, 25, 26, 27, 28, 29, 30, 31, 37, 38, 39, 40, 41, 42, 43, 46, 47, 48, 49, 50, 51, 52, 53.

Aearo Limited

First Avenue, Poynton, Stockport, SK12 1FJ

Tel: 01625 878 320
Fax: 01625 877348
E-mail: kieron_lonergan@aero.co.uk
Contact: Brian Carey, Director

Ear Products; formerly Cabot Safety.

Equipment

50.

Aico Ltd

Mile End Business Park, Maesbury Road, Oswestry, Shropshire, SY10 8NN

Tel: 01691 657466
Fax: 01691 662933/ 679559 Adm/Sales
E-mail: enquiries@aico.co.uk
Contact: Elizabeth Musgrave, Sales Team
Fax: 01691 679559 (Sales)

Fire alerting devices.

Equipment

2, 7.

Aird Walker and Ralston Ltd

12f Lawson Street, Kilmarnock, Ayrshire, KA1 3JP

Tel: 01563 522236
Fax: 01563 521304
Contact: Robert Jarvie, Sales Team

Equipment

1, 5.

Alan Saunders Associates

The Coach House, Worthy Park, Kingsworthy, Winchester, Hampshire, SO21 1AN

Tel: 01962 889466
Fax: 01962 889477
E-mail: 101361.3136@compuserve.com
Contact: Alan Saunders, Director

Provide consultancy advice on a wide range of noise and vibration aspects. Acoustics is treated as a quantitative subject where results are predictable and the subject of formulation. The practice offers advice in the following fields: architectural and building acoustics, transportation noise, environmental noise and workplace and industrial noise. Alan Saunders Associates is a member of the Association of Noise Consultants.

Alfred Peters plc

Acoustic House, Hunmanby Industrial Estate, Hunmanby, Filey, North Yorkshire, YO14 0PH

Tel: 01723 890141
Fax: 01723 891742
E-mail: sales@cirrusresearch.co.uk
Contact: James Tingay, Sales Team

Audiometers, speech/auditory trainers.

Equipment

51.

Amberguard Limited

Elk Mill, Broadway, Royton, Oldham, Lancashire, OL2 5HS

Tel: 0161 620 4328

AMC Communications Ltd

64 Exeter Road, London, N14 5JS

Tel: 020 8361 8881
Fax: 020 8361 4523
Contact: Antony Clayden

Loop installation and hire. Areas covered: London, southern England.

Equipment

25, 27, 28, 29, 31.

Ampetronic Ltd

Whitehouse Wharf, Millgate, Newark, Nottinghamshire, NG24 4TY

Tel: 01636 610062
Fax: 01636 610063
E-mail: ampetronic@aol.com
Contact: Patricia Percy, Commercial Director

Manufacturer of induction loop amplifiers and ancillary equipment for the professional market. Offers a full consultancy service from telephone advice to full system design using a unique computer program for complex installations such as low-spillover, multiple rooms, metal loss correction and unusual or difficult building design. Does not install, but can advise on suitable professional installers.

Equipment

25, 29.

Amplivox Ltd

29-30 Station Approach, Kidlington, Oxfordshire, OX5 1JD

Tel: 01865 842411
Fax: 01865 841853
E-mail: sales@amplivox.ltd.uk
Website: www.amplivox.ltd.uk

Amplivox is a UK manufacturer of a comprehensive range of screening and diagnostic audiometers, tympanometers, Real Ear Hearing Aid Test Systems and distributor for tympanometers. Provides a comprehensive test and calibration service for Amplivox instruments.

Equipment

49, 50, 51, 52, 53.

Annalex Systems

15 Blackthorn Road, Launton, Bicester, Oxfordshire, OX6 0DA

Tel: 01869 243637
Textphone: 01869 243637
Fax: 01869 243637

Expertise based on 35 years working for the hearing impaired. Provides a service for all environmental aids. Secondary general aspects include sound system installation and maintenance (a signer).

Anthony Best Dynamics Ltd

Holt Road, Bradford-on-Avon, Wiltshire, BA15 1AJ

Tel: 01225 867575
Fax: 01225 864912
E-mail: info@abdynan.demon.co.uk
Contact: Anthony Best, Director

Anthony Best Dynamics employs engineers specialising in noise, vibration and engineering dynamics. Offers a complete design, research and development, prototype manufacture and testing service including: mathematical modelling of vibrating systems, rotating machinery, hydraulic pumps; seismic response prediction; finite element analysis; statistical energy analysis; design, development and application of vibration isolators, suspension systems, engine mountings, noise and vibration in vehicles, active noise and vibration control; fatigue testing; design of quiet fans and blowers; computer analysis systems for noise and vibration testing of machines on the production line or laboratories, and testing of elastomers, springs, dampers. Anthony Best Dynamics is a member of the Association of Noise Consultants.

Anti-Noise Ltd

67 Great Underbank, Stockport, Cheshire, SK1 1PE

Tel: 0161 480 8454

Equipment

50.

Antwerp Bionic Systems

Drie Eikenstraat, 661, B-2650 Edegem, Vlaanderen, Belgium

Tel: 0032 3 825 2616
Fax: 0032 3 825 0630
Contact: Dirk Lanens

Philips Hearing Implants is a developer, manufacturer and distributor of cochlear implant systems. Currently Philips Hearing Implants is offering the Laura Cochlear Implant System, an advanced eight-channel cochlear implant system, developed at the University of Antwerp. The system is using the continuous interleaved sampling speech strategy, generally considered to be the most advanced currently available.

Equipment

44.

APT Acoustics

Alpina, Rochester Way, Crowborough, East Sussex, TN6 2DR

Tel: 01892 652545
Fax: 01892 652545
E-mail: apt@btinternet.com
Contact: Fred Traexler, Director

APT Acoustics has provided independent consultancy in noise, acoustics and vibration since 1971. Working on such areas as noise and vibration investigations, measurement of room reverberation and sound insulation, sound level predictions, noise nuisance assessment, specification of noise criteria, hearing conservation, design of remedial measures, environmental impact studies, design of noise and vibration control measures for systems or unitary equipment and representations in court or hearings. Comprehensive in-house instrumentation and computer programs for analysis and calculations are provided. APT Acoustics is a member of the Association of Noise Consultants.

ARCO

P O Box 21, Waverly Street, Hull, North Humberside, HU1 2SJ

Tel: 01482 327678
Fax: 01482 218536
Website: www.arco.co.uk
Contact: N Kelly, Director

Personal protective equipment chainstore. Please contact the head office at the above number for details of your nearest store.

Equipment

50.

Ascom Tele-Nova Ltd

Clockhouse Court, 45 Westerham Road, Sevenoaks, Kent, TN13 2QB

Tel: 01732 742014
Fax: 01732 455865
E-mail: peter.wilson@ascomtele-nova.com
Contact: Brian Lester, Director

Equipment

8, 19.

Ashdown Environmental Ltd

The Oast House, Hodore, Upper Hartfield, East Sussex, TN7 4AR

Tel: 01892 770881
Fax: 01892 770885
E-mail: enquiries@ashdown-
           environmental.co.uk
Website: www.ashdown-environmental.co.uk
Contact: Philip Evans, Director

Ashdown is a specialist environmental consultancy, providing independent, professional advice to public and private sector clients both in the UK and internationally. Specialist areas include: air and water pollution, noise and vibration, contaminated land and waste management, ecology, environmental impact assessment, monitoring and audit, risk management, training and occupational hygiene.

Aspinwall and Company Ltd

16 Crucifix Lane, London Bridge, London, SE1 3JW

Tel: 020 7940 5400
Fax: 020 7940 5414
E-mail: trevor.curson@aspinwall.co.uk
Contact: Trevor Curson, Director

One of the largest environmental management consultancies in the UK. The acousticians have wide ranging capabilities in environmental noise and building acoustics work. Aspinwall's services range from simple noise monitoring through noise assessment relating to development proposals, subjective nuisance assessment, research and development and presentation of expert witness evidence. An in-depth experience of local authority requirements and procedures allows for effective presentation of information in written reports, and also as necessary at planning appeals, public enquiries and court hearings. Aspinwall and Company is a member of the Association of Noise Consultants.

Association of Noise Consultants

6 Trap Road, Guilden Morden, Royston, Hertfordshire, SG8 0JE

Tel: 01763 852958
Fax: 01763 853252
E-mail: 10331.1253@compuserve.com

The Association of Noise Consultants aims to improve and control the standard of service offered by its members and to protect the interests of the clients whilst promoting the reputation of the profession. Members provide technical advice on all aspects of acoustics, noise and vibration.

Astro Communications

New Britannia House, Askew Road West, Gateshead, Tyne and Wear, NE8 2PD

Tel: 0191 230 5544
Textphone: 0191 230 5522
Fax: 0191 230 5500

Audifon UK Ltd

Unit 5, Gatwick Metro Centre, Balcombe Road, Horley, Surrey, RH6 9GA

Tel: 01293 821000
Fax: 01293 821010

Agents for: Unitron (Canada); Electone (USA); Sonic 'Natura' (USA).

Equipment

38, 39, 40.

Audio Medical Devices Ltd

Enterprise House, 511-513 Upper Elmers End Road, Beckenham, Kent, BR3 3HF

Tel: 020 8663 0760
Fax: 020 8663 0163
Contact: Harvey Franklin, Hearing Aid Dispenser

Manufactures all types of hearing aids. Its service department can ensure servicing of all makes of hearing aids. Also makes noise generators for use in tinnitus management. The company has a full ear mould lab, is registered to ISO 9002 and EN46002 and is a registered medical devices manufacturer.

Equipment

24, 29, 37, 38, 39, 40, 42, 43, 46, 50.

Audio-Visual Technology Ltd

280 Forest Road, London, E17 5JN

Tel: 020 8520 4321
Fax: 020 8520 9484
E-mail: hire@the-av.co.uk
Contact: David Phillips, Sales Manager

Loop installation and hire. Area covered: UK-wide.

Equipment

1, 2, 4, 5, 7, 8, 9, 11, 18, 24, 25, 26, 27, 28, 29, 30, 31.

Audix Communications

Station Road, Wendens Ambo, Saffron Walden, Essex, CB11 4LG

Tel: 01799 540888

Equipment

22, 25, 27, 28, 29.

AVT Communication Systems Ltd

11 East Butts Road, Rugeley, Staffordshire, WS15 2LU

Tel: 01889 583158
Fax: 01889 583158
E-mail: john@avtcomm.demon.co.uk
Website: www.avtcomm.demon.co.uk

AVT Communication Systems Ltd is a market leader in specialist communication installations for the hard of hearing. John Machin, the founder of the business, has over 18 years of practical and technical experience in the design, specification and installation of audio frequency induction loop systems. The company also provides infra-red, FM and sound field system installations.

Equipment

20, 21, 22, 24, 25, 26, 27, 28, 29, 30, 31.

B & J Stevenson

19 Peverel Road, Cambridgeshire, CB5 8RN

Tel: 01223 241901
Fax: 01223 241901
E-mail: MatthewStevenson1@compuserve.com
Contact: Barry Stevenson, Proprietor

Manufacture, supply and installation of induction loop equipment, sound systems and associated equipment.

Equipment

20, 21, 22, 27, 28, 29.

B and H Designs

2 Pepys Way, Baldock, Hertfordshire, SG7 5AB

Tel: 01462 893039
Fax: 01462 893039
Contact: Brian Howarth, Partner

B and H Designs primarily manufactures a comprehensive range of environmental aids for the hearing impaired. It has a multi-purpose alerting system, a range of alarm clocks (including deafblind), dedicated door bell and baby alarms and a home sleep system. In addition to these items it supplies a number of other products.

Equipment

1, 3, 4, 5, 6, 7, 8, 12, 24, 25, 27.

BCF Technology Ltd

8 Brewster Square, Brucefield Industrial Estate, Livingston, West Lothian, EH54 9BJ

Tel: 01506 460023
Fax: 01506 460045

Datamed Easi-com and Multi-com.
Equipment
18.

BCL Acoustic Services

Acoustics Section, P O Box 5248, 581 Tyburn
Road, Birmingham, B24 9RF
Tel: 0121 303 9900
Fax: 0121 384 9054

BCL offers a wide range of services in the field of
acoustics and noise control specialising in the
following areas: environmental noise and
vibration; building acoustics; occupational noise;
expert testimony and environmental impact
assessment of development proposals. BCL is a
member of the Association of Noise Consultants.

BDP Acoustics Ltd

Sunlight House, Quay Street, Manchester, M60 3JA
Tel: 0161 834 8441
Fax: 0161 832 4280
Contact: David Cash, Office Chairman

BDP Acoustics works alongside architects,
planners and engineers on a variety of projects
including performing arts venues, studios and
multiplex cinemas. Its main areas of consultancy
are: architectural acoustics, environmental noise,
industrial and building services, noise and
vibration and representation at public enquiries.
BDP Acoustics is a member of the Association of
Noise Consultants.

Bell Audio

Owners, High Street, Newburn, Newcastle upon
Tyne, Tyne and Wear, NE15 8LN
Tel: 0191 229 0850
Fax: 0191 229 0984
Contact: Dave Proctor

Loop installation and hire. Areas covered: Tyne
and Wear, Teeside, UK-wide if contract work.

Bernafon UK Ltd

Unit 6, Westerham Trade Centre, The Flyers Way,
Westerham, Kent, TN16 1DE
Tel: 01959 561942
Fax: 01959 561943
Contact: Michael Williams, Sales Manager and
Audiologist

Agents for: Bernafon (Swiss); Bosch (German).
Equipment
18, 37, 38, 39, 40.

Bickerdike Allen Partners

121 Salusbury Road, London, NW6 6RG
Tel: 020 7625 4411
Fax: 020 7625 0250
E-mail: bap@london.demon.co.uk
Contact: D Ward, Company Secretary

BAP's consultancy team offers a complete service,
covering all stages in the design and construction
of buildings, investigation and resolution of
acoustic problems in exisiting buildings.
Commissions are undertaken in the fields of
planning and noise, sound insulation, industrial
noise, architectural acoustics and
electroacoustics. BAP is a member of the
Association of Noise Consultants.

Bilsom

90 High Street, Odiham, Hook, Hampshire, RG29
1LP
Tel: 01256 693200
Fax: 01256 693300
Contact: Gary Fletcher, Director

A brand of Dalloz Safety, Earplugs and Muffs.
Equipment
50.

BioAcoustics Ltd.

26 Guildford Street, Luton, Bedfordshire, LU1 2NR
Tel: 01582 431000
Fax: 01582 488227
E-mail: ol@bioacoustics.com
Contact: Owen Lang, Sales Team

BioAcoustics Ltd provides communication
solutions relating to noise, speech and hearing.
Its aim is to improve intelligibility and
understanding by enhancing the listening
environment. BioAcoustics's bespoke systems are
now widely used in schools, universities,
community halls, council chambers, sports
grounds, places of worship, cinemas, courtrooms,
nursing homes and home entertainment. Opening
hours are 9am to 5pm (Lunch 1 to 2pm).
Equipment
1, 2, 5, 20, 21, 22, 24, 25, 26, 27, 29, 31.

Bird Acoustics

Hemley Hill, Shootacre Lane, Princes Risborough,
Buckinghamshire, HP27 9EH
Tel: 01844 342487
Fax: 01844 342487
E-mail: 100331.1253@compuserve.com
Contact: Susan Bird, Director

12

Bird Acoustics offers a wide range of consultancy services in the field of noise control and acoustics, specialising in acoustics and noise control in buildings. It can provide expert testimony to support planning applications and planning conditions, and can provide measurement, assessment and remedial advice in cases of noise nuisance. It also has extensive experience in workplace noise and in the field of noise-induced hearing loss. Bird Acoustics is a member of the Association of Noise Consultants.

Border Hearing Services

7-13 Lawson Court, Dunbar, East Lothian, EH42 1JT

Tel:	01368 862906
Fax:	01368 864909
Contact:	Graeme Cockburn

Border Hearing Services manufactures ear moulds for the NHS and produces personalised hearing protection. Can also supply environmental aids, loop systems, noise defenders and swim plugs.

British Hearing Aid Manufacturers Association

Knowles Electronic Company, Victoria Road, Burgess Hill, West Sussex, RH15 9LP

Tel:	01444 235432
Fax:	01444 248724
Contact:	A K Grant-Salmon, Chairman

Informal industry association providing platform for UK manufacturers to discuss key industry issues which are in the interests of serving the hard of hearing.

BT Age and Disability

9th Floor, Burne House, Bell Street, London, NW1 5BZ

Tel:	0800 671504
Textphone:	0800 243123
Fax:	020 8205 4853
E-mail:	disability@bt.com
Website:	www.bt.com

BT has a wide range of products and services to make it easier for people to use the phone, whatever the difficulty. A free booklet giving detailed information is available on request. Call free on: 0800 671504 and ask for the 'BT guide for disabled people'.

C & P Hearing Equipment Centre

27 Woodlands Road, Rubery, Rednal, Birmingham, West Midlands, B45 9HA

Tel:	0121 608 1575
Textphone:	0121 628 4771
Fax:	0121 608 1575
E-mail:	colin@whitehouse75.freeserve.co.uk
Website:	www.whitehouse75.freeserve.co.uk
Contact:	Colin Whitehouse

A family business with first-hand experience of the needs of the hearing impaired community and their families. Has a wide and varied range of products on show for customers to try out. This ensures their needs are met to the full. A stockist of most leading brands.

Equipment

1, 2, 3, 4, 5, 6, 7, 8, 9, 12, 13, 16, 18, 20, 21, 22, 23, 24, 25, 26, 27, 29, 30, 32, 34.

C C Consultants

28 Keynshambury Road, Cheltenham, Gloucestershire, GL52 6HB

Tel:	01872 223669
Fax:	01872 223800
E-mail:	100555.3512@compuserve.com
Contact:	David Millner, Sales Team

Sidekick personal attack alarms, magnotherapy products to improve people's health.

Caradon Friedland Ltd

Houldsworth Street, Stockport, Cheshire, SK5 6BP

Tel:	0161 432 0277
Fax:	0161 431 4385
Website:	www.caradon.com
Contact:	Paul Atherton, Electronics Manager

Friedland offers a range of easy-to-operate and install door chimes, and wire-free products that operate on FM radio waves include flashing strobe light unit for RNID members. All products come complete with one-year guarantee and lifetime after-sales support. Just call the technical customer helpline for simple help and advice on: 0161 432 0277, 8am to 5pm.

Equipment

1.

Carter-Voce Ltd

111-113 Chiltern Drive, Berrylands, Surbiton, Surrey, KT5 8LS

Tel:	020 8390 8671
Fax:	020 8390 2383
E-mail:	info@cartervoce.co.uk

Carter-Voce supplies and installs induction loop and sound equipment for permanent or hire installations throughout the UK in all types of environment.

Equipment

25, 26, 27, 28, 29.

Castle Group Ltd

Salter Road, Eastfield, Scarborough, North Yorkshire, YO11 3UZ

Tel: 01723 584250
Fax: 01723 583728
E-mail: sales@castlegroup.co.uk
Website: www.castlegroup.co.uk
Contact: Simon Bull, Sales Team

Castle manufactures a range of accurate, quality sound level meters starting at reasonable prices. Castle audiometry equipment includes the Excalibur audiometer which works via a PC or laptop, giving it the ultimate power and flexibility.

Equipment

48, 50, 51.

CEL Instruments Ltd

35-37 Bury Mead Road, Hitchin, Hertfordshire, SG5 1RT

Tel: 01462 422411
Fax: 01462 422511
Website: www.cel.ltd.uk
Contact: Teresa Horton, Marketing Manager

Sound level meters.

Equipment

46, 48.

Chapman and Smith

Safir Works, South Street, East Hoathly, Lewes, East Sussex, BN8 6EW

Tel: 01825 840323
Fax: 01825 840827
Website: www.chapman.smith.co.uk
Contact: G Mason, Director

Manufacturers of industrial safety equipment which includes a wide range of ear muffs and ear plugs. Literature is available on request.

Equipment

50.

Cirrus Research plc

Acoustic House, Hunmanby Industrial Estate, Hunmanby, Filey, North Yorkshire, YO14 0PH

Tel: 01723 891655
Fax: 01723 891742
E-mail: soler@cirrusresearch.co.uk
Contact: James Tingay, Sales Team

Sound level meters.

Equipment

48.

Civil Engineering Dynamics

83-87 Wallace Crescent, Carshalton, Surrey, SM5 3SU

Tel: 020 8647 1908
Fax: 020 8395 1556
E-mail: ced.co.@virgin.net
Contact: Mr Dudman, Engineer

A firm of noise and vibration consultants dealing with all aspects of monitoring, assessment and control related to a broad range of situations. Civil Engineering Dynamics is a member of the Association of Noise Consultants.

12

Clofield Ltd

St John's Road, Chesterfield, Derbyshire, S41 8PB

Tel: 01246 260045
Textphone: 01246 450789
Fax: 01246 450789
E-mail: clofield.ltd@virgin.net
Contact: Mark Findley, Production Manager

Clofield Ltd designs and manufactures the silent alert paging system for deaf and deafblind people. The system alerts the user of sounds around the home and workplace. A small vibrating pager responds to radio transmitters connected to various sound sources which include doorbells, telephones, and smoke and baby alarms.

Equipment

1, 2, 4, 5, 6, 7, 8, 9.

Cochlear (UK) Ltd

Mill House, 8 Mill Street, London, SE1 2BA

Tel: 020 7231 6323
Textphone: 020 7231 6323
Fax: 020 7231 3371
Website: www.cochlear.com.au
Contact: Rory Kehoe, Sales Team

Nucleus 24 Cochlear Implant System.

Equipment

44.

Cole Jarman Associates

95 The Street, West Horsley, Surrey, KT24 6DD
Tel: 01483 281381
Fax: 01483 281717
E-mail: colejarman@compuserve.com
Contact: Neil Jarman, Partner

Offer expertise and experience in planning and noise, building acoustics, transportation and industrial noise and vibration. Cole Jarman Associates can also provide expert testimony in planning enquiries, licensing and litigation. Cole Jarman Associates is a members of the Association of Noise Consultants.

Colin MacPherson Sound Systems

12 Moyness Park Crescent, Blairgowrie, Perthshire, PH10 6LY
Tel: 01250 873714
Fax: 01250 873714
Contact: Colin MacPherson

Installation, supply and repair of induction loop systems in the home or public buildings. Free demonstrations. Twenty-four-hour answering service.

Equipment

24, 25, 26, 27, 28, 29, 30, 31.

Communication Services

C S House, 32 Arlington Drive, Alvaston, Derby, DE24 0AU
Tel: 01332 751412
Fax: 01332 751412
Contact: B Reid, Director

Loop installation and hire. Areas covered: UK-wide.

Equipment

24, 25, 26, 27, 28, 29, 31.

Communications MVC

Derwen House, Willow Crescent, Five Oak Green, Tonbridge, Kent, TN12 6TD
Tel: 01892 832775
Fax: 01892 836775
E-mail: mvccomms@btconnect.com
Contact: Maurice Van Cooley, Director

Loop installation. Areas covered: London, Kent, East Sussex. Supplies, installs and maintains sound systems, PA systems, CCTV, aerial systems and access controls.

Equipment

8, 21, 25, 27, 29.

Connevans Ltd

54 Albert Road North, Reigate, Surrey, RH2 9YR
Tel: 01737 247571
Textphone: 01737 243134
Fax: 01737 223475
E-mail: mary@connevans.com
Website: www.connevans.com
Contact: Mary Cann, Director

Connevans is a major UK manufacturer and supplier of a wide range of equipment for the deaf and hearing impaired. With over 30 years' experience of specialising in meeting the needs of the deaf community, its comprehensive mail order catalogue covers everything from hearing aid care kits to personal vibrating pagers and radio microphone systems.

Equipment

1, 2, 3, 4, 5, 6, 7, 8, 9, 12, 13, 20, 21, 22, 23, 24, 25, 26, 27, 32, 33, 47, 48, 52, 53.

Conrad Acoustics

13 Nash Green, Bromley, Kent, BR1 4ED
Tel: 020 8466 1433
Fax: 020 8466 6418
E-mail: acoustix@conrad.demon.co.uk
Contact: Andrew Conrad, Director

Conrad Acoustics provides acoustics design services offering special expertise in performing arts auditoria, media studios and post-production facilities, including: feasibility studies, sound distribution analysis, reverberation analysis, sound insulation and vibration isolation, specification, site monitoring and field testing for quality assurance. The practice provides noise and vibration control design services for industrial and commercial applications, with special expertise in listed and historic buildings and environmental noise impact assessments for town and country planning applications, appeals and inquiries. The practice undertakes field measurements of noise and vibration for fault diagnosis, community, traffic, environmental and industrial noise surveys. Conrad Acoustics is a member of the Association of Noise Consultants.

Contacta Communication Systems

50 Churchill Square, Kings Hill, West Malling, Kent, ME19 4YU
Tel: 01732 223900
Fax: 01732 223909
Website: www.contacta.co.uk
Contact: Andrew Thomas, Sales Director

Equipment

23, 25, 27, 28.

D G Controls
Cadley Hill Road, Swadlincote, Derbyshire, DE11 9TB

Tel: 01283 550850
Fax: 01283 550776
E-mail: mail@deegee.com
Website: www.deegee.com
Contact: D Guyett, Managing Director

Flashing beacon lamps and tower beacon indicators with rotating, xenon strobe, pulsed and static filament or LED interiors. Beacon lamp/sounder combined units. Telephone ring-initiated flashing beacons, designed for industrial, commercial, community welfare and other applications where a visual indication of a ringing telephone is required.

Equipment
9.

Danavox (Great Britain) Ltd
6 Christchurch Road, Northampton, NN1 5LL

Tel: 01604 636351
Fax: 01604 250957
E-mail: danavox_gb@compuserve.com
Website: www.DANAVOX.com
            www.MADSEN.com
Contact: Trevor Baillie, Sales and Marketing
            Manager
Tel: 01604 623791

Danavox-Madsen is a major supplier of hearing instruments. It is the sole supplier of the full range of hearing testing equipment from Madsen Electronics. Together with EMIS of Glasgow, which is its calibration service and repair partners, now provides a full range of products and services to the hearing impaired community.

Equipment
37, 38, 39, 40, 42.

Deaf Awareness Technology
59 Hennings Park Road, Oakdale, Poole, Dorset, BH15 3QX

Tel: 01202 682795
Fax: 01202 682795
E-mail: paul@deaftech.force9.co.uk
Website: www.deaftech.force9.co.uk
Contact: Linda Cox, Sales Team

Supplier and installer of equipment for people who are hearing impaired to include assistive devices (three types), loop amplifiers for home use, reception desk, office and large loops for churches, and public buildings. Visual alerts for doorbells, phone, intercom, child alert and nurse call.

Equipment
1, 2, 3, 5, 6, 7, 8, 9, 12, 22, 23, 24, 25, 26, 27.

Delphi Tool Company Ltd
Slackcote Lane, Delph, Oldham, Lancashire, OL3 5TW

Tel: 01457 971666

Water proof radio link for sports training/coaching.

Delta Design
Primrose Hill, Kings Langley, Hertfordshire, WD4 8HD

Tel: 01923 269522
Fax: 01923 260167
E-mail: sales@deltadesign.co.uk
Website: www.deltadesign.co.uk
Contact: Janet Walsby, Sales Director

Delta Design is Europe's largest manufacturer of Xenon beacons. Included in the range are small, low-profile Xenon beacons for security and fire systems, door entry controls, warden-controlled monitors and alarm panels. The latest product, to partner the Ministrobe, is the Microstrobe, a small, compact Xenon flashing panel-mount beacon.

Equipment
5.

Dennis R Robinson and Associates
169 Sherwood Avenue, Northampton, NN2 8TB

Tel: 01604 843807
Fax: 01604 843807
E-mail: denis-rr@skynet.co.uk
Contact: Dennis Robinson, Director

Specialist in acoustical design and in the control of noise and vibration, offering professional advice, appraisal and assistance including: architectural acoustic surveys, design and remediation; building services noise and vibration control; construction noise surveys and predictions; entertainment noise evaluation; environmental noise and vibration studies; machinery noise and vibration nuisance investigations; occupational noise and vibration assessments; planning and development noise evaluation and expert witness testimony at hearings and tribunals. Dennis R Robinson and Associates is a member of the Association of Noise Consultants.

12

DM Marketing

PO Box 1200, Benfleet, Essex, SS7 1JZ
Tel: 01268 565888

DSN Computers

10 The Hollies, Welwyn Garden City, Hertfordshire, AL8 7TA
Tel: 0941 115927
Textphone: 0941 102600 ext 115927 T pager
Fax: 0870 0553571
E-mail: dsn@daveysn.demon.co.uk
Contact: Davey North, Managing Director

DSN Computers is run by a deaf businessman to supply computers and related accessories. Also runs at many computer fairs in south-east England. Please call for details.

Dunvegan Ltd

Dunvegan House, Great Howard Street, Liverpool, Merseyside, L3 7EU
Tel: 0151 207 4069
Fax: 0151 207 2604
Contact: Jason Longworth

Dunvegan is a specialist communications company offering a wide range of services for a variety of communication requirements. Services offered include: advice, design, consultancy, supply, installation and maintenance of both induction loops and infra-red systems for commercial installation nationwide.

Equipment

5, 8, 12, 13, 14, 16, 18, 19, 21, 22, 23, 24, 25.

EAR Division

First Avenue, Poynton Industrial Estate, Poynton, Stockport, Cheshire, SK12 1YJ
Tel: 01625 878320
Fax: 01625 877348
See also under: Aearo Ltd.

Equipment

20, 23.

Eastfield-Rossmill Ltd (Technical Services)

Elesmere House, 40 Southampton Road, Ringwood, Hampshire, BH24 1JD
Tel: 01425 478000
Fax: 01425 478391
Contact: Colin Harrison, Technical Director

Loop installation and hire. Areas covered: Midlands, London, south-east and south-west England.

Equipment

2, 8, 9, 20, 21, 22, 24, 25, 26, 27, 28, 29, 30, 31, 48.

Easylink Electronics

Factory 7, Grange Road, Geddington, Kettering, Northamptonshire, NN14 1AL
Tel: 01536 744788
Fax: 01536 744788
Contact: Mike Dines, Director

Equipment

1, 2, 3, 4, 5, 6, 7, 8, 9, 11, 12, 19, 20, 21, 22.

Electrical and Acoustic Services Ltd

105 Fermor Way, Crowborough, East Sussex, TN6 3BH
Tel: 01892 661950
Fax: 01892 667641
Contact: R Howard

Loop installation. Areas covered: London, south-east England.

Equipment

9, 25, 27, 28.

Electronic Services

35 Vicarage Road, Wednesfield, Wolverhampton, West Midlands, WV11 1SE
Tel: 01902 726846
Fax: 01902 727483
E-mail: terry.electronicservices@alkomm.co.uk
Contact: Terry Billau, Partner

Electronic Services is a long-established sound systems contractor and specialises in induction loop and infra-red hearing aid systems. Clients include many local authorities and public bodies (except churches), and systems for hire are usually available.

Equipment

24, 25, 26, 27, 28, 29, 30, 31.

Elite-Sound Communications

Wormald Park, Grimshaw Lane, Newton Heath, Manchester, M40 2WL
Tel: 0161 455 4242
Fax: 0161 455 4349
Contact: Paul Enderby

Loop installation and hire. Infra-red installation and hire service of existing installation. Voice alarm and public address.

12

Equipment

25, 26, 27, 28, 29, 31.

Emtec Laboratories

Spirella Building, Bridge Road, Letchworth,
Hertfordshire, SG6 4ET
Tel: 01462 684293

Entec UK Ltd

Gables House, Kenilworth Road, Leamington Spa,
Warwickshire, CV32 6JX
Tel: 01926 435990
Fax: 01926 435991
E-mail: wilsk@entecuk.co.uk
Contact: Ken Taylor, Director

Entec is an international, multi-disciplinary
environmental consultancy that specialises in
managing business issues. Entec is a member of
the Association of Noise Consultants.

Environmental Resources Management Ltd

8 Cavendish Square, London, W1M 0ER
Tel: 020 7465 7200
Fax: 020 7465 7250
E-mail: smd@ermuk.com
Website: www.ermuk.com
Contact: Roger Barracliffe, Director

ERM is a multi-disciplinary consultancy focusing
on the environment, dealing with technical
projects and policy issues. ERM offers expertise
across the range of environmental disciplines, as
well as occupational health-and-risk and hazard
assessment. The practice has worked a great deal
in the field of environmental acoustics, having
undertaken many evaluations of the construction
and operation of transportation sources (roads,
rail, aircraft), industrial sources, residential
developments and recreational noise for both
public and private sector clients. ERM can
undertake occupational noise-building acoustic
work, drafting regulations and expert evidence for
public enquiry and litigation work. ERM is a
member of the Association of Noise Consultants.

Equipment for Equality

20 Fenlake Business Centre, Fengate,
Peterborough, Cambridgeshire, PE1 5BQ
Tel: 01733 893006
Textphone: 01733 893006
Fax: 01733 893018

Equipment for Equality provide a one-stop shop
for a wide range of domestic and industrial
assistive products. EQ also has a national

installation service for induction loops, paging and
infra-red systems. Please contact them for a free
catalogue showing the latest alerting, listening
and telephone products.

Equipment

1, 2, 3, 4, 5, 6, 7, 8, 9, 12, 13, 20, 21, 22, 23, 24,
25, 26, 27, 29, 30, 31, 46.

Equus Partnership, The

Park House, Greenhill Crescent, Watford,
Hertfordshire, WD1 8QU
Tel: 01923 213625
Fax: 01923 213863
Contact: Chris Hookway, Partner

An experienced independent consultancy
providing practical advice in architectural
acoustics, building acoustics, environmental
noise, noise at work, acoustic testing, industrial
noise and expert testimony. The Equus
Partnership is a member of the Association of
Noise Consultants.

European Captioning Institute

17-19 Foley Street, London, W1P 7LH
Tel: 020 7323 4657
Fax: 020 7323 4658
E-mail: caption@compuserve.com
Contact: J Higham, Office Manager

Aims to facilitate access to video home
entertainment for deaf and hard of hearing
people. Provides 'open' subtitles as well as
'closed-captions' (hidden subtitles). Believes that
all television and video programming should be
accessible.

Evets Communications Ltd

Enfield House, 303 Burton Road, Derby, DE23 6AG
Tel: 01332 363981
Textphone: 01332 363981
Fax: 01332 293267
E-mail: deaf-alerter.com
Contact: Tony Eyre, Sales Manager

Deaf Alert.

Equipment

8.

Ferrosound

Unit 3, Enterprise Complex, 24 Walmgate, York,
YO1 2TJ
Tel: 01904 610110
Textphone: 01904 626623
Fax: 01904 640058
Contact: M Holdsworth

Loop installation. Areas covered: 50-mile radius of
York. Infra-red listening devices and audio-
induction loops.

Fire Alarm Installations (UK) Ltd

Pound Place, Mill Lane, Poutridge Green,
Horsham, West Sussex
Tel: 01403 711224

Fishwick, John L

27 Holbeck Avenue, Blackpool, Lancashire, FY4
4LS
Tel: 01253 761545
Fax: 01253 300792

Loop installation. Public address consultant.
Areas: Lancashire, Cumbria.
Equipment
24, 25, 27, 29, 30, 31.

Fleming and Barron

Unit A2, Fourth Floor, Linton House, 39-51
Highgate Road, London, NW5 1RT
Tel: 020 7482 4030
Fax: 020 7284 1239
E-mail: fandb@dbf-acoustics.demon.co.uk

Consultants in noise and vibration control, sound
insulation and acoustics related to buildings,
building services, building technology,
transportation and planning. The practice
specialises in the acoustic design of arts and
leisure facilities for the community, schools and
colleges and in railway noise and vibration. There
are laboratory facilities for acoustic model testing
of sound propagation and auditorium acoustics at
1:50 scale. Fleming and Barron is a member of the
Association of Noise Consultants.

Fulford Sound Service

13 Alexandra Road, Capel-le-Ferne, Folkestone,
Kent, CT18 7LN
Tel: 01303 249999
Fax: 01303 249999
Contact: Bill Fulford

Loop installation. Areas covered: Kent, Sussex.

Fulleon Synchrobell

40 Springvale Industrial Estate, Cwmbran, NP44
5BD
Tel: 01633 872131
Fax: 01633 866346
E-mail: sales@fulleon.co.uk
Contact: Stuart Strong, Director

Supplier of industrial fire alarm systems.
Equipment
9.

GB Electronics Ltd

287 Oldham Road, Royton, Oldham, Lancashire,
OL2 6AJ
Tel: 0161 652 3888
Fax: 0161 652 3887
Contact: Gordon Buckley, Proprietor
Equipment
26.

Gordon Morris Ltd

Twyford House, Ham Street, Baltonsborough,
Glastonbury, Somerset, BA6 8QG
Tel: 01458 850396
Textphone: 01458 850396
Fax: 01458 850652
E-mail: info@gordonmorris.co.uk
Contact: Julie Middleton, Business Development

Specialist suppliers, installers and manufacturers
of audio induction loop, infra-red and sound
reinforcement systems, both domestic and
commercial. From 30 square metres to 650 square
metres, includes car loop kit, conference folder-
free loan service, across the counter loop: hire of
portable commercial loop; also supplier of Nokia
Mobile Inductive Loopset. Its aim is to enhance
quality of life for those with a hearing situation.
Equipment
1, 6, 7, 8, 9, 12, 13, 16, 18, 20, 21, 22, 24, 25, 26,
27, 28, 29, 30, 31.

Grainger Communications

Unit 29b, Gortrush Industrial Estate, Omagh,
County Tyrone, BT78 5EJ
Tel: 028 8224 4800
Fax: 028 8224 4810
E-mail: gcom@iol.ie
Contact: Martin Grainger, Proprietor

Loop installation. Areas: Northern Ireland,
Republic of Ireland.

Equipment

22, 24, 25, 26, 27, 28, 29.

Guymark UK

Indalo House, 50 Heath Road, Caterham, Surrey, CR3 5RQ

Tel: 01883 346969
Fax: 01883 346979
E-mail: Guymarkuk.dle@btinternet.com
Contact: David Lloyd-Evans, Director

Sound censors custom-made in the canal hearing protectors.

Equipment

48, 49, 50, 51.

Hann Tucker Associates

Duke House, 1-2 Duke Street, Woking, Surrey, GU21 5BA

Tel: 01483 770595
Fax: 01483 729565
E-mail: hanntucker@aol.com

Hann Tucker Associates can advise on all aspects of applied acoustics, noise and vibration control, associated with, in particular, architecture and buildings; building services; industry; the performing arts; transportation and the environment. Consultants are available as expert witnesses for public enquiries and other legal proceedings. Hann Tucker Associates is a member of the Association of Noise Consultants.

Hearing Aid Technology Ltd

Unit 6, Borers Yard, Borers Arms Road, Copthorne, Crawley, West Sussex, RH10 3LH

Tel: 01342 717073
Fax: 01342 717074
E-mail: hat@hearing.aid.tech.demon.co.uk
Contact: Ian Uffingdell, Sales Team

Agent for Rexton Hearing Instruments.

Equipment

38, 39, 40, 43.

Hearing Products International

95 Heaton Road, Stockport, Cheshire, SK4 4JH

Tel: 0161 442 3724
Fax: 0161 442 4600
E-mail: hpi.ok@ibm.net
Contact: Chris Rohde, Managing Director

HPI Ltd is a progressive and expanding company that designs and distributes a wide range of its own specialised products to meet the needs of the hearing impaired community. Products include state-of-the-art personal listeners, a vibrating alarm clock, a home loop system, a personal infra-red system and a speech amplifier.

Equipment

3, 7, 20, 21, 22, 23, 24, 25, 26, 27, 28, 29, 30, 32, 48.

Hector Tanner & Co Ltd

23-24 Barnack Trading Centre, Novers Hill, Bristol, Avon, BS3 5QE

Tel: 0117 966 1751
Textphone: 0117 966 7303
Fax: 0117 966 7404
Contact: Andrew Tanner, Director

Hector Tanner & Co Ltd manufactures the Mountcastle Silent Bell range of visual door systems for the deaf and hard of hearing people. The comprehensive range includes add-on units for telephones and door entry systems and the SMA2 Fire Alarm Control Panel.

Equipment

1, 2, 5, 6, 7, 9.

Hepworth Acoustics Ltd

St James Court, Wilderspool Causeway, Warrington, WA4 6PS

Tel: 01925 650360
Fax: 01925 632284
E-mail: hepworth_acoustics@poboxes.com
Contact: Peter Hepworth, Director

Hepworth Acoustics specialises in providing solutions for planning and noise nuisance problems in the areas of entertainment, environmental, industrial and transportation noise, in addition to dealing with all aspects of building acoustics. Hepworth Acoustics is a member of the Association of Noise Consultants.

Hi Linc Brunel Technic Ltd

56 Ravenswood Road, Redland, Bristol, Avon, BS6 6BP

Tel: 01272 245828

Hilltop Audio Supplies

40 Trowell Park Drive, Trowell, Nottingham, NG9 3RA

Tel: 0115 939 4672
Contact: David Wright, Proprietor

Our range of combined sound/loop equipment was developed to allow churches to have worthwhile dual systems at any level of complexity, without cost being the prohibitive factor. Though unconventional, these methods now form the most highly developed and cost-effective systems specifically designed for churches.

Equipment

24, 25, 26, 27, 28, 29.

Howard Leight

Clarence Mill, Clarence Road, Bollington, Macclesfield, Cheshire, SK10 5JZ

Tel: 01625 560518
Fax: 01625 560519
Website: www.HowardLeight.com

Equipment

50.

HPS Protection

Churchgate Mill Complex, Lavenders Brow, Stockport, Cheshire, SK1 1YW

Tel: 0161 477 9490

Hutchison Paging (UK) Ltd

Telesales Department, The Chase, John Tate Road, Foxholes Business Park, Hertford, SG13 7NN

Tel: 0800 282826 ext 178
Textphone: 0992 502020
Fax: 0992 502233

Hutchison Paging is a paging network operator. It provides a national subscription service and rents or sells alphanumeric and numeric pagers for use on its network. Text messages are handled via its bureau, which is manned 24 hours per day. A variety of supplementary services and support packages are available.

Equipment

16, 19.

HW Audio Ltd

174-176 St Georges Road, Bolton, Lancashire, BL1 2NZ

Tel: 01204 385199
Fax: 01204 364057
Website: www.karaokeshop.com
Contact: Chris Harfield, Director

Supply and installation of induction loop systems, public address and other hearing assistance systems. Equipment for permanent installation or short-term hire. Upgrades to present installations undertaken.

Equipment

24, 25, 26, 27, 28, 29, 31.

HW Music Centre Ltd (Wightsound)

3 Baneswell Road, Newport, Gwent, NP9 4BP

Tel: 01633 262023

Loop installation and hire. Areas covered: Wales and western England

John Ward & Sons (Stourbridge) Ltd

P O Box 12, Gainsborough Trading Estate, Rufford Road, Stourbridge, West Midlands, DY9 7NB

Tel: 01384 374284
Fax: 01384 395368
E-mail: admin@wardglore.co.uk
Contact: David Guest, Director

Equipment

50.

JSP Consultants

2 Millards Way, Upton Scudamore, Warminster, Wiltshire, BA12 0DR

Tel: 01985 847405
Fax: 01985 847405
Contact: John Pollard, Director

Noise and vibration consultancy is offered in the areas of environmental issues, planning requirements, construction site and traffic noise predictions, factory noise studies and vibration monitoring. Particular expertise exists in structure-borne noise transmission, statistical energy analysis modelling, aircraft and helicopter noise studies. JSP is a member of the Association of Noise Consultants.

Keith Monks Sound Systems

29 Tower Park, Fowey, Cornwall, PL23 1JD

Tel: 01726 833783
Fax: 01726 833800
Contact: Keith Monks

Well-established company supplying and installing loop and sound systems mainly in churches all over the UK. Has a chain of approved dealers in areas not easily covered. A free advisory service is available. Export service with agents in various countries. On approved list as an installer, with organisations and public bodies.

Equipment

20, 21, 22, 23, 24, 25, 26, 27, 28, 29, 31, 46, 48, 53.

Keith Monks Sound Systems (Hampshire)

Unit 7, Beechnut Industrial Estate, Beechnut Road, Aldershot, Hampshire, GU12 4JA

Tel: 01252 334123
Fax: 01726 833800
Contact: Keith Monks, Director

Has a small loop for hire. Areas covered: UK-wide.

Ken Dibble Acoustics

P O Box 541, Rugby, Warwickshire, CV21 3YJ

Tel: 01788 541133
Fax: 01788 541314
E-mail: KDAcoustic@aol.com
Contact: Ken Dibble, Practice Principal

Established in 1977, KDA is an independent consultancy in general acoustics, noise control and noise exposure, specialising (but by no means limited to) the performing and recorded arts, entertainment and leisure activities. The practice principal is a Chartered Engineer, Fellow of the Institute of Acoustics and Member of the Academy of Experts and has investigated and provided expert evidence in industrial injury legislation arising from hearing loss claims.

Laboratories MXM

2720 Chemin de Saint Bernard, 06224 Vallauris Cedex, France

Tel: 0033 4 93 95 18 18
Fax: 0033 4 93 95 38 01
Contact: David Veran

Manufacturing and commercialisation of fully digital multi-channel cochlear implants, brain stem implants and accessories (antenna, cables, FM system adaptor, programming system and software).

Equipment

44.

Lavis Medical Systems

Langdon Road, Bradworthy, Holsworthy, Devon, EX22 7SF

Tel: 01409 241655
Fax: 01409 241608
Contact: Helen Belcher, National Hearing Aid Adviser and Sales Manager, Philips and LMS Products
Tel: 01704 880859 (24-hour ansaphone)

Agent for: Philips (Holland); Coselgi (Italy); 3M Products. Opening hours are: 8.30am to 5pm Monday to Friday. Lavis is based in Devon but has other retail activities in Surrey, Sheffield and the Midlands.

Equipment

37, 38, 39, 40, 43.

Leventhall, Dr H G

150 Craddocks Avenue, Ashtead, Surrey, KT21 1NL

Tel: 01372 272682
Fax: 01372 273406
E-mail: h.g.leventhall@dial.pipex.com

Dr Leventhall has long experience in noise and vibration control, including general work in environmental, building, transport and industrial noise and vibration, litigation and as an expert witness. He also has special expertise in low-frequency noise and active control of noise and vibration. Training course in acoustics and noise can be provided. Dr Leventhall is a member of the Association of Noise Consultants.

Location Sound

53 Fallodon Way, Henleaze, Bristol, Avon, BS9 4HT

Tel: 0117 962 4411
Fax: 0117 962 4411
E-mail: locationsound@btconnect.com
Contact: Nick Langley

Assists organisations and individuals who can benefit from audio frequency induction loop and infra-red systems. Happy to discuss requirements and install systems in churches, shops, offices, nursing homes, theatres and public buildings throughout the south of England and south Wales.

Equipment

1, 5, 6, 7, 8, 20, 21, 22, 24, 25, 26.

MAR Design Services

7 Elmscroft Gardens, Potters Bar, Hertfordshire, EN6 2JP

Tel: 01707 658543
Fax: 01707 658543

Equipment

1, 5, 9.

Marconi Hillend Enterprise

AF18, Taxi Way, Hillend Industrial Park, Hillend, Dunfermline, Fife, KY11 5JE

Tel: 01383 823008

Phone amplifiers.

Martec Environmental Engineering

Gerrard Place, East Gillibrands Estate,
Skelmersdale, Lancashire, WN8 9SU

Tel: 01695 725121
Fax: 01695 50219
E-mail: noise@globalnet.co.uk
Contact: Mel Kenyon, Partner

Martec can advise on the following: noise and vibration assessments, surveys, planning applications and litigation support. Building acoustics - insulation and property development. Environmental noise impact, industrial and power generation projects; noise at work assessments and residential complaints. Martec is a member of the Association of Noise Consultants.

Equipment

46, 48, 50.

McDonald, J M, and Associates

Unit 13C5, Balmakeith Industrial Estate, Nairn,
IV12 5QW

Tel: 01667 451717
Fax: 01667 451717
E-mail: mcdonassoc@clara.net
Contact: John McDonald
Tel: 01463 231314

Provides a service in the supply, installation and repair of assistive listening and visual alert systems to the hard of hearing throughout Scotland.

Equipment

1, 2, 4, 5, 6, 8, 11, 20, 21, 22, 24, 25, 26, 27, 28, 29, 30, 31, 46, 48.

Med-El UK Ltd

Bridge Mills, Holmfirth, Huddersfield, West
Yorkshire, HD7 2TW

Tel: 01484 686223
Fax: 01484 686056
Website: www.medel.com
Contact: Cassandra Brown, Business Manager

High Rate Combi 40+ Cochlear Implants.

Equipment

41, 43, 44.

MHC Electronics

51 Kempton Grove, Cheltenham, Gloucestershire,
GL51 0JX

Tel: 01242 227754
Fax: 01242 227754

Millbank Electronics

Bellbrook Industrial Estate, Uckfield, East Sussex,
TN22 1QL

Tel: 01825 764811
Fax: 01825 761620
E-mail: millbank-
            electronics@compuserve.com
Contact: Sarah Harwood, Products Manager

Millgrant Wells Ltd

P O Box 3, 7 Stanley Road, Rugby, Warwickshire,
CV21 3UE

Tel: 01788 561185
Fax: 01788 543218

Speech/auditory trainers.

Moflash Co Ltd

Unit 18, Klaxon Tysley Industrial Estate, 751
Warwick Road, Tyseley, Birmingham, West
Midlands, B11 2HA

Tel: 0121 707 6681
Fax: 0121 707 8305
Contact: A Evans, Chairman

Equipment

6.

Moir Hands and Associates

Bridge House, 1 Station Road, Amersham,
Buckinghamshire, HP7 0BQ

Tel: 01494 725530
Fax: 01494 432210
E-mail: project@moirhands.co.uk
Contact: Steven Moore, Partner, Noel Hill
            Partners

The practice provides independent specialist advice in all aspects of acoustics, noise and vibration control, particularly in the areas of planning, industry and commerce and leisure. Moir, Hands and Associates is a member of the Association of Noise Consultants.

Motion Media Technology

Horton Hall, Horton, Bristol, BS37 6QN

Tel: 01454 338506
Textphone: 01454 338590
Videotel: 01454 338537 9am to 7pm
Fax: 01454 313678
E-mail: kenb@motionmedia.co.uk
Website: www.motionmedia.co.uk
Contact: Ken Burgin, Videophone contact

The design and supply of videophones and video conferencing systems. These use the latest technology and use the established international H 320 standard to provide high performance video over ISDN and BT highway lines. Visit the Website for more details.

Equipment

14.

MTL International Ltd

Unit 6, Crusader Industrial Estate, Hermitage Road, London, N4 1LZ

Tel: 020 8800 8090
Fax: 020 8890 6465
Contact: WRL Phillips, Sales Manager

Loop installation. Areas covered: London and south-east England, but UK-wide if contract work.

Equipment

20, 21, 22, 25, 26, 27, 29, 31.

Mustang Communications

Industrial Estate, Cayton Low Road, Scarborough, North Yorkshire, YO11 3UT

Tel: 01723 582555
Fax: 01723 581673
Contact: Martin Tetley, Sales and Marketing Manager

Equipment

26, 29.

NES Acoustics

Kylemore Road, Dublin 12, Eire

Tel: 00353 1 450 4922
Fax: 00353 1 450 4929

NES specialises in the areas of architectural and building acoustics, industrial noise control, building services noise, electroacoustics, noise at work assessments, integrated pollution control licensing, environmental impact assessments and litigation. NES is a member of the Association of Noise Consultants.

Newland Electronics Ltd

The Exchange, Benton Road, Benton, Newcastle Upon Tyne, Tyne and Wear, NE7 7XB

Tel: 0191 215 0088
Fax: 0191 266 4298
Contact: Adrian Stewart

Loop installation and hire. Areas covered: England and Scotland.

Newtech International

Southern House, 48 Old Milton Road, New Milton, Hampshire, BH25 6DX

Tel: 01425 620210
Textphone: 01425 620210
Fax: 01425 638443
Contact: Liz Foot, Office Manager

Provides a complete service for its customers. Through its own design and manufacturing facility it offers a wide range of products, from television aids to sophisticated pocket pagers. If you need help or just advice please call and ask for a copy of the free brochure.

Equipment

1, 2, 3, 4, 5, 6, 7, 8, 9, 12, 17, 20, 21, 22, 23, 24, 25, 26, 27, 29, 30, 31.

Niagara Manufacturing Ltd

Colomendy Industrial Estate, Rhyl Road, Denbigh, LL16 5TS

Tel: 01745 813666
Fax: 01745 816106
Contact: Peter Nelson, Sales and Marketing Manager

Manufactures a range of adjustable beds, reclining chairs and portable equipment fitted with Niagara cycloid action massage. Also manufactures a vibrating alarm designed to alert deaf people when their urgent attention is required. The Vibralarm range also offers an alarm clock for the deaf and hard of hearing.

Equipment

3, 6, 7.

Nicolet Biomedical

Nicolet House, Budbrooke Industrial Estate, Budbrooke Road, Warwick, CV34 5XH

Tel: 01926 494111
Fax: 01926 402262
E-mail: paul-wainwright@dial.pipex.com
Contact: Paul Wainwright, Sales Manager (UK)

Nicolet Biomedical manufactures, sells and supports a range of diagnostic instruments for auditory evoked potential and vestibular testing.

Noise Advisory Services

Thetford Road, Coney, Weston, Bury St Edmunds, Suffolk, IP31 1DN

Tel: 01359 221311
Fax: 01359 221824
E-mail: NoiseInfo@aol.com
Contact: Stephen Grundy, Director

12

NAS is an independent acoustics consultancy practice, advising on all noise, vibration and acoustics matters. It has particular expertise in building and architectural acoustics, noise nuisance investigation, industrial acoustics, on-site acoustic testing and noise/vibration monitoring. It frequently provides expert testimony to planning enquiries and court hearings.

Northern Acoustics

117 Townhead, Kirkintilloch, Glasgow, Lanarkshire, G66 1NX

Tel:	0141 776 2556
Textphone:	0141 775 2365
Fax:	0141 775 2365
E-mail:	northern-acoustics@wiz.net.uk
Website:	www.wiz.net.uk/northern-acoustics
Contact:	K Monroe

Textphones, phone flash. Mr Monroe is a registered hearing aid dispenser and is available for consultation from 9.15am to 5pm Monday to Friday, other times by appointment. He is able to service all makes of hearing aid and will undertake home visits.

Equipment

1, 2, 3, 4, 5, 6, 7, 8, 9, 11, 12, 18, 21, 22, 23, 24, 25, 26, 27, 29, 30, 32, 37, 38, 39, 40, 42, 43.

Oscar Faber Acoustics

Marlborough House, Upper Marlborough Road, St Albans, Hertfordshire, AL1 3UT

Tel:	020 8784 5784
Fax:	020 8784 5700
E-mail:	enquiries@faber-e.oscarfaber.co.uk
Website:	www.oscarfaber.co.uk
Contact:	John Lloyd, Associate Director

Services offered include acoustic design advice in respect to medium and large scale building projects with particular emphasis on development in acoustically difficult environments. Noise prediction for control in building services design, industrial noise emission, vibration measurement and environmental noise issues also receive particular emphasis. Oscar Faber Acoustics is a member of the Association of Noise Consultants.

Oticon Ltd

P O Box 20, Hamilton, Lanarkshire, ML3 7QE

Tel:	01698 283363
Fax:	01698 284308
E-mail:	oticonuk@dial.pipex.com
Contact:	Alison Miller, Customer Support Manager

Equipment

37, 38, 39, 40, 43.

Outside In (Cambridge) Ltd

Unit 21, Scotland Road Estate, Dry Drayton, Cambridge, CB3 8AT

Tel:	01954 211955
Fax:	01954 211956
E-mail:	info@outsidein.co.uk
Website:	www.outsidein.co.uk

Outside In specialises in all things concerning the body clock, including SAD (winter depression), shiftwork, jetlag and some sleep disorders. The Natural Alarm Clock copies a sunrise to use light to wake people up. Most users are not hearing impaired.

Equipment

3.

Oxford Sound Company, The

Unit 11, Threshers Yard, Kingham, Oxfordshire, OX7 6YF

Tel:	01608 659025
Fax:	01608 659806
E-mail:	soundco@btinternet.com
Contact:	Andrew Riley

A reputable installer of induction loops for all public buildings. An established business with an excellent client base. Nationwide installation service.

Equipment

25, 26, 27, 29, 31.

Page One (System Technology)

78 Glebe Lane, Maidstone, Kent, ME16 9BA

Tel:	01622 728200
Textphone:	01622 720490
Fax:	01622 720950
Contact:	Chris Taylor, Managing Director

Distribution and public address, inductive loop, CCTV and door entry equipment. The design and installation of public address, speech reinforcement, inductive loop and CCTV systems.

12

Equipment

8, 22, 24, 25, 26, 27, 28, 29.

Palantype Possum Controls Ltd

8 Farmborough Close, Aylesbury Vale Industrial Park, Stocklake, Aylesbury, Buckinghamshire, HP20 1DQ
Tel: 01296 481591
Textphone: 01296 393223
Fax: 01296 394349
Contact: Philip Robinson, Director

Palantype keyboards.

PAS Sound Engineering Ltd

Unit 7, 92 Liverpool Road North, Maghull, Liverpool, Merseyside, L31 2HN
Tel: 0151 526 7924
Fax: 0151 526 5553
Contact: J Vaudrey, Managing Director

PAS Sound Engineering is a specialist audio company providing the design, installation and maintenance of commercial and professional audio systems including induction loops. The company has numerous clients including government agencies, local authorities and other organisations.

Equipment

25, 26, 27, 28, 29, 31.

PC Werth Ltd

Audiology House, 45 Nightingale Lane, London, SW12 8SP
Tel: 020 8675 5151
Fax: 020 8675 7577
E-mail: info@pcwerth.co.uk
Website: www.pcwerth.co.uk
Contact: Andrew Taylor, Director, Special
                  Instruments Division

Agents for: Phonak; Widex. Consumer Information Freephone for public enquiries about hearing aids: 0800 454338. Opening times are 9am to 5pm, Monday to Friday.

Equipment

20, 21, 22, 23, 24, 25, 26, 37, 38, 39, 40, 41, 42, 43, 46, 47, 48, 49, 50, 51, 52, 53.

Permic Emergency Lifting Ltd

P O Box 3, Chesterfield, Derbyshire, S40 1EX
Tel: 01246 270914
Fax: 01246 275879

Equipment

1, 2, 9.

Peter Knight Industries

10 New Farm Lane, Nuthall, Nottinghamshire, NG16 1DY
Tel: 0115 938 3551
Textphone: 0115 919 6028
Fax: 0115 938 3551
Contact: Peter Knight, Sales Department

Designers and manufacturers of visual/tactile aids for deaf people. An extensive range of approved products respond to doorbells, telephones, smoke alarms, alarm clocks, door entry-phones and baby alarms. Available for hard wired and remote control installations. Special adaptions offered to meet individual needs.

Equipment

1, 2, 3, 4, 5, 6, 7, 9.

Philip Dunbavin Acoustics Ltd

Vincent House, 212 Manchester Road, Warrington, Cheshire, WA1 3BD
Tel: 01925 418188
Fax: 01925 417201
E-mail: 100625.1040@compuserve.com
Contact: Andrew Raymond

PDA offers a wide range of services including design work and troubleshooting in the following areas: occupational noise, architectural and mechanical services, environmental noise, legal services, quiet product development and electro-acoustics. PDA is a member of the Association of Noise Consultants.

Phillips Communication and Security Systems

Cromwell Road, Cambridgeshire, CB1 3HE
Tel: 01223 245191
Fax: 01223 413551
E-mail: neil.almond@pp-cmb.ie.phillips.com
Contact: Sandra Fernie, Personnel Officer

Equipment

25, 27, 31.

Phoenix Accessories (Safety) Ltd

Waterloo Mills, Waterloo Road, Pudsey, West Yorkshire, LS28 8DQ
Tel: 01532 574475

12

Phonak UK Ltd

Cygnet Court, Lakeside Drive, Warrington,
Cheshire, WA1 1PP

Tel: 01925 623600
Fax: 01925 245700
Website: www.phonak.com
Contact: David Charmer, Director

Equipment

38, 39, 40, 41, 43.

Plantronics International

Interface Business Park, Binknoll Lane, Wootton
Bassett, Swindon, Wiltshire, SN4 8QQ

Tel: 01793 848999
Fax: 01793 848853
E-mail: headset.helpline@plantronics.com

Plantronics, provider of communications headsets,
provides products for formal and informal call
centres, as well as home offices, mobile and DECT
applications. Plantronics also specialises in
producing products for the hard of hearing. The
Walker Clarity telephone amplifies high frequency
sounds, where the majority of hearing problems
occur.

Portshel Industries

Portland Training College, Nottingham Road,
Mansfield, Nottinghamshire, NG18 4TJ

Tel: 01623 491255
Fax: 01623 491255
E-mail: enquiry@portshel.emnet.co.uk
Website: www.emnet.co.uk/portshel
Contact: Paddy Crabtree, General Manager

As a leading supplier of assistive listening devices
and systems for the hearing impaired, Portshel is
committed to providing quality products and value
for money. As a BS EN ISO 9002 registered
company, it aims to achieve high standards of
quality, professionalism and customer care.

Equipment

22, 24, 25, 26, 27, 28, 29.

Professional Lighting and Sound Association

38 St Leonards Road, Eastbourne, East Sussex,
BN21 3UT

Tel: 01323 410335
Fax: 01323 646905
E-mail: info@plasa.org
Website: www.plasa.org.uk
Contact: Nora Phillips, Membership Services
            Manager

The Professional Lighting and Sound Association
(PLASA) is a long-established trade association
representing companies spanning the entire
breadth of the entertainment technology industry.
Current membership consists of around 430 of the
sector's top companies from all corners of the
globe which manufactures, supplies, hires and
installs professional lighting, sound, presentation,
special effects and staging equipment. A call to
PLASA will provide the right contacts for induction
loops, infra-red systems and voice alarms.

Protector Sabre

Pimbo Road, West Pimbo, Skelmersdale,
Lancashire, WN8 9RA

Tel: 01695 50284

Equipment

50.

Pure-Tec Ltd

Isberg House, Kingston Street, Hull, North
Humberside, HU1 2DB

Tel: 01482 210444
Textphone: 01482 225775
Fax: 01482 225875
Contact: Paul Hatley

Supplier of Sound Pillow, a pillow with stereo
speakers (audio) fitted inside. Plugs into
Walkman or hi-fi system. The user can listen to
any audio recording through the pillow.

Puretone Ltd

10 Henley Business Park, Trident Close, Medway
City Estate, Rochester, Kent, ME2 4ER

Tel: 01634 719427
Fax: 01634 719450
E-mail: mailbox@puretone.ltd.uk
Website: www.puretone.ltd.uk/puretone/
Contact: S Choudhry, Hearing Aid
            Dispenser/Sales Director

Puretone has been making hearing aids for over
20 years and is one of Britain's biggest exporters
in the industry, supplying over 25 countries.
Based in Rochester, Puretone was proud to be
awarded the Queen's Award for Industry in 1996
and hold quality control certificates ISO9001 and
BS EN 46001.

Equipment

1, 3, 7, 21, 22, 23, 24, 25, 26, 29, 37, 38, 39, 40,
41, 42, 43, 46, 48, 49, 50, 51, 52, 53.

PW Sound Engineers

32 Glen Road, Fleet, Hampshire, GU13 9QR

Tel: 01252 811557
Fax: 01252 811557
Contact: P White

Loop installation. Areas: south and south-east England.

Quantech Ltd

10 Whitehouse Centre, Stannington, Morpeth, Northumberland, NE61 6AW

Tel: 01670 789171
Fax: 01670 789172
E-mail: pet@quantech.co.uk
Website: www.quantech.co.uk
Contact: Peter Scargill, Director

Equipment

46.

R G Jones Sound Engineering

16 Endeavour Way, London, SW19 8UH

Tel: 020 8971 3100
Videotel: 020 8971 3125/ 3111
Fax: 020 8971 3101
E-mail: telecoms@rgjones.co.uk
Website: www.rgjones.co.uk
Contact: Ron Purbrick

Sound reinforcement and audio loop systems - hire and sales. Audio and video conference systems. Video phones.

Equipment

8, 14, 24, 25, 26, 27, 28, 29.

Racal Panorama Ltd

Christie Place, Durban Road, Bognor Regis, West Sussex, PO22 9QT

Tel: 01243 828911

Resound Viennatone Ltd

1 Weston Business Park, Weston-on-the-Green, Oxfordshire, OX6 8SY

Tel: 01869 343500
Fax: 01869 343466
E-mail: resuk@resounduk.com

Agent for: Resound; Viennatone. Supplier of hearing aids to the UK and Eire. This includes manufacture and service of products at UK laboratory.

Equipment

37, 38, 39, 40, 42, 43, 46, 50.

Richard Miller Audio Systems

17 Massey Street, Newark, Nottinghamshire, NG24 1PE

Tel: 01636 613094
Fax: 01636 613094
E-mail: datalink@rmaudiosystems.freeserve.co.uk
Contact: Richard Miller

Design, supply and installation of commercial and professional sound reinforcement, paging, background music and induction loop systems (BS 7594). Technical support, on-site operator/user training, service and maintenance scheme are all included in the design, supply and installation package.

Equipment

8, 21, 22, 24, 25, 26, 27, 29, 30, 31.

RNID Sound Advantage

1 Metro Centre, Welbeck Way, Peterborough, Cambridgeshire, PE2 7UH

Tel: 01733 361199
Textphone: 01733 238020
Fax: 01733 361161
E-mail: solutions@rnid.org.uk
Website: www.rnid.org.uk
Contact: David Thompson, Head of Business Development

RNID Sound Advantage sells a wide range of assistive devices for deaf and hard of hearing people. There are over 200 products in its range, including television listening devices and loop systems, flashing doorbells and alarm clocks, smoke detector systems, subtitling video recorders, textphones and portable telephone amplifiers. All products are tested by technical experts to ensure they are safe. The company offers initial information and, if required, a free site survey and quotation for costs. Areas covered: UK-wide.

Equipment

1, 2, 3, 4, 5, 6, 7, 8, 9, 12, 16, 18, 20, 21, 22, 23, 24, 25, 26, 27, 29, 30, 31, 32.

Robbotronic Company

14 Blatchford Close, Industrial Estate, Horsham, West Sussex, RH13 5RG

Tel: 01403 210420
Contact: Bryan Robinson, Managing Director

Established in 1972, Robbotronic Co. have designed, supplied and installed loop systems (to BS 7594) and infra-red systems (to BS 6418 and 7693) in theatres, cathedrals, churches, council offices and chambers, hospitals, sheltered housing, registry offices, and so on. Prior to quotation, site visits are made to ensure the system will operate correctly.

Equipment

21, 22, 23, 24, 25, 26, 27, 29, 30, 31, 43, 47.

Roger Dey Sound and Communications Engineers

P O Box 492, Canterbury, Kent, CT2 7GS

Tel: 01227 277611
Fax: 01227 277611
E-mail: RDEY669152@aol.com
Contact: Jason Dey, Service Engineer

Sale, installation and maintenance of sound and communication systems, specialising in churches, schools and public venues. Demonstration service available including loop systems.

Equipment

24, 25, 26, 27, 28.

RS Components

P O Box 99, Corby, Northamptonshire, NN17 9RS

Tel: 01536 201234
Fax: 01536 405678
Contact: Martin Haynes, Director

Equipment

2, 50.

Rupert Taylor FIOA

Spring Garden, Fairwarp, East Sussex, TN22 3BG

Tel: 01825 712435
Fax: 01825 712542
E-mail: 100675.1765@compuserve.com
Contact: Rupert Taylor, Director

Offers advice in industrial noise and vibration, building acoustics, transportation noise, town planning and community noise and noise control in product development. Rupert Taylor is a member of the Association of Noise Consultants.

Safe and Sound Products Ltd

Clifton Lodge, Clifton, Ashbourne, Derbyshire, DE6 2GL

Tel: 01335 300730
Fax: 01335 300730
Contact: Roy Clegg, Director

Equipment

1, 2, 3, 4, 5, 7, 8, 9, 11, 12, 13, 18, 19, 25, 31.

Sandy Brown Associates

1 Coleridge Gardens, London, NW6 3QH

Tel: 020 7624 6033
Fax: 020 7625 6688
E-mail: post@sandybrown.co.uk
Contact: Richard Galbraith, Partner

Cover all major areas of acoustics, noise and vibration: expert evidence before parliamentary select committees; environmental impact assessments; noise nuisance problems. Sandy Brown Associates is a member of the Association of Noise Consultants.

Sarabec Ltd

15 High Force Road, Middlesbrough, Cleveland, TS2 1RH

Tel: 01642 247789
Textphone: 01642 251310
Fax: 01642 230827
Contact: Deborah Barningham, Sales Manager

Manufacturer and supplier of comprehensive range of equipment for deaf and hard of hearing people.

Equipment

1, 3, 4, 5, 6, 7, 8, 12, 13, 18, 21, 22, 24, 29, 32.

Securicor Alarms Ltd

Sutton Park House, 15 Carshalton Road, Sutton, Surrey, SM1 4LD

Tel: 020 8390 8822

Genesis vibrating paper system.

Select Hearing Systems Ltd

Dept N1, The Science Park, Hutton Street, Blackburn, Lancashire, BB1 3BY

Tel: 01254 675196
Fax: 01254 675197
Contact: Andrew Hall

Conversor wireless listening device director, for use with loops.

Sennheiser UK Ltd

3 Century Point, Halifax Road, High Wycombe, Buckinghamshire, HP12 3SL

Tel: 01494 551551
Fax: 01494 551550
E-mail: info@sennheiser.co.uk
Website: www.sennheiser.co.uk

Infra-red listening devices.

Equipment

21.

Sevenside Safety Supplies Ltd

Malmesbury Road, Kingsditch Trading Estate,
Cheltenham, Gloucestershire, GL51 9PL

Tel: 01242 525811
Fax: 01242 224184
Contact: Clive Dunning, Director

Sharps Redmore Partnership

The White House, London Road, Copdock,
Ipswich, Suffolk, IP8 3JH

Tel: 01473 730073
Fax: 01473 730030
Contact: Doug Sharp, Director

The partnership offers an independent specialist
consultancy in the following aspects of acoustics:
environmental, building and industrial acoustics.
Sharps Redmore is a member of the Association of
Noise Consultants.

Sherborne Sound

The Creamery, 67a Melton Road, West Bridgford,
Nottingham, NG2 6EN

Tel: 0115 981 5555
Fax: 0115 982 7007
Contact: Kevin Beevers, Proprietor

The company designs and installs quality sound
and loop systems in commercial, worship,
educational, leisure and entertainment venues. A
specialist in church/listed buildings where
attention to detail and craftsmanship are shown to
best advantage. Infra-red hearing systems also
supplied. Areas covered for loop installation and
hire: Midlands, within a 70 to 80 mile radius of
Nottingham.

Equipment

21, 24, 25, 26, 27, 28, 29, 30, 31.

Sietech Hearing Ltd (Head Office)

Langley House, Stanneylands Road, Wilmslow,
Cheshire, SK9 4HH

Tel: 01625 548273
Fax: 01625 530693
Contact: Louise Shaw, Products Manageress
            208 High Street, Croydon, Surrey, CR0
            1NE

Agent for: Siemens; Amplivox.

Signet (AC) Ltd

5 Tower Road, Glover Industrial Estate,
Washington, Tyne and Wear, NE37 2SH

Tel: 0191 417 4551
Fax: 0191 417 0634
E-mail: signet@dial.pipex.com
Contact: Tremayne Crossley, Marketing
            Coordinator

Signet manufactures the popular PDA range of
induction loop systems offering top quality sound,
simple installation and proven reliability. The
range incorporates five different units ranging
from the PDA100 for bank counters, ticket offices
and desks to the PDA1000 for large installations
such as churches, theatres and conference centres

Equipment

24, 25, 29.

Smith and Nephew Richards Ltd

6 The Technopark, Newmarket Road, Cambridge,
CB5 8PB

Tel: 01223 568100
Fax: 01223 568098
Contact: Sue Phillips, Sales Team

Ineraid Multichannel Implant.

Sound Advice

F1 Fareham Heights, Standard Way, Fareham,
Hampshire, PO16 8XT

Tel: 01329 221791
Fax: 01329 823394
E-mail: soundadvice@athene.co.uk
Contact: Jon Hunnisett

Sound Advice specialises in the supply and
installation of loop induction and infra-red
systems and is a member of the Professional
Sound and Light Association - PLASA. It is a
Department of the Environment (CMIS) approved
installer, listed with Southern Arts, Hampshire
Constabulary, the MOD and the RNID, and is an
approved contractor of several local authorities,
including Hampshire County Architects
Department.

Equipment

25, 27, 28, 29, 31.

12

Sound Induction Systems

30 Poplar Road, Newtown, Powys, SY16 2QG
Tel: 01686 628012
Fax: 01686 610515
E-mail: Phil@soundinductionsystems.freeserv
            e.co.uk
Contact: Philip Nicholes

The company designs, supplies and installs induction loop systems and sound systems. Installations from domestic loops in houses to complete sound and loop installations in theatres, churches, schools and halls. Temporary loop, sound and recording facilities are provided for such events as conferences and AGMs.

Equipment

1, 13, 20, 21, 22, 23, 24, 25, 26, 27, 28, 31, 35.

Sound Research Laboratories Ltd

70-77 Cowcross Street, London, EC1M 6BP
Tel: 020 7251 3585
Fax: 020 7336 8880
Contact: Malcolm Every, Director

SRL is an independent acoustic consultancy which can help with all areas of noise and vibration: environmental; building; industrial; legal and planning. It has a test laboratory and extensive measurement equipment. SRL is a member of the Association of Noise Consultants.

Sound Workshop Ltd, The

19-21 Queens Road, Halifax, West Yorkshire, HX1 3NS
Tel: 01422 345021
Fax: 01422 363440
Contact: David Mitchell, Managing Director

Designs, installs and maintains public address, induction loop, infra-red, telephone, CCTV, video and lighting systems. Aims to provide the end user with the simplest and most cost-effective solutions.

Equipment

1, 2, 3, 4, 5, 6, 7, 8, 9, 12, 13, 14, 15, 17, 18, 19, 20, 21, 22, 23, 24, 25, 26, 27, 29, 30, 31, 35.

Soundtrack (Audio Visual) Ltd

23 Farriers Way, Temple Farm Industrial Estate, Southend-On-Sea, Essex, SS2 5RY
Tel: 01702 619583
Fax: 01702 619584
Contact: Colin Cooper

Long-established professional sound engineers committed to the provision of clear speech in public places including council offices, churches

186

and community centres. As well as audio frequency induction loops and infra-red assistive listening systems, from manufacturers such as Ampetronic and Sennheiser, Soundtrack also installs closed circuit systems.

Equipment

8, 21, 22, 25, 26, 27, 28, 29, 31.

Southdowns Environmental Consultants Ltd

Suite A3, 16 Station Road, Lewes, East Sussex, BN7 2DB
Tel: 01273 488186
Fax: 01273 488187
E-mail: secl@tcp.co.uk
Contact: Patrick Williams, Director

SEC is an independent firm of environmental consultants which specialises in the provision of acoustic consultancy services to the public and private sectors. SEC staff have extensive experience in providing advice on the assessment of environmental noise and vibration impacts associated with railways, highways, manufacturing industries, quarries, power generation, residential, leisure and commercial developments. Southdowns is a member of the Association of Noise Consultants.

Southwestern Bell UK

2 Enfield Industrial Estate, Redditch, Worcestershire
Tel: 01527 584854

Spectrum Acoustic Consultants Ltd

27-29 High Street, Biggleswade, Bedfordshire, SG18 0JE
Tel: 01767 318871
Fax: 01767 317704
E-mail: Spectrum@SpectrumAcoustic.com
Contact: Andrew Corkhill, Managing Director

Provides advice on environmental and occupational noise control design/specification for large capital projects throughout the power generation, chemical, petrochemical, pharmaceutical, transportation, water, food and drink industries. Spectrum is a member of the Association of Noise Consultants.

12

Stanger Science and Environment

The Lansdowne Building, Lansdowne Road,
Croydon, Surrey, CR0 2BX

Tel: 020 8256 4851
Fax: 020 8256 4862
Contact: Andrew Colthurst, Director

Stanger provides independent professional
consultancy advice in all areas of transportation,
construction and in industrial noise, health and
safety, architectural and building services
acoustics and vibration. Stanger is a member of
the Association of Noise Consultants.

Starkey Laboratories Ltd

William F Austin House, Bramhall Technology
Park, Pepper Road, Hazel Grove, STOCKPORT,
Cheshire, SK7 5BX

Tel: 0161 483 2200
Fax: 0161 483 9833
E-mail: sales@starkey.co.uk
Website: www.starkey-uk.com
Contact: Jennifer Cranshaw, Sales and
Marketing Manager

Custom hearing aids, repairs of all makes of ear
moulds, paediatric programme audiometers,
testing equipment, test boxes, behind-the-ear
hearing aids, education courses.

Equipment

37, 38, 39, 40, 42, 43, 50, 51, 53.

Summit

6 Key Hill Drive, Hockley, Birmingham, West
Midlands, B18 5NY

Tel: 0121 554 6946
Fax: 0121 523 8340

TAMs, listening devices.

Equipment

2, 4, 5, 7, 9, 11.

Symonds

Symonds House, Wood Street, East Grinstead,
West Sussex, RH19 1UU

Tel: 01342 327161
Fax: 01342 333496
E-mail: jgriffit@stmgroup.mhs.compuserve.co
m

Symonds offers services in engineering, planning,
environment, transportation and project
management and control. Its work on noise and
vibration includes: measuring, predicting and
advising on the impact of engineering works,
highway schemes, new or altered rail networks
and infrastructure developments. Expert evidence
is available for public inquiries and other legal
processes. Symonds is a member of the
Association of Noise Consultants.

Equipment

25, 26, 27, 29, 48, 50, 51.

Tandy Corporation (UK) Ltd

Tandy Centre, Leamore Lane, Bloxwich, Walsall,
West Midlands, WS2 7PS

Tel: 01922 710000
Fax: 01922 710789
Website: www.tandyuk.co.uk
Contact: Karen Lamerick, Marketing

General electrical.

Equipment

13, 16, 18, 19, 35.

Taylor Bros Installations (Bolton) Ltd

Unit 5, Burden Industrial Estate, Manchester
Road, Bolton, Lancashire, BL3 2QP

Tel: 01204 380726
Fax: 01204 380724
Contact: Karl Boden, Manager

Loop installation. Areas: UK-wide.

Equipment

24, 25, 27, 29, 31.

TeleMole Ltd

35 Dene Street, Dorking, Surrey, RH4 2DB

Tel: 01306 880454
Fax: 01306 880454
E-mail: design@telemole.com
Website: www.telemole.com
Contact: Paul Davis
Tel: 01929 481284

Design and manufacture of teletext adaptors.
Standard product through distributors. (See
Connevans.) Designer products supplied direct.
Consumer electronics design is complex but so
exciting that no consumer should be denied
access - talk to the chief architect, through the
Mole Hole (Website). Newsletter, briefings and
upgrades for club members.

Equipment

32, 33.

12

Teletec International Ltd

Sendale House, 49 Coldacock Drive, Coldacock
Bus Park, Milton Keynes, Buckinghamshire, MK7
8LF

Tel: 01908 270003
Textphone: 01908 270005
Fax: 01908 270010
Contact: Mr Jones, Managing Director

Distributes textphones through a dealer network
and direct sales. Provides after-sales care service,
after-sale repairs, customer service and technical
advice.

Equipment

1, 2, 4, 6, 8, 12.

Tim Smith Acoustics

7 Swancombe, Clapton-in-Gordano, Bristol, BS20
9RR

Tel: 01275 848229
Fax: 01275 843945

The practice offers specialist consultancy services
on all aspects of building acoustics and noise
control, particularly architectural acoustics,
broadcasting and communications and
environmental noise. TSA is a member of the
Association of Noise Consultants.

Tjaden Ltd

62a Chatsworth Road, London, E5 0LS

Tel: 020 8533 7234
Fax: 020 8533 7234
Contact: Keith Tjaden

Primary NICEIC-approved electrical installation
contractor (Class I). Specialist in high grade
domestic installations, with service and retail
facility. Specialising also in AFILS and infra-red
installations (with or without PA), mainly for public
areas/buildings. Particularly relevant with DDA95
PT 3 and building regulations Part M (BSS9
Amendment) this year (1999). Available to teach
organisations the correct application of AFILS and
I-R and microphone technique for speakers.

Equipment

1, 2, 5, 8, 13, 20, 21, 22, 24, 25, 26, 27, 28, 29, 31.

Toad Innovations Ltd

Spectrum Business Estate, Bircholt Road,
Maidstone, Kent, ME15 9YP

Tel: 01622 683044
Fax: 01622 683950
Contact: Terry Lewton, Senior Technician

Equipment

16.

Toby Churchill Ltd

20 Panton Street, Cambridge, CB2 1HP

Tel: 01223 316117
Fax: 01223 518133
Contact: Simon Churchill, Sales

Keyboard-based communication aids, generating
an artificial voice.

Universal Aids Ltd

8-14 Wellington Road South, Stockport, Cheshire,
SK4 1AA

Tel: 0161 480 9228
Fax: 0161 476 5707
Contact: C Turner, General Manager

Manufacturer and supplier of equipment to assist
the hearing impaired and disabled for over 30
years. Products include: door and telephone
intercom warning systems, induction loops, smoke
alarms and alarm clocks. Contractors to
government organisations, local authorities and
hospitals.

Equipment

1, 2, 3, 5, 6, 7, 23, 24, 38, 39, 40, 42, 43.

Vaughan Sound Installations Ltd

3-4 Heol Rhosyn, Dafen Park, Llanelli, Dyfed, SA14
8QG

Tel: 01554 775235
Fax: 01554 740501
E-mail: vsi@pa-installations.co.uk
Contact: Richard Vaughan

Supplies and installs public address systems,
professional sound and lighting systems, CCTV
systems, intercoms, fire alarms, nurse call systems
and inductive loop systems. Loop installation and
hire for the West of England and Wales.

Equipment

2, 5, 6, 8, 9, 13, 14, 20, 21, 22, 24, 25, 26, 27, 28,
29, 30, 31.

Verhas, Dr H P

Gasthuisstraat 32, 9200 Sint-Gillis-Dendermonde,
Belgium

Tel: 0032 5 222 4864
Contact: H Verhas, Director
Gasthuisstraat 32, B-9200 Sint-Gillis-
Dendermonde, Vlaanderen, Belgium

Independent services in all aspects of sound,
noise, vibration and dynamics as a consultant
designer and development engineer. Services
include: measurements, analysis and research and

development, and cover the following areas: architectural and building, industrial and the environmental sector. Dr Verhas is a member of the Association of Noise Consultants.

Vibrock Limited

Shanakiel, Ilkeston Road, Heanor, Derbyshire, DE75 7DR
Tel: 01773 711211
Fax: 01773 711311
E-mail: vibrock@btinternet.com
Contact: David Johnson, Director

Offers advice in the following areas: project consultancy, public enquiries, environmental impact assessments, assisting with planning applications, specifying project criteria and limits, and advice on reduction and control in matters relating to industry or the environment. Vibrock is a member of the Association of Noise Consultants.

Vibronoise Limited

Brook House, Off Brookfield Road, Cheadle, Cheshire, SK8 2PE
Tel: 0161 491 3100
Fax: 0161 428 1198
E-mail: sales@vibronoise.co.uk
Website: www.vibronoise.co.uk
Contact: A Pratt, Director

Vibronoise's main experience is in troubleshooting, dynamic analysis and handling total responsibility projects. Occupational and environmental work is undertaken and professional witnesses can be supplied to deal with many noise and vibration issues regarding planning and litigation. Vibronoise is a member of the Association of Noise Consultants.

W A Hines and Partners

2 Theobald Court, Theobald Street, Borehamwood, Hertfordshire, WD6 4RN
Tel: 020 8953 2022
Fax: 020 8207 6170
E-mail: HinesPrtn@aol.com
Contact: Peter Hines, Director

Provide a comprehensive acoustic and noise control consultancy service. The practice has an extensive range of noise monitoring and measuring equipment, and offers a full consultancy service in all aspects of acoustics from inital surveys and reports to final testing. W A Hines is a member of the Association of Noise Consultants.

W S Atkins Engineering Sciences

Woodcote Grove, Ashley Road, Epsom, Surrey, KT18 5BW
Tel: 01372 726140
Fax: 01372 740055
E-mail: wsatkinsinfo@wsatkins.co.uk
Contact: Alan Rudge, Chairman

W S Atkins is part of one of the largest integrated consultancies in Europe, covering the fields of engineering, architecture and planning. It acts on behalf of private, national and international companies, individuals, local authorities, govenment bodies and agencies. Services offered by its noise department include: noise and vibration surveys; prediction of environmental transportation and industrial noise; hearing conservation; noise control to specified standards; building and room acoustics; environmental impact assessment; design, procurement, installation and computer software development of noise-monitoring systems; construction noise; active attenuation systems; provision of evidence at public enquiries and court cases; contract research and special projects. W S Atkins is a member of the Association of Noise Consultants.

12

Walker Beak Mason Partnership, The

Hunters Park, Yew Tree Lane, Spratton, Northampton, NN6 8HL
Tel: 01604 821987
Fax: 01604 821990

The partnership specialises in noise and vibration work for environmental statements, planning appeals, public inquiries and court cases; mineral extraction and association operations, waste disposal and construction sites, transportation noise, environmental noise monitoring, commericial development, architectural acoustics and industrial noise surveys. Walker Beak Mason is a member of the Association of Noise Consultants.

Walsh, J L

25 Crosthwaite Park West, Dun Laoghaire, Co Dublin, Eire
Tel: 00 353 1 280 7820
Fax: 00 353 1 284 2072

Provides a quality audio signal to the listener. This service is provided in churches, houses of religion and in the domestic environment.
Equipment
1, 8, 21, 22, 24, 25, 26.

Wessex Electronics Ltd

114-116 North Street, Downend, Bristol, Avon, BS16 5SE

Tel: 0117 957 1404
Fax: 0117 957 3843
E-mail: wesbry@wessex.telme.com
Contact: Malcolm Butt, Sales Director

Speech/auditory trainers.

Equipment

47.

Wight Audio Services

Unit 4, Grahamstown Road, Sedbury, Chepstow, NP6 7AD

Tel: 01291 625490
Fax: 01291 625490
Contact: Nick Wight

Design, supply, installation, hire and service of all types of professional sound equipment, including AFILS and infra-red. Specialist in the supply and installation of sound systems for factories, warehouses, places of worship, restaurants, offices, and so on. Also, supplier of audio-conferencing facilities.

Equipment

21, 25, 27, 28, 29, 31

Wigwam Acoustics Ltd

St Anne's House, Ryecroft Avenue, Heywood, Lancashire, OL10 1QB

Tel: 01706 624547
Fax: 01706 365565
E-mail: sales@wigwam.co.uk
Website: www.wigwam.co.uk
Contact: Michael Spratt, Managing Director
Tel: 01706 624547/ 365565

Equipment

20, 21, 24, 25, 26, 27, 28, 29, 30, 31.

Williams Hearing Aid Services

67a Bexley High Street, Bexley, Kent, DA5 1AA

Tel: 01322 558596
E-mail: gwilliams@clara.net

Williams manufactures and supplies all types of noise generators and tinnitus maskers.

Wimtec Environmental Limited

St Peter's House, 6-8 High Street, Iver, Buckinghamshire, SL0 9NG

Tel: 01753 737744
Fax: 01753 792321
E-mail: 101675.163@compuserve.com
Website: ourworld.compuserve.com/homepages/wimtec
Contact: Richard Clough, Director

Wimtec Environmental Limited is one of the UK's largest environmental consultancies. It provides services in occupational hygiene, noise, vibration, contaminated land, asbestos, water quality, air quality, energy use, environmental management, environmental assessment, site investigation, and geo-consultancy.

Wintonfield Systems

Albyn Industrial Estate, Broxburn, West Lothian, EH52 5PQ

Tel: 01506 852000
Fax: 01506 855506
E-mail: info@wintonfield.co.uk
Contact: Doreen Armstrong, Sales Director

Equipment

1, 3, 4, 5, 6, 7, 8, 9, 32, 34.

WS Steele Ltd

Unit 5-05 Oakbank Industrial Estate, Garscube Road, Glasgow, Lanarkshire, G20 7LU

Tel: 0141 353 3393
Fax: 0141 353 3396
Contact: Graham Steele, Managing Director

One area of expertise is the supply and installation of inductive loop and infra-red equipment including counter, television and reception systems as installed in public buildings and churches.

Equipment

22, 24, 25, 27, 28, 30, 31, 34, 35, 48.

WSP Environmental

Buchanan House, 24-30 Holborn, London, EC1N 2HS

Tel: 020 7314 5000
Fax: 020 7314 5005
E-mail: environmental@london.wspgroup.com
Contact: Christopher Cole, Director

The following lists show which organisations supply or manufacture different types of equipment

They are listed under the following headings:

Alerting Devices
Telecommunications
Listening Devices
Television
Hearing Aids
Implanted Devices
Audiological Equipment
Noise Consultants

Companies supplying alerting devices

A and M Hearing
Advanced Hearing Systems
Aico Ltd
Aird Walker and Ralston Ltd
AJ Sound and Vision Ltd
Annalex Systems
Ascom Tele-Nova Ltd
Audio-Visual Technology Ltd
B and H Designs
BioAcoustics Ltd.
C & P Hearing Equipment Centre
C C Consultants
Caradon Friedland Ltd
Clofield Ltd
Communications MVC
Connevans Ltd
D G Controls
Deaf Awareness Technology
Delta Design
Dunvegan Ltd
Eastfield-Rossmill Ltd (Technical Services)
Easylink Electronics
Electrical and Acoustic Services Ltd
Equipment for Equality
Evets Communications Ltd
Fulleon Synchrobell
Gordon Morris Ltd
Hearing Products International
Hector Tanner & Co Ltd
Location Sound
MAR Design Services
McDonald, J M and Associates
Moflash Co Ltd
Newtech International
Niagara Manufacturing Ltd
Northern Acoustics
Outside In (Cambridge) Ltd
Page One (System Technology)
Permic Emergency Lifting Ltd
Peter Knight Industries
Pure-Tec Ltd
Puretone Ltd
R G Jones Sound Engineering

Richard Miller Audio Systems
RNID Sound Advantage
RS Components
Safe and Sound Products Ltd
Sarabec Ltd
Securicor Alarms Ltd
Sound Induction Systems
Sound Workshop Ltd, The
Soundtrack (Audio Visual) Ltd
Summit
Teletec International Ltd
Tjaden Ltd
Universal Aids Ltd
Vaughan Sound Installations Ltd
Walsh, J L
Wintonfield Systems

Companies supplying telecommunications devices

A and M Hearing
Advanced Hearing Systems
AJ Sound and Vision Ltd
Ascom Tele-Nova Ltd
Audio-Visual Technology Ltd
B and H Designs
BCF Technology Ltd
Bernafon UK Ltd
BT Development and Procurement
C & P Hearing Equipment Centre
Connevans Ltd
Deaf Awareness Technology
DSN Computers
Dunvegan Ltd
Easylink Electronics
Equipment for Equality
Gordon Morris Ltd
Hutchison Paging (UK) Ltd
Marconi Hillend Enterprise
Motion Media Technology
Newtech International
Northern Acoustics
Plantronics International
R G Jones Sound Engineering
RNID Sound Advantage
Safe and Sound Products Ltd
Sarabec Ltd
Sound Induction Systems
Sound Workshop Ltd, The
Tandy Corporation (UK) Ltd
Teletec International Ltd
Tjaden Ltd
Toad Innovations Ltd
Toby Churchill Ltd
Vaughan Sound Installations Ltd

Companies supplying listening devices

A and M Hearing
Advanced Hearing Systems
AJ Sound and Vision Ltd
AMC Communications Ltd
Ampetronic Ltd
Audio Medical Devices Ltd
Audio-Visual Technology Ltd
Audix Communications
AVT Communication Systems Ltd.
B & J Stevenson
B and H Designs
Bell Audio
BioAcoustics Ltd.
C & P Hearing Equipment Centre
Carter-Voce Ltd
Colin MacPherson Sound Systems
Communication Services
Communications MVC
Connevans Ltd
Contacta Communication Systems
Deaf Awareness Technology
Dunvegan Ltd
EAR Division
Eastfield-Rossmill Ltd (Technical Services)
Easylink Electronics
Electrical and Acoustic Services Ltd
Electronic Services
Elite-Sound Communications
Equipment for Equality
Ferrosound
Fishwick, John L
Fulford Sound Service
GB Electronics Ltd
Gordon Morris Ltd
Grainger Communications
Hearing Products International
Hilltop Audio Supplies
HW Audio Ltd
HW Music Centre Ltd (Wightsound)
Keith Monks Sound Systems
Location Sound
McDonald, J M and Associates
MTL International Ltd
Mustang Communications
Newland Electronics Ltd
Newtech International
Northern Acoustics
Oxford Sound Company, The
Page One (System Technology)
PAS Sound Engineering Ltd
PC Werth Ltd
Phillips Communication and Security Systems
Portshel Industries
Professional Lighting and Sound Association
Puretone Ltd
PW Sound Engineers
R G Jones Sound Engineering
Richard Miller Audio Systems
RNID Sound Advantage
Robbotronic Company

Roger Dey Sound and Communications Engineers
Safe and Sound Products Ltd
Sarabec Ltd
Select Hearing Systems Ltd
Sennheiser UK Ltd
Sherborne Sound
Signet (AC) Ltd
Sound Advice
Sound Induction Systems
Sound Workshop Ltd, The
Soundtrack (Audio Visual) Ltd
Symonds
Taylor Bros Installations (Bolton) Ltd
Tjaden Ltd
Universal Aids Ltd
Vaughan Sound Installations Ltd
Walsh, J L
Wight Audio Services
Wigwam Acoustics Ltd
WS Steele Ltd

Companies supplying television aids

AJ Sound and Vision Ltd
C & P Hearing Equipment Centre
Connevans Ltd
Hearing Products International
Northern Acoustics
RNID Sound Advantage
Sound Induction Systems
Sound Workshop Ltd, The
Tandy Corporation (UK) Ltd
TeleMole Ltd
Wintonfield Systems
WS Steele Ltd

Companies supplying hearing aids

A and M Hearing
AB Transistor
Advanced Hearing Systems
Audifon UK Ltd
Audio Medical Devices Ltd
Bernafon UK Ltd
Border Hearing Services
Danavox (Great Britain) Ltd
Hearing Aid Technology Ltd
Lavis Medical Systems
Med-El UK Ltd
Northern Acoustics
Oticon Ltd
PC Werth Ltd
Phonak UK Ltd
Puretone Ltd
Resound Viennatone Ltd
Robbotronic Company
Sietech Hearing Ltd (Head Office)
Starkey Laboratories Ltd
Universal Aids Ltd

Companies supplying implanted devices

Advanced Bionics UK Ltd
Antwerp Bionic Systems
Cochlear (UK) Ltd
Smith and Nephew Richards Ltd

Companies supplying audiological equipment

3M Occupational Health & Environmental Safety Group
A and M Hearing
Advanced Hearing Systems
Aearo Limited
AJ Sound and Vision Ltd
Alfred Peters plc
Amplivox Ltd
Anti-Noise Ltd
ARCO
Audio Medical Devices Ltd
Bilsom
Castle Group Ltd
CEL Instruments Ltd
Chapman and Smith
Cirrus Research plc
Connevans Ltd
Eastfield-Rossmill Ltd (Technical Services)
Equipment for Equality
Guymark UK
Hearing Products International
Howard Leight
HPS Protection
John Ward & Sons (Stourbridge) Ltd.
Keith Monks Sound Systems
Laboratories MXM
Martec Environmental Engineering
McDonald, J M and Associates
Millgrant Wells Ltd
Nicolet Biomedical
PC Werth Ltd
Protector Sabre
Puretone Ltd
Quantech Ltd
Resound Viennatone Ltd
Robbotronic Company
RS Components
Sevenside Safety Supplies Ltd
Starkey Laboratories Ltd
Symonds
Wessex Electronics Ltd
WS Steele Ltd

Noise Consultants

Acoustic Consultants Ltd
Acoustical Investigation and Research Organisation Ltd
Acoustics and Noise Partnership
Alan Saunders Associates
Anthony Best Dynamics Ltd

APT Acoustics
Ashdown Environmental Ltd
Aspinwall and Company Ltd
Association of Noise Consultants
BCL Acoustic Services
BDP Acoustics Ltd
Bickerdike Allen Partners
Bird Acoustics
Civil Engineering Dynamics
Cole Jarman Associates
Conrad Acoustics
Dennis R Robinson and Associates
Entec UK Ltd
Environmental Resources Management Ltd
Equus Partnership, The
Fleming and Barron
Hann Tucker Associates
Hepworth Acoustics Ltd
JSP Consultants
Ken Dibble Acoustics
Leventhall, Dr H G
Moir Hands and Associates
NES Acoustics
Noise Advisory Services
Oscar Faber Acoustics
Philip Dunbavin Acoustics Ltd
Rupert Taylor FIOA
Sandy Brown Associates
Sharps Redmore Partnership
Sound Research Laboratories Ltd
Southdowns Environmental Consultants Ltd
Spectrum Acoustic Consultants Ltd
Stanger Science and Environment
Tim Smith Acoustics
Verhas, Dr H P
Vibrock Limited
Vibronoise Limited
W A Hines and Partners
W S Atkins Engineering Sciences
Walker Beak Mason Partnership, The
Wimtec Environmental Limited

12

Resource Centres

This is a new section in the directory. As more equipment for deaf and hard of hearing people becomes available it is useful for people to be able to try out different pieces of equipment in order to see what works for them. This section lists resource centres around the country. If you know of a centre near you that is not listed here, please get in touch with RNID and we will include it in the next edition.

This section is listed alphabetically by resource centre within country and county sections.

England

➢ Bedfordshire

Disability Resource Centre Dunstable

Poynters House, Poynters Road, Dunstable, Bedfordshire, LU5 4TP

Tel:	01582 470900
Textphone:	01582 470968
Fax:	01582 470977
E-mail:	drc_beds@compuserve.com
Contact:	Sue Mills, Information Manager

A focal point for disability services in Bedfordshire. The building houses many services both statutory and voluntary. We provide a comprehensive disability information service throughout Bedfordshire, plus an equipment display area where people can try out equipment and obtain professional advice from an occupational therapist. Hours 10am to 4pm, Monday to Friday.

➢ Blackburn

See Lancashire

➢ Buckinghamshire

RNID Information and Environmental Equipment Service, Buckinghamshire

Walton House, Walton Street, Aylesbury, Buckinghamshire, HP21 7QQ

Tel:	01296 434839 information only
Textphone:	01296 436722
Fax:	01296 436358
Contact:	Amanda Edwards, Environmental Equipment Officer
Tel:	01296 437175

RNID is working with deaf people and other organisations to identify, liaise, network and advise on how to adapt and improve their services to make them accessible to deaf people. The information officer answers enquiries on issues relating to deafness and attends local events. You can make appointments to visit the Equipment Display Room at Walton House to see which pieces of equipment might be of use to you. Hearing aid batteries are also available. On behalf of social services, the equipment officers will assess and, where appropriate, supply environmental equipment for prelingually profoundly deaf adults and children living in Milton Keynes and Buckinghamshire. Hard of hearing/deafened adults will be assessed if they live anywhere in Buckinghamshire. They will also register anybody with a hearing loss on the deaf and hard of hearing register.

➢ Cambridgeshire

CAMTAD Cambridge

Buchan House, Buchan Street, Cambridge, CB4 2XF

Tel:	01223 460616
Fax:	01223 712113 ("Attn. CAMTAD")
Website:	www.yell.co.uk/sites/hearinghelpcambridge/
Contact:	Sue Hempstead, Organiser

CAMTAD exists to help anyone with a hearing loss in Cambridge and the surrounding area. It provides information, advice, training including awareness training, equipment and an information exchange with other organisations. CAMTAD demonstrates equipment at its 16 centres and it also has a mobile display in order to reach people who are less mobile in outlying areas. Its services are also available to other organisations, professionals working with deaf people and the general public. CAMTAD produces a bi-monthly newsletter.

CAMTAD Fenland

24 Woodlands Court, Wisbech, Cambridgeshire, PE13 3SD

Tel:	01354 692091
Contact:	Joan Brown

Channel Islands
Hearing Resource Centre Jersey
Westmount Road, Jersey, Channel Islands, JE1 3UH

Tel: 01534 623030

Fax: 01534 623031

The centre provides a focus for both public and voluntary organisations as well as professionals and provides the following services: information to improve the quality of life for people with a hearing impairment, working displays of assistive devices, a comprehensive library of books and videos, counselliing and information for parents, teaching of communication skills in British Sign Language and lipreading, a meeting place for groups and individuals, training sessions for volunteers and Link nurses, careers advice, guidance and employment, speech and language therapy, audiology clinics, advice on in-the-ear and digital hearing aids, sale of hearing aid batteries, tinnitus relaxation classes and a base for the Home Visit Support Scheme.

Cumbria
Cumbria Hearing Services
HillCrest, 75 High Brigham, Brigham, Cockermouth, Cumbria, CA13 0TG

Contact: Glyn Hewitt

Derby
See Derbyshire

Derbyshire
CAMTAD Chesterfield
Offices 4 and 5, Market Hall, Chesterfield, Derbyshire, S40 1AR

Tel: 01246 555934

Textphone: 01246 555933

Fax: 01246 555934

Contact: Janet Millard, Coordinator

Increases public awareness and understanding of the problems of deafness; visits hearing aid users; provides help and encouragement; visits residential and sheltered homes and hospitals and demonstrates environmental equipment.

CAMTAD Derby
Derbyshire Royal Infirmary, London Road, Derby, DE1 2QQ

Tel: 01332 254689

Aims and activities as for CAMTAD Chesterfield, above.

Derbyshire Centre for Integrated Living
Long Close, Providence Street, Ripley, Derbyshire, DE5 3HY

Tel: 01773 740246

Textphone: 01773 748452

Fax: 01773 570185

Hasland Resource Centre
Heather Vale Road, Hasland, Chesterfield, Derbyshire, S41 0HZ

Hearing Help Amber Valley
The Hearing Help Centre, 156 Derby Road, Ripley, Derbyshire, DE5 8HU

Tel: 01773 570976

Textphone: 01773 570976

Fax: 01773 570976

Contact: E Richardson, Service Manager

Hearing Help has nine clinics throughout Amber Valley providing practical help, information and support. Its workers also visit residential homes, wardened flats and clients' own homes. It also provides a monthly social/self-help group, a weekly lipreading group and a quarterly newsletter.

13

Two Can Resources Unit
St Helen's House, King Street, Derby, DE1 3EE

Tel: 01332 205305 ext 229

Textphone: 01332 291109

Fax: 01332 292507

Contact: Sandra Creighton, Administrative Officer

The resource unit, based within Derby Deaf Social Club and St Helen's House, allows deaf people to become involved with every aspect of community education. Services include: community education classes, adult basic education, one-to-one tuition, sign language courses, support within community education classes, which are based within county provision, a graphics service and computer-based training.

➤ Devon

Acorn Resource Centre

George Street, Exeter, Devon, EX1 1DA
Tel: 01392 384481
Textphone: 01392 384481

Contact: E Pike, Information Officer

Community-based services for people with sensory loss. One-to-one focused work to timescaled goals. Referral basis from social services. Follow-on work with rehabilitation officers. Services at the centre include group work, developing a network of support and help for individuals.

Hearing and Sight Centre

Pounds House, 162 Outland Road, Peverell, Plymouth, Devon, PL2 3PX
Tel: 01752 788999
Textphone: 01752 768573
Fax: 01752 780470
Contact: Maggie Paine, Coordinator

This is an information, advice and equipment service which helps people with a sight and/or hearing impairment make informed choices and maintain independence. Families, carers, friends and professionals are also welcome to use the service. The service is confidential and impartial and is provided by trained advisors. Support groups and classes are held at the centre as are training courses in sensory impairment and British Sign Language. Visitors can use a reference library which includes practice journals as well as academic and research literature on sensory impairment. There is an equipment display where people can view and try out a range of environmental aids. If required, the aids can be taken away from the centre on short-term loan for home trial. There is also a selection of toys, videos and books available on short-term loan for parents and children. Other services available from the centre include battery replacement and retubing for people with NHS hearing aids. There is a home support visiting scheme for people with new hearing aids supplied by the NHS and a hearing therapy clinic (both these services are available by appointment via Derriford Hospital, Plymouth). There is also the Tinnitus Support Group, which provides mutual support and the sharing of ideas for people with tinnitus.

National Federation of Access Centres

Rm 8, Babbage Building, University of Plymouth, Drake Circus, Plymouth, Devon, PL4 8AA
Tel: 01752 232278
Textphone: 01752 232285
Fax: 01752 232279
E-mail: swarn@plymouth.ac.uk
Website: www.plym.ac.uk
Contact: Sarah Warn, Administrator

The National Federation of Access Centres (NFAC) is a nationwide network of specialist centres offering independent assessment and training facilities in the use of enabling and information technologies for people with learning difficulties and/or disabilities. Access centres are recognised by the the DfEE and Student Awards Agency for Scotland (SAAS) as the main provider of assessments to identify a student's entitlement to the Disabled Student Allowance (DSA).

➤ East Sussex

Firstfields Resource Centre

42 London Road, Hailsham, East Sussex, BN27 3BU

Hearing Resource Centre Eastbourne

19 Hartfield Road, Eastbourne, East Sussex, BN21 2AR
Tel: 01323 638230
Textphone: 01323 638230
Fax: 01323 642968
Contact: John Leonard, The Hearing Resource Centre Coordinator
Tel: 01323 722505

The Hearing Resource Centre provides a permanent display of assistive devices and where possible will loan equipment for short periods of time. Open or Drop-in days are Tuesdays and Wednesdays 10am to 4pm with appoinments available other than these days. The centre also provides deaf awareness training to CACDP standards either at the centre or in house. A volunteer project is in operation whereby volunteers visit residential homes, nursing homes, hospitals, day centres, etc. to carry out basic hearing aid maintenance. This includes visits to housebound people, especially in rural areas. The most recent project includes a communication worker working throughout the Wealden which is a mainly rural area of East Sussex. Communication groups have been set up where people are encouraged to use 'Total Communication' and to include lipreading and sign language. The aims of this project is to increase

13

communication skills, provide advocacy and to involve users as volunteers. Hearing Resource Centre is part of the LINK Centre.

➢ Essex

Hearing Help Essex

Suite E, Imperial House, Victoria Road, Chelmsford, Essex, CM1 1NY

Tel: 01245 348440

Textphone: 01245 348440

Fax: 01245 280747

Contact: Pauline Connor, Director

We offer follow-up and home visits to people with an acquired hearing loss, cleaning and retubing NHS hearing aids. Our volunteers hold regular Hearing Help sessions at several day care centres. Members of the public can visit our Resource Centre. We also offer deaf awareness training courses.

RNID Sensory Services Redbridge

Access and Information Centre, Ground Floor, Connaught House, Broomhill Road, Woodford Green, Essex, IG8 0XR

Tel: 020 8498 9911

Textphone: 020 8498 9922

Videotel: 020 8504 0329

Fax: 020 8498 9955

Contact: Maria Oxland, Centre Manager

The RNID Sensory Services Centre provides information and advice for blind, deaf and deafblind people living in the London Borough of Redbridge. It has around 200 items of equipment on display as well as providing services and support to local deaf, deafblind and blind people, their families, carers and professionals.

Royal Association in Aid of Deaf People

Tel: 01206 509509

Textphone: 01206 577090

Fax: 01206 769755

E-mail: info@royaldeaf.org.uk

Website: www.royaldeaf.org.uk

See entries under Regional Organisations.

➢ Gloucestershire

Gloucestershire Independent Living

Cayley Hall, Shepherd Road, Gloucester, GL2 5DW

Tel: 01452 311101

Fax: 01452 301990

A country-wide mobile exhibition of small aids to daily living. Visitors are welcome to call in and try out items and discuss their needs with an occupational therapist. The service offers independent advice on all aspects of daily living and services available.

➢ Hampshire

Breakthrough Trust

Tel: 01252 313882

Textphone: 01252 313882

Fax: 01252 337546

E-mail: scbthu@aol.com

Contact: Celia Pinto, Regional Manager

See entries under Regional Organisations.

Communication Aid Centre

Tremona Road, Shirley, Southampton, Hampshire, SO16 6YD

Tel: 023 8085 2288

Fax: 023 8079 4756

Contact: Alison Proudman, Speech and Language Therapist

Tel: 023 8079 6455

A centre for people of any age living within the Southampton and South West Hampshire Health District who are severely speech impaired. Maintains a supply of specialised communication aids for demonstration and assessment purposes. Referrals through healthcare professionals, eg speech and language therapists, GPs, consultants. Clients seen on appointment basis only.

13

> Hertfordshire

Hertfordshire Hearing Advisory Service

The Woodside Centre, The Commons, Welwyn Garden City, Hertfordshire, AL7 4SE

Tel: 01707 324582
Textphone: 01707 375486
Fax: 01707 390644
E-mail: info@hhas.demon.co.uk

Hertfordshire Hearing Advisory Service offers free practical help and advice on aspects of hearing loss. Trained volunteers provide basic hearing aid maintenance and advice on hearing aid use and assistive equipment at The Woodside Centre, on-board the mobile unit, and sites across the country. Training in deaf awareness and loop system management available.

> Isle of Wight

RNID Sound Advice

34 The Mall, Carisbrooke Road, Newport, Isle of Wight, PO30 1BW

Tel: 01983 529533
Textphone: 01983 529533
Fax: 01983 533100
Contact: Joyce Love, Project Manager

Sound Advice provides information and demonstrations of daily living equipment for deaf and hard of hearing people. It is jointly funded by RNID and the Isle of Wight County Council Social Services Department.

> Kent

Beckenham Access Centre

Beckenham Hospital, Trapnell Wing, Croydon Road, Beckenham, Kent, BR3 3QL

Tel: 020 8289 8050
Textphone: 020 8289 8090
Fax: 020 8289 8060

Provides information, support and communication support for hearing impaired people. There is also a Tinnutus and Hard of Hearing Group meeting from 1 to 3.30pm on Mondays on an irregular basis. Please ring for details of the next meeting. There is also a Job Club open between 10am and 4pm on Wednesdays (closed for lunch from 12.30 to 1.30pm), new clients should attend the Job Club between 1.30pm and 2.30pm; a deafblind group meets fortnightly on Mondays, and the Bromley Deaf Club meets on the first and third Tuesday afternoon of every month. A Deaf Women's Group meets fortnightly on Thursday mornings. If anyone is interested please contact the Access Centre for more details.

198

Bexley Deaf Centre

Tel: 01322 550879
Textphone: 01322 550879
Fax: 01322 525583
Contact: Janette Nimmo, Information Officer

See entry under Deaf Clubs.

Hi Kent Canterbury

46 Northgate, Canterbury, Kent, CT1 1BE

Tel: 01227 760046
Textphone: 01227 760046
Fax: 01277 760068
E-mail: hikent@btinternet.com
Website: www.btinternet.com/~hikent/
Contact: Jon Lambert, Centre Manager

Hi Kent aims to raise awareness of the needs of deaf and hearing impaired people, and to enable all people with hearing loss to lead a full and integrated life. This is achieved by providing advice, information and practical support, assistive equipment assessments and provision, awareness and sign language training.

Hi Kent Maidstone

18 Brewer Street, Maidstone, Kent, ME14 1RU

Tel: 01622 691151
Textphone: 01622 691151
Fax: 01622 672436
E-mail: hikent@btinternet.com
Website: www.btinternet.com/~hikent/
Contact: Daphne Lewis, Information Officer

The Maidstone office is the head office for the Hi Kent charity. It provides services for deaf and hard of hearing people of all ages, but is unable to provide any financial support. The centre can provide information, advice, educational services, equipment, awareness training, an information exchange and tinnitus advice. The centre runs sign language courses CACDP Stage I and II. Open to the public from 9am to 5pm Monday to Friday. An occasional newsletter is produced. Hi Kent also has a mobile resource centre, satellite resource centres, hearing aid clinics for basic retubing and advice on hearing aids and a volunteer visiting scheme, and can assess for the provision of equipment by social services in Kent and Medway areas for the over 65s.

➤ Lancashire

Aids to Communication in Education Centre - North

1 Broadbent Road, Watersheddings, Oldham, Lancashire, OL1 4HU

Tel:	0161 627 1358
Fax:	0161 627 0363
E-mail:	ace-north@dail.pipex.com
Website:	dspace.dialpipex.com/town/terrace/ac 969

ACE Centre North provides independent assessments, training, advice and information on the uses of assistive technology for individuals with physical and/or communication impairments. The assessment team consists of a speech therapist, teacher, occupational therapist and disability advisor.

RNID Community Outreach Services

1st and 2nd Floor, Wellington Street, St Johns, Blackburn, Lancashire, BB1 8AF

Tel:	01254 6786249
Textphone:	01254 670299
Fax:	01254 6786249

➤ Lincolnshire

CAMTAD Lincoln

St Matthias Centre for Deaf People, Burton Road, Lincoln, LN1 3TX

Tel:	01522 541561
Textphone:	01522 541561
Fax:	01522 530644
Contact:	S King, Project Manager

CAMTAD is an organisation which uses trained volunteer staff to provide advice and information about all aspects of deafness. It welcomes anyone who is directly or indirectly affected by deafness and needs support or assistance.

➤ London

Computer Centre for People with Disabilities

72 Great Portland Street, London, W1N 5AL

Tel:	020 7911 5161
Videotel:	020 7637 8061

The Computer Centre for People with Disabilities (CCPD) provides specialist employment training in IT up to NVQ levels 2 and 3. Two courses are run solely for deaf students; the employment training in IT course for local unemployed adults and the pilot course (Leonardo funded) for deaf graduates as information officers. CCPD supports disabled students generally but works with a range of specialist agencies for deaf people on a range of projects.

Disabled Living Foundation

380-384 Harrow Road, London, W9 2HU

Tel:	020 7289 6111
Textphone:	020 7432 8009
Fax:	020 7266 2922
E-mail:	advice@dlf.org.uk
Website:	www.atlas.co.uk/dlf/
Contact:	Mary Queally, Head of Advice Services
Tel:	020 7432 8005
E-mail:	maryq@dlf.org.uk

The aim of the Disabled Living Foundation is to make everyday life easier for disabled people, older people and carers, by giving expert and impartial advice about equipment for daily living. The Helpline telephone number is: 0870 603 9177 (Voice) and 0870 603 9176 (textphone). It is open from 10am to 4pm, Monday to Friday. The Equipment Centre displays a wide range of useful equipment for older people and people with disabilities. Mondays, Tuesdays and Fridays are open days from 10am to 3.30pm. Appointments can be made for Wednesday or Thursday by telephoning the main office numbers. They do not sell equipment directly. The DLF has now produced a CD-ROM of equipment. It has over 14,000 items listed with suppliers' names and addresses and includes self-help groups also.

London Centre for Micro Assisted Communication

Eltham Green Complex 4th Floor, 1a Middleton Park Avenue, Eltham, London, SE9 5HL

Tel:	020 8850 9229
Fax:	020 8850 9220
E-mail:	cenmac@cenmac.demon.co.uk
Website:	www.cenmac.demon.co.uk
Contact:	Myra Tingle
E-mail:	myra@cenmac.demon.co.uk

CENMAC supports learners whose educational progress is hindered by their physical inability to communicate effectively through speech and writing. By identifying appropriate technological aids CENMAC helps each to gain equal access to the curriculum. For up-to-date training programme, contact CENMAC or visit the website.

13

Sensory Advice Bureau

Winkfield Resource Centre, 33 Winkfield Road,
London, N22 5RP

Tel: 020 8829 9381

Textphone: 020 8829 9381

Located within the Winkfield Resource Centre, the bureau is for people with physical disabilities. It has some equipment suitable for deaf people on display and an assessment of need can be carried out by specialist staff. The centre is open for equipment advice on Tuesdays, Thursdays and Fridays from 9.30am to 1pm (phone first to check availablility). There is a general Deaf Drop-in on Mondays from 9.30am to 1pm and on Thursdays from 1pm to 4.30pm. A Deaf Women's Group meets 1pm to 4.30pm on Wednesday.

Waltham Forest Disability Resource Centre

1a Warner Road, London, E17 7DY

Tel: 020 8520 8347

Textphone: 020 8520 3860

Fax: 020 8520 7091

Contact: Margaret Elias, Training Officer

Provides activities for people with physical and/or sensory disabilities living in the borough of Waltham Forest. To provide a training scheme for people with physical and/or sensory disabilities to enable them to seek open employment after gaining the necessary skills and self-confidence required.

➢ North Yorkshire
Resource Centre for Deafened People

Bootham House, 61 Bootham, York, YO30 7BT

Tel: 01904 626583

Fax: 01904 626583

The resource centre has display equipment, not for loan or purchase, but so that you can try it and see which works best for you. There is a voluntary visiting service for housebound hearing impaired people, lipreading classes (from September to May) at York College of Further and Higher Education (01904 770200), Thursday coffee mornings and help with caring with your hearing aid.

➢ Oxfordshire
Oxford Access Centre

Omerod School, Waynflete Road, Headington, Oxford, OX3 8DD

Tel: 01865 762508

Fax: 01865 750188

E-mail: ace-cent@dircon.co.uk

Website: www.rmpl.co.uk/eduweb/sites/acecent

Contact: Andrew Lypley

The ACE (Aids to Communication in Education) Centre provides a focus of information and expertise in the use of technology as an aid to communication. It provides a wide variety of services including in-depth assessments of the communication needs of individual young people in education, training of professionals and parents, and research and development.

➢ Plymouth
See Devon

➢ Shropshire
Disability Resource Centre Shrewsbury

Lancaster Road, Shrewsbury, Shropshire, SY1 3NJ

Tel: 01743 444599

Textphone: 01743 444569

Contact centre for details of lipreading classes in Shropshire.

➢ South Yorkshire
RNID Rotherham

Kirk House, Browning Road, Herringthorpe, Rotherham, South Yorkshire, S65 2LG

Tel: 01709 821232

Textphone: 01709 821232

Fax: 01709 821232

Contact: Alex McMurdo

We provide information on local and national services for deaf and hard of hearing people. Facilitate access to community care services in Rotherham. Provide demonstrations of equipment such as loop systems, text phones, smoke alarms and TV amplifiers, etc. to the residents of Rotherham. Provide a text phone advice service.

➤ Southampton
See Hampshire

➤ Staffordshire
Flash Ley Resource Centre
Hawksmoor Road, Stafford, ST17 9DR

Tel:	01785 356830
Textphone:	01785 356830
Fax:	01785 356841
E-mail:	hivipd.service@staffordshire.gov.uk
Contact:	Debra York, Coordinator for Hearing Impairment Services

Staffordshire ASSIST is a post-16 support service for hearing impaired, visually impaired and physically disabled students and trainers. ASSIST supports students in further education, higher education, and training establishments. ASSIST provides a variety of specialist support to deaf students - communication support workers, teachers of the deaf, lipspeakers and notetakers.

➤ Surrey
Merton Hard of Hearing Resource Centre
Crown House, London Road, Morden, Surrey, SM4 5DX

Tel:	020 8540 1650
Fax:	020 8540 6861

A drop-in centre where people with hearing difficulties (and their families and friends) can come for advice, information and support, and try out some of the equipment that might help them. Opening hours are from 10am to 2pm on Mondays, Wednesdays and Fridays. For more information drop in or telephone the coordinator.

Rentwood Resource Centre
School Lane, Fetcham, Leatherhead, Surrey, KT22 9JX

➤ Tyne and Wear
Communicate (Northern England Assistive Technology)
The Lodge, Regional Neurological Rehabilitation Centre, Hunters Road, Newcastle Upon Tyne, Tyne and Wear, NE2 4NR

Tel:	0191 219 5640/1
Fax:	0191 219 5647
Contact:	Liz Panton

Helps identify if a communication aid will help, and if so which one. Talks through problems and solutions. Tries devices. Provides information and advice to professionals, carers, communication aid users and their families. Specialises in work with people of all ages with severe speech impairment - aiming to achieve functional improvements in communication in daily life.

Newcastle General Hospital
Westgate Road, Newcastle upon Tyne, Tyne and Wear, NE4 6BE

Tel:	0191 273 8811 ext 22489
Contact:	Richard Major, Regional Technical Aid Service, Regional Medical Physics Department

The Regional Technical Aid Service covers the area of the former NHS Northern Region and can provide complete solutions to some disability problems where these are not commercially available. Referral to the service is normally through therapists working in the community and further details, including referral forms, can be obtained from the named contact.

South Tyneside Home Loan Equipment Centre
Gordon Street, South Shields, Tyne and Wear, NE33 4JP

Tel:	0191 454 0927
Textphone:	0191 454 0927

South Tyneside Resource Centre
18 Barrington Street (above Registrars office), South Shields, Tyne and Wear, NE33 1AN

Tel:	0191 455 3090
Textphone:	0191 455 2090

Worker available twice weekly to demonstrate equipment. Equipment loaned through Home Loan Equipment Centre - see separate entry.

13

➤ Warwickshire

Abilitynet

P O Box 94, Warwick, CV34 5WS

Tel: 0800 269545 Helpline
01926 312847

Textphone: 0800 269545 Freephone

Fax: 01926 311345

E-mail: enquiries@abilitynet.co.uk

Website: www.abilitynet.co.uk.

Abilitynet is a national charity offering professional expertise in the use of computers by people with all kinds of disabilities. They can provide advice and information. They help anyone with a query relating to computers and disability - employers, professionals in community care, teachers, professional and voluntary organisations, disabled people themselves and their carers. They also provide awareness training and organise conferences.

➤ West Midlands

Access to Communication and Technology

Oak Tree Lane Centre, 91 Oak Tree Lane, Selly Oak, Birmingham, West Midlands, B29 6JA

Tel: 0121 627 8235

Fax: 0121 627 8892

E-mail: actcomtec@aol.com

Contact: Clive Thursfield, Doctor

Provides services for people without verbal communication or disabled people who want access to computers.

Birchfield Resource Centre

Wolverley Crescent, Oldbury, West Midlands, B69 1DH

Coventry Centre for Integrated Living

Faseman Avenue, Tile Hill North, Coventry, West Midlands, CV4 9RB

Tel: 024 7647 1411

Textphone: 024 7647 1008

Fax: 024 7642 2583

Services to Deaf People's Team offers an assessment and care management service to deaf and deafened people aged 18-65 years and an advisory service to under 18s and over 65s.

Disability Resource Centre Yardley

Bierton Road, Yardley, Birmingham, West Midlands, B25 8PQ

Tel: 0121 789 7365

Fax: 0121 789 0104

Contact: D Heap

Fax: 0121 785 0104

Hearing Impaired Unit Dudley

Queens Cross Centre, Wellington Road, Dudley, West Midlands, DY1 1RB

Tel: 01384 813465

Textphone: 01384 242654

Fax: 01384 813465

The Hearing Impaired Unit is a Dudley Metropolitan Borough Council resource and support service. It has a display of environmental equipment; support groups for deaf and hard of hearing people; information room; sign language and lipreading classes. We run a 10-weekly Better Hearing programme for hard of hearing and deafened people.

Rehabilitation Services For Deafened People

Oak Tree Lane Centre, 91 Oak Tree Lane, Selly Oak, Birmingham, West Midlands, B29 6JA

Tel: 0121 627 8930

Textphone: 0121 627 8932

Fax: 0121 627 8931

Contact: Christine Mann, Coordinator/Administrator

A regional NHS service, the centre provides clinical rehabilitation services in individually tailored programmes - audiology, hearing therapy, psychological counselling and speech and language therapy. The centre also provides training services for professionals and lay groups in issues related to acquired hearing loss. Staff at the centre can provide advice on the management of acquired hearing loss and associated problems such as tinnitus, and auditory rehabilitation in people with learning disabilities. The centre provides tinnitus retraining therapy, family sessions dealing with acquired hearing loss and hearing tactics and individual psychological counselling to assist adjustment to acquired hearing loss.

➢ West Yorkshire
Disabled Access to Technology Association
Broomfield House, Bolling Road, Bradford, West Yorkshire, BD4 7BG

Tel: 01274 370019

Textphone: 01274 370019

Provides information about computers and software.

William Merrit Disabled Living Centre
St Mary's Hospital, Green Hill Road, Armley, Leeds, West Yorkshire, LS12 3QE

Tel: 0113 279 3140

Fax: 0113 231 9291

Website: members.ad.com/wmdlc/welcome.htm

Permanent exhibition of products/equipment for potential users to see, try, and be assessed with, to enable informed choice about what items suit each individual. Impartial, accurate and professional advice and information is provided by telephone, post and on visits. Visits by appointment or open days.

➢ York
See North Yorkshire

Eire

➢

National Disability Resource Centre
44 North Great Georges Street, Dublin 1, Eire

Scotland

➢ Lanarkshire
Scottish Centre for Technology for the Communication Impaired
WESTMARC, Southern General NHS Trust, 1345 Govan Road, Glasgow, Lanarkshire, G51 4TF

Tel: 0141 201 2619

Fax: 0141 201 2649

E-mail: sctci@waacis.edex.co.uk

Contact: Janet Scott

➢ Midlothian
Key Comm
St Giles Centre, 40 Broomhouse Crescent, Edinburgh, Midlothian, EH11 3UB

Tel: 0131 443 6775

Fax: 0131 443 5121

E-mail: djans@keycomm.demon.co.uk

Contact: Debbie Jans, Coordinator, Specialist Speech and Language Therapist

KEYCOMM exists to help people with communication impairments make use of technology to contribute to and control their environments. The service is multi-agency funded and is overseen by a strategic management committee.

➢ Morayshire
Moray Resource Centre
Maisondieu Road, Elgin, Morayshire, IV30 1RX

Tel: 01343 551376

Textphone: 01343 551339

Fax: 01343 542014

Contact: Val Swanston, Assistant Social Worker of the Deaf

The Aberdeen and North East Deaf Society has an agency agreement to provide the following range of social services: social work, equipment, interpreters, sign language, lipspeaking, and services for deafblind people. Contact: Rosemary Burt, Principal Officer at the Society's other centre: 13 Smithfield Road, Aberdeen, Scotland AB2 2NR. Tel: 01224 494566/495675 (Voice/Textphone).

National Organisations

This section gives details of national groups representing or working with deaf people such as Hearing Concern, the British Deaf Association and the National Association of Deafened People. It also gives information on professional bodies such as the British Association of Audiology and the British Society of Hearing Therapists.

This section is organised by country within the UK i.e. England, Northern Ireland, Scotland and Wales. Most of the organisations based in England will cover the whole of the UK.

England

Abilitynet

Tel: 0800 269545 Helpline
              01926 312847
Textphone: 0800 269545 Freephone
Fax: 01926 311345
E-mail: enquiries@abilitynet.co.uk
Website: www.abilitynet.co.uk.
Contact: Bill Fine, Senior Consultant

See entry under Resource Centres.

AFASIC - Unlocking Speech and Language

347 Central Markets, Smithfield, London, EC1A 9NH

Tel: 020 7236 6487
Fax: 020 7236 8115
E-mail: info@afasic.org.uk
Website: www.afasic.org.uk/afasic
Contact: Lorna Spenceley

AFASIC campaigns for improved speech therapy services and better special educational facilities for children and young people with specific speech and language disorders. It organises conferences and workshops for parents and professionals, provides an advice and information service, and works to help young people with language disorders train for and gain employment. Parent and professional members meet for mutual support and fundraising activities in many parts of the UK. As well as Activity Week holiday, Activity Days are organised for members' children throughout the year.

Age Concern England

Astral House, 1268 London Road, London, SW16 4ER

Tel: 020 8765 7200
Fax: 020 8679 6069
Website: www:ace.org.uk
Contact: Karen Bradshaw, Information Manager

AIDS Ahead

BDA Health Promotion, 1 Worship Street, London, EC2B 2AB

Tel: 020 7588 3521
Textphone: 020 7588 3520

Advice, information, counselling and other support services on sexual health issues (HIV/AIDS, sexual abuse, rape, drugs, etc) for deaf people. Training and awareness sessions can be arranged.

Alliance of Deaf Service Users and Providers

Centre for Deaf People, Centenary House, North Street, Leeds, West Yorkshire, LS2 8AY

Tel: 0113 243 8328
Textphone: 0113 243 8328
Fax: 0113 243 3553
Contact: Nick Pickard, Deaf Service Team
              Monument House, 5 Upper High Street, Winchester, Hampshire, SO23 8UT
Tel: 01962 845554
Textphone: 01692 845554

ADSUP is committed to developing positive working alliances between actual and potential users, providers and purchasers of personal social services to deaf people. Also to identifying and promoting good practice for inter-agency work between health and social services, education authorities and the private and voluntary sectors in all areas of social policy and social care as they relate to deaf people.

Alliance of Disability Advice and Information Providers

Park Lodge, St Catherine's Hospital, Tickhill Road, Doncaster, South Yorkshire, DN4 8QN

Tel: 01302 570800
Textphone: 01302 570800
Fax: 01302 570801
E-mail: ADAIP@aol.com
Contact: Martin Haresign, Development Worker

To promote and support the development of information services to meet the needs of disabled people. To promote communication and co-operation between national and local disability information services through conferences and training events. To promote networking between services through the production of a quarterly newsletter for members.

Arrow Trust

Bridgwater College, Bath Road, Bridgwater, Somerset, TA6 4PZ

Tel: 01278 446261

Textphone: 01278 446261

Fax: 01278 446261

The Arrow technique is a method of learning used to improve literacy, listening and communication skills in people of all ages and abilities. Training courses are available throughout the UK. The Arrow Trust itself can provide information, advice, educational services, training-including awareness training, and equipment. It also organises workshops and conferences and undertakes research.

Arthritis Care

18 Stephenson Way, London, NW1 2HD

Tel: 020 7916 1500

Fax: 020 7916 1505

E-mail: agreenwood6@compuserve.com

Contact: Ann Greenwood, Information Manager

Arthritis Care is the only national charity working proactively with and for people with arthritis, providing development courses, self-help groups and finding improvements in self-management. In addition we work through 650 local branches and groups with more than 7,000 volunteers, providing information, counselling, publications, holidays, respite care, support and assistance for more than 100,000 people each year.

Asian Deaf Women's Association

c/o Stratford Advice Arcade, 107-109 The Grove, London, E15 1HP

Tel: 020 8221 0581

Textphone: 020 8555 9680

Fax: 020 8221 0582

Contact: Sarla Meisuria, Information and Outreach Worker

The aim of the group is to help deaf Asian women around Britain; to reduce isolation and depression among Asian women; to help with their identities and assist them in awareness of the deaf world and Asian culture. The activities include drop-ins, Women's Group (on Tuesdays), workshops,

training, trips, teaching British Sign Language and assisting in all major areas such as counselling.

Association of British Sign Language Tutors

39 Rowell Way, Chipping Norton, Oxfordshire, OX7 5BD

Tel: 01608 644468

Fax: 01608 644468

Contact: Jacqueline Swinbourne, Secretary

The Association, set up in May 1989, provides information, support and advice to BSL tutor-members on sign language teaching issues. Promotes professional standards, promotes and safeguards the interests of BSL tutor-members, and makes representations on matters relating to sign language assessments. Membership is open to all those involved in BSL teaching.

Association of Disabled Professionals

BCM ADP, London, WC1N 3XX

Tel: 01924 283253

Textphone: 01924 270335

E-mail: AssDisProf@aol.com

This organisation aims to improve the careers prospects of disabled people and represents their interests in all aspects of training and employment

Association of Lipspeakers

Flat 4, 21 Christchurch Avenue, London, NW6 7QP

Tel: 020 8459 7191

Textphone: 020 8459 7191

Contact: Lynn Jackson, Information Officer

The Association of Lipspeakers (ALS) is a membership organisation which promotes the development and training of lipspeakers and offers them support. We publish information for agencies and employers, the legal profession, and users of lipspeakers. 'ALS News' is produced twice a year. We hold two workshops and a conference each year. Full Membership is open to anyone with a lipspeaking qualification; associate membership is open to people who have an interest in lipspeaking.

Association of Sign Language Interpreters

91 Orchard Way, Burwell, Cambridge, CB5 0EQ

Tel: 01638 742480

Textphone: 01638 742480 after 6pm

Fax: 01638 742480

E-mail: aslisec@hotmail.com

Contact: Jim Dunne, Secretary

The Association of Sign Language Interpreters is the professional association and support network for sign language interpreters in England, Wales and Northern Ireland. They aim to encourage good practice in sign language interpreting and represent the views of sign language interpreters and the profession.

Association of Speech and Language Therapists in Independent Practice

58 Cheshire Street, Market Drayton, Shropshire, TF9 1PR

Tel: 01630 655858

Association of Teachers of Lipreading to Adults

P O Box 506, Hanley, Stoke-on-Trent, Staffordshire, ST2 9RE

Contact: Kathryn Bradbury, Information Officer

The aims of ATLA: to provide a professional and recognised association for qualified teachers of lipreading to adults; to maintain and develop standards of lipreading teaching to adults; to promote understanding of the needs of people with an acquired hearing loss, whether partial or total; to advance the awareness of the benefits of lipreading and other communication skills in the rehabilitation of people with an acquired hearing loss; to coordinate and disseminate up to date information on all aspects of acquired deafness and on teaching methods and materials for members of the association; to provide support for qualified lipreading teachers, enabling them to serve the needs of hearing impaired people. A newsletter, 'Catchword', is produced by ATLA for its members.

Benefits Enquiry Line for People with Disabilities

Room 908, Victoria House, Ormskirk Road, Preston, Lancashire, PR1 2QP

Tel: 0800 882200
Textphone: 0800 243355
Fax: 01772 238953
Contact: Cathy Webster, Customer Services Manager
Tel: 01772 238994

BEL provides advice and information about all social security benefits for people with disabilities, their carers and representatives. BEL has no access to personal records and can provide general advice only. BEL also provides help over the telephone for people needing help to fill in disability-related claim packs. Help with filling in forms can also be provided in braille or large print. The lines are open Monday to Friday from 8.30am to 6.30pm and from 9am to 1pm on Saturday. BEL holds external focus groups twice a year where it consults with customers about the service they receive and asks for suggestions on how it can be improved.

Black and Asian Sign Language Interpreters' Network

194 Ravens Way, London, SE12 8HD

BASLIN is the professional network for Black and Asian sign language interpreters. BASLIN aims to: create a network and professional body of Black and Asian sign language interpreters; provide a forum for Black and Asian sign language interpreters to raise and discuss issues pertinent to our work in the interpreting field; provide mutual support and to encourage and empower each other, thereby enabling personal and professional development; develop a pool of expertise and experience, which can be made available to service users and providers. It welcomes all Black and Asian sign language interpreters who hold a minimum of CACDP Stage 3 certificate and who are committed to professional development.

Breakthrough Trust

Alan Geale House, The Close, Westhill Campus, Bristol Road, Selly Oak, Birmingham, West Midlands, B29 6LN

Tel: 0121 472 6447
Textphone: 0121 472 6447
Fax: 0121 415 2323
E-mail: TThompbthu@aol.com
Contact: Terry Thompson, Trust Director

From regional centres, Breakthrough works to improve the lives of deaf people through: contact with a wide variety of integrated social activities; information on culture and language with available technology and services; and training - developing skills which enable deaf and hearing people to work together.

British Acoustic Neuroma Association

Sherwood House, Ransom Wood Park, Southwell Road West, Mansfield, Nottinghamshire, NG21 0HJ

Tel: 01623 632143
Fax: 01623 635313
E-mail: danchris9@aol.com

British Aphasiology Society

High Heaton, Newcastle-upon-Tyne, Tyne and Wear, NE7 7DN

Tel: 0191 284 3111 ext 26644

British Association of Audiological Physicians

National Hospital of Neurology and Neurosurgery, Queen Square, London, WC1N 3BG

Tel: 020 7837 3611

Fax: 020 7829 8720

E-mail: rosdavies@mcmail-com

Contact: Rosalyn Davies, Honorary Secretary Department of Neuro-Otology

Fax: 020 7829 8775

The aims of the Association are: to provide an opportunity for consultants in audiological medicine to discuss items of mutual interest; to provide an opinion relevant to audiological medicine to those bodies which might wish to request such; to concern itself with training programmes and professional standards within specialty; to disseminate information about the specialty. The Association also provides advice, education, conducts research and holds awareness training on its subject area.

British Association of Audiological Scientists

Wrexham Maelor Hospital, Audiology Department, Wrexham, Clwyd, LL13 7TD

Tel: 01734 660622

Fax: 01734 351915

E-mail: www.isvr.soton.ac.uk/BAAS

Contact: John Day, Chair

Tel: 01734 966 0622

Fax: 01352 750469

BAAS is established to promote the following aims and objectives: to develop, support and promote delivery of high quality, effective healthcare and research in audiology in the UK; to develop, support and promote an appropriate training base for the profession with CPD and maintenance of standards; to support individual members on professinal matters, represent its members in dealings with other bodies; to provide a forum for the discussion of professional matters for audiological scientists.

British Association of Audiology Technicians

c/o Audiology Department, Port Talbot Hospital, Hospital Road, Port Talbot, West Glamorgan, SA12 6PD

Contact: Janet Evans, Publicity Officer Audiology Department

Tel: 01639 762667/ 762276

BAAT exists to advance and protect the professional interests of its members. It advises on the education and training of audiologists, promotes and maintains standards, and conducts professional examinations for which BAAT is the awarding body. The majority of its members are British-based and work in the NHS.

British Association of Community Doctors in Audiology

23 Stokesay Road, Sale, Cheshire, M33 6QN

Tel: 0161 962 8915

Fax: 0161 291 9398

Contact: Pam Williams, Secretary

The Association provides information and educational services for members and professionals working in the field. It also organises conferences.

British Association of Educational Audiologists

c/o STS, Western Annexe, County Hall, Glenfield, Leicester, LE3 8RF

Tel: 0116 265 6131

Textphone: 0116 265 6131

Fax: 0116 265 6958

E-mail: simonblake@baea.freeserve.co.uk

Contact: Simon Blake

British Association of Otorhinolaryngologists - Head and Neck Surgeons

The Royal College of Surgeons of England, 35/43 Lincolns Inn Fields, London, WC2A 3PN

Tel: 020 7404 8373

Fax: 020 7404 4200

E-mail: orl@bao-hns.demon.co.uk

Website: www.orlt-baohns.org.uk

Contact: Barbara Komoniewska, Administrative Secretary

The Association aims to promote the highest quality and standards of medical and surgical practice of the specialty for the benefit of patients and to encourage its future advancement through

14

education, research and audit.

British Association of Teachers of the Deaf

41 The Orchard, Leven, Beverley, East Riding of Yorkshire, HU17 5QA

Tel:	01865 792890/ 01964 544243
Fax:	01865 792890/ 01964 544243
E-mail:	batodsec@compuserve.com
Website:	www.rmplc.co.uk/orgs/batod
Contact:	Paul Simpson, Hon Secretary
	18 Moberly Close, 134c Cowley Road, Oxford, OX4 1HX

BATOD is the sole UK association representing the interests of Teachers of the Deaf. Regional and national meetings are organised to promote the education of deaf children and young people. Strong links are maintained between BATOD and government and voluntary agencies to contribute to policy development in this field.

British Computer Society Disability Group

c/o Room C126, EASAMS Ltd, West Hanningfield Road, Great Baddow, Chelmsford, Essex, CM2 8HN

Tel:	01245 242950
Fax:	01245 478317
E-mail:	geoffrey.busby@gecm.com
Website:	www.abilitynet.co.uk
Contact:	Christine Goldsmith, Subscription Secretary

The British Computer Society (BCS) Disability Group is a voluntary organisation which aims to identify and promote ways in which computer technology can improve the quality of life of people with disabilities. It promotes the concept of universal access through 'design for all'. For further details of the group's activities, please contact Christine Goldsmith.

British Council of Organisations of Disabled People

Litchurch Plaza, Litchurch Lane, Derby, DE24 8AA

Tel:	01332 295551
Textphone:	01332 295581
Fax:	01332 295580
E-mail:	jenny@bcodp.demon.co.uk

BCODP was founded in 1981 to provide a national representative voice of organisations controlled and managed by disabled people. It promotes the equality and integration of disabled people in society through dialogue with government and other bodies, campaigning and research. It has an information centre providing details of disability issues being addressed by, or of concern to, the disabled people's movement and its organisation.

British Deaf Association

1-3 Worship Street, London, EC2A 2AB

Tel:	020 7588 3520
Textphone:	020 7588 3529
Fax:	020 7588 3527
E-mail:	inf@bda.org.uk
Website:	www.bda.org.uk
Contact:	Nick Sturley, Information Officer

The overall objective of the BDA is to advance and protect the interests of the Deaf Community and to ensure greater awareness of their rights and responsibilities. The BDA believes deaf people should be enabled, through equal access, to take their full place as members of the wider national community. It provides information and advice, organises conferences, undertakes research, campaigns on issues affecting deaf people and provides information exchange. They also run services for young people, deaf gay/bi-sexual men, a health promotion project, and the London Deaf Access Project for production of videos. Their services are available to all.

British Deaf History Society

49 Whitton Close, Doncaster, South Yorkshire, DN4 7RB

E-mail:	chris@ionic.demon.co.uk
Website:	www.ionic.demon.co.uk/index.htm
Contact:	A Boyce

British Deaf History Society's objectives are to encourage the study of and to foster interest in Deaf history; to encourage the preservation of records and materials related to the deaf and of historical value; to produce publications in connection with Deaf history. BDHS activities: three 'Deaf History Journal' issues are distributed to members every year; workshops for local Deaf history are arranged; books and documents on deaf history are printed; campaigns for preservation of deaf materials; projects on Deaf history are supported and funded wherever applicable; collaborates with the established local Deaf history centres and international Deaf History Societies; collaborate with universities and colleges and schools on Deaf history studies; catalogues on deaf issues are compiled and updated in collaboration with libraries and archives.

14

British Deaf Sports Council

7a Bridge Street, Otley, West Yorkshire, LS21 1BQ

Tel: 01943 850214

Textphone: 01943 850081

Fax: 01943 850828

Contact: Roland Haythornthwaite, Executive Director

The BDSC promotes sports and leisure opportunities for deaf people through regional clubs, national championships and international championships (including the World Games of the Deaf which are recognised by the International Olympic Committee and run under their auspices). The BDSC newsletter is available quarterly.

British Dyslexia Society

98 London Road, Reading, Berkshire, RG1 5AU

Tel: 01734 668 271

British Educational Communication and Technology Agency

University of Warwick Science Park, Milburn Hill Road, Coventry, West Midlands, CV4 7JJ

Tel: 024 76416994

Fax: 024 7641 1418

E-mail: becta@becta.org.uk

Website: www.becta.org.uk

Contact: Terry Waller, Special Needs

Tel: 024 7641 6994

Contact us for information regarding computers and software.

British Medical Association

BMA House, Tavistock Square, London, WC1H 9JP

Tel: 020 7387 4499

Fax: 020 7383 6400

Website: www.bma.org.uk

The BMA is a professional association of doctors, representing their interests and providing services for its 111,000-plus members. This includes 4,500 from overseas and 10,500 who are medical students. More than 80% of British doctors are members. The BMA is an independent trade union, a scientific and edcuational body, a publishing house, a limited company funded largely by its members. The BMA does not: register doctors, that is the responsibility of the General Medical Council; discipline doctors, that is the province of the employer/health authority and/or the GMC; recommend individual doctors to patients.

British Psychological Society

St Andrew's House, 48 Princess Road East, Leicester, LE1 7DR

Tel: 0116 254 9568

Fax: 0116 247 0787

E-mail: mail@bps.org.uk

Website: www.bps.org.uk

A professional body and learned society for psychologists in the UK.

British Society for Mental Health and Deafness

Tel: 020 8682 6925

Fax: 020 8682 6950

Contact: Jean Drewett, Administrator

See entry under Mental Health.

British Society of Audiology

80 Brighton Road, Reading, Berkshire, RG6 1PS

Tel: 0118 966 0622

Fax: 0118 935 1915

E-mail: bsa@b-s-a.demon.co.uk

Website: www.b-s-a.demon.co.uk/index.html

Contact: Ann Allen, Administrative Secretary

Furtherance of science and audiology and of clinical audiological practice. The enhancement of audiological practice by education and research.

British Society of Hearing Aid Audiologists

Bridle Croft, Burgh Heath Road, Epsom, Surrey, KT17 4LS

Tel: 01372 725348

Contact: Alan Crego-Bourne, Secretary

BSHAA is the trade association for hearing aid dispensers in the private sector. It campaigns to encourage education and training in the application of hearing aid audiology. It organises conferences, study courses and examinations for trainee dispensers. A members' newsletter is published. Information is provided to the public, professionals and people involved in academic research.

14

British Society of Hearing Therapists

Audiology Department, Musgrove Park Hospital, Musgrove Park, Taunton, Somerset, TA1 5DA

Tel: 01823 342188
Textphone: 01823 342158
Fax: 01823 336877
Contact: Lisa Richards, BSHT Information Officer

A hearing therapist's role is to provide a comprehensive rehabilitation service for adults who have learning difficulties and/associated disorders, such as tinnitus and balance problems. Most hearing therapists work as part of a multi-disciplinary team comprising health, social service and voluntary workers.

British Stammering Association

15 Old Ford Road, London, E2 9PJ

Tel: 020 8983 1003

British Tinnitus Association

Tel: 0800 018 0527 Freephone
             0114 273 0122
Fax: 0114 279 6222
E-mail: tinnitus@dial.pipex.com
Contact: Val Rose, Operations/ Publications
             Manager

See entry under Tinnitus.

Broadcasting Support Services

252 Western Avenue, London, W3 6XZ

Central Council for Education and Training in Social Work

Derbyshire House, St. Chad's Street, London, WC1H 8AD

Tel: 020 7278 2455
Fax: 020 7278 2934
E-mail: info-london@ccetsw.org.uk
Contact: Ngozi Odigbo, Project Officer
Tel: 020 7520 3522

The central body responsible for co-ordinating the education and training in Social Work.

Centre for Accessible Environments

Nutmeg House, 60 Gainsford Street, London, SE1 2NY

Tel: 020 7357 8182
Textphone: 020 7357 8182
Fax: 020 7357 8183

Centre for Studies on Inclusive Education

1 Redland Close, Elm Lane, Redland, Bristol, Avon, BS6 6UE

Tel: 0117 923 8450
Fax: 0117 923 8460

CHANGE

First Floor, 69-85 Old Street, London, EC1V 9HU

Tel: 020 7490 2668
Textphone: 020 7490 3483
Videotel: 020 7490 1745
Fax: 020 7490 3581
E-mail: contact@changeuk.demon.co.uk
Contact: Pauline Latchem

CHANGE is a national organisation for people with learning disabilities, especially those who are blind or deaf. It supports people with learning disabilities to set their own standards of care; it provides training for managers, staff and people who work with people with learning disabilities. CHANGE also works on various projects with other organisations, gives out information and campaigns for equal rights. All CHANGE's information is easily accessible through the use of short words and sentences and illustrations. CHANGE will also support people with learning disabilites and staff to access British Sign Language.

Child 2000

P O Box 350, Buckingham, MK18 5EL

Tel: 020 7272 7774
Textphone: 020 7272 9648
Fax: 020 7272 6012

14

ChildLine

2nd Floor, Royal Mail Building, Studd Street, London, N1 0QW

Tel: 0800 1111 Helpline
 020 7239 1000 Administration

Textphone: 0800 400 222 7.30am-9.30pm

Fax: 020 7239 1001 Administration

Website: www.childline.org.uk

Contact: Jenny Seale, Information Officer

ChildLine is the free, national helpline for children and young people in danger or distress. It provides a confidential phone counselling service for any child with any problem 24 hours a day, every day. Trained counsellors provide support and advice and refer children in danger to appropriate helping agencies. ChildLine also brings to public attention issues affecting children's welfare and rights.

Cleft Lip and Palate Association

235-237 Finchley Road, London, NW3

Tel: 020 7431 0033

Fax: 020 7431 8881

E-mail: clapa@mcmail.com

Website: www.clapa.mcmail.com

Contact: Gareth Davies

CLAPA is a support organisation for all those with - and affected by - cleft lip and palate. The charity was set up in 1979 as a partnership between parents and health professionals concerned with the care and treatment of cleft lip and palate.

Communication Forum

P O Box 854, 3 Dufferin Street, London, EC1Y 8NB

Communication Matters

c/o Lancashire Schools IT Centre, 103 Preston New Road, Blackburn, Lancashire, BB2 6BJ

Tel: 01254 673303

Augmentative and alternative communication.

Council for the Advancement of Communication with Deaf People (CACDP)

Durham University Science Park, Block 4, Stockton Road, Durham, DH1 3UZ

Tel: 0191 383 1155

Textphone: 0191 383 7915

Fax: 0191 383 7914

E-mail: durham@cacdp.demon.co.uk

Contact: Sarah Marshall, Publicity Officer

CACDP aims to improve communication between deaf and hearing people by the development of training and examinations in communication skills. It offers certification in sign communication skills (sign language, lipspeaking and communicating with deafblind people) and carries out the training, selection, monitoring and registration of examiners. CACDP maintains a register of qualified interpreters and publishes annually a national directory of sign language interpreters, lipspeakers and interpreters for deafblind people who are not only of a required standard but are also available to undertake interpreting assignments. CACDP also produces a membership magazine called 'CACDP Standard'.

Deaf Broadcasting Council

70 Blacketts Wood Drive, Chorleywood, Rickmansworth, Hertfordshire, WD3 5QQ

Tel: 01923 283127

Textphone: 01923 283127

Fax: 01923 283127

E-mail: dmyers@cix.co.uk

Website: www.waterlow.com.dbc

Contact: Ruth Myers, Honorary Secretary

The DBC is a consumer organisation to which all the major organisations for and on behalf of deaf, deafened and hard of hearing people are affiliated. Its aim is to ensure that the voice of the consumer is heard by broadcasters and that suitable access is provided to the full range of programmes.

Deaf Diabetic Group

BID Centre for Deaf People, Ladywood Road, Birmingham, West Midlands, B16 8SZ

Textphone: 0121 246 6101

Fax: 0121 246 6125

E-mail: bid@bid.org.uk

Website: www.bid.org.uk

Contact: Ruth Beer, BID Information Officer

A new group set up in Birmingham, with support from the British Diabetic Associaiton and Birmingham Institute for Deaf People. Aims to

14

bring in speakers and produce information videos presented in British Sign Language, posters and leaflets written in plain English, or any other language the community requires, for example Hindi.

Deaf Education Through Listening and Talking (DELTA)

P O Box 20, Haverhill, Suffolk, CB9 7BD

Tel: 01440 783689

Contact: Wendy Barnes, National Director

DELTA is a nationwide support group of teachers and parents of deaf children which provides wide-ranging support, information and advice to guide parents in helping their deaf children to develop normal spoken language, and to live independently within hearing society.

Deaf Ex-Mainstreamers Group

DEX, P O Box 102, Barnsley, South Yorkshire, S72 9YT

This group runs contact reunions and socials for deaf people who have been through mainstream schools.

Deafblind UK

Tel: 01733 358100/ 0800 132320 Helpline
Textphone: 01733 358100/ 358858
Fax: 01733 358356
E-mail: jackie@deafblnd.demon.co.uk
Contact: Maureen Jobson, Service Manager

See entry under Deafblind Resources.

DeafMail

47 Bennetts Way, Shirley, Croydon, Surrey, CR0 8AE

Tel: 0800 515152
            020 8777 2994 via Typetalk
Textphone: 020 8777 2994
Fax: 020 8777 2994
E-mail: deafmail@cix.co.uk
Website: www.deafmail.org.uk
Contact: Roy Staines, Coordinator

Deaf Mail is an E-mail orientated deaf organisation which is respected for the quality of its services and information content. Deaf Mail provides facilities for its members to meet electronically in a friendly and helpful atmosphere and represents them on their consumer issues as well as providing whatever assistance that is needed.

Defeating Deafness

330-332 Gray's Inn Road, London, WC1X 8DA

Tel: 020 7833 1733
Textphone: 020 7915 1695
Fax: 020 7278 0404
E-mail: defeating.deafness@ucl.ac.uk
Website: www.ilo.ac.uk/ddeaf/index.htm

Defeating Deafness is the only national charity dedicated to helping deaf and hearing impaired people through research. Supported entirely by voluntary contributions, it aims to encourage and finance research into the prevention, diagnosis, treatment and cure of hearing difficulties and to educate people about hearing problems by providing information and advice.

Disability Awareness in Action

DPIEUC, 11 Belgrave Road, London, SW1V 1RB

Tel: 020 7834 0477
            020 7821 9812
Fax: 020 7821 9539

Down's Syndrome Association

155 Mitcham Road, London, SW17 9PG

Tel: 020 8682 4001
Fax: 020 8682 4001
E-mail: info@downs-syndrome.org.uk
Contact: Carol Boys, Director

The object of the Association is to create and develop the conditions which will enable people with Down's Syndrome to attain their full potential

Foundation for Communication for the Disabled

Beacon House, Pyrford Road, West Byfleet, Surrey, KT14 6LD

Tel: 01932 336512

FCD helps people with communication problems. Clients have a range of need, including help with impaired reading from dyslexia, impaired writing from physical or visual disability, and impaired speaking. The charity gives unbiased assessments, training and support in the use of computers.
The FCD also prepares, free to disabled people, tailored specialist support materials and continuing advice. Seminars and updates on new computer technology are open to disabled people, healthcare professionals, teachers, social workers and anyone else involved in solving communication problems.

14

Friends for Young Deaf People

East Court Mansion, College Lane, East Grinstead, West Sussex, RH19 3LT

Tel:	01342 323444
Textphone:	01342 312639
Fax:	01342 410232
Contact:	Morag Rosie, President

FYD encourages and enables young deaf people to equip themselves to become active members of society. Our training programme helps build their self-confidence and independence, enabling them to take positive control of their lives. Various projects and activities are organised throughout the country.

Genetic Interest Group

Unit 4D Leroy House, 436 Essex Road, London, N1 3QP

Tel:	020 7704 3141
Textphone:	020 7430 0092
Fax:	020 7359 1447
E-mail:	mail@gig.org.uk
Website:	www.gig.org.uk
Contact:	Saskia Ottignon, Administrator

The Genetic Interest Group is the umbrella body for charities, voluntary organisations and support groups for individuals and families affected by genetic conditions. It provides awareness raising and training programmes for lay and professional groups, and information (by post or over the telephone) to individuals, students and professionals. It can also provide information about access to services and support for individuals and families affected by or at risk from genetic disorders, and for the professionals working with them.

Hearing Aid Council

Witan Court, 305 Upper Fourth Street, Central Milton Keynes, Buckinghamshire, MK9 1EH

Tel:	01908 235700
Fax:	01908 233770
Contact:	Christopher Reid, Registrar

The Council has power under the Hearing Aid Council Act 1968 to grant admission to the Register, thus granting authority to dispense hearing aids in the private sector. It is an offence for unqualified personnel who are not registered to practise. Admission to the Register is by training and examination. The Council has disciplinary powers which include expulsion from the Register. It does not, however, act on behalf of individual members of the public in obtaining recompense. If difficulties arise out of the private dispensing of a hearing aid, the Council is always interested in the facts, with a view to taking any action that might be appropriate using its powers as granted by the 1968 Act.

Hearing Aided Young Adults

7-11 Armstrong Road, Acton, London, W3 7JL

Tel:	020 8743 1110
	01245 344600 Helpline
Textphone:	020 8742 9151
Fax:	020 8742 9043
E-mail:	hearing.concern@ukonline.co.uk
Website:	www.ukonline.co.uk/hearing.concern
Contact:	Gary West, Membership Services Manager, Hearing Aided Young Adults
Tel:	020 8743 1110

Hearing Aided Young Adults (HAYA!) is the youth section of Hearing Concern, with groups across the UK, and is run by and for young people from 18-29 years of age. Level of hearing loss is not important, communication is by speech, lipreading and Sign Supported English. The group is not really suitable for strong British Sign Language users. HAYA! runs a membership scheme and organises activities, social and educational weekend trips. It also has a pen friend scheme.

Hearing Concern

7-11 Armstrong Road, Acton, London, W3 7JL

Tel:	020 8743 1110
	01245 344600 Helpline
Textphone:	020 8742 9151
Fax:	020 8742 9043
E-mail:	hearing.concern@ukonline.co.uk
Website:	www.ukonline.co.uk/hearing.concern
Contact:	Mike Theobald, Chairman

Hearing Concern is a self-help membership organisation which assists and promotes all activities that relieve and support hard of hearing people. It provides advisers, deaf awareness training initiatives and encouragement for campaigns and research, clubs, liaisons with professional organisations, quarterly magazines, advice and useful information for all adult ages.

14

Hearing Concern National Telephone Helpline

Suite E, Imperial House, Victoria Road, Chelmsford, Essex, CM1 1NY

Tel: 01245 344600

Textphone: 01245 344600

Fax: 01245 280747

Hearing Dogs for Deaf People

The Training Centre, London Road (A40), Lewknor, Oxfordshire, OX9 5RY

Tel: 01844 353898

Textphone: 01844 353898

Fax: 01844 353099

E-mail: info@hearing-dogs.co.uk

Website: www.hearing-dogs.co.uk

Contact: Gillian Lacey, Deaf Liaison Officer

Hearing Dogs for Deaf People trains carefully selected dogs to alert severely, profoundly or totally deaf people to the everyday sounds which hearing people may take for granted such as the alarm clock, doorbell, etc. Potential owners are carefully assessed. They must have the desire to look after a dog properly. Hearing dog recipients receive assistance in the care and support of their dogs, with free veterinary check-ups and vaccinations. The scheme has been in operation since 1982. It is totally reliant on funding from the general public, companies clubs, etc.

Institute of Acoustics

Agriculture House, 5 Holywell Hill, St Albans, Hertfordshire, AL1 1EU

Tel: 01727 848195

Fax: 01727 850553

Institute of Hearing Research

Medical Research Council, University Park, Nottingham, NG7 2RD

Tel: 0115 922 3431

Fax: 0115 951 8503

E-mail: janep@ihr.mrc.ac.uk

Website: www.ihr.mrc.ac.uk/welcome.htm

Contact: Jane Paulson, Administrator

Website: www.ihr.mrc.ac.uk

The Medical Research Council is a government-funded body that exists to conduct medical and related biological research in the UK. The MRC Institute of Hearing Research exists to do long-range applicable research on hearing and hearing disorders designed to improve both basic understanding and applications in the healthcare system.

214

Institute of Laryngology and Otology

330-332 Gray's Inn Road, London, WCIX 8EE

Tel: 020 7915 1308

Fax: 020 7837 9276

E-mail: anthony.wright@ucl.ac.uk

Website: www.ilo.ucl.ac.uk/index.htm

Contact: S Overington, Adminstrator

Tel: 020 7915 1308 ext 4218

The Institute conducts postgraduate teaching and research. Its services are available to professionals and people involved in academic research. The Institute also holds the RNID Library which is open to the general public.

Jewish Deaf Association

Julius Newman House, Woodside Park Road, off High Road, North Finchley, London, N12 8RP

Tel: 020 8446 0502

Textphone: 020 8446 0502

Videotel: 020 8446 0765

Fax: 020 8445 7451

E-mail: jda@dircon.co.uk

Contact: Pat Goldring, Executive Director

The JDA is a totally independent organisation, housed in a purpose-built centre, working from North London. Services include: a weekly social club for profoundly deaf people, offering a Kosher meal, lectures on deaf issues and games; computer courses; visits to places of interest; sign language classes; lipreading classes; hard of hearing cultural club; tinnitus self-help group; deaf awareness programmes; resource centre; Koleinu - a support group for deaf youngsters and their families. Most of their activities and services are open to people of all faiths. The Resource Centre is fitted with equipment that is available from the local social services (London Borough of Barnet) and the Resource Centre Co-ordinator, Helen Rabin, carries out assessments for equipment and makes recommendations to the social services department on behalf of the client. The centre is fully accessible and people may become members of the JDA.

LASER

8 Church Lane, Kimpton, Hitchin, Hertfordshire, SG4 8RP

Tel: 01438 832676

Textphone: 01438 832676

Contact: Riki Kittel, Treasurer

LASER is a forum for the development of the use of bilingualism in the education of deaf children. Membership comprises deaf people, professionals working within the field and parents of deaf children. LASER runs conferences and workshops and publishes a tri-annual newsletter 'Laserbeam' with professional articles, up-to-date research and news.

Lipservice

Milton House, Stratfield Saye, Reading, Berkshire, RG7 2BT

Tel: 01256 882740

Fax: 01306 884317

Contact: Alison Tongue

Lipservice has produced two fully subtitled videos to assist hard of hearing people. ' Look Hear: an introduction to lipreading', is a one-hour video teaches the viewer the fundementals of lipreading, in easy steps. Endorsed by the RNID, this video will improve the quality of life not only of the hearing impaired person but also that of the friends and relations who often share the problems. 'How to cope with hearing loss', introduced by Desmond Wilcox, is a 45-minute video shows how life for anybody with a hearing problem can be made easier. It provides useful tips on how to cope with everyday problems more successfully. It also includes a section on lipreading and shows the latest gadgets and technical innovations to help people with a hearing loss. Each video is priced at £19.00; however, if you buy both of them together the cost is £30.00 including post and packing. Cheques should be made payable to Lipservice and sent to the above address.

Local Government Association

26 Chapter Street, London, SW1P 4ND

Tel: 020 7235 1066

Textphone: 020 7235 1066

Fax: 020 7664 3227

Website: www.lga.gov.uk

Contact: Nick Georgiou, Information Department

Low Frequency Noise Sufferers Association

6 Hyatt Place, Shepton Mallet, Somerset, BA4 5XY

Tel: 01749 345643 Evenings

Contact: Elizabeth Griggs

Makaton Vocabulary Development Project mvdp

31 Firwood Drive, Camberley, Surrey, GU15 3QD

Tel: 01276 681368

E-mail: mvdp@makaton.org

Website: www.makaton.org

Contact: Margaret Walker, Director

The project aims to support users of the Makaton Vocabulary Programme through a network of Makaton tutors (national and international), by providing training, and developing and supplying resource materials. Workshops are held throughout the country. Details are available from Margaret Walker at the above address.
The centre promotes, maintains and advances the general welfare and education of deaf people, by providing access to information and instruction in the use of Cued Speech. The Centre provides day, evening, weekend, residential and regional courses in Cued Speech.

Ménière's Society

98 Maybury Road, Woking, Surrey, GU21 5HX

Tel: 01483 740597

Textphone: 01483 771207

Fax: 01483 755441

Contact: Brenda Shield, Director

The Society strives to promote greater understanding and awareness of this condition and related balance disorders. It also maintains links with similar organisations all over the world. The Ménière's Society was founded to help people who suffer from Ménière's Disease and associated balance disorders. For details of membership please contact the Society at the above address.

Michael Palin Centre for Stammering Children

Finsbury Health Centre, Pine Street, London, EC1R 0JH

Tel: 020 7530 4238

Fax: 020 7833 3842

The Centre sees children from the ages of 2 years 6 months to 18, and can offer an initial assessment funded by the charity that is part of the organisation. The Centre is not private, rather it is NHS based but with charity funding. It offers intensive courses for children aged between 9 and 14 during the Easter and summer vacations and will also see adults living within the Camden and Islington Health Trust area.

14

National Association for Special Educational Needs

NASEN House, Amber Close, Amington, Tamworth, Staffordshire, B77 4RP

Tel: 01827 311500

Fax: 01827 313005

NASEN aims to promote the development of children and young people with special educational needs (SEN) and support those who work with them. It organises local, regional and national activities throughout the UK. NASEN has branches throughout the UK and through these local and national networks, teachers, parents, governors and other professionals can receive up-to-date information on SEN provision and practice in the UK. NASEN also has four professional committees: curriculum, professional development, policy and research. A range of publications is available, as are the three journals produced by NASEN.

National Association of Citizens Advice Bureaux

115-123 Pentonville Road, London, N1 9LZ

Tel: 020 7833 2181

Fax: 020 7883 4371

See entry under Information, Advice and Legal Services.

National Association of Deafened People

P O Box 50, Amersham, Buckinghamshire, HP6 6XB

Tel: 01494 723613

Textphone: 01494 723613

Fax: 01494 431932

The NADP is an Association run by and for deafened people. The Association offers help, advice and support for those who have lost most of all of their useful hearing. It runs a help desk providing information and publications on benefits, employment, communication and environmental aids and cochlear implants, etc. It supports a network of local self-help groups and produces a quarterly newsletter for members.

National Association of Tertiary Education for Deaf People

c/o SASU, Coventry Technical College, The Butts, Coventry, West Midlands, CV1 3GD

Contact: Christine Fenton, Membership Secretary

NATED promotes and develops opportunities for deaf students in further, higher and continuing education and training. NATED has influenced examination boards to allow adaptations to exam papers for deaf students. Each year there are three open meetings on themes relating to post-16 education and three newsletters, one each term.

National Autistic Society

276 Willesden Lane, London, NW2 5RB

Tel: 020 8451 1114

National Centre for Cued Speech

29-30 Watling Street, Canterbury, Kent, CT1 2UD

Tel: 01227 450757

Fax: 01227 784407

Contact: June Dixon-Millar, Director

The Centre provides advice, information, speakers, courses and certification in Cued Speech. Research has shown that Cued Speech, which is a sound-based communication tool, enables children and adults to absorb and use spoken language accurately and effectively with hearing people, not only orally but also for writing and reading.

National Cochlear Implant Users Association

Marjorie Sherwin House, 83 Sherwin Road, Nottingham, NG7 2FB

Fax: 01494 484993

E-mail: alisonh@horsleys.demon.co.uk

To provide a forum for cochlear implant users, their partners, families and other interested people. To publicise the value of cochlear implants as cost-effective treatment for suitable patients. To provide information about implants. We also have links with local cochlear implant users' support groups and their programmes.

National Committee of Professionals in Audiology

80 Brighton Road, Reading, Berkshire, RG6 1PS

Tel: 0118 966 0622

Fax: 0118 935 1915

National Council for Voluntary Organisations

Regents Wharf, 8 All Saints Street, London, N1 9RL

Tel: 020 7713 6161
Textphone: 020 7278 1289
Fax: 020 7713 6300
E-mail: ncvo@compuserve.com
Website: www.ncvo-vol.org.uk
Contact: Roger Hitt, Information Services Manager

National Deaf Children's Society

15 Dufferin Street, London, EC1Y 8UR

Tel: 020 7250 0123 Helpline
020 7490 8656
Textphone: 020 7250 0123 Helpline
Videotel: 020 7251 4303
Fax: 020 7251 5020
E-mail: ndcs@ndcs.org.uk

The National Deaf Children's Society is the UK's leading organisation for deaf children, their families and carers. Since 1944, the Society has been working to enable deaf children to maximise their skills and abilities, and provide support, information and advice to parents and carers on all aspects of childhood deafness.

National Deaf Children's Sports Association

Thorn Park School, Thorn Lane, Bradford, West Yorkshire, BD9 6RY

Tel: 01274 497866

Contact: Michael Pulford, Secretary

The Association organises sporting activities such as cricket, athletics, football and cross-country competitions for schools and units.

National Deaf Mental Health Services

Denmark House, Mendelsohn Way, Edgbaston, Birmingham, West Midlands, B15 2QZ

Tel: 0121 627 2930
Textphone: 0121 627 2871
Fax: 0121 627 2934
Contact: Peter Jackson, Community Services Manager, Deaf Service

See entry under Mental Health

National Disability Council

Level 4, Caxton Street, Tothill Street, London, SW1H 9NA

Tel: 020 7273 5636
Textphone: 020 7273 5645
Fax: 020 7273 5929
Website: www.open.gov.uk/ndc/ndchome.htm
Contact: Michael Flemming

Ministerial responsibilities for disability issues have transferred to the Department of Education and Employment, and the National Disability Council offices are now based at the DfEE at the above address.

National Meningitis Trust

Fern House, Bath Road, Stroud, Gloucestershire, GL5 3TJ

Tel: 01453 751738
Fax: 01453 753588
Contact: Susan Bath, Helpline Manager
Tel: 01453 768000

The National Meningitis Trust has three main aims: supporting sufferers and their families, increasing public awareness and raising vital funds for research. A 24-hour nurse-led Helpline is in operation for anyone concerned about meningitis on 0845 6000800.

National Subtitling Library for Deaf People

Tel: 0161 449 9650
Textphone: 0161 449 9650
Fax: 0161 449 9650
Contact: Beryl Roberts, Administrator

See entry under Arts and Leisure.

NHS Direct Health Information Service

Tel: 0800 665544 Freephone

Anyone can call the freephone number at any time from 10am-5pm, Monday to Friday. Staff will be able to either give an immediate reply, direct you to another source for the information you need, call you back, send information through the post or do further research. The Health Information Service is purely an information service. Its staff are not doctors and cannot diagnose illnesses or give personal counselling. They can, however, tell you how to contact clinics, counselling services or self-help groups which may be able to help. The Service operates on a local basis. Calls are automatically routed to the nearest office so that information about hospital services, self-help groups and many other matters is all relevant to

14

your own area.

Paget Gorman Society

2 Dowlands Bungalows, Dowlands Lane,
Smallfield, Horley, Surrey, RH6 9SD

Tel: 0134 284 2308

Website: www.pgss.org

The Paget Gorman Society exists to help children
and young people with speech and language
disorders to communicate and develop language
skills through the use of Paget Gorman Signed
Speech (PGSS).

Royal Association for Disability and Rehabilitation

12 City Forum, 250 City Road, London, EC1V 8AF

Tel: 020 7250 3222

Textphone: 020 7250 4119

Fax: 020 7250 0212

E-mail: radar@radar.org.uk

Website: www.radar.org.uk

Contact: Bert Massie, Director

RADAR is one of the principal charities in the field
of disability. It campaigns for disabled people's
rights and for the full integration of disabled
people in all aspects of society. It has an
information and advisory service and a small team
of regional officers, and is particularly active in the
areas of legislation, education, employment,
housing, mobility, access and holidays. RADAR
produces many informative publications and a
monthly newsletter which covers a wide range of
information including legal and parliamentary
news, forthcoming conferences, courses, the
international scene, the arts and sport.

Royal College of Speech and Language Therapists

7 Bath Place, Rivington Street, London, EC2A 3DR

Tel: 020 7613 6413

Fax: 020 7613 3854

E-mail: info@rcslt.org

Website: www.rcslt.org

Contact: Jenifer Ellender, Information Officer

The College can link speech and language
therapists with specific advisers in hearing
impairment and special interest groups
throughout the UK. It can also give information on
whether a speech and language therapist is
registered and can give details of the local NHS
speech and language therapy manager.

Royal National Institute for Deaf People

19-23 Featherstone Street, London, EC1Y 8SL

Tel: 020 7296 8000

Textphone: 020 7296 8001

Videotel: 020 7490 1641

Fax: 020 7296 8199

E-mail: helpline@rnid.org.uk

Website: www.rnid.org.uk

Contact: RNID Helpline
             P O Box 16464, London, EC1Y 8TT

Tel: 0870 60 50 123

Textphone: 0870 60 33 007

Website: www.rnid.org.uk/

The Royal National Institute for Deaf People (RNID)
is the largest charity representing the 8.7 million
deaf and hard of hearing people in the UK. As a
membership charity, we aim to achieve a radically
better quality of life for deaf and hard of hearing
people. We do this by campaigning and lobbying
vigorously, by raising awareness of deafness and
hearing loss, by providing services and through
social, medical and technical research.

Royal National Institute for the Blind

224 Great Portland Street, London, W1N 6AA

Tel: 020 7388 1266

Textphone: 0800 515152

Fax: 020 7388 4921

E-mail: helpline@rnib.org.uk

Website: www.rnib.org.uk

Contact: RNIB Helpline

Tel: 0345 66 99 99

The Royal National Institute for the Blind aims to
help all blind and partially sighted people in the
UK. It aims to challenge blindness in three ways:
through challenging the disabling effects of sight
loss by providing information and practical
services to help people get on with their own lives;
challenging all who put barriers in the path of
blind and partially sighted people; challenging the
underlying causes of blindness by working
towards its prevention, cure or alleviation. The
Institute provides over 60 services for people with
visual loss including training, an employment
network, rehabilitation services equipment,
communication services including the printing of
braille, moon and large print manuscripts, leisure
services and social services including residential
care. Provides information on access to the arts
for visually impaired people.

Save the Children Fund

Mary Datchelor House, 17 Grove Lane, London, SE5 8RD

Tel: 020 7703 5400

Fax: 020 7703 2278

Website: www.savethechildren.org.uk

Save the Children works in the UK and across the world. Emergency relief runs alongside long-term development and prevention work to help children, their families and communities to be self-sufficent. We learn from the reality of children's lives and campaign for solutions to the problems they face. We gain expertise through our projects around the world and use that knowledge to educate and advise others.

Sense

Tel: 020 7272 7774

Textphone: 020 7272 9648

Fax: 020 7272 6012

E-mail: enquiries@sense.org.uk

Website: www.sense.org.uk

Contact: Colin Anderson, Information Manager

See entry under Deafblind Resources.

SKILL

4th Floor, Chapter House, Crucifix Lane, London, SE1 3JW

Tel: 020 7450 0620

Textphone: 020 7450 0620

Fax: 020 7450 0650

E-mail: admin@skill.org.uk

For further information contact the Helpline on 020 7978 9890 from 1.30 to 4.30pm.

Speakeasy - The Association of Speech Impaired

34 Newark Street, London, E1 1BB

Tel: 020 7377 7177

Contact: Catherine Humphries, Secretary
              Pentre Farm, Pentre, Bucknell,
              Shropshire, SY7 0BU

Tel: 01547 520332

Speakeasy aims to provide a network of support and selfhelp for patients, their families and friends. The organisation wants to improve public awareness of speech problems, and create a channel through which speech impaired people can advise those providing services. Speakeasy also acts as a pressure group to improve facilities, working towards the opening of social centres for speech impaired people.

Special Communication Needs

Barn Oast, Woodfalls, Laddingford, Maidstone, Kent, ME18 6DA

Tel: 01622 873232

Textphone: 01622 873232

Fax: 01622 873153

Contact: Stefanie Hugh, Chief Executive

SCN was awarded a three-year lottery grant to provide free sign language training to parents of deaf children, unpaid carers and volunteers working with deaf people. It can provide information, advice, education and training, which includes awareness training. Its services are open to all. SCN also offers various sign language courses, including intensive classes in Stage I and II. It also runs short refresher courses.

Sympathetic Hearing Scheme

7-11 Armstrong Road, Acton, London, W3 7JL

Tel: 020 8740 4447

Textphone: 020 8740 4447

Fax: 020 8742 9043

E-mail: hearing.concern@ukonline.co.uk

Website: web.ukonline.co.uk/hearing.concern

Contact: Annabel Corbalan, Head of
              Sympathetic Hearing Scheme

The Sympathetic Hearing Scheme is the Deaf Awareness Project of Hearing Concern and is a key provider of deaf awareness, deaf equality training to service providers and other organisations. Also available: plastic card for use by deaf and hard of hearing people, leaflets on clear communication, and a training video.

TEC National Council

10th Floor Westminster Tower, 3 Albert Embankment, London, SE1 7SX

Tel: 020 7735 0010

Fax: 020 7735 0090

Website: www.tec.co.uk/index.html

The Children's Society

Edward Rudolph House, 69-85 Margery Street, London, WC1X 0JL

Tel: 020 7837 4299

Fax: 020 7837 0211

Website: www.the_children's_society.org.uk

14

The Elizabeth Foundation

Southwick Hill Road, Cosham, Portsmouth, Hampshire, PO6 3LL

Tel: 023 9237 2735
Textphone: 023 9237 2735

The Elizabeth Foundation provides a Family Centre for pre-school deaf children and their families; a parent-infant programme for children from 0-2 years and nursery education for children from 3-5 years. It also has a music studio where children learn to listen through musical vibrations; a counselling service for giving help, guidance and support to parents; a correspondence course for families of deaf children; and a direct referral Early Detection of Deafness Clinic.

The Samaritans

10 The Grove, Slough, Berkshire, SL1 1QP

Tel: 0345 909090 Helpline
 01753 216500 Administration
Textphone: 08457 909192
Fax: 01753 819004
E-mail: jo@samaritans.org
Website: www.samaritans.org.uk
Contact: Su Ray, Information Officer

The Samaritans provide emotional support in complete confidence 24 hours a day every day of the year to anyone passing through a crisis and at risk of despair and suicide. A range of leaflets are produced for callers including a leaflet for deaf and hard of hearing people. In addition to contact by textphone, all branches can be visited during the daytime and evening and a few branches have volunteers who can sign. Contact can also be made by letter. The address and phone number of your local Samaritan branch is listed in the telephone directory.

Treacher Collins Family Support Group

c/o Sue Moore, 114 Vincent Road, Norwich, Norfolk, NR1 4HH

Tel: 01603 33736

UK Council on Deafness (UKCOD)

The Business Centre, Room 13, Second Floor, 5 Blackhorse Lane, London, E17 6DS

Tel: 020 8527 6680
Textphone: 020 8527 6631
Fax: 020 8527 6680
Contact: Shenaz Hayatoolah, Chief Executive

UKCOD aims to improve and extend cooperation between member organisations in promoting and representing the interests of deaf, deafened, deafblind and hard of hearing people. Our objective is to provide a forum for debate and a focus for action by promoting understanding and acceptance of the different perspectives on issues connected with deafness. The Council members work together to achieve change on matters of shared concern.

United Kingdom Noise Council

Cirrus Research plc, Acoustic House, Bridlington, Hunmanby, North Yorkshire

Contact: A Wallis, Researcher

Working Party on Signed English

1 Rousbury Cottages, School Lane, Stewartby, Bedford, MK43 9NG

Contact: Information Officer
 Healthlands School, Heathlands Drive, St Albans, Hertfordshire, AL3 5AY

Signed English is a system which uses traditional and generated signs with the intention of showing grammatical features of English that may not otherwise be perceivable to a child through either listening or lipreading. The content vocabulary is based on that used in British Sign Language (BSL) but signs are presented in English order with the addition of standardised markers and generated signs together with finger-spelling to reproduce accurately the components of grammatical English. Signed English is not a language in its own right (as English and BSL are) but is a tool that can be used to help deaf children access features of English within an educational setting. Its services are available to other organisations and professionals such as teachers and speech therapists, working with language disordered children.

Write Away

1 Thorpe Close, London, W10 5XL

Tel: 020 8964 4225

Write Away started in 1991 as a national pen-friend club for children with disabilities. It has now opened the service to adults also. Write Away also gives comprehensive advice about letter-writing.

British Deaf Association (NI)

Wilton House, 5 College Square North, Belfast, County Antrim, BT1 6AR

Tel:	028 9043 4767
Textphone:	028 9043 4755
Videotel:	028 9043 8796
Contact:	Majella McAteer

The Visible Voices project aims to work with local Deaf communities, Eastern Health and Social Services, and its four community service trusts, and commissioners/providers of health and other social services to provide them with training for the Deaf communites.

Council for the Advancement of Communication with Deaf People (NI)

Wilton House, 5 College Square North, Belfast, County Antrim, BT1 6AR

Tel:	028 9043 8161
Textphone:	028 9043 8161
Fax:	028 9043 8161
Contact:	Priscilla Mullan, Development Officer

CACDP in Northern Ireland provides training in sign language in Northern Ireland. It runs workshops and conferences, and provides training in deaf awareness and sign language. The Council undertakes research and also provides an information exchange with other organisations. CACDP aims to promote training in communication skills and also conducts examinations in these skills and maintains a register of qualified interpreters.

Hearing Dogs for Deaf People (NI)

12 Main Street, Crawfordsburn, Bangor, County Down, BT19 1JE

Tel:	028 9185 3669
Contact:	Ambi Jamieson, Information Contact

National Deaf Children's Society (NI)

Wilton House, 5 College Square North, Belfast, County Antrim, BT1 6AR

Tel:	028 9031 3170
Textphone:	028 9027 8177
Fax:	028 9031 3170
Contact:	Pauline Walker, Development Officer

This is the Northern Ireland office of the NDCS, which exists to provide support to local deaf children, young people and their families. The office can provide information, advice, educational services, training, including awareness training, equipment and an information exchange. It also organises conferences and workshops and undertakes campaigning activities. Its services are also available to other organisations, professionals working with deaf children, anyone involved in academic research and any interested members of the public.

Northern Ireland Deaf Youth Association

Wilton House, 5 College Square North, Belfast, County Antrim, BT1 6AR

Tel:	028 9043 8566
Textphone:	028 9023 6453
Fax:	028 9043 8566
E-mail:	ni.deafyouth@dnet.co.uk
Contact:	Barry Campbell, Youth Development Officer

NIDYA aims to meet the social, educational and psychological needs of Northern Ireland's young deaf people and to enchance their quality of life and choices in a youth work context by the provision of training. The Association also organises international youth exchanges and special events. It provides a Deaf Youth Work Service through youth clubs, as well as training courses, and information and advice. A newsletter is published quarterly.

14

RNID Northern Ireland

Wilton House, 5 College Square North, Belfast, County Antrim, BT1 6AR

Tel:	028 9023 9619
Textphone:	028 9023 9619
Videotel:	028 9043 8354
Fax:	028 9031 2032
Website:	www.rnid.org.uk
Contact:	Nicola Hall, Regional Information Officer

RNID Regional Offices provide the following services to deaf, deafblind and hard of hearing people, their family, friends and professionals: Information Services: information officers provide information by telephone, letter, factsheets and leaflets. They also attend exhibitions and conferences and give talks to promote RNID services. Communication Services Units provide a full range of services for deaf, deafblind and hard of hearing people through sign language interpreters, deafblind communicators, lipspeakers, notetakers, and speech-to-text transcription. Training Services provide training in disability and deaf awareness as well as telephone techniques and work-based sign language through a network of regional training officers, most of whom are deaf. Assistive devices are available from RNID Sound Advantage. The Ulster Institute for the Deaf merged with RNID Northern Ireland in February 1998 creating a united force for the advancement of the Deaf community in Northern Ireland.

Sense (NI)

The Manor House, 51 Mallusk Road, Mallusk, County Antrim, BT36 9RU

Tel: 028 9083 3430
Textphone: 028 9083 3430
Fax: 028 9084 4232
E-mail: SENSNI@dial.pipex.com
Website: www.sense.org.uk

See entry under Deafblind Resources.

Skill Northern Ireland

Unit 2, Jennymount Court, North Derby Street, Belfast, County Antrim, BT15 3HN

Scotland

Deafblind UK (Scotland)

21 Alexandra Avenue, Lenzie, Kirkintilloch, Glasgow, Strathclyde, G66 5BG

Tel: 0141 777 6111
Textphone: 0141 777 6111
Fax: 0141 775 3311
E-mail: info@deafblindscotland.org.uk
Website: www.deafblindscotland.org.uk
Contact: Drena O'Malley, Development Manager, Scotland

This is the Scottish office for Deafblind UK developing services in Scotland. Services include: information, advice, training, rehabilitation, holidays and respite care, communication skills and training for teachers and professionals. Deafblind UK also provides leaflets, organises conferences and produces written articles for the press.

RNID Scotland

9 Clairmont Gardens, Glasgow, Lanarkshire, G3 7LW

Tel: 0141 332 0343
Textphone: 0141 332 5023
Videotel: 0141 353 2935
Fax: 0141 331 2640
Website: www.rnid.org.uk
Contact: Dorothy Davidson, Regional Information Officer

Textphone: 0141 353 2225

For details of services provided by RNID Scotland, please refer to the notes section of RNID Northern Ireland.

Scottish Association for the Deaf

Clerwood House, 96 Clermiston Road, Edinburgh, Midlothian, EH12 6UT

Tel: 0131 314 6075
Textphone: 0131 314 6078
Fax: 0131 314 6077
Contact: Lorna Sutherland, Administrator

SAD works to assist all people with a hearing loss in Scotland. It provides information, advice, equipment and awareness training. It also organises conferences, undertakes campaigning activities and provides an information exchange with other organisations. Its services are also available to other organisations, professionals working with deaf people and the general public.

Scottish Association of Sign Language Interpreters

45 York Place, Edinburgh, Midlothian, EH1 3HP

Tel: 0131 557 6370
Textphone: 0131 557 6370
Fax: 0131 557 4110
Contact: Doreen Mair, Director

The Scottish Association of Sign Language Interpreters aims to foster and enhance sign language interpreting services in Scotland. The Association maintains a Register of Interpreters, arranges for the provision of interpreter services, and provides training, supervision and support of trainee interpreters, professional development courses for registered interpreters as well as workshops and seminars for interpreters and other professionals involved in work with deaf people. The Association will also provide information and advice on interpreting and related matters.

14

Scottish Sensory Centre

Moray House Institute of Education, Holyrood Road, Edinburgh, Midlothian, EH18 8AQ

Tel:	0131 651 6501
Textphone:	0131 557 8147
Fax:	0131 651 6502
Website:	www.ssc.mhie.ac.uk
Contact:	Ruth Simpson, Office Administrator

The Centre promotes and supports new developments and effective practices in the education of children and young people with visual, hearing and dual sensory impairment. The Centre organises courses, conferences, workshops and seminars and provides information on education and related topics through the library and sensory information database.

Wales

Age Concern Cymru

Transport House, 1 Cathedral Road, Cardiff, CF1 9SD

Tel:	029 2037 1566
Fax:	029 2039 9562
E-mail:	accymru@demon.co.uk
Contact:	Debbie Meehan, Information Officer

Arts Council of Wales

9 Museum Place, Cardiff, South Glamorgan, CF1 3NX

Arts Disability Wales

Chapter ARTS Centre, Market Road, Canton, Cardiff, CF5 1QE

Tel:	029 2037 7885
Textphone:	029 2025 1800
Fax:	029 2039 5211
Website:	www.arts.disability@enablis.co.uk
Contact:	Jeanette Thomas, Coordinator

ADW is the national arts and disability organisation in Wales. It promotes equal opportunities in the arts for disabled people living in Wales. Services include training courses, information and advice and consultancy.

Blissymbolics Communication Resource Centre

Western Avenue, Llandaff, Cardiff, CF5 2YB

Originally created by Charles Bliss as a means of international communication, now used with non-speaking children with physical disablities.

British Association of Teachers of the Deaf (BATOD) Wales

Ty Morfa, Hafan Deg, Aberkenfig, Bridgend, CF32 9AW

Contact:	Rose Taylor, Chairman
	Education Directorate, Merthyr Tydfil CBC, Ty Keir Hardie, Riverside Court, Avenue de Clichy, Merthyr Tydfil, Mid Glamorgan, CF47 8XD

British Deaf Association Wales

Shand House, 2 Fitzalan Place, Cardiff, CF2 1BD

Tel:	029 2046 2929
Textphone:	029 2048 8437
Videotel:	029 2045 8091 10am-5pm
Fax:	029 2049 9873
Contact:	R Jones, Community Services Officer

Community advocacy and youth development services aim to train and develop deaf advocates and youth workers.

Cambrian Education Foundation for Deaf Children

'Montreux', 30 Lon Cedwyn, Sketty, Swansea, West Glamorgan, SA2 0TH

Contact:	Pamela Brown, Clerk to the Trustees

The Foundation works to help children and young people (to age 25) throughout Wales with any form of hearing loss. Financial assistance is given for those in schools or units, pre-school, further education or higher education or preparing for entry into a profession, trade, business, or employment of any kind. Personal grants are made for clothing, equipment and tools, electronic equipment, text books, courses, travelling expenses, playgroups in holidays, etc. Assistance is also available for voluntary organisations for approved educational courses, including music and other arts. Applications are dealt with on the basis of need.

Disability Wales

Llys Ifor, Crescent Road, Caerphilly, Mid Glamorgan, CF83 1XL

Tel:	029 2088 7325
Fax:	029 2088 8702

Disability Wales is the national organisation of disability groups working to promote the rights, inclusion, equality and support of all disabled people in Wales.

14

223

National Association of Citizens Advice Bureaux Wales

Unit 7, St Asaph Business Park, Glascoed Road, St Asaph, Denbighshire, LL17 0LJ

Tel: 01745 586400

Fax: 01745 585554

Contact: Ann Morgan, Director

Offers help to people with their rights, with information and advice on legal matters, benefits, welfare, housing and other issues.

National Deaf Children's Society Wales

Room 2, 1st Floor, 43 Charles St, Cardiff, South Glamorgan, CF1 4EB

Tel: 029 2037 3474

Textphone: 029 2038 4277

Fax: 029 2037 3474

Contact: Paula Brown, Welsh Development Officer

63 Risca Road, Newport, Gwent, NP9 4HY

We provide full and balanced information to parents of deaf children and deaf young people in order to make their lives better, to have better opportunities, full access to education, etc.

RNID Cymru

3rd Floor, 33-35 Cathedral Road, Cardiff, CF1 9HB

Tel: 029 2033 3034

Textphone: 029 2033 3036.

Videotel: 029 2064 5298

Fax: 029 2033 3035

Website: www.rnid.org.uk

For details of RNID services please refer to notes under entry for RNID Northern Ireland.

Wales Council for the Deaf

Glenview House, Courthouse Street, Pontypridd, Mid Glamorgan, CF37 1JW

Tel: 01443 485687

Textphone: 01443 485686

Fax: 01443 408555

E-mail: wcdeaf@pop3.poptel-org.uk

Contact: Norman Moore, Director

The Council's main aim is to support all activities of benefit to people with a hearing loss in Wales with the object of enabling them to live fuller and more independent lives. Publications include 'Wales HI', ' Welsh Book of Signs', 'Information Guide' and a directory for text terminal users.

Wales Council for Voluntary Action

Llys Ifor, Crescent Road, Caerphilly, Mid Glamorgan, CF83 1XL

Contact: Graham Benfield, Chief Officer

Wales Council for Voluntary Action (WCVA) is the voice of the voluntary sector in Wales. It represents and campaigns for voluntary organisations, volunteers and communities in Wales. WCVA leads the sector in providing advice, information and training: lobbying decision-makers at all levels; safeguarding and increasing resources for the sector; responding positively to new challenges.

Regional Organisations

Many of the organisations listed in this section are long-established societies and associations for deaf people. They provide a wide range of services, are often the providers of social work services in their area under agency agreement, and a range of activities including social clubs, youth activities and information services. Some groups also represent the needs and views of deaf people in particular forums.

This section is listed alphabetically by organisation within country sections.

England

Berkshire Disability Information Network

Church Hill House, Crowthorne Road, Bracknell, Berkshire, RG12 7EP

Tel: 01344 301572/ 426500
Textphone: 01344 427757
Fax: 01344 302293
E-mail: ask@bdin.demon.co.uk
Website: www.azariah.org.uk/bdin/index.html

Berkshire Disability Information Network (BDIN) is a registered charity whose mission aim is to provide information to disabled people and carers throughout Berkshire in any manner they require (such as word of mouth, printed sheets, Braille, cassette tape), via workers trained in disability awareness, communications skills and use of a computerised database, benefits calculations packages, fully indexed library, equipment registers both for the United Kingdom and the European Union, a full range of holiday brochures detailing accessible venues throughout the world, the 'Patient Wise' guide and so on. The organisation is controlled by disabled people and carers and is currently part-funded by a variety of sources.

Birmingham Institute for the Deaf

Ladywood Road, Birmingham, West Midlands, B16 8SZ

Tel: 0121 246 6100
Textphone: 0121 246 6101
Fax: 0121 246 6125
E-mail: bid@bid.org.uk
Website: www.bid.org.uk
Contact: Bryan Sheppard, Chief Executive

BID can provide information, advice, educational services, training (including awareness training) and equipment. They run workshops and undertake campaigning work. Their services are available to all deaf and hard of hearing people in the Birmingham area as well as other organisations, professionals working with deaf people and the general public. BID are the social service providers for Birmingham and Solihull social service departments. They also have a communication support unit and an employment department. BID produce a quarterly magazine 'Sign Times' available to all users. They are an independent interpreting agency.

Breakthrough Trust Aldershot

Princes Gardens, 2a High Street, Aldershot, Hampshire, GU11 1BJ

Tel: 01252 313882
Textphone: 01252 313882
Fax: 01252 337546
E-mail: scbthu@aol.com
Contact: Celia Pinto, Regional Manager

Breakthrough Trust Cambridge Heath

28 All Saints Close, London, N9 9AT

Tel: 020 7791 0105
Textphone: 020 7791 0103
Fax: 020 7791 0103
Contact: Philip Merriweather

This centre is open for drop-in callers Monday to Thursday from 10am to 4pm. Appointments are neccessary at other times.

Breakthrough Trust Ealing

West London Advice Centre, 2 Erconwald Street, East Acton, London, W12 0BS

Tel: 020 8749 4111
Textphone: 020 8740 4820
Fax: 020 8749 4111

This resource centre is open on Tuesday, Wednesday and Thursday from 10am to 2pm. Other times by appointment.

Breakthrough Trust Farnborough

67 Albert Road, Farnborough, Hampshire, GU14 6SL

Tel: 01252 510051
Textphone: 01252 313882
Fax: 01252 524642
E-mail: scbthu@aol.com
Contact: Celia Pinto, Regional Manager

15

Breakthrough Deaf-Hearing Integration is a national voluntary organisation which encourages partnership between deaf and hearing people. Innovative programmes of contact, information and training enable people to improve their quality of life.

Breakthrough Trust London Region

The Hall, Peyton Place, London, SE10 8RS

Tel: 020 8853 5661
Textphone: 020 8853 2683
Videotel: 020 8858 7689
Fax: 020 8853 5661
E-mail: longbthu@aol.com.uk
Contact: David Buxton

The contact and information officer provides advice and assistance on all issues relating to deafness and can demonstrate a range of environmental equipment (such as teletext TV, pager, telephones, loop systems). The Resource Centre is open from 2 to 4pm on Mondays and Wednesdays and from 10am to 12 noon on Tuesdays and Thursdays. Other times by appointment only. You may exchange your hearing aid batteries at the Centre Monday to Thursday from 10am to 12 noon and from 2 to 4pm. Re-tubing is available. The Hearing Aid Surgery by Beryl Read is held on the third Tuesday of each month from 10am to 12 noon. The following courses are offered for in-house or in-service training: deaf awareness, sign language, BSL stages I and II courses. Deaf tutors are able to provide a course tailored to your group's specific needs. Your staff will learn to feel confident in using the appropriate communication techniques with people who are deaf or hard of hearing. There is a choice: one day to three days. Following consultations, a ten per cent deposit would be required for an advance booking. If you wish to apply for a course individually, call Rene Tye for further details.

Breakthrough Trust West Midlands

1 College Walk, Bristol Road, Selly Oak, Birmingham, West Midlands, B29 6LE

Tel: 0121 472 5488
Textphone: 0121 415 5900
Fax: 0121 472 5488
E-mail: Wmidsbthu@aol.com

To develop innovative work with deaf and hearing people which enables them to improve their quality of life through contact, information and training.

Cornwall Association for Deaf and Hard of Hearing People

31 Wellington Terrace, Falmouth, Cornwall, TR11 3BN

Tel: 01326 312470
Textphone: 01326 312471
Fax: 01326 312470
Contact: Rennie Fry, Coordinator/ Secretary

The Association serves deaf and hard of hearing people throughout Cornwall. It will assist deaf and hard of hearing people financially, either individually, or in groups or clubs for specific needs, such as training, that are not met by social services or Care in the Community. It provides information, advice and awareness training, and also runs workshops, undertakes campaigning and provides an information exchange with other organisations.

Cumbria Deaf Association

3 Compton Street, Carlisle, Cumbria, CA1 1HT

Tel: 01228 522885
Textphone: 01228 522885
Fax: 01228 590501
Contact: Ann Blair, Director
Textphone: 01228 522885

The Association provides support to all deaf people in the Cumbria area including deaf people with special needs. It is able to provide financial assistance to groups exisiting either under the umbrella of Cumbria Deaf Association or providing direct services. The Association also provides information, advice, educational services, training, including awareness training, equipment and an information exchange. It also provides workshops, undertakes campaigning activities, provides communication support and organises social activities. A newsletter is produced on an irregular basis. Lipreading: classes for Kendal and South Lakeland are held at Cumbria Deaf Association at the above address. Lipreading classes are available at this centre on Mondays 7.30 to 9.30pm and Tuesdays 1.30 to 3.15pm. Sign language classes are also available.

15

Deafness Support Network (Main Office)

144 London Road, Northwich, Cheshire, CW9 5HH

Tel: 01606 47831
Textphone: 01606 350823
Videotel: 01606 330515
Fax: 01606 49456
Website: www.deafsoc.co.uk
Contact: Craig Crowley, Head of Community Services

DSN provides a wide range of services which include communication support, residential rehabilitation/respite care, social clubs and social services. There are also other branches of the DSN in Chester and Warrington, and social clubs in Congleton, Crewe and Macclesfield. The organisation has a full network of video telephones, access to which can be made from selected libraries. People should contact their nearest branch of DSN for details. For details of the other branches of DSN, Cheshire Interpreting Service and Stepping Stones (residential rehabilitation), please look under their individual entries.

Deafness Support Network Chester

Southview Road, Chester, Cheshire, CH1 4JG

Tel: 01244 371372
Textphone: 01244 375347
Videotel: 01244 390506
Fax: 01244 378215
Website: www.deafsoc.co.uk
Contact: Martin Colville, Director

One of the regional branches of the DSN. For details of services local to the Chester area, please contact this office.

Deafness Support Network Warrington

13 Wilson Patten Street, Warrington, Cheshire, WA1 1PG

Tel: 01925 634640
Textphone: 01925 232551
Videotel: 01925 626995
Fax: 01925 626992
Website: www.deafsoc.co.uk
Contact: Martin Colville, Director

A regional office of the DSN. For details of services in the area local to Warrington, please contact this office.

East Lancashire Deaf Society

The Resource Centre, Swallow Drive, Blackburn, Lancashire, BB1 6LE

Tel: 01254 252620
Textphone: 01254 262460
Fax: 01254 693200
E-mail: eldeaf@aol.com

A mother and toddler group is held fortnightly on Wednesdays from 11am till 3pm. Social Services has an office within the club buildings and provision of equipment and services for deafblind people is available from there. The Society now has an office in Burnley.

Gloucester Deaf Association

Colin Road, Armwood, Gloucester, GL51 5SY

Gloucester Diocesan Association for the Deaf

Gloucester Centre for Deaf People, Colin Road, Barnwood, Gloucester, GL4 7JN

Tel: 01452 372999
Textphone: 01452 372999
Fax: 01452 372288

Hampshire Deaf Association

Fairbairn Centre, 18 Augustine Road, Northam, Southampton, Hampshire, SO14 0PL

Tel: 023 8022 6803
Textphone: 023 8033 9872
Fax: 023 8023 2848
E-mail: hantsdeafass@compuserve.com
Website: www.info-quest.com./deafsociety
Contact: Roger Mallard, Chief Executive

The Association provides support to 28 deaf clubs in the area. It can provide some financial, emotional and social support to individuals and families. The Association provides information, advice, training, including awareness training, and an information exchange. An information centre was opened in April 1998. The Association also organises workshops and conferences, undertakes campaigning activities and runs the Hampshire Sign Language Project which aims to develop a resource centre for sign language materials. A newsletter is produced on a quarterly basis.

15

Huddersfield and District Society for the Deaf

53a Trinity Street, Huddersfield, West Yorkshire, HD1 4DN

Tel: 01484 542713
Textphone: 01484 542713

Contact: Yvonne Groom, Secretary

Deaf people of all ages and ethnic backgrounds are welcome to join the society which provides information, advice, awareness training and a social meeting place.

Hull and East Yorkshire Institute for the Deaf

63 Spring Bank, Kingston Upon Hull, East Riding of Yorkshire, HU3 1AG

Tel: 01482 223911
Textphone: 01482 223911

Contact: Gordon Watts, Supervisor

Provision of social and recreational facilities for hearing impaired people over 16 years of age. Assistance and advice is also given for any social, health and welfare problems. Amenities include: a chapel, bar, multi-purpose hall, TV room, snooker room, meeting room, showers and kitchen.

Leicester and County Mission for the Deaf

Centre for Deaf People, 135 Welford Road, Leicester, LE2 6BE

Tel: 0116 255 6776
Textphone: 0116 254 5126
Videotel: 0116 247 0626
Fax: 0116 255 6940
E-mail: knight@centrefordeafpeopleleicester.
              btinternet.com
Contact: Philip Kilgour, Director
E-mail: philip.kilgour@leicesterdeaf.freeserve.
              co.uk

The Centre for Deaf People provides a county-wide service to people who are deaf, hard of hearing and their families and carers in Leicester, Leicestershire and Rutland. Services include: social work service, equipment, information, communication support, partial care, lipreading and BSL classes.

Merseyside Society for Deaf People

Queens Drive, West Derby, Liverpool, Merseyside, L13 0DJ

Tel: 0151 228 0888
Textphone: 0151 228 0888
Videotel: 0151 220 2019 (9am to 5pm)
Fax: 0151 228 4872
E-mail: j.g.lewis@btinternet.com
Contact: Lynn Greenbank, Chief Executive
Videotel: 0151 220 2019 (9am to 5pm)

The two centres of Merseyside Society for Deaf People in Liverpool and Birkenhead provide social work services, technical advice, sign language courses and deaf awareness training within Merseyside. There are a wide range of social activities for all age groups and religious services are held twice monthly.

Midlands Regional Association for the Deaf

75 Midhurst Road, Kings Norton, Birmingham, West Midlands, B30 3RA

Tel: 0121 458 4557
Textphone: 0121 458 4557
Fax: 0121 458 4557
Contact: Robin Caley, Honorary Secretary

MRAD is th RNID's regional body in the Midlands. We act as a forum for all organisations concerned with deafness, plus local authorities and health authorities. We arrange four workshops per year on topics related to deafness.

Mobility Unit - DETR

Zone 1-11 Great Minster House, 76 Marsham Street, London, SW1P 4DR

Tel: 020 7890 4914
Textphone: 020 7890 6100
Fax: 020 7890 6102
E-mail: mu.detr.gtnet.gov.uk
Contact: Ann Frye, Head of Unit
Tel: 020 7890 4461
E-mail: mu.detr@gtnet.gov.uk

Norfolk Deaf Association

217 Silver Road, Norwich, Norfolk, NR3 4TL

Tel: 01603 404440
Textphone: 01603 406677
Fax: 01603 404433
E-mail: nda@netcentral.co.uk
Contact: Gordon Hunter, Manager

15

Our aim is to improve the lives and well-being of the deaf, deafened and hard of hearing through education, employment, training and communication services. Raising awareness of deaf culture, and lobbying to improve statutory services.

North Regional Deaf Association

144 London Road, Northwich, Cheshire, CW9 5HH

Tel: 01606 330362

Textphone: 01606 330362

Fax: 01606 49456

Contact: John Banham, Organiser

The North Regional Deaf Association seeks to create a forum for discussion and debate concerning services and policies for deaf and hard of hearing people by local authorities, health services, voluntary societies, and regional deaf organisations. It seeks to promote the interests, welfare and education of deaf and hard of hearing people through influencing its members and national organisations or media who can have effect on services or policies, and to advance the advocacy and self-representation by deaf and hard of hearing people into areas where they can affect the quality of life and standard of services for deaf people. The Association has recently developed an advocacy scheme, providing information, advice, educational services, training and advocacy. It organises conferences and workshops, undertakes research and campaigning, and operates an information exchange. Its services are available to all people with a hearing loss and deafblind people. The advocacy service is dedicated to people with a hearing loss. It covers any area of personal problem or crisis. The service is open to agencies in the region.

North West Regional Association of Community Health Councils

Lancaster Buildings, 77 Deansgate, Manchester, Lancashire, M3 2BW

Tel: 0161 833 4689

Textphone: 0161 833 4689

Fax: 0161 833 3839

E-mail: NWAssoc.chc.@ compuserve.com

Contact: Marilyn Taylor, Project Officer

A forum for Community Health Council.

Northamptonshire and Rutland Mission to the Deaf

St Marks Centre for Deaf People, Green Street, Northampton, NN1 1SY

Tel: 01604 250303

Textphone: 01604 636828

Fax: 01604 239041

E-mail: northants-deaf.demon.co.uk

Contact: Frank Tanner, Chaplain

Social club meets Saturdays from 6 to 11pm, all ages welcome. Church services at St Marks Church, Green Street, on Sundays at 10am. The Retired Group meets on the second and fourth Thursday in the month from 2 to 5pm. The deafblind club meets the second Tuesday in the month 2 to 5pm. Youth Group meets on Wednesday at 7pm and a hard of hearing club meets once a month on a Thursday from 10am to 12 noon. St John's Guild for the Blind meets on the first Friday of the month at 2pm. A summer holiday Sunshine Club for children meets once a week for six weeks in the summer, and the NDCS Northampton branch meets monthly. Other church services, social clubs and hard of hearing clubs take place elsewhere in the diocese. The club covers the diocese of Peterborough.

Northumbria Deaf Mission

St Andrews Church, Newgate Street, Newcastle-upon-Tyne, Tyne and Wear, NE1 5SS

Tel: 0191 221 0397

Textphone: 0191 221 0397

Fax: 0191 221 0444

Contact: Jennifer Bell, Secretary

Tel: 0191 221 0444

Our task is to be the primary instrument of the Church of England in the Dioceses of Durham and Newcastle in meeting the spiritual needs and pastoral care of deaf and hard of hearing people.

Northumbria Deaf Social Club

c/o Butlers, 18 Nun Street, Newcastle-upon-Tyne, Tyne and Wear, NE1 5AQ

Contact: W Coward

              47 Umfraville Dene, Prudhoe,
              Northumberland, NE42 5JF

Tel: 0191 221 0397

15

Nottinghamshire Deaf Society

22 Forest Road West, Nottingham, NG7 4EQ

Tel: 0115 970 0516

Textphone: 0115 970 0516

Fax: 0115 942 3096

The Society provides information, workshops and awareness training. It also acts as a community centre. The Nottinghamshire Sign Language Interpreting Service is based in the same building and provides a range of communication support. Activities at the club include: a regular social club on Wednesdays and Saturdays starting at 7pm, a youth club on Thursdays from 7pm, a whole range of sporting activities and church services on the second and fourth Sunday of every month. Other groups include: over 60s, Asian Women carers, a work club, Parents and Carers and a Christian Group. There is also a service for unemployed deaf people, a health/advocacy service and a summer holiday playscheme. The society produces a quarterly newsletter.

RNID Midlands

1st Floor, Monaco House, Bristol Street, Birmingham, West Midlands, B5 7AS

Tel: 0121 622 2726

Textphone: 0121 622 1191

Fax: 0121 622 5774

Website: www.rnid.org.uk

Contact: Victoria Owen, Regional Information Officer

Tel: 0121 622 5662

RNID regional offices provide a range of services to deaf, deafblind and hard of hearing people, their family, friends and professionals.
Information Services: information officers provide information by telephone, letter, factsheets and leaflets. They also attend exhibitions, conferences and give talks to promote RNID services.
Communication Services Units provide a full range of services for deaf, deafblind and hard of hearing people through sign language interpreters, deafblind communicators, lipspeakers, notetakers, and speech-to-text transcription.
Training Services provide training in disability and deaf awareness, telephone techniques and work-based sign language through a network of Regional Training Officers, most of whom are deaf. Assistive devices are available from RNID Sound Advantage.

RNID North

National Computing Centre, Armstrong House, Oxford Road, Manchester, M1 7ED

Tel: 0161 242 2313

Textphone: 0161 242 2314

Videotel: 0161 236 5687

Fax: 0161 242 2317

Website: www.rnid.org.uk

Contact: Jenny Harkison, Regional Information Officer

Tel: 0161 242 2316 (V) 242 2272 (T)

Contact: Sue Davies, Regional Information Officer

See notes under RNID Midlands for information on services available from RNID regional offices. Another service provided by RNID North is provided in cooperation with Rotherham Metropolitan Borough Council (MBC). This is the RNID/Rotherham 'One Stop Shop' Project, Kirk House, Browning Road, Herringthorpe, Rotherham S65 2LG. Tel: 01709 821232 (voice/textphone). Contact: Alex McMurdo, Resource/Advice Officer. The One Stop Shop has a dual role. It offers access to information, national agencies, including RNID, and local facilities. It also offers facilities to view assistive devices. The project is funded by Rotherham MBC and is managed by RNID.

RNID South - London Office

19-23 Featherstone Street, London, EC1Y 8SL

Tel: 020 7296 8000

Textphone: 020 7296-8001

Videotel: 020 7490 1641

Fax: 020 7296 8128

Website: www.rnid.org.uk

Contact: Fiona Nichols, Administrator

See notes under RNID Midlands for information on services available from RNID regional offices.

RNID South - Bath Office

13b Church Farm Business Park, Corston, Bath, Avon, BA2 9AP

Tel: 01225 874460

Textphone: 01225 874460

Videotel: 01225 874804

Fax: 01225 874246

Website: www.rnid.org.uk

Contact: Julie Swinburne, Regional Information Officer

See notes under RNID Midlands for information on services provided by RNID regional offices.

15

Royal Association in Aid of Deaf People (Head Office)

Centre for Deaf People, Walsingham Road, Colchester, Essex, CO2 7BP

Tel: 01206 509509

Textphone: 01206 577090

Fax: 01206 769755

E-mail: info@royaldeaf.org.uk

Website: www.royaldeaf.org.uk

Contact: Tom Fenton, Chief Executive

RAD is a charity committed to meeting the individual needs of people affected by deafness. Our purpose is to help deaf people make effective and enjoyable contact with each other and with the world at large regardless of age, race, sex or creed. RAD provides services which include: advocacy, chaplaincy, counselling, information, interpreting, leisure facilities and support groups.

Royal Association in Aid of Deaf People London, St Saviours

St Saviour's Centre for Deaf People, 1 Armstrong Road, London, W3 7JL

Tel: 020 8743 2209

Textphone: 020 8740 1603

Fax: 020 8742 9150

Contact: Rev Chris Colledge

Textphone: 020 8810 8879

Support of people who are deaf and deafblind. The RAD provides centres where deaf and deafblind people come and socialise as well as supporting one another. The London Services Team provides support in the community and RAD Chaplaincy seeks to give pastoral and spiritual support.

Royal Association in Aid of Deaf People, Chelmsford

St Mark's Centre for Deaf People, Cottage Place, Chelmsford, Essex, CM1 1NL

Tel: 01245 283777

Textphone: 01245 257704

Fax: 01245 346609

A resource centre is open to the public for demonstrations from 10am to 3pm on Monday and Wednesday. Appointments are not neccessary on these days. A hearing therapist is available on Mondays, Wednesdays and Fridays. Jane Smith provides tinnitus counselling and general hearing aid work. Work is done with people with learning disabilities and domiciliary visits can be arranged. Communication classes are also held here. An interpreting service is available and can be

contacted on: 01245 284953.

Royal Association in Aid of Deaf People, Gillingham

49-51 Balmoral Road, Gillingham, Kent, ME7 4NT

Tel: 01634 280231

Textphone: 01634 581033

Videotel: 01634 281069

Fax: 01634 281651

E-mail: office@rad-clu.demon.co.uk

Contact: Graham Olive, Centre Manager

RAD (Kent) is a charitable organisation for deaf people living in Kent. Services provided include: support worker, deaf club and other leisure activities, community learning (computers), deaf awareness and sign language training, interpreting services and a chaplaincy.

Royal Association in Aid of Deaf People, London St Bede's

St Bedes Centre for Deaf People, 412 Clapham Road, London, SW9 9DA

Tel: 020 7627 1716

Textphone: 020 7627 1706

Videotel: 020 7498 1910

Fax: 020 7622 4969

E-mail: RAD.London@virgin.net

Website: www.royaldeaf.org.uk/royaldeaf

RAD strives to meet the individual needs of deaf people through the provision of services and the use of RAD Deaf Centres, of which there are four in London. RAD also provides a Pastoral Care team; advice, advocacy and deaf awareness; and has its own interpreting agency.

Royal Association in Aid of Deaf People, Romford

Sims Close, Romford, Essex, RM1 3QT

Tel: 01708 752046

Textphone: 01708 731894

Fax: 01708 756950

E-mail: info@royaldeaf.org.uk

Website: www.royaldeaf.org.uk

Contact: Diane Davies, Secretary

Romford Deaf Club meets on Wednesday, Friday and Saturday.

15

Royal Association in Aid of Deaf People, Southend

Oakhurst Road, Southend-On-Sea, Essex, SS2 5DT

Tel: 01702 613656
Textphone: 01702 613656
Fax: 01702 461108
Contact: Eleanor Cross, Centre Administrator

We provide social, recreational and educational activity, sign language teaching, lipreading classes and deaf awareness training, support for families by arranging monthly meetings, resource centres and interpreting. Our aim is to provide support, help and advice to all families coping with hearing loss.

Royal Association in Aid of Deaf People, Surrey

316 High Street, Dorking, Surrey, RH4 1QX

Tel: 01306 881958
Textphone: 01306 876287
Fax: 01306 881958
Contact: Heather Wadey

RAD provides specialist services for deafblind people and deaf people with learning difficulties in Surrey. It also provides awareness training. An Access Centre for Deaf People is based at 320 Dorking High Street, providing information, equipment display, drop-in work experience and computer training.

Salisbury Diocesan Association for the Deaf and Hard of Hearing

Tel: 01722 411977 ext 205
Textphone: 01722 411977 ext 205
Fax: 01722 331159
Contact: Diana James, Administrator

See entry under Religious Organisations.

Somerset Disability Consultative Network

34 Clyce Road, Highbridge, Somerset, TA9 3DH

Tel: 01823 335393
Fax: 01823 353393
E-mail: farthings@lineone.net
Contact: John Beaman
Fax: 01823 335393

The SDCN is a county-wide working group representing the interests of disable people in Somerset. Members attend various Somerset County Council committees as part of the consultation process. Consultation also takes place with health authorities and through local forums, the district councils.

South East Regional Association for the Deaf

67 Netheravon Road, London, W4 2NB

Tel: 020 8995 4443
Textphone: 020 8995 4443
Fax: 020 8995 4443
E-mail: michesterne@aol.com
Contact: Reginald McLaughin, Chairman

SERAD enables the needs of hearing impaired people to be heard in council chambers of the South East of England. It achieves this by providing a forum where councillors meet with representatives from voluntary organisations, people from statutory bodies and social workers, as well as people having impaired hearing; SERAD issues information digests and publishes booklets of value to deaf people; it holds open meetings where specific subjects are discussed and matters of concern are aired, and views, needs and opinions are put forward; and SERAD generally encourages elected councillors to share experiences and to report on their own Council's work in the area relating to provisions for and help to hearing impaired people. Although SERAD is active in a variety of fields, its principle role is as a forum enabling a variety of people from different jobs, concerns and activities to meet together and exchange thoughts, views, opinions and ideas, and to learn, apply and promote helpful and useful procedures within the South East region of England.

Stoke-on-Trent and Staffordshire Deaf Society

Wellesley Street, Shelton, Stoke on Trent, Staffordshire, ST1 4NF

Tel: 01782 219161
Textphone: 01782 281125
Videotel: 01782 206575
Fax: 01782 281125
E-mail: christopher.harrison@dial.pipex.com
Contact: Tom Wordley, Chief Executive

The Society provides information, education and workshops, awareness training, assertiveness training, sign language classes, communication services, advocacy and outreach work, social centre provision and transport for elderly and infirm people. Details of lipreading classes in Staffordshire area available from here.

Suffolk Deaf Association Ipswich

49 Fonnereau Road, Ipswich, Suffolk, IP1 3JN

Tel: 01473 251179

Textphone: 01473 251179

Fax: 01473 251179

The Association provides a comprehensive range of information, advice, counselling, social activities, spiritual, educational services and training, including awareness training, and equipment. It can provide financial support to deaf people. The Association also has premises in Bury St Edmunds and Lowestoft. Stage I BSL courses: Tuesdays 7 to 9pm and Saturdays 10am to12 noon. Lipreading classes held on Monday and Tuesday - contact the centre for details.

Suffolk Hearing Support Scheme

49 Fonnereau Road, Ipswich, Suffolk, IP1 3JN

Tel: 01473 583561

Textphone: 01473 583561

Contact: Mike Morton, Coordinator

Wessex Association of Deafened People

2 Farrs Orchard, Merriott, Somerset, TA16 5RG

Textphone: 01460 76560

Contact: Wendy Lord

The WADP draws its membership from Somerset or Dorset and holds two conferences a year for deafened people. The organisation can provide information, advice and awareness training. It organises conferences, campaigns and will exchange information with other organisations.

West Norfolk Deaf Association

8 Jubilee Drive, Dersingham, King's Lynn, Norfolk, PE31 6YA

Textphone: 01553 660483

Fax: 01553 660483

E-mail: stephen@deafcentre.freeserve.co.uk

Contact: Julia Paul

To set up a community centre for deaf people. To raise awareness of deafness in the general public. To be a central point of contact for information.

West Regional Association for Deaf People

13b Church Farm Business Park, Corston, Bath, Avon, BA2 9AP

Tel: 01225 874460

Textphone: 01225 874460

Fax: 01225 874246

Contact: Bernard Harding, Chairman

The West Regional Association for the Deaf aims to coordinate and provide a forum for statutory authorities and voluntary organisations for deaf people within the region, on matters relating to deafness. The Association organises meetings for representatives, seminars, and offers information and advice to member organisations. The Association also supports and/or sponsors study or training days on specific topics and gives grants to projects of specific local or regional interest. It acts throughout the region as advocates for deaf and hard of hearing people within the framework of Care in the Community and education. This role is approved by the RNID.

West Sussex Deaf and Hard of Hearing Association

Elizabeth House, 13 Heath Road, Haywards Heath, West Sussex, RH16 3AX

Tel: 01444 415582

Textphone: 01444 415593

Fax: 01444 415587

E-mail: wsdeaf@dial.pipex.com

Contact: Peter Ford, General Manager

The Association can provide information, advice, training including awareness training, and equipment to deaf and hard of hearing people in the West Sussex area. The Resource Centre is open to the public; appointments are neccessary. Its services are also available to other organisations, professionals working with deaf and hard of hearing people and any other interested bodies. The Association is occasionally able to give small grants to individuals whose work will benefit deaf and hard of hearing people in the area. It produces a bi-annual magazine 'News and Views' available free of charge. There is a group of volunteers who can visit house-bound clients to check and re-tube hearing aids and offer advice on equipment.

15

Wirral Centre for the Deaf

Merseyside Society for Deaf People, 15-17 Grange Road West, Birkenhead, Merseyside, L41 4BY

Tel: 0151 201 2552
Textphone: 0151 201 2552
Videotel: 0151 650 0737
Fax: 0151 201 2557

Social workers available on Tuesday and Thursday from 9.30am to 12.30pm and 2 to 4.30pm. Hard of Hearing Club meets on Tuesday afternoons from 1.30 to 3.30pm. Elderly pensioners club meets on a Thursday from 1.30 to 4.30pm and the Deaf/Blind group on Thursday morning from 10am to 12 noon. Sign language practice group is every Monday afternoon from 1.30 to 2.30pm. There is also a Saturday Club which meets from 7 to 10pm.

Worcester and Hereford Association for Deaf People

13 Castle Street, Worcester, WR1 3AD

Tel: 01905 723351
Textphone: 01905 723351
Fax: 01905 723351
Website: www.deafsoc.co.uk/worcester/worc.htm
Contact: Pauline Bannon, Adminstrator

WHAD provides from its two bases in Hereford and Worcester a range of services for deaf and hard of hearing people. This includes: advice and information, the interpreting service (WHIS), a display of environmental equipment, newsletterand local children's holiday. A meeting room is available.

Northern Ireland

Developing Awareness in Sensory Impairment (DAISI)

54 Campsie Road, Omagh, County Tyrone, BT79 0AG

Tel: 028 8225 2479
Fax: 028 8225 2479
Contact: Maria King, Project Officer

A project jointly promoted by Guide Dogs for the Blind Association, the National Association for Deaf People and the Royal National Institute for Deaf People. Supported by the Northern Ireland Voluntary Trust through the European Union Special Support Programme for Peace and Reconciliation.

Aberdeen and North East Deaf Society

13 Smithfield Road, Aberdeen, Grampian, AB21 2NR

Tel: 01224 494566
Textphone: 01224 495675
Fax: 01224 494661
Contact: Rosemary Burt, Principal Officer
Textphone: 01224 495676
Fax: 01224 483894

Maintains a service agreement with Aberdeen City, Aberdeenshire and Moray councils to provide social work services for deaf and hearing impaired people throughout Grampian. The Society operates from its premises in both Aberdeen and Elgin, and provides a range of drop-in surgeries throughout Aberdeenshire and Moray. It is responsible for assessment and provision of environmental equipment. The society has a resource centre, church, social and leisure facilities and a newly developed interpreter service. A variety of self-help groups meet at the centre as well as lipreading and sign language classes.

Deaf Connections

100 Norfolk Street, Glasgow, Strathclyde, G5 9EJ

Tel: 0141 420 1759
Textphone: 0141 429 6682
Videotel: 0141 418 0597 (office hours)
Fax: 0141 429 6860
Contact: Gordon Chapman, Chief Executive
Videotel: 0141 418 0597

Deaf Connections is the new title of the Glasgow and West of Scotland Society for the Deaf. We provide a range of specialist services for deaf and hearing impaired people. These include: communication support, community development projects (youth services, befriending), residential and respite care for elderly deaf and deafblind people. We also have a large social facility which caters for a wide range of social and sporting needs.

Edinburgh and East of Scotland Deaf Society

49 Albany Street, Edinburgh, Lothian, EH1 3QY

Tel: 0131 556 3128
Textphone: 0131 557 4202
Fax: 0131 557 0419
E-mail: admin@escotdeafsoc.demon.co.uk
Contact: Liz Gibson

We work towards equality of opportunity for all deaf, deafblind, hard of hearing and deafened

15

people. We provide social work support, community development activities, specialist equipment, communication support services, residential care, advice, information and recreational facilities. We endeavour to work in partnership with service-users and to provide a responsive and quality service.

Moray Resource Centre

Tel: 01343 551376
Textphone: 01343 551339
Fax: 01343 542014
Contact: Val Swanston, Assistant Social Worker of the Deaf

See entry under Resource Centres.

Wales

Cyswllt Deaf Children's Society and Family Centre

Cottage Hospital, St Davids Road, Caernarfon, Gwynedd, LL55 1BH
Tel: 01286 676416
Textphone: 01286 676416
Fax: 01286 676416
Contact: Richard Lloyd-Jones, Coordinator

Cyswllt is run by parents of deaf children for the benefit of hearing impaired children in Gwynedd and Anglesey from birth to the end of their formal education. We offer individual support and financial grants. We also organise recreational activities.

Glamorgan Mission to the Deaf

1 Lan Park Road, Graigwen, Pontypridd, Rhondda, Cynon,Taff, CF37 2DH
Tel: 01443 404222
Textphone: 01443 404222
Contact: Alun Taylor, Manager

To provide profoundly deaf and speech impaired people in the Glamorgan area the means for social, recreational, welfare and training support without religious or other distinction.

North Wales Deaf Association

The Bungalow, Plas Tre Marl, Broad Street, Llandudno Junction, Gwynedd, LL31 9HL
Tel: 01492 573998
Textphone: 01492 580016
Videotel: 01492 572097
Fax: 01492 573998
Website: web.ukonline.co.uk/nwda/contents.html
Contact: Jane Priestley, Coordinator

North Wales Deaf Association aims to improve the quality of life for deaf, deafened, hard of hearing and deafblind people living in North Wales by providing deaf awareness training, communication support services, advice and information, education consultancy, lobbying for equal access to services and employment, promoting the Welsh deaf identity.

Swansea Deaf Club

58 Rowan Tree Close, Neath, West Glamorgan, SA10 7SQ
Tel: 01792 470477
Contact: Helen Mort, Secretary

Provides a religious and social centre for the deaf community. Provides premises for the National Deaf Children's Society. West Glamorgan Deaf Children's Society activities. Church services every Sunday.

15

Organisations Abroad

This section gives details of organisations representing deaf people all over the world. It is sometimes difficult to verify the details of some groups, particularly in countries experiencing unrest or war. Where possible we have used local spellings of names and places.

This section is listed alphabetically by organisation within country sections.

Algeria

Algeria Deaf Sports
National Federation, 16 avenue Malika Gald, Scala, Algiers, Algeria

Federation Nationale des Sourds D'Algerie
Centre Familial de Ben-Aknoun, Route des 2 Bassins Ben-Aknoun, Algiers, Algeria
Tel: 00213 2 911710
Fax: 00213 2 914218
Contact: Allik Cherif, Président Commission Chargée des Relations Extérieures

Organisation Nationale des Sourds-Muets d'Algerie
Centre Familial de Ben-Aknoun, B P 172, Al Biar, Algiers, Algeria

Argentina

Confederaciøn Argentina de Sordomudos
Costa Rica 5631, 1414 Buenos Aires, Argentina
Tel: 0054 1 931 2158
Fax: 0054 1 931 7119
Contact: Maria Massone

The institution is in charge of the community's problems in general. Intervenes in fundamental investigations and decisions relating to education, laws and employment. Has assumed the recognition of the Argentine Sign Language so as to facilitate the education of deaf children in our country.

Australia

Acoustic Neuroma Association of Australasia, Inc
c/o Better Hearing, 5 High Street, Prahran, Victoria 3181, Australia
Tel: 0061 3 510 1577/ 3499/ 6076
Fax: 0061 3 510 6076
E-mail: anaa@vicnet.net.au
Contact: Audrey Pollard, Secretary
            81 Viviani Crescent, Heathmont, Victoria 3135, Australia
Tel: 0061 3 870 1803

Offer support and information to people who are facing or have undergone surgery for an acoustic neuroma. Make the general public aware of the symptoms of this tumour enabling them to seek medical attention, as early diagnosis and treatment makes the outcome so much better for the patient.

Adult Education Centre for Deaf and Hearing Impaired Persons Inc
Homebush West Public School, Exeter Road, Homebush West, NSW 2140, Australia
Tel: 0061 2 764 4635/ 4972/ 8426

Audiological Society of Australia Inc
Level 2, 11-19 Bank Place, Melbourne, Victoria 3000, Australia
Tel: 0061 3 9642 4866
Fax: 0061 3 9642 4922
Contact: Robert Cowan, Federal President
            P O Box 306, Market Street, Victoria 8007, Australia

Our audiologist members are employed in a wide range of settings within Australia, including private practice, Commonwealth agencies (Office for Hearing Services, Australian Hearing Services), State agencies (WorkCover), public hospitals, private hospitals, private practice, hearing aid or other health-related companies, community service agencies (eg Deaf-Blind Association), and in academic education and research. In addition, audiologists may be involved in public health or industrial settings. The ASA has an international reputation for the excellence of our member audiologists in both the clinical service provision and research areas, and for our participation in international audiological activities. The ASA has been selected to host the XXVI International Congress of Audiology in 2002, as well as other international meetings.

Auslan Parents and Friends
P O Box 94, Ormond, Victoria 3204, Australia

Australian Association of Teachers of the Deaf
P O Box 4120, Parramatta, NSW 2124, Australia
Tel: 0061 7 875 5835/ 5924

Australian Association of the Deaf, Inc.
Suite 601, Level 6, 225 Clarence Street, Sydney, NSW 2000, Australia
Tel: 0061 2 9262 3506
Textphone: 0061 2 9262 3507
Fax: 0061 2 9262 3508
E-mail: aad@fl.net.au
Website: www.aad.org.au
AAD is a national consumer organisation, founded in 1986. It represents people who are deaf and use Australian Sign Language (Auslan). AAD provides use of a specialist advocacy service which focuses on the needs of the deaf community throughout Australia, and aims to achieve equality of opportunity and full participation in society for people who are deaf. AAD will host the XIII World Congress of the World Federation of the Deaf in July 1999.

Australian Association of Workers with the Deaf
P O Box 432, Petersham, NSW 2049, Australia
Tel: 0061 2 560 6433/ 564 2202

Australian Caption Centre
Level 4, 187 Thomas Street, Haymarket, Sydney, NSW 2000, Australia
Tel: 0061 2 9212 5277
Textphone: 0061 2 9212 3198
Fax: 0061 2 9281 2198
E-mail: infoserv@auscap.com.au
Website: www.auscap.com.au
Contact: Louise French, Information Coordinator

Australian Communication Exchange Ltd
252 Annerley Road, Dutton Park, Queensland 4102, Australia
Tel: 0061 7 3405 8333
Textphone: 0061 7 3405 8302
Fax: 0061 7 3405 8402
E-mail: ace.brisbane@mailbox.uq.edu.au

Australian Deaf Sports Federation Ltd
101-117 Wellington Parade South, East Melbourne, Victoria 3002, Australia
Tel: 0061 3 9650 2524
Fax: 0061 3 9654 2868/ 3650 6843
E-mail: adsf-melb@msn.com
Contact: Lance Hately, Administrator

Australian Deafness Research Foundation
354 Victoria Street, Darlinghurst, NSW 2001, Australia
Tel: 0061 2 332 2881

Australian Federation of Deaf Societies
59 Cadbury Road, Claremont, Tasmania 7011, Australia
Tel: 0061 3 6249 5144
Textphone: 0061 3 6249 1174
Fax: 0061 3 6249 8818
E-mail: tasdeaf@tassie.net.au
Contact: Greg Keane, Secretary/Treasurer

Australian Hearing Services
126 Greville Street, Chatswood, NSW 2067, Australia

Australian Sign Language Advisory Body
P O Box 432, Petersham, NSW 2049, Australia
Tel: 0061 7 875 5654/ 5773/ 5924

Australian Sign Language Interpreters Association (NSW)
59 Cadbury Road, Claremont, Tasmania 7011, Australia
Tel: 0061 2 9893 8555
Textphone: 0061 2 9893 8858
Fax: 0061 2 9893 8333
Contact: Joe Sabolec, Correspondence Secretary

16

Better Hearing Australia

National Administration Office, 10 Gordons Road, Lower Templestowe, Victoria 3107, Australia

Tel: 0061 3 9852 1436

Fax: 0061 3 9852 1224

E-mail: rexc@bigpond.com

Contact: Rex Christensen, Vice President Administration

The mission of Better Hearing Australia is to maximise the quality of life of people who have a hearing disability; to encourage the adoption of lifestyles and work practices; to prevent unnecessary hearing loss; and to initiate effective communication for people who have a hearing disability.

Centre for Deafness Studies and Research

Faculty of Education, Griffith University, Queensland 4111, Australia

Tel: 0061 7 3875 5654

Textphone: 0061 7 3875 5654

Fax: 0061 7 3875 5924

E-mail: d.power@edn.gu.edu.au

Website: www.gu.edu.au/gwis/cdsr/CDSR.html

Contact: Des Power, Director

Cochlear Implant Club and Advisory Service

34 Scullin Place, Wahroonga, NSW 2076, Australia

Tel: 0061 2 9489 2583

Fax: 0061 2 9487 6724

CICADA provides: newsletter, regular social gatherings which serve as a meeting ground for sharing any problems encountered by people during the adjustment period to artifical sound, and ongoing sharing of experiences and information. Open to cohlear implantees, new or prospective implantees, their families and friends.

Deafness Forum of Australia

Suite 7b, 17 Napier Close, Deakin, Canberra, ACT 2600, Australia

Tel: 0061 6 2813934

Textphone: 0061 6 2813156

Fax: 0061 6 2814309

E-mail: deaforum@ozemail.com.au

Deafness Resources Australia

Ground Floor, 33 Argyle Street, Parramatta, NSW 2150, Australia

Tel: 0061 2 9204 2970

Fax: 0061 2 9204 2972

Kids of Deaf Adults International

24 Carinda Drive, Glenhaven, New South Wales 2156, Australia

Contact: Judie Bonser

La Trobe University

Bundoora, Victoria 3083, Australia

Renwick College

361-365 North Rocks Road, North Rocks, NSW 2151, Australia

The Deaf-Blind Association

P O Box 267, Clifton Hill, Melbourne, Victoria 3068, Australia

Tel: 00 61 3 9482 1155

Textphone: 0061 3 9489 3091

Fax: 00 61 3 9486 2092

E-mail: dba@internex.net.au

Website: www.internex.net.au/~dba/dba/htm

Contact: John Finch

DBA provides support to deafblind people and people with other disabilities, and their families. The support includes accommodation, community support, respite care, day services, general assistance and advice.

Tinnitus Association Victoria Inc

c/o Better Hearing Australia, 5 High Street, Prahran, Victoria 3181, Australia

Tel: 0061 3 9510 1577

Fax: 0061 3 9510 6076

Tinnitus Association Victoria Inc assists people suffering from tinnitus, with information and support through newsletters, advice line, tinnitus information packs and quarterly meetings. Membership helps provide support and services.

16

Austria

International Federation of the Hard of Hearing
Radegunder Strasse 10, 8045 Graz, Austria
Tel: 0043 316 67 13 27

Landesverband der Gehörlosenvereine in Niederösterreich
Herr Johan Groisse, Kaltenbrunngasse 7, 3100 St Polten, Austria

Landesverband der Gehörlosenvereine in Oberösterreich
Herr Klaus Haidenthaler, Stifterstrasse 12, 4020 Linz, Austria
Tel: 0043 732 77 70 41

Landesverband der Kärntner Gehörlosenvereine
Frau Gerlinde Wiessenegger, Waidmannsdorfer Strasse 137, 9020 Klagenfurt, Austria
Tel: 0043 1 463 26 15 37

Österreichischer Gehörlosen Sportverband
Waldgasse 13, 1100 Wien, Austria
Fax: 0043 1 402 64 18 17

Österreichischer Gehörlosenbund
Sekretariat Professor Peter Dimmel, Auf der Heide 9, 4060 Leonding/Linz, Austria
Tel: 0043 1 622 08 53
Fax: 0043 1 602 34 59
Contact: Trude Dimmel, Secretary

Steirischer Gehörlosen Sport u. Kulturverein
Steinberg Strasse 9, 8052 Graz, Austria
Tel: 0043 316 57930
Fax: 0043 316 572547
E-mail: St.GSKV@ffphal01.tu.graz.ac.at
Website: www.cis.tu-raz.ac.at/if/harik/homepage/
Contact: Christian Stalzer, Head of Organisation

Tiroler Landesverband der Gehörlosenvereine
Ing Etzelstrasse 67, 6020 Innsbruck, Austria
Tel: 0043 512 586162
Textphone: 0043 512 586162
Fax: 0043 512 587025
Contact: Romana Monz, Secretary
Tel: 0043 512 587025

Verband der Gehörlosenvereine im Lande Salzburg
Kulturzentrum der Gehörlosen, Schopperstrasse 21, 5020 Salzburg, Austria
Tel: 0043 662 455150/ 12
Fax: 0043 662 455150/ 12
Contact: Reinhard Grobbauer Reinhard, President

Promotion of deaf culture by meetings, celebrations, sports, cultural events, theatre, social events, etc. Assistance for deaf individuals through interpreting services and social work, information and an information centre. Improvement of the life situation of deaf people through political work and several projects.

Weiner Interessengemeinschaft Hörgeschädigter
Herr Michael Brunner, Waldgasse 13, 1100 Wien, Austria

Wiener Gehörlosenverein
Frau Florica Wolf, Waldgasse 13, 1100 Wien, Austria

Bangladesh

Bangladesh Deaf Sports Federation
Room No. 68, Outer Stadium, Dhaka, Dhaka-1000, Bangladesh
Fax: 00880 800 83 31 70

Bangladesh National Federation of the Deaf
62 Bijoy Nagar, Dhaka-1000, Bangladesh
Contact: Anwara Idris, Director

16

Belarus

Deaf Sports Federation of the Republic of Belarus

Uralskaya Str. 3, Minsk 220038, Republic of Belarus

Fax: 00375 17 227 6184

The Belarusian Society of the Deaf

12 Volodarskogo St, Minsk 220050, Belarus

Contact: Serguei Sapouto, Chairman of the
             Board of Administration

The Belarusian Society of the Deaf (BELSD) is a self-governed public organisation, established in 1931 on a voluntary basis. BELSD represents the deaf at national, regional and local levels, defends their rights particularly in the field of employment, medical care, housing, education, and rehablitation. The government recognises the advisory role of BELSD in making laws and decisions on disability matters, and takes special measures to ensure equal constitutional rights of disabled people as members of their country.

Belgium

European Forum of Sign Language Interpreters

c/o Kasteellaan 120, 9000 Gent, Belgium

Tel: 0032 9 224 43 10
Fax: 0032 9 231 41 63

European Union of the Deaf

Franklin Straat 110, 1040 Brussels, Belgium

Tel: 0032 2 735 18 72
Textphone: 0032 2 733 55 35
Fax: 0032 2 735 53 54
E-mail: eudeaf@pophost.eunet.be

Federation Francophone des Sourds de Belgique

79 Rue du Commerce, B - 1040 Brussels, Belgium

Tel: 0032 2 513 05 24
Textphone: 0032 2 511 72 03 minitel
Fax: 0032 2 511 72 03

Federation of Flemish Deaf and Hard of Hearing

Jules Destreelaan 65c, 9050 Gentbrugge, Belgium

Tel: 0032 9 232 0497
Textphone: 0032 9 232 0497 minitel
Fax: 0032 9 231 6473
E-mail: fevlado@unicall.be
Website: www.ap.be/fevlado
Contact: Filip Verstraete, President

Our aims: to defend the interests and the rights of deaf people as a language minority group; spread information about deafness and deaf culture to both hearing and deaf people; organise sign language courses, deaf awareness courses, workshops, etc; set up projects about sign language research and training programmes; lobby for legislation in favour of deaf people (eg recognition of sign language).

International Federation of Otorhinolaryngological Societies

MISA/NKO, Oosterveldlaan 24, 2610 Wilrijk, Belgium

Tel: 0032 3 443 3611

Contact: Peter Alberti, General Secretary

RFSS Belgique

Boeverstraat 28, 8790 Waregem, Belgium

Fax: 0032 5 660 6132

Bolivia

Federación Bolivana de Sordos

Tumusla 279, Casilla 2374, Cochabamba, Bolivia

Tel: 00591 42 55862
Textphone: 00591 42 55747
Fax: 00591 42 55862

Brazil

Federação Nacional de Eduçãcao e Integrasçãao dos Surdos

Rua Major Avila 379, Tijuca, Rio de Janeiro, Brazil

Tel: 0055 21 234 7786
Textphone: 0055 21 284 2801
Fax: 0055 21 284 2801
E-mail: fenis@pobox.com
Contact: Antonio Abreu, Director-President

Bulgaria

Union of the Deaf in Bulgaria
12-14 Denkooglu St, 1000 Sofia, Bulgaria
Tel: 00359 2 545092/ 650181

Burkina Faso

Association Nationale des Deficients Auditifs du Burkina
01 BP 3758, Ouagadougou, Burkina Faso

Contact: Abel Kafando

Cameroon

Cameroon National Association of the Deaf
BP 6011, Yaoundé, Republic of Cameroon
Tel: 00237 446436
Fax: 00237 446669

Canada

Advocacy Resource Centre for the Handicapped
40 Orchard View Boulevard, Suite 255, Toronto, Ontario, M4R 1B9, Canada
Tel: 001 416 482 1254/ 8255
Fax: 001 416 482 2981

Alexander Graham Bell Association
145 Clearwater Road, Saskatoon, Saskatchewan, S7K 3Y8 Canada
Tel: 001 306 242 2422

Contact: Wendy White

Association of Visual Language Interpreters of Canada
2435 Holly Lane, Suite 205, Ottawa, Ontario, K1V 7P2, Canada
Tel: 001 613 526 4867
Textphone: 001 613 526 2498
Fax: 001 613 526 4718

Canadian Association of Speech Language Pathologists and Audiologists
25 Mainstreet West, Suite 1215, Hamilton, Ontario, L8P 1H1, Canada
Tel: 001 905 523 5790
Fax: 001 905 523 5792
E-mail: www.caslpa.ca

Canadian Association of the Deaf
203-250 Bank Street, Suite 205, Ottawa, Ontario, K2P 1X3, Canada
Tel: 001 613 565 2882
Fax: 001 613 565 1207
E-mail: jroots@cyberus.ca
Website: www.cad.ca
Contact: James Roots, Executive Director

We are the national research, resource, and communication organisation of Canada's 300,000 deaf citizens. Our mandate is to promote and protect the rights, interests and concerns of deaf Canadians whose preferred method of communication is sign language. The CAD also provides consultation and information on deaf needs and interests to the public, business, media, educators, governments and others. We conduct research and collect data regarding deaf issues; issue reports on these studies; and provide expertise on them; and develop and implement pilot programmes. We offer assistance to deaf organisations and service agencies across the country. We also provide a major library and resource centre on deafness at our office in Ottawa, Ontario.

Canadian Cultural Society of the Deaf Inc
House 144, 11337-61 Avenue, Edmonton, Alberta, T6H 1M3, Canada
Textphone: 001 403 436 2599 TTY
Fax: 001 403 430 9489
E-mail: ccsd@connect.ab.ca
Website: www.connect.ab.ca/~ccsd/
Contact: Helen Pizzacalla, President
            11 Keholme Crescent, Thorold, Ontario, L2V 4CI, Canada
E-mail: hpizzaca@netcom.ca

Canadian Cultural Society of the Deaf (CCSD) consists of seven provincial cultural societies across Canada. CCSD's primary objective is to ensure that the cultural needs of deaf and hard of hearing people are being met. The organisation concentrates its efforts in the areas of the performing arts, sign language, deaf literature, the visual arts and heritage resources.

16

Canadian Deaf Sports Association
303-1600 James Naismith Drive, Gloucester, Ontario, V3C 4B7, Canada
Tel: 001 613 748 5736
Textphone: 001 613 748 5789 TTY
Fax: 001 613 526 4718

Canadian Deafblind and Rubella Association
P O Box 1625, Meaford, Ontario, N0H 1Y0, Canada
Tel: 001 519 538 3431

Canadian Deafened Persons Association
16 Gloucester Court, Richmond Hill, Ontario, L4C 8L4, Canada
Textphone: 001 905 737 7878 TTY
Fax: 001 905 781 3783
Contact: Jerry Krueger
Fax: 001 905 737 6223

Canadian Education and Research Society for the Hearing Impaired
The Elizabeth Buckley School, 4054 Carey Road, Victoria, British Columbia, V8Z 4G2, Canada
Tel: 001 604 727 2215
Textphone: 001 604 727 2215 TTY

Canadian Hard of Hearing Association
2435 Holly Lane, Suite 205, Ottawa, Ontario, K1V 7P2 Canada
Tel: 001 613 526 1584
Textphone: 001 613 526 2692 TTY
Fax: 001 613 526 4718

Canadian Hearing Society
271 Spadina Road, Toronto, Ontario, M5R 2V3, Canada
Tel: 001 416 964 9595
Textphone: 001 416 964 0023 TTY
Fax: 001 416 964 2525
E-mail: info@chs.co

Canadian International Hearing Services
54 Strathburn Boulevard, Weston, Ontario M9M 2K7, Canada
Tel: 001 416 743 9755
Fax: 001 416 743 1232
Contact: Gordon Kerr

Captioning Resource Centre
443 Reynolds Street, Oakville, Ontario, L6J 3M5, Canada
Tel: 001 905 338 1246
Textphone: 001 905 338 1246 TTY
Fax: 001 905 338 7483
E-mail: NormTra@captions.org

Hearing Ear Dogs of Canada
P O Box 907, Oakville, Ontario, L6J 5E8, Canada
Tel: 001 416 842 7344
Textphone: 001 416 842 1585 TTY
Fax: 001 416 842 3373

International Hearing Society (Canada)
147 Hunter Street East, Peterborough, Ontario, K9H 1G7, Canada
Tel: 001 705 745 3244
Contact: Dianne Bernath

National Captioning Centre
409 King Street West, Suite 409, Toronto, Ontario, M5V 1K1, Canada
Tel: 001 416 599 0223
Fax: 001 416 599 0781

Ontario Association of the Deaf
271 Spadina Road, Toronto, Ontario, M5R 2V3, Canada
Textphone: 001 416 513 1893

Prince Edward Island Association for the Hearing Impaired
P O Box 2613, Charlottetown, Prince Edward Island, C1A 8C3, Canada
Tel: 001 902 892 4988
Textphone: 001 902 892 4988 TTY
Contact: Sharon MacInnis

Tinnitus Association of Canada
23 Ellis Park Road, Toronto, Ontario, M6S 2V4, Canada
Tel: 001 416 762 1490
Fax: 001 416 769 1109
E-mail: chasm@pathcom.com
Website: www.kadis.com/ta/tinnitus.htm
Contact: Elizabeth Eayrs

The objects of the Association are to collect and assess material about tinnitus and its treatments; to provide this information to every Canadian who suffers from head and ear noise; to encourage tinnitus research; to promote and assist the setting up of local support groups for people with tinnitus.

Chile

Asociación de Sordomudos de Chile

Avenida J P Aleddanori 1251, Nunoa, Santiago, Chile

Tel: 0056 2 237 0593

Fax: 0056 2 238 4232

China

China Association of the Deaf

44 Beichizi Street, Dongcheng District, Beijing 100006, People's Republic of China

Tel: 0086 1 513 9719/ 513 9722

Contact: Fu Zhiwei, Chief Executive

Colombia

Federación Colombiana

Deportiva de Sordos, Apartado Aereo # 5908, Cali, Colombia

Federación Nacional de Sordos de Colombia

Avenida 13, No. 80-60, Oficina 300, Bogotá DC, Colombia

Tel: 0057 1 256 1470

Textphone: 0057 1 256 1467

Fax: 0057 1 257 1024

E-mail: fenascol@impsat.net.co

Contact: Henry Royet, General Director

The Federation can provide the following services: Information and Guiding Centre, Training Centre (courses, workshops, conferences and advice about different topics related to deafness), develop and sell teaching materials, assistive devices for deaf and hard of hearing people, and development of local and national projects to improve the quality of life of deaf people.

FFD Nacional de Sordos de Colombia

Apartdo Aereo 76825, Bogotá, Colombia

Tel: 0057 1 257 1024

Fax: 0057 1 256 1470

Congo

Association Nationale des Déficients Auditifs de Congo

BP 1446, Brazzaville, Congo

Tel: 00242 810 923

Contact: Jacques Ekoko

Costa Rica

Asociaciøn de Sordos de Costa Rica

Apartado 6552-1000, San José, Costa Rica

Côte d'Ivoire

Association Nationale des Sourds de Côte d'Ivoire

01 BP 7912, Abidjan 01, Côte d'Ivoire, Africa

Croatia

Croatian Deaf Sports League

Palmoticeva 4, 41000 Zagreb, Croatia

16

Cyprus

Pan-Cyprian Organisation of Deaf

P O Box 1014, Nicosia, Cyprus

Fax: 00357 2354 610

Czech Republic

Federacion Svaz Neslys Sportovcu

Spartakiadni Stadion, Vychodni Triuna, CS-160 17 Praha 6, Czech Republic

Fax: 00420 2 235 7557

International Commission on Acoustics

Plzenska 66, 151 24 Praha 5, Czech Republic

Democratic Republic of Congo

L'Association Nationale des Sourds du Zaïre

BP 8276, Kinshasa, Democratic Republic of Congo, Africa

Denmark

Dansk Døve-ldraetsforbund

Genaratorvej 2a, DK-2730 Herlev, Denmark

Fax: 0045 4 494 4346

Danske Døves Landsforbund

Rantzausgade 60 - 1, P O Boks 704, DK-2200 København N, Denmark

Tel: 0045 3 524 0910
Textphone: 0045 3 524 0919
Fax: 0045 3 524 0920
E-mail: lf@deaf.dk
Contact: Knud Sondergaard, Chief Executive

Døvefilm Video

Rentemestervej 2, 2400 Københaven NV, Denmark

Tel: 0045 35821055
Fax: 0045 35821855
E-mail: deaftvdk@inet.uni2.dk

Production of TV programmes in sign language aired weekly on Danish broadcast organisation. The programmes are aimed at adults, youth and children. Production of daily news.

Døves Centre for Tegnsprog og Tegnstottet Kommunikation

Kastelsvej 60 A, DK-2100 Københaven O, Denmark

University level - interpreters, sign language training, etc.

European Deafblind Network

c/o Prinsessegade 28, 9400 Norresundby, Denmark

Tel: 0045 98 19 20 99
Fax: 0045 98 19 20 57
E-mail: lex.grandia@tp44.frukt.org

Information Centre for Acquired Deafblindness

Tel: 0045 4 485 6030
Fax: 0045 4 485 6099
E-mail: dbcent@inet.uni2.dk
Website: www.dbcent.dk
Contact: Ole Mortensen, Information Manager

See entry under Deafblind Resources.

Institutionen for Døve

Generatorvej 2a, DK-2730 Herlev, Denmark

Dominican Republic

Asociación Pro-Educación de los Sordomudos

Apdo No 596, Santo Domingo, RD, Dominican Republic

Ecuador

Federación Nacional de Sordos del Ecuador

Apartado 1703-841-A, Sucural 3, Quito, Ecuador

Eire

International Phonetic Association

Centre for Language and Communication Studies, Arts Building, Trinity College, Dublin, Eire

Tel: 00353 1 608 1348
Fax: 00353 1 677 2649
E-mail: anichsid@tcd.ie.
Website: www.arts.gla.ac.uk/IPA/ipa.html
Contact: Ailbhe Chasaide, Treasurer

The Association provides information and undertakes research in the field of phonetics. The organisation is open to other academics engaged in work in this field.

Irish Deaf Society

30 Blessington Street, Dublin 7, Eire

Tel: 00353 1 860 1878
Textphone: 00353 1 860 1910
Fax: 00353 1 860 1960
E-mail: irideas@indigo.ie
Website: www.indigo.ie/~wflynn/deaf/index.html#top
Contact: Helena Saunders

16

Irish Deaf Sports Association

8 Dun Eamer Drive, Dundrum, Dublin 16, Eire

Fax: 00353 1 735 7374

Irish Hard of Hearing Association

35 North Frederick Street, Dublin 1, Eire

Tel: 00353 1 872 3800

Fax: 00353 1 872 3816

Waterford Association for the Deaf

Henrietta Street, Waterford, Eire

Contact: Theresa O'Connor, Club Secretary

England

Commonwealth Society for the Deaf/Sound Seekers

138 Buckingham Palace Road, London, SW1W 9SA

Tel: 020 7259 0200

E-mail: sound.seekers@btinternet.com

Website: www.tcol.co.uk/comorg/csd.htm

Contact: J Davis, Chief Executive

In partnership with governments, associations and schools of commonwealth countries. Aims to prevent deafness and treats infective ear disease. Volunteer specialist surgeons, doctors, audiologists and teachers. Answers calls for help. Training of audiologists and technicians. Provision for audiological equipment, hearing aids and educational material.

Deafblind International

11-13 Clifton Terrace, Finsbury Park, London, N4 3SR

Tel: 020 7272 7774

Fax: 020 7272 6012

E-mail: dbi@sense.org.uk

Formerly the International Association for the Education of the Deaf Blind, Deafblind International provides information, runs workshops and conferences and an information exchange with other organisations. It provides services to all including academics and professionals working in the field. It publishes 'Deafblind Education' bi-annually.

European Federation of Audiology Societies

Tinnitus and Hyperacusis Centre, 32 Devonshire Place, London, W1N 1PE

Tel: 020 7486 4233

Fax: 020 7486 2218

E-mail: jon.hazell@ucl.ac.uk

Website: www.efas.org

Contact: Jonathan Hazell, General Secretary

EFAS was founded during the British Society of Audiology conference in Cambridge 1992 and now has 22 member countries. The scope of EFAS is to promote cooperation, exchange of experience, a knowledge of audiology within Europe, both as a scientific field and as a hearing health service offered to the public. EFAS represents the national societies of audiology in the 22 member countries.

European Federation of Parents of Deaf Children

Carpenters Cottage, Hemplands Lane, Privett, Alton, Hampshire, GU34 3NU

Tel: 01730 828286

Textphone: 01730 828286

Fax: 01730 828019

E-mail: kloening@pt.lu

Contact: John Butcher, Vice President

European Working Party in Paediatric Otorhinolaryngology

55 Harley Street, London, W1N 1DD

Tel: 020 7580 1481

Contact: John Evans, Board Member

Initiatives for Deaf Education in the Third World

Chapel Cottage, 7 King Street, Much Wenlock, Shropshire, TF13 6BL

Tel: 01952 727093

Fax: 01952 728473

Contact: Doreen Woodford, Secretary/ First Trustee

Tel: 01952 727093 / 728473

Exists to facilitate the activities of its partners. These are individuals working in their own countries who themselves contribute to spreading information, sharing skills, ideas and experiences within their own countries and across borders. Initiatives enables these partners to meet together from time to time for planning and conferring. Materials are prepared and circulated.

16

Youth Exchange Council

The British Council, 10 Spring Gardens, London, SW1A 2BN

Tel: 020 7389 4030
Textphone: 020 7389 4030
Fax: 020 7389 4033

Estonia

Estonian Association of the Deaf

2 Nômme Tee Street, Tallinn 13426, Estonia

Tel: 00372 2 655 2510/ 6552 509
Fax: 00372 2 655 2510
E-mail: klüt@uninet.ee
Contact: Liivi Hollman

Aims: to develop cooperation between deaf and partially deaf people in Estonia; cooperation with the government and municipal governments; to have a say in working out the social policy in Estonia, to develop and introduce sign language; to organise cultural and sports events; to help in finding work; rehabilitation; cooperation with other non-governmental organisations.

Estonian Deaf Sport Union

Sihi St. 49, Tallinn EE 0016, Estonia

Ethiopia

Ethiopian National Association of the Deaf

P O Box 21359, Addis Ababa, Ethiopia

Tel: 00251 118572

Contact: Alemayehu Teferi

To advoate for the rights and human dignity of deaf people. To work closely in cooperation with non-governmental organisations and other interested groups for the general well-being of the deaf. Ordinary members of the WFD.

Finland

IFHOH-Europe (International Federation of the Hard of Hearing, European Region)

Ilkantie 4, Fin-00400 Helsinki, Finland

Tel: 00358 9 580 3310
Fax: 00358 9 580 3331

Suomen Kuurojen Urh.

PL 57, SF-00401 Helsinki, Finland

Tel: 00358 0 580 3770

The Finnish Association of the Deaf

P O Box 57, 00401 Helsinki, Finland

Tel: 00358 9 580 3570
Fax: 00358 9 580 3576
E-mail: kuurojenliitto@kl-deaf.fi
Website: www.kl-deaf.fi
Contact: Raili Ojala, International Officer
Fax: 00 358 9 580 3774

The Finnish Association of the Deaf is the central organisation for 53 local deaf clubs, and the advocacy organisation for equal rights and services in sign language for deaf people. It provides the following services: information in sign language (video production unit, deaf magazine); education (Centre for Finnish Sign Language, courses and materials, FiSL dictionary work, Folk High School for the Deaf); culture (Cultural Centre of the Deaf, Museum for the Deaf, library and information service); 15 rehabilitation counsellors. It is active in international cooperation (development cooperation projects, WFD President's Office, European and Nordic cooperation with the nearby regions of St Petersburg and Karelia and with Estonia).

World Federation of the Deaf

Ilkantie 4, P L 65, SF-00401 Helsinki, Finland

Tel: 00358 9 58031
Fax: 00358 9 580 3770

France

Comite Permanent de Liason des Orthophonistes/Logopedes de l'UE CPLOL

2 Rue des deux Gares, 75010 Paris, France

Tel: 0033 1 40 35 63 75
Fax: 0033 1 40 37 41 42

Fédération Nationale des Sourds de France

1 Rue du 11 November, 92120 Montrouge, France

Tel: 0033 1 46 55 00 57
Textphone: 0033 1 46 55 00 57 minitel
Fax: 0033 1 46 55 00 57
Contact: Brigitte Pelletier, Responsable Administrative

Respresents deaf people and makes their needs known to the relevant public authorities. Information centre for both deaf and hearing people.

Fédération Sportif des Sourds de France

84 rue de Turenne, Paris 75003, France

Tel: 0033 1 42 72 30 75

World Federation of the Deaf France

13d chemin du Levant, 01210 Ferney-Voltaire, France

Tel: 0033 4 50 40 01 05

Fax: 0033 4 50 40 01 07

Contact: Carol-lee Aquiline, General Secretary

Germany

Deutscher Gehörlosen-Bund e. V

Paradeplatz 3, 24768 Rendsburg, Germany

Tel: 0049 331 589722

Textphone: 0049 331 589751

Fax: 0049 331 589745

E-mail: info@Gehörlosen-Bund.de

Website: www.Gehörlosen-Bund.de

Contact: Ulrich Hase, President

The society provides information and advice, runs conferences and an information exchange and also undertakes political work.

Deutscher Gehörlosen-Sportverband

Postfach 34 02 31, 4300 Essen 1, Germany

Fax: 0049 201 78 33 02

European League of Stuttering Associations

c/o BV Stotterer-Selbsthilfe, Gereonswall 112, 50670 Koln, Germany

Tel: 0049 221 139 1106

Fax: 0049 221 139 1370

International Association of Physicians in Audiology

c/o Prof K Schorn, ENT University Hospital, Klinikum Grosshadern, Marchinoinstrasse 15, 81377 Munich, Germany

Tel: 0049 89 70953860/ 861

Fax: 0049 89 70958825

Contact: S Stephens, President

c/o Welsh Hearing Institute, University Hospital of Wales, Cardiff, CF4 4XW

Tel: 029 2074 2374

International Federation for Pastoral Care of the Hard of Hearing Inc

Krokusstrasse 1, 48527 Nordhorn, Lower Saxony, Germany

Tel: 0049 5921703212

Fax: 0049 5921777024

Contact: Karl-Heinz Kooten, Federation Director

Nurnberger Strasse 6, 48529 Nordhorn, Lower Saxony, Germany

Ghana

Ghana National Association of the Deaf

P O Box AN 7908, Accra North, Ghana

Tel: 00233 21 243450

Fax: 00233 21 243450

Contact: Francis Boison, National President

The Ghana National Association of the Deaf (GNAD), which is the mouthpiece of all deaf persons in Ghana, has instituted concrete measures aimed at seeking the welfare and well-being of its members through a number of activities. Notably: deafness awareness raising; the development of sign language; interpreter training programme; to facilitate communication between the public and deaf community; mobilisation and membership drive; leadership training efforts; to develop the Women's Wing of the Association; training in income-generating activities; cultural and sporting activities, among others.

16

Greece

Greek Federation of the Deaf
57 Salomou St, 104-32 Athens, Greece
Tel: 0030 1 523 39 50
Fax: 0030 1 523 39 68
E-mail: hfd@hol.gr
Contact: Antonis Kab, General Secretary

Hellenic Athletic Federation for the Deaf
Aristogitonos 11-13, T Q 31 172, 100 35 Athens, Greece

Fax: 0030 1 865 7382

Guinea

Association Guinéenne des Sourds
BP 1868, Conakry, Guinea, West Africa
Tel: 00224 44 27 81
Contact: Abraham Bangour

Hong Kong

Hong Kong Deaf Sports Association
Rm. 1001C, 10/F, Ho King Comm. Centre, 2-16 Fa Yuen Str, Mongkok, Kowloon, Hong Kong
Fax: 00852 37 82 05 09

Hong Kong Mutual Assistance Society of the Deaf
General Post Office, P O Box 5016, Hong Kong

Hungary

Halasserultek Testnevelesi es Sportbizottsaga
Benczur u. 21, 1068 Budapest Vl, Hungary
Tel: 0036 1 112 5643
Fax: 0036 1 142 1989

Hallasserultek Orszagos Szovetsege
Benczur u. 21, 1068 Budapest, Hungary
Tel: 0036 1 112 5643/ 36 1 342 1989
Contact: Ivan Vasak, Chief Executive

Iceland

Felag Heyrnarlausra
Laugavegur 26, 101 Reykjavik, Iceland
Tel: 00354 561 3560
Fax: 30054 551 3567
E-mail: Feheyrn@ismennt.is
Contact: Hafdís Gísladóttir, Managing Director

The Icelandic Deaf Organisation was founded in 1960. Its main goal is to improve the life status of deaf people in Iceland, get the government to acknowledge the Icelandic Sign Language as the mother language of deaf people and fight for better service for them, including better access to aid equipment such as computers.

Iceland Deaf Sports Club
Klapparstigur 28, 101 Reykjavik, Iceland
Fax: 00354 113 567

India

All India Federation of the Deaf
18 Northend Complex, Ramakrishna Ashram Marg, New Delhi 110001, India
Tel: 0091 99 3364766
Contact: Onkar Sharma, Hon General Secretary

All India Sports Council of the Deaf
18 Northend Complex, Ramikrishna Ashram Marg, New Delhi 110001, India
Fax: 0091 11 94 11 11

Nambikkai Foundation
Palavoor 627 121, Tirunelveli Kattabomman District, Tamil Nadu, South India
Contact: Selwyn Morgan

Indonesia

Indonesian Welfare Association of the Deaf
Jalan Jambrut No 5b, Jakarta 10430, Indonesia

Padesan Educational Foundation
JL Tebet Timur 4/21, Jakarta (Selatan) 12820, Indonesia
Contact: Baron Sutadisasra

Iran

Iranian Deaf Sports Federation
Damavand Street, Silence Sports Complex, Tehran, Iran

Fax: 0098 21 83 43 33

Iranian National Centre for the Deaf
P O Box 14155-5819, 14179 Tehran, Iran

Contact: Mahmoud Pakzad, General Secretary

Welfare Organisation of Iran
Fayazbakhsh Avenue, Tehran, P O Box 11365 - 9187, Iran

Tel: 00672001-9/ 676974

Contact: H Aghabakshi, Head of International Relations

Israel

Association of the Deaf in Israel
P O B 9001, 13 Sd. Yad Lebanim, Tel Aviv 61090, Israel

Tel: 00972 37303355
Fax: 00972 37396419
Contact: Yad Eliyahu

Deaf people working voluntarily for the improvement of the deaf community is the cornerstone of our Association. Our organisation is run on a voluntary basis by the deaf members elected democratically and working for the deaf and hearing impaired community. Our objectives: to strive for the betterment of the hearing impaired person's life within the deaf community and within society as a whole; to promote legislation and advocacy for deaf people; to raise society's awareness of the deaf person's abilities as well as their limitations; to develop unique services for the deaf population.

Sport Organisation for the Deaf in Israel
Hellen Keller Centre, P O Box 9476, Tel Aviv 61093, Israel

Fax: 00972 3631 0940

Ente Nazionale Sordomuti
Via Gregorio VII 120, 00165 Rome, Italy

Tel: 0039 6 32 66 697/ 66 698
Fax: 0039 6 638 09 31

Federazione Sport
Silenziosi d'Italia, Viale della Tecnica 250/260, Velodromo Olimpico, 1-00 144 Rome, Italy

Tel: 0039 65 92 15 07
Fax: 0039 65 91 64 74

Japan

Japan Athletic Association of the Deaf
S K Bulding 130, Yamabuki-cho/Shinjuku-ku, Tokyo 162, Japan

Fax: 0081 33 26 73 445

Japanese Federation of the Deaf
8F S K Building, 130 Yamabuki-cho, Shinjuku-ku, Tokyo 162, Japan

Tel: 0081 33 26 88 847
Fax: 0081 33 26 73 445
E-mail: jfd@tky2.3.web.ne.jp
Website: www.2.tky.3web.ne.jp/~jfd/
Contact: Masayuki Matsumoto, General Secretary

The Japanese Federation of the Deaf can provide information, educational services, training including deaf awareness, and an information exchange. It also organises conferences and workshops and undertakes research and campaigning activities. It also has an office in Kyoto.

16

Kenya

Kenya National Association of the Deaf
Queensway House Office, P O Box 53448, Nairobi, Kenya

Contact: Dominic Majiwa, Chief Executive

Kenya Sports Federation
P O Box 59855, Nairobi, Kenya

Latvia

Latvijas Nedzirdigo
Sporta Federacija, Kandavagiela 27, 226083 Riga, Latvija

Latvijas Nedzirdigo Savieniba
Jana Seta 5, Riga 1050, Latvija
Tel: 00371 0132 212 485
Contact: Arnolds Pavlins, President

Lebanon

Andeweg Mediterranean Training For Teachers of the Deaf In the Middle East, Teacher Training College
P O Box 434, Hazmieh, Lebanon
Tel: 00961 5 920336
Fax: 00961 5 920625
Contact: A Andeweg

The Andeweg Mediterranean Training programme was established to ensure a supply of well-educated teachers of the deaf. Trainee-teachers of the deaf are enrolled in the Teacher Training College, which was started in 1960, for a two-year course in Special Education. Specialist tutors, many from overseas, lecture at the College. Students graduate with a Teacher of Deaf Diploma or a B Ed in Special Education if they follow an extended course for a further two years.

The Andeweg Institute for the Deaf
P O Box 11, 4623 Beirut, Lebanon
Tel: 00961 5 920735
Fax: 00961 5 920625
Contact: A Andeweg

Our school started in 1957 to provide oral education for deaf children from the age of 2 years six months to 18. Every available means of communication is used to encourage and enable our pupils to interact and communicate effectively, on equal terms with their peers. Our goal is to foster positive interaction, communication, development of skills and understanding and optimum independence.

Liberia National Association of the Deaf

P O Box 10-4569, 1000 Monrovia 20, Liberia, West Africa

Contact: W Wioh, President

Libya

Association de L'Oeuvre des Sourds-Muets au Liban
P O Box 33141, Al-Roudah, P C 73452, Libya

Lithuania

Lithuania Deaf Sports Federation
Sv Kazimiero Street 3, Vilnius 2600, Lithuania

Lithuanian Deaf Association
Sv Kazimiero Street 3, Vilnius 2600, Lithuania
Tel: 00370 2 628115
Fax: 00370 2 220493
Contact: Petras Gasiunas, Chairman

Luxembourg

FEAPDA
c/o Centre de Logopédie, Val Saint Andre, 1128 Luxembourg
Tel: 00352 445566/ 250908
Contact: Gaston Schuller, President

Verein der Gehorlosen und Schwerhorigen Luxemburg/ Association des Deficients Auditiefs Luxembourg
B P 2790, 1027 Luxembourg

Malawi

Education Centre for the Deaf in Malawi
c/o Box 225, Rumphi District Hospital, Rumphi, Malawi
Tel: 00265 372222
Fax: 00265 372338
Contact: Wiseman Nkhonjera

Several projects in existence; one of the aims is to maximise the benefit of these projects by creating a videophone directory for public distribution for deaf pupils in the community.

16

Maryview School For the Deaf

P O Box 5554, Limbe, Malawi

Contact: G N Mbewe

Malaysia

Sabah Society for the Deaf

P O Box 13971, 88846 Kota Kinabalu, Sabah, Malaysia

Tel: 0060 88 230894

Fax: 0060 88 252972

Contact: Lu Kong

Sabah Society for the Deaf was founded in 1975. The services provided are: assisting deaf people to look for employment; setting up pre-school for deaf children; giving counselling and sign language lessons to parents of both deaf and hearing children; providing vocational programmes for deaf people; opening a bakery for deaf people.

SHIMA

9b Tingkat 2, Komplek Sri Selangor, Jalan San Peng, 55200 Kuala Lumpur, Malaysia

Tel: 0060 3222 6536

Malta

Deaf Peoples Association (Malta)

Dar Joe Vassallo, 45 Lascaris Wharf, Valletta VLT01, Malta

Tel: 00356 245823

Textphone: 00356 245823

Fax: 00356 245823

E-mail: nayd@kemmunet.net.mt

Website: www.angelfire.com/mt/mnayd/index. html

Contact: Karl Borg
             Sarah Flat 1, Blanche Street, Sliema SLM05, Malta

Tel: 00356 336179

Textphone: 00356 336179

Fax: 00356 316820

E-mail: karl.l.borg@usa.net

The Deaf People Association (Malta) is an organisation working to ensure equal opportunities to all deaf people to live independently with the necessary support. This entails campaigning for good education, sign language use, development and interpreting, good audiological services together with anti-discrimination legislation. It also provides

awareness training together with information and support to its members, both deaf people and their families.

Mexico

Asociación Mexicana de Sordos

Ap Postal M-2290, C P 06002, Admin de Correos 1, México, DF, Mexico

Tel: 0052 5 588 97 51/ 52 5 30 22 34

Contact: Armando Vieyra, Chief Executive

Federación Mexicana de Sordos

Dep Para Sordos, A C, Agustin Melgar No 66-1, Col. Condesa/C P 06140, México, DF, Mexico

Fax: 0052 905 525 65 82

Moldova

Society of the Deaf of the Republic of Moldova

Str Hincesti 1, 277028 Chisinau, Moldova

Tel: 00373 2 729927/ 735371

Mongolia

Mongolian Association of the Blind and the Deaf

Ulaanbaatar - 210136, Mongolia

Namibia

Namibian National Association of the Deaf

P O Box 70220, Khomasdal, Windhoek, Namibia

Tel: 00264 61 217621

Contact: Martin Tjivera

Netherlands

Acquired Deafblind Network

Stichting Doof-Blinden, Professor Bronkhorstlaan 10, 3723 MB Bilthoven, The Netherlands

The Network is part of Deafblind International. It organises conferences and provides information on acquired deafblindness to interested professionals. The committee members are professionals working in different European countries. They publish and maintain a contact list of people working in the field, detailing their activities and current interests.

16

Dovenschap

Churchilllaan 11, 5e etage, Postbus 323, 3500 AH
Utrecht, The Netherlands

Tel: 0031 30 297 0800
Textphone: 0031 30 297 0600
Fax: 0031 30 297 0030
E-mail: info@dovenschap.nl
Website: www.dovenschap.nl
Contact: Tineke Ouwehand, Office Manager

Dovenschap is the national organisation of deaf
people in Holland. It is an umbrella organisation
of deaf clubs, young deaf people, elderly deaf
people, Christian deaf people, deaf sports clubs,
gay deaf people, and deafblind people.

Koninklijke Nederlandse Doven

Sport Bond, Plein 40-45, 1, 1064 SW Amsterdam,
The Netherlands

Fax: 0031 20 61 36 166

Signing Books for the Deaf

Signing Books, Slakkenstraat 58, 6431 NJ
Hoensbroek, Netherlands

Tel: 0031 45 522 84 59/ 0031 40 4123
               6751
Fax: 0031 45 523 30 29
E-mail: signingbooks@sign-lang.uni-
               hamburg.de
               Helpdesk: helpdesk-sb@sign-lang.uni-
               hamburg.de
Website: www.sign-lang.uni-
               hamburg.de/signingbooks/

Signing Books for the Deaf is a EU-Telematics
Applications-funded programme. The aim of the
project is to research current provision in Europe,
identify and evaluate best practice - and to make
this knowledge widely available as a resource to
producers, publishers, presenters and viewers. In
this way examples of good practice can be
extended throughout the community. The project
publishes an information resource on the Signing
Books Website. The project has a helpdesk that
will help anyone involved in the production of new
sign language videos.

New Zealand

New Zealand Association of the Deaf

P O Box 20051, Glen Eden, Auckland, New Zealand

New Zealand Deaf Sports

P O Box 15275, New Lynn, Auckland, New Zealand
Fax: 0064 9636 8557

Nicaragua

Asociación de Sordo de Nicaragua

Repto Pancasan, III Etapa del Sandy, Cuadras
arriba 1 1/2, Cuadra al Lago, Managua, Nicaragua
Tel: 00505 2 70666

Niger

Association des Sourds du Niger

B P 2361, Niamey, Niger

Nigeria

Imo Broadcasting Corporation

Oweri-Egbu Road, P O Box 329, Owerri, Imo State,
Nigeria
Tel: 00234 83 232801
Contact: Ajie Nzeribe, Director of Programmes
               P M B 1129, Owerri, Imo State, Nigeria

Nigeria National Association of the Deaf

c/o Tola Odusanya, Federation College of
Education (special), P M B 1089 Oyo, Oyo State,
Nigeria

Contact: Tola Odusanya, General Secretary

Norway

Norges Dove-Idrettforbund

Sven Brungst 7, 0166 Oslo 1, Norway
Tel: 0047 22 11 16 33
Textphone: 0047 22 42 06 91
Fax: 0047 22 11 16 33

Norwegian Association of the Deaf

P O Box 6850, St Olavs Place, 0130 Oslo, Norway
Tel: 0047 22 11 17 75
Fax: 0047 22 11 16 33
Contact: Svein Peterson, General Secretary

Pakistan

All-Pakistan Deaf and Dumb Welfare Society
47 Ahmed Block, New Garden Town, Lahore, Pakistan

Pakistan Association of the Deaf
P O Box 10583, Pechs, Karachi 75400, Pakistan

Fax: 0092 21 256 1036
Contact: Sohail Kochra, President

The Association is very involved in educating deaf adults and their families. Also works towards empowerment of women. Currently involved in promoting computer literacy amongst all deaf adults. Also developing a park and sports facilities for Special People in Karachi. PAD has spread its wings and hopefully will render services nationwide in Pakistan, focusing on education and job placement of deaf people. PAD is a non-governmental organisation without any support from the government.

Pakistan Deaf Sports Council
Ida Rieve School for the Deaf, Old Exhibition, Karachi-3, Pakistan

Paraguay

Centro de Sordomudos del Paraguay
TTE Garay 2717, Asunción, Paraguay
Tel: 00595 21331223

Peru

Asociaciøn de Sordos del Peru
Apartado Postal 3668, Lima 1, Peru
Tel: 00511 4222152
Fax: 00511 4222152
Contact: Elizabeth Aldun

Philippines

Philippine Association of the Deaf
Dao Street, San Antonio Village, Makati, Metro Manila, Philippines

Polski Zwiazek
Sportowy Glchych, ul. Flory 3-lllp, 00-586 Warzawa 11, Poland
Fax: 0048 22 489 427

Polski Zwiazek Gluchych
ul. Podwale 23, 00-261 Warsaw, Poland
Tel: 0048 22 8310896
Fax: 0048 22 6357536
Contact: Jozef Hendzel, Secretary

The Association provides help and support to its members and other deaf people through the following establishments which it runs: 68 centres for rehabilitation of deaf and hard of hearing children; 126 centres for rehabilitation and support of deaf adults; 97 clubs in which deaf people participate in various cultural and other activities, thus developing their artistic talents and enhancing their social life; 9 workshops in which deaf people can work and earn their living and which at the same gime generate profits for the Association.

Portugal

Associação de Familias e Amigos dos Surdos
Avenue Infante Santo n. 68, 5 C, 1350 Lisboa, Portugal
Tel: 00351 19217935
Fax: 00351 19207400
Contact: Luis Clara, Chairman of Directors

Associação Portuguesa de Surdos
Avenida da Liberdade 157-2, 1250 Lisboa, Portugal
Tel: 00351 1 3557244
Fax: 00351 1 3153244
E-mail: apsurdoscen@mail.telepac.pt

Associação Portuguesa dos Surdos
Rua da Alegria 19-2, 4000 Porto, Portugal
Fax: 00351 2208 0627

16

Romania

Romanian National Association of the Deaf

Asociatia Surzilor din Romania, Italiana Str Nr 3, Sektor 2, Bucharest 70216, Romania

Tel: 0040 1 3113061
Textphone: 0040 1 3113061
Fax: 0040 1 3113061
Contact: Florea Barbu, President

Our focus is on social integration of deaf people into hearing society. All activities (social, cultural, sport) are scheduled in an annual calendar: modern and folk dance contests, Miss Beauty contest, literature and history competition, creative compositions, sport, day of retired persons, interpreting services in any circumstances (police, court, hospital).

Russia

All-Russia Federation of the Deaf

10-A, 1905 Goda Street, 123022 Moscow, Russia
Tel: 007 095 252 06 74/ 214 32 35

Contact: Victor Smaltser
                   10-A , 1905 Goda Street, 123022
                   Moscow, Russia

Ordinary members of the WFD. The All-Russian Society of the Deaf aims at protecting the rights and interests of deaf and hard of hearing people, their social rehabilitation and integration. Conducts production activity at a number of specialised enterprises belonging to the ARSD.

Senegal

Association Nationale des Sourds du Senegal

BP 7052, Dakar, Senegal

Contact: Papa Faye, General Secretary

Singapore

Singapore Association for the Deaf

227 Mountbatten Road, Singapore, 397998
Tel: 0065 3448274
Fax: 0065 3457706
E-mail: admin@rainbow.sad.org.sg
Website: www.sad.org.sg
Contact: Jenny Ho, Executive Director
Tel: 0065 3448274/ 3457706
E-mail: jennyho@rainbow.sad.org.sg

Slovak Republic

Slovak Union of the Deaf and Hard of Hearing

Budatinska 59/a, 851 06 Bratislava, Slovak Republic

Tel: 00421 7 839926
Fax: 00421 7 839927
Contact: Milan Ruckay, Secretary General

The mission of the Slovak Union of the Deaf and Hard of Hearing is to actively help deaf and hard of hearing people to enable them to take part in the life of society in an integrated and fully valid way, and to undertake systematic advocacy of their specific interests and needs. The law on Sign Language of the Deaf approved by the Slovak Parliament in 1995 was initiated and promoted by the Slovak Deaf Organisation.

Slovenia

Zveza Drustev Slusno

Prizadetih Slovenije, Drenikova 24, 61000 Ljubljana, Slovenia

Fax: 00386 61 558282

Zveza Glumim in Naglusnih Slovenije

Drenikova 24, 1000 Ljubljana, Slovenia
Tel: 00386 61 554243
Fax: 00386 61 558281
Contact: Aljosa Redzepovic, Secretary

South Africa

Deaf Federation of South Africa

20 Napier Road, Richmond, Johannesburg, South Africa

Tel: 0027 11 482 1610
Fax: 0027 11 726 5873
E-mail: deafsa@icon.co.za

South Africa Deaf Sport Federation

P O Box 28453, Sunnyside, Pretoria 0132, South Africa

South Korea

Korea Welfare Association of the Deaf
681-50 Yok Sam-Dong, Kang Nam-Gu, Seoul, Republic of Korea
Tel: 0082 2 556 4758/ 3493
Fax: 0082 2 555 4241
Contact: Ingi Park, Director

Spain

Asociación de Personas Afectadas por Tinitus (APAT)
Apdo Correos 57, 08320 El Masnou, Barcelona, Spain
Tel: 0034 93 555 4955
Contact: Lucia Puig, President

Comité Español de Deportes Silenciosos
Barquil. n 19-l. lzqda, 28004 Madrid, Spain
Tel: 0034 91 531 0995
Fax: 0034 91 531 0995

Confederación Nacional de Sordos de España
Alcala, 160-1F, 28028 Madrid, Spain
Tel: 0034 91 356 5776
Textphone: 0034 91 356 5832
Videotel: 0034 91 724 0000/ 1225/ 1281
Fax: 0034 91 355 4336
E-mail: cnse@cnse.es
Website: www.cnse.es
Contact: Luis Canon, President

Information and advice, educational services, training, including awareness training, information exchange, organised workshops and conferences, research and campaigning activities. The services of the CNSE are available to public institutions and state and private schools.

Sri Lanka

Central Federation of the Deaf
'The Rosary', National Housing Scheme, Katunayaka, Sri Lanka

Contact: J Francis, General Secretary

Sudanese National Society for the Deaf
P O Box 2600, Khartoum, Sudan
Tel: 00249 11 460073
Fax: 00249 11 772381
Contact: Talat Taha, President

Swaziland

Swaziland National Association of the Deaf
P O Box 3622, Mbabane, Swaziland
Tel: 00268 42573
Fax: 00268 44719
E-mail: box33@icafe.co.sz

To provide interpretation facilities to deaf people in Swaziland. To assist with job applications. To raise awareness amongst hearing people. To establish income-generating projects for deaf people. To initiate research into Swazi Sign Language.

Sweden

Sveriges Dovas Idrottsforbund
Idrottens Hus, 123 87 Farsta, Sweden
Tel: 0046 87 24 85 40

Sveriges Dovas Riksforbund
Box 300, 793 27 Leksand, Sweden
Tel: 0046 8 442 14 61
Textphone: 0046 8 442 14 60/71
Fax: 0046 8 442 14 99

Switzerland

Fédération Suisse des Sourds
Secrétariat Général, C P 3, 1603 Grandvaux, Switzerland
Tel: 0041 21 799 3091
Fax: 0041 21 799 3091
Contact: Elisabeth Faoro, Secretary

At national level, the Swiss Federation of the Deaf primarily fights for: equal rights for disabled persons, recognition and acceptance of our language and our culture, more subtitles on TV and more visual information, development of interpreter services, better training, better professional and social integration, more solidarity.

16

SGSV
Klaus Notter, Sonnrainweg 4, 9008 St Gallen, Switzerland

Tel: 0041 71 242913

Syria

Syrian Federation of Societies for the Welfare of the Deaf
P O Box 31350, Damascus, Syria

Tel: 0093 11 4427952

Contact: Fayez el-Kafi

Taiwan

National Association of the Deaf in the Republic of China
2nd Floor No 70, Yen-Ping South Road, Taipei, Taiwan

Tel: 00886 2 383 2508

Fax: 00886 2 375 1698

Contact: Yu-Shan Ku, Director General

Taipei Chinese Sports
Association of the Deaf, 320 Chung-Ching N Road, Sec 3, 10318 Taipei, Taiwan

Tel: 00886 2 531 2959

Tanzania

Tanzania Association of the Deaf (CHAVITA)
P O Box 21591, Dar es Salaam, Tanzania

Tel: 00255 51 850829

Fax: 00255 51 112434

CHAVITA is a non-governmental organisation dedicated to the advancement of thousands of deaf people in the United Republic of Tanzania. CHAVITA is striving towards achieving its development strategies and to become the pressure group of deaf people in the country.

Thailand

National Association of the Deaf in Thailand
6-4 Soi Seang Utai Thip, Din Deang 1 Rd, Sam Sen Nai Phyathai, Bangkok 10400, Thailand

Tel: 0066 2 248 3094

Tunisia

Association Voix du Sourd de Tunisie
12 rue Mahmoud Bourguiba, 1000 Tunis, Tunisia

Tel: 00216 1 347 907

Contact: Moncef Ezzeddine

Turkey

Turkish National Federation of Deaf and Dumb Associations
Malta Fevzipasa Caddesi, Kinalizade Sokak, No 2-3 Fatih, Istanbul, Turkey

Turkiye Sagir-Dilzis
Spor Kulupleri Federasyonu, Gazet. E. Dernek Sokak 15/4, Beyoglu, Istanbul, Turkey

Tel: 0090 212 340 4063

Uganda

Uganda National Association of the Deaf
Namirembe, P O Box 7339, Kampala, Uganda

Contact: Emmanuel Lwanga

Ukraine

Ukraine Deaf Sports Federation
P Tichina Str 28, Ap 112, 253173 Kiev, Ukraine

Contact: P Sandugei

Ukrainian Society of the Deaf
Central Board, 74 V Vasylkivska St, 252150 Kiev, Ukraine

Tel: 00380 44 220 56 73/ 227 26 16

Fax: 00380 44 227 53 16

Contact: Ann Merezhko

To unite hearing impaired and speech impaired citizens, assist them in getting social and vocational rehabilitation, promote their general, professional and cultural level so that they can obtain the maximum information to help them broaden their outlook and enrich their spiritual world. To provide deaf people with legal and social protection, etc.

16

Uruguay

Asociación de Sordomudos del Uruguay
Casilla de Correo 897, Montevideo, Uruguay
Tel: 00598 2383212
Fax: 00598 2354218

Uruguay Organisation Deportiva de Sordos
Calle Guri 2317, C P 11 200, Montevideo, Uruguay

USA

ABLEDATA
8455 Colesville Road, Suite 935, Silver Spring, MD 20910-3319, USA
Tel: 001 301 608 8998 ext 100
Textphone: 001 301 608 8912
Fax: 001 301 608 8958
E-mail: abledata@macroint.com.us
Website: www.abledata.com
Contact: Katherine Belknap, Assistant Project Director

ABLEDATA is an electronic database of assistive technology and rehabilitation equipment products for children and adults with physical, cognitive and sensory disabilities. The database currently lists more than 24,000 products from 3,000 companies and may be searched via the ABLEDATA website.

Alexander Graham Bell Association for the Deaf
3417 Volta Place NW, Washington, DC 20007, USA
Tel: 001 202 337 5220/ 8314
Fax: 001 202 337 8314
E-mail: agbell@aol.com

Gathers and disseminates information on hearing loss, promotes better public understanding of hearing loss in children and adults, provides scholarship, financial and parent-infant awards and promotes early detection of hearing loss in infants.

American Academy of Audiology
8201 Greensboro Drive, Suite 300, McLean, VA 22102, USA
Tel: 001 703 610 9022/ 800 222 2336
Fax: 001 703 610 9005
E-mail: lac@audiology.com
Contact: Barry Freeman, President

American Academy of Otolaryngology - Head and Neck Surgery, Inc
1 Prince Street, Alexandria, VA 22314-3357, USA
Tel: 001 703 836 4444
Textphone: 001 703 519 1585
Fax: 001 703 683 5100
E-mail: entnews@aol.com
Website: www.entnet.org
Contact: Michael Maves, Executive Vice President

The American Academy of Otolaryngology - Head and Neck Surgery, Inc represents more than 7,500 ear, nose and throat specialists. Promotes the art and science of medicine related to otolaryngology - head and neck surgery, including providing continuing medical education courses and publications. Distributes patient leaflets relating to ear problems and makes referrals to physicians.

American Association of the Deafblind
7202 Buchanan Street, Landover Hills, MD 20784-2236, USA
Tel: 00 1 301 588 6545
Fax: 00 1 301 588 8705
E-mail: aadb@aerols.com
Contact: Jeffrey Bohrman, President

American Deafness and Rehabilitation Association
P O Box 27, Roland, AR 721355, USA
Tel: 001 501 868 8850/ 8812
Fax: 001 501 868 8812
E-mail: adarahuie@aol.com
Contact: Marie Huie, Office Manager

American Hearing Research Foundation
55 E Washington Street, Suite 2022, Chicago, IL 60602, USA
Tel: 001 312 726 9670
Fax: 001 312 726 9695
Contact: William Lederer, Executive Director/Editor

16

American Society for Deaf Children

2848 Arden Way, Suite 210, Sacramento, CA 95825-1373, USA

Fax: 001 916 482 0121

E-mail: asdc1@aol.com

Contact: Elaine Ocuto, President

American Society for Deaf Social Workers

1306 Morningside Drive, Silver Spring, MD 20904, USA

Tel: 001 202 373 7215

American Speech-Language Hearing Association

10801 Rockville Pike, Rockville, MD 20852, USA

Tel: 001 800 638 8255

Textphone: 001 800 638 8255

Fax: 001 301 897 7348

Contact: Katharine Butler, President

American Tinnitus Association

P O Box 5, Portland, OR 97207-0005, USA

Tel: 001 503 248 9985

Fax: 001 503 248 0024

E-mail: tinnitus@ata.org

Website: www.ata.org

Contact: Gloria Reich, Executive Director

ATA provides information and lists of service providers; publishes quarterly journal and bibliography; funds research and coordinates support groups.

Arkansas Rehabilitation Research and Training Center for Persons who are Deaf and Hard of Hearing

University of Arkansas, 4601 W Markham Street, Little Rock, AR 72205, USA

Tel: 001 501 686 9691

Fax: 001 501 686 9698

E-mail: rehabres@cavern.uark.edu

Website: www.uark.edu/depts/rehabres

Contact: Douglas Watson, Director

The centre conducts research in the areas related to enhancing employability of deaf and hard of hearing persons - preparation, entry, and advancement in careers. Conducts in-service training and disseminates publications and materials related to the vocational rehabilitation of deaf and hard of hearing persons. Provides graduate training in rehabilitation counselling.

258

Association of Late-Deafened Adults

10310 Main Street, P O Box 274, Fairfax, VA 22030, USA

Tel: 001 404 289 1596

Fax: 001 404 284 6862

Contact: Candis Shannon, Editor

Auditory-Verbal International, Inc

2121 Eisenhower Avenue, Suite 402, Alexandria, VA 22314, USA

Tel: 001 703 739 1049

Textphone: 703 739 0874

Fax: 001 703 739 0395

Contact: Renee Levinson, Executive Director

Better Hearing Institute

5021-B Backlick Road, Annandale, VA 22043, USA

Tel: 001 703 642 0580

Fax: 001 703 750 9302

E-mail: betterhearing@juno.com

Website: www.betterhearing.org

Contact: Michele Hartlove, Executive Director

Since 1973, the BHI, a non-profit educational association, has been a resource to the public, the media, and hearing health professionals and has provided free information about hearing loss, hearing care providers, hearing aids, and tinnitus. North Americans with uncorrected hearing problems receive hearing help on BHI's Hearing Helpline or by logging on the Institute's Hearing Help-On-Line Internet site.

Boys Town National Research Hospital

555 N 30th Street, Omaha, NE 68131, USA

Tel: 001 402 498 6511/ 6543

Fax: 001 402 498 6638

E-mail: peb@boystown.org

Website: www.boystown.org

Contact: Patrick Brookhouser, Director

Centre for Bicultural Studies

5506 Kenilworth Avenue, Suite 100, Riverdale, MD 20737, USA

Tel: 001 301 277 3945/ 3944/ 301 699 5226

Contact: M Bienvenu, President

Children of Deaf Adults (CODA)

P O Box 30715, Santa Barbara, California, CA 93130, USA

Tel:	001 805 682 0997
Website:	www.gallaudet.edu/-rgpricke/coda /index.html
Contact:	Millie Brother, Founder of CODA International

CODA International is an organisation established for the purpose of promoting family awareness and individual growth in hearing children of deaf parents. This purpose is accomplished through providing educational opportunities, promoting self-help, organising advocacy efforts and acting as a resource for the membership and various committees.

Cochlear Implant Club International

5335 Wisconsin Avenue NW, Suite 440, Washington, DC 20015-2034, USA

Tel:	001 202 895 2781
Textphone:	001 202 895 2781
Fax:	001 202 895 2782
E-mail:	pwms.cici@worldnet.9tt.net
Website:	www.cici.org
Contact:	Peg Williams, Executive Director

CICI provides information and support to help its members work together to meet the shared challenges of having and using a cochlear implant. Its members are implant users, candiadates for implanting, families, professionals, and the general public. CICI publishes a quarterly magazine, 'Contact', and holds a biennial convention.

Comité International des Sports des Sourds

16117 Orchard Grove Road, North Potomac, MD 20878, USA

Contact:	Donalda Ammons, Secretary General

Conference of Educational Administrators of School and Programs for the Deaf, Inc

P O Box 1778, St Augustine, FL 32085-1778, USA

Tel:	001 904 810 5200
Textphone:	001 904 810 5200
Fax:	001 904 810 5525
Contact:	Gertrude Galloway, President

Conference of Educational Administrators Serving the Deaf

1600 S Highway 275, Council Bluffs, IA 51503, USA

Tel:	001 712 366 0571/ 3218
Contact:	William Johnson, President

Convention of American Instructors of the Deaf

P O Box 377, Bedford, TX 76095-0377, USA

Tel:	001 817 354 8414
Fax:	001 817 354 8414
E-mail:	caid@swbell.net

The Convention of American Instructors of the Deaf is the organisation for teachers, administrators, educational interpreters, residential personnel and other concerned professionals involved in education of the deaf. The CAID provides biennial conventions. Benefits of membership includes issues of the 'American Annals of the Deaf', the oldest educational journal in the US, quarterly newsletters, special interest groups, convention proceedings.

CPB/ WGBH National Center for Accessible Media

125 Western Avenue, Boston, MA 02134, USA

Tel:	001 617 492 9258
Textphone:	001 617 492 9258
Fax:	001 617 782 2155
E-mail:	ncam@wgbh.org
Website:	www.wgbh.org/ncam
Contact:	Larry Goldberg, Director of Media Access
E-mail:	Larry_Goldberg@wgbh.org

A division within the WGBH Educational Foundation that works to make media accessible to under-served populations, such as disabled persons, minority language users, and people with low literacy skills. NCAM researches and develops new technologies that create access to public mass media (TV, radio, movies, newspapers, etc), investigates how existing access technologies may benefit other populations, and conducts community outreach to educate people about media access issues.

16

DB-LINK

Teaching Research, 345 North Monmouth Avenue, Monmouth, OR 97361, USA

Tel: 00 1 800 438 9376/ 854 7013
Textphone: 001 800 854 7013
Fax: 00 1 503 838 8150
E-mail: dblink@tr.wou.edu
Website: www.tr.wou.edu/dblink/

DB-LINK identifies, coordinates and disseminates information related to children and young people who are deafblind. Parents, service providers, administrators and others interested in services are invited to contact DB-LINK for information. DB-LINK is a collaborative effort involving the Helen Keller National Center, Perkins School for the Blind and Teaching Research. DB-LINK is a co-sponsor of the publication 'Deaf-blind Perspectives'.

Deaf and Hard of Hearing Entrepreneurs Council

814 Thayer Avenue, Suite 303, Silver Spring, MD 20910, USA

Tel: 001 301 474 8278
Fax: 001 301 474 3330
E-mail: srattner@aol.com
Contact: Steven Rattner, President

Deaf Entertainment Foundation

8306 Wilshire Boulevard, Suite 906, Beverly Hills, CA 90211-2382, USA

Tel: 001 213 782 1344
Textphone: 001 213 782 0298
Videotel: 001 323 782 1344
Fax: 001 213 782 1344
E-mail: deafent@aol.com
Website: www.deafentertainment.org
Contact: Ken Elks, Executive Director/Publisher
Textphone: 001 323 655 1542

Deaf Entertainment Foundation's purpose consists of three points: 1) to recognise and encourage excellence of the deaf and hard of hearing talents; 2) to promote awareness and deaf culture in the entertainment industry; and 3) to achieve unity between the deaf/hard of hearing and hearing communities.

Deaf Women United Inc

P O Box 44, East Hampton, CT 06424, USA

Textphone: 001 206 726 0093
Fax: 001 206 726 0017
Website: www.tr.wou.edu/dblink/

Deafness and Communicative Disorders Branch

Office of Special Education and Rehabilitation, Department of Education, 330 C St SW, Room 3228, Washington, DC 20202-2736, USA

Tel: 001 202 205 9152/ 205 8352
Fax: 001 202 205 9772
E-mail: Victor_Galloway@ED.GOV

Promotes improved and expanded rehabilitation services for deaf and hard of hearing people and individuals with speech or language impairments. Provides technical assistance to Rehabilitation Services Administration staff, state rehabilitation agencies, other public and private agencies, and individuals. Also provides funding for interpreter training and demonstration rehabilitation programmes such as programmes for low-functioning adults who are deaf.

Deafness Research Foundation

15 W 39th Street, New York, NY 10018, USA

Tel: 001 212 768 1181/ 800 535 3323
Fax: 001 212 768 1782
Contact: Jane Fortune, Chairman

Deafpride Inc

800 Florida Avenue NE, Washington, DC 20002-3695, USA

Tel: 001 202 675 6700
Fax: 001 202 547 0547
Contact: Willie Logan, President

Episcopal Conference of the Deaf

P O Box 27469, Philadelphia, PA 19118-0069, USA

Tel: 001 215 247 1059
Textphone: 001 215 247 6454
Fax: 001 315 449 1602
E-mail: RAPickerin@aol.com
Contact: Virginia Nagel, President
            100 Wilson Place, Syracuse, NY 13214-1925, USA
Tel: 001 315 449 1602
E-mail: RevGinger@aol.com

Gallaudet University Alumni Association

Gallaudet University, 800 Florida Avenue NE, Washington, DC 20002-3695, USA

Tel:　　　001 202 651 5060/ 5061

Fax:　　　001 202 651 5062

E-mail:　　alumweb@gallux.gallaudet.edu

Website:　www.gallaudet.edu/~alumweb

Contact:　Mary Pugin, Executive Director

The GUAA is a non-profit organisation which represents more than 13,000 alumni of Gallaudet University. Governed by an elected Board of Directors, the GUAA sponsors programmes and activities that support the mission of Gallaudet University.

HEAR NOW

9745 E Hampden Avenue, Suite 300, Denver, CO 80231-4923, USA

Tel:　　　001 303 695 7797/ 800 648-HEAR

Fax:　　　001 303 695 7789

E-mail:　　jostelter@aol.com

Website:　www.leisurelan.com~hearnow

Contact:　Elaine Hansen, Assistance Programs Coordinator

HEAR NOW is a Denver-based, national non-profit organisation that provides hearings for legal residents of the US with very limited financial resources. An application process for assistance is followed. Help is also available for cochlear implants. Hearing aids are collected for recycling.

Hearing Education and Awareness for Rockers

P O Box 460847, San Francisco, CA 94146, USA

Tel:　　　001 415 773 9590

Fax:　　　001 415 552 4296

E-mail:　　hear@hearnet.com

Website:　www.hearnet.com

Contact:　Kathy Peck, Executive Director

Hearing Education and Awareness for Rockers (HEAR) is a non-profit public benefit health organisation dedicated to raising awareness about the dangers of debilitating and often irreversible hearing loss and tinnitus due to exposure to excessively loud sound levels in music; whether it is from playing, attending concerts, using stereo earphones, or playing amplification systems too loudly. HEAR provides information, hearing referrals, hearing protection and educational videos. A catalogue is available upon request. HEAR also undertakes research into this area.

Hearing Industries Association

515 King Street, Suite 420, Alexandria, VA 22314, USA

Tel:　　　001 703 684 5744

Fax:　　　001 703 684 6048

E-mail:　　hiallears@aol.com

Contact:　Carole Rogin, President

Heath Resource Center

1 Dupont Circle, Suite 800, Washington, DC 20036, USA

Tel:　　　001 202 939 9320/ 800 544 3284

Fax:　　　001 202 833 4760

E-mail:　　heath@ace.nche.edu

Website:　www.acenet.edu/programs/HEATH

Contact:　Daniel Gardner, Information Specialist

The HEATH Resource Center operates the national clearing house on post-secondary education for individuals with disabilities. Support from the United States Department of Education enables the center to serve as an information exchange about educational support services, policies, procedures, adaptations, and opportunities at American campuses, vocational-technical schools, and other post-secondary training entities. The Center gathers and disseminates this information to help people with disabilities develop to their fullest potential through post-secondary education and training.

Helen Keller National Center for Deaf-Blind Youths and Adults

Tel:　　　　00 1 516 944 8900

Textphone: 001 516 944 8637

Fax:　　　　00 1 516 944 7302

E-mail:　　abigailp@aol.com

Website:　www.helenkeller.org\national

Contact:　Barbara Hausman, Director of Public Relations

Tel:　　　00 1 516 944 8900 ext 325

See entry under Deafblind Resources.

House Ear Institute

2100 West Third Street, Fifth Floor, Los Angeles, CA 90057, USA

Tel:　　　001 213 483 4431/ 484 2642/ 1 800 55 2

Fax:　　　001 213 483 8789

Contact:　John House, President

16

International Catholic Deaf Association, United States Section

8002 S Sawyer Road, Darien, IL 60561-5227, USA

Tel: 001 630 887 9472
Fax: 001 630 887 8850
E-mail: kgkush@aol.com
Website: members.aol.com/KgKush
Contact: Kathleen Kush, Manager, US Section

International Deaf Pilots Association

R R #1, Box 99 E-1, Jacksonville, IL 62650, USA

E-mail: idpa@mediasoft.net

International Hearing Society (USA)

20361 Middlebelt Road, Livonia, MI 48152, USA

Tel: 001 810 478 2610/ 800 521 5247
Fax: 001 810 478 4520

Professional association of specialists who test hearing and select, fit, and dispense hearing instruments. The society conducts programmes of competence qualifications, education, and training, and promotes specialty-level accreditation.

International Lutheran Deaf Association

1333 S Kirkwood Road, St Louis, MO 63122, USA

Tel: 001 314 965 9917 ext 1315/ 965 9000
Textphone: 001 888 899 5031 TTY
Fax: 001 314 965 0959
Contact: Dennis Konkel, President

The purpose of ILDA is: to coordinate and strengthen the religious activities and services in congregations; to promote their growth to the highest level of the service to their Lord; to promote the Christian faith and life of deaf people, both Lutheran and non-Lutheran; to carry on our mission-focused ministry throughout the world.

Jewish Deaf Congress

9420 Reseda Boulevard, Suite 422, Northridge, CA 91324, USA

Tel: 001 818 993 2517
Textphone: 001 818 993 8517
Fax: 001 818 993 2695
Contact: Barbara Boyd, President

John Tracy Clinic

806 West Adams Boulevard, Los Angeles, CA 90007, USA

Tel: 001 213 748 5481/ 747 2924
Textphone: 001 800 522 4582
Fax: 001 213 749 1651
Website: www.johntracyclinic.org
Contact: Maura Martindale, Director of Education Department

John Tracy Clinic is an educational facility for pre-school deaf children and their families. Worldwide correspondence courses in English and Spanish are offered to parents whose children are of pre-school age and are hard of hearing, deaf or deafblind. Two 3-week international family summer programmes are offered in Los Angeles to families worldwide. All Clinic services are free of charge to families of deaf or deafblind children.

Junior National Association of the Deaf and Youth Leadership Camp

7202 Buchanan Street, Landover Hills, MD 20784-2236, USA

Tel: 001 301 587 1788
Textphone: 001 301 587 4875
Fax: 001 301 587 4873
E-mail: juniornad@juno.com
Contact: Michele Listisard, Youth Programs Coordinator

League for the Hard of Hearing

71 West 23rd Street, New York, NY 10010-4162, USA

Tel: 001 212 741 7650
Textphone: 001 212 255 1932
Fax: 001 212 255 4413
E-mail: postmaster@lhh.org
Website: www.lhh.org
Contact: Keith Muller, Executive Director

The League for the Hard of Hearing is the oldest hearing rehabilitation agency in the country, offering a comprehensive programme of services to enable infants, children and adults to better function in a hearing world. Annually the League provides services to over 13,000 individuals and their families from all economic, social and ethnic groups regardless of the degree of hearing loss or choice of communication style.

16

National Association for Hearing and Speech Action

10801 Rockville Pike, Rockville, MD 20852, USA

Tel: 001 800 638-Talk
Textphone: 001 800 638-Talk

National Association of the Deaf

7202 Buchanan Street, Landover Hills, MD 20784-2236, USA

Tel: 001 301 587 1788
Textphone: 001 301 587 1789
Fax: 001 301 587 1791
E-mail: nadhq@juno.com
Website: www.nad.org
Contact: Nancy Bloch, Executive Director

National Association of the Deaf Captioned Films/Video Program

1447 E Main Street, Spartanburg, SC 29307, USA

Tel: 001 800 237 6213
Textphone: 001 800 237 6819
Fax: 001 800 538 5636
E-mail: nadcfv@aol.com

National Captioning Institute Inc

1900 Gallows Road, Suite 3000, Vienna, VA 22182, USA

Tel: 001 703 917 7600/ 9878
Fax: 001 703 917 9878
Contact: Betty Hallman, Vice President, Marketing

NCI, a non-profit corporation founded in 1979, is the nation's largest provider of closed-captioned television services for the broadcast, cable and home video industry. Also researches the educational benefits of captioned TV, and works to expand the captioning serviced around the world.

National Catholic Office of the Deaf

7202 Buchanan Street, Landover Hills, MD 20784-2236, USA

Tel: 001·301 577 1684
Textphone: 001 301 577 4184
Fax: 001 301 577 1690
E-mail: nora.letourmeau@deafworld.com
Contact: Arvilla Rank, Executive Director

Assists in the coordination of the efforts of people and organisations involved in the church's ministry with deaf and hard of hearing people; serves as a resource centre for information concerning spiritual needs and religious educational materials and assists bishops and pastors with their pastoral responsibilities to people who are deaf or hard of hearing.

National Centre for Law and Deafness

800 Florida Avenue NE, Washington, DC 20002-3695, USA

Tel: 001 202 651 5373/ 5381
Contact: Sy DuBow, Legal Director

National Congress Of Jewish Deaf

33 South Landing Road, Rochester, NY 14610, USA

Contact: Judy Slomovic, Executive Secretary

National Cued Speech Association USA

Nazareth College, Speech and Language Department, 4245 East Avenue, Rochester, NY 14618, USA

Tel: 001 716 586 2525 Work/ 389 2776 Home
Contact: Mary Daisey, Executive Director

National Fraternal Society of the Deaf

1118 South Sixth Street, Springfield, IL 62703, USA

Tel: 001 217 789 7429
Textphone: 001 217 789 7438
Fax: 001 217 789 7489
Website: www.nfsd.com
Contact: Al Nevel, Grand President

Provides life insurance to deaf and hard of hearing people, their families, and others associated with hearing loss. Serves in advocacy capacity on issues relating to deafness, provides scholarships, prints quarterly newsletter, engages in fraternal activities, and presents various awards.

National Hearing Aid Society

20361 Middlebell Road, Livonia, MI 48152, USA

Tel: 001 313 478 2610/ 4520
Contact: Michael Stone, President

16

National Information Center for Children and Youth with Disabilities

P O Box 1492, Washington, DC 20013, USA

Tel: 001 800 695 0285
Textphone: 001 202 884 8200
Fax: 001 202 884 8441
E-mail: nichy@aed.org
Website: www.aed.org/nichcy

National Information Center on Deafness

Gallaudet University, 800 Florida Avenue NE, Washington, DC 20002-3695, USA

Tel: 001 202 651 5051
Textphone: 001 202 651 5052
Fax: 001 202 651 5054
E-mail: nicd.infotogo@gallaudet.edu
Website: www.gallaudet.edu/~nicd

The National Information Center on Deafness (NICD), located on the Gallaudet University campus, is a centralised source of accurate, up-to-date, objective information on topics dealing with deafness and hearing loss. NICD responds to questions from the general public and deaf and hard of hearing people, their families, and professionals who work with them. NICD collects, develops, and disseminates information on deafness, hearing loss, and services and programmes related to people with hearing loss. The Center maintains contacts with a multitude of resources and experts on the University campus and across the country. When appropriate, we make referrals to other organisations and agencies.

National Information Clearing House on Children who are Deafblind

Teaching Research, 345 N Monmouth Avenue, Monmouth, OR 97361, USA

Tel: 001 800 438 9376
Textphone: 001 854 7013
Fax: 001 503 838 8150
Website: www.tr.wosc.osshe.edu/tr/dbp/index.htm
Contact: John Reiman, Director

National Institute on Deafness and Other Communication Disorders

31 Center Drive, MSC 2320 (Room 3C31), Bethesda, MD 20892-2320, USA

Tel: 001 301 496 7243
Textphone: 001 301 402 0252
Fax: 001 301 402 0018
Website: www.nih.gov/nidcd

The NIDCD conducts and supports research and research training on normal and disordered mechanisms affecting hearing, balance, smell, taste, voice, speech and language. NIDCD provides information and disseminates materials to educate the public and health professionals about these seven research areas.

National Rehabilitation Information Center

8455 Colesville Road, 935, Silver Spring, MD 20910-3319, USA

Tel: 001 301 588 9284
Textphone: 001 301 495 5626/ 800 346 2742
Fax: 001 301 587 1967
Website: www.naric.com/naric
Contact: Mark Odum, Information Specialist

National Technical Institute for the Deaf

Lyndon Baines Johnson Building, 52 Lomb Memorial Drive, Rochester, NY 14623-5604, USA

Tel: 001 716 475 6906
Textphone: 001 716 475 6906
Fax: 001 716 475 5623
E-mail: ntidmc@rit.edu
Website: www.rit.edu/NTID
Contact: Robert Davila, Vice President
Fax: 001 716 475 5623/ 6500

NTID aims to provide deaf students with outstanding state-of-the-art technical and professional education programmes, complemented by a strong arts and sciences curriculum, that prepares them to live and work in the mainstream of a rapidly changing global community and enhances their interest and skill in continuing lifelong learning. Secondarily, NTID prepares professionals to work in fields related to deaf people; undertakes a programme of applied research designed to enhance the social, economic and educational accommodation of deaf people; and shares its knowledge and expertise through outreach and other information dissemination programmes.

16

National Theatre of the Deaf

P O Box 659, 5 West Main Street, Chester, CT 06412, USA

Tel: 001 860 526 4971/4974 /0066
Fax: 001 860 526 0066
E-mail: Deaftcon@aol.com
Website: www.NTD.org
Contact: Camille Jeter, Artistic Director, Education/Outreach
Tel: 001 860 526 4971
Textphone: 001 860 526 4975

Concentrates on artistic and theatrical professional development of deaf actors and actresses. Tours the United States and abroad. Also presents Little Theatre of the Deaf productions in schools, theatres, museums and libraries. Sponsors a professional school that includes playwriting with full scholarships available for deaf people interested in theatre. Outreach and residency programmes available. Deaf theatre conference annually.

Piedmont Center for Mental Health Services

307 Miller Road, Mauldin, SC 29365, USA

Tel: 001 864 297 5044
Videotel: 001 864 288 9321
Fax: 001 864 297 8969
E-mail: mhinterp@mindspring.com

Rainbow Alliance of the Deaf

10908 Bucknell Drive, Suite #1312, Wheaton, MD 20902, USA

Tel: 001 702 804 6476 evenings/weekends
Fax: 001 702 804 7832
E-mail: eahinca@aol.com
Website: www.rad.org
Contact: Scot Pott, President
            8117 Heavenly Star Circle, Las Vegas, NV 89128, USA

Registry of Interpreters for the Deaf Inc

8630 Fenton Street, Suite 324, Silver Spring, MD 20910-3919, USA

Tel: 001 301 608 0050
Fax: 001 301 608 0508
E-mail: ridcmp@aol.com
Contact: Wendy Yanis

A professional organisation that certifies interpreters, provides information on interpreting to the general public, and publishes a national directory of certified interpreters.

Rehabilitation Engineering Research Center on Hearing Enhancement and Assistive Devices

Lexington Center Inc, 30th Avenue and 75th Street, Jackson Heights, NY 11370, USA

Tel: 001 718 899 8800 ext 212
Fax: 001 718 899 3433
E-mail: lexrsch@transit.appliedtheory.com
Website: gramercy.ios.com/~reslex
Contact: Harry Levitt, Project Director

Rehabilitation Research and Training Center on Mental Health

California School of Professional Psychology, 6160 Cornerstone Court East, San Diego, CA 92121 3725, USA

Tel: 001 619 623 2777
Textphone: 001 619 554 1540
Fax: 001 619 642 0266
E-mail: rtrybus@mail.cspp.edu
Contact: Raymond Trybus, Director

Self Help for Hard of Hearing People Inc

7910 Woodmont Avenue, Suite 1200, Bethesda, MD 20814, USA

Tel: 001 301 657 2249
Textphone: 001 301 657 2249
Fax: 001 301 913 9413
E-mail: national@shhh.org
Website: www.shhh.org
Contact: Donna Sorkin, Executive Director
Tel: 001 301 657 2248
Textphone: 001 301 657 2248

Committed to making mainstream society more accessible to people who are hard of hearing and to improving the quality of hard of hearing people's lives through education, advocacy and self-help.

Tele-Consumer Hotline

901 Fifteenth Street NW, Suite 230, Washington, DC 20005, USA

Tel: 001 202 223 4371/ 466 6020
Fax: 001 800 332 1124
Contact: Sylvia Rosenthal, Executive Director

16

Telecommunications for the Deaf, Inc

8719 Colesville, Suite 300, Silver Spring, MD 20910-3919, USA

Tel: 001 301 589 3786
Textphone: 001 301 589 3006
Fax: 001 301 589 3797
E-mail: tdial@aol.com
Contact: Claude Stout, Executive Director

The Caption Center

125 Western Avenue, Boston, MA 02134, USA

Tel: 001 617 492 9225
Textphone: 001 617 492 9225
Fax: 001 617 562 0590
E-mail: caption@wgbh.org
Website: www.wgbh.org/caption
Contact: May Watkins, Communications Manager

A non-profit service of the WGBH Educational Foundation and the world's first television captioning agency. Produces captions for every segment of the entertainment and advertising industries and offers clients an array of services including off-line captions, real-time captions, deafblind, dual language captions and open captions. Publishes and distributes free of charge information on captioning for consumers and the television/cable industry: Consumer Information Services, Caption Centre News and TechFacts. Information about captioning for video professionals. All are available in printed form or at our website.

The Ear Foundation

1817 Patterson Street, Nashville, TN 37203, USA

Tel: 001 615 329 7809
Textphone: 001 800 545-HEAR
Fax: 001 615 329 7935
Contact: Michael Glasscock, President

The SEE Center for the Advancement of Deaf Children

P O Box 1181, Los Alamitos, CA 90720, USA

Tel: 001 562 430 1467
Fax: 001 562 795 6614
Contact: Esther Zawolkow, Director

Information and referral centre for parents and educators of hearing impaired children. Conducts workshops on the use of Signing Exact English, educational interpreting, education-related communication topics. Sign skill evaluations for teachers/teachers' aides, educational interpreters also available.

TRIPOD

2901 N Keystone Street, Burbank, CA 91504-1620, USA

Tel: 001 818 972 2080
Fax: 001 818 972 2090
Contact: Megan Williams, President

University of Gallaudet

Public Relations Office, 800 Florida Avenue NE, Washington, DC 20002-3695, USA

Tel: 001 202 651 5000
E-mail: publicre@gallaudet.edu
Website: www.gallaudet.edu
Contact: Muriel Strassler, Director, Public Relations

Established in 1864, Gallaudet is the only accredited liberal arts university in the world designed exclusively for deaf and hard of hearing students. Gallaudet is a multi-purpose educational institute and resource centre serving deaf and hard of hearing people in the US and around the world. Gallaudet's two campuses are located in Washington, DC. The orginal campus is at Kendall Green in Northeast Washington while the newer Northwest Campus is seven miles from Kendall Green and is home to the School of Preparatory Studies and other programmes including the English Language Institute, which offers full-time instruction in English as a second language, American Sign Language, and cultural studies to international deaf students. The university is committed to development of the intellect; to research aimed at improving the lives of deaf and hard of hearing people; and to providing service to them, their families and friends, and the professionals who work with them

USA Deaf Sports Federation

3607 Washington Blvd, Suite 4, Ogden, UT 84403-1737, USA

Textphone: 001 801 393 7916
Fax: 001 801 393 2263
E-mail: deafsports@juno.com
Contact: Bobbie Scoggins, President
Textphone: 1 801 393 7916

The spirit of the USADSF incorporates universal values of self-respect, sportsmanship and competition which transcend all boundaries of geography, nationality, gender, age, race and religion. The USADSF believes that by developing

16

recreational opportunities, sports training and competition at all levels, deaf and hard of hearing people can benefit physically, mentally, socially and spiritually in an environment which cultivates equality, mutual respect and acceptance. The USADSF also believes in the consistent and on-going training and development of deaf and hard of hearing individuals as leaders, coaches, officials and participants who serve as role models for our future generations.

Vestibular Disorders Association

P O Box 4467, Portland, OR 97208-4467, USA

Tel: 001 503 229 7705/ 800 837 8428

Fax: 001 503 229 8064

E-mail: veda@vestibular.org

Website: www.vestibular.org

Contact: Jerry Underwood, Executive Director

VEDA provides information to people with inner ear disorders such as labyrinthitis, Meniere's disease and BPPV. It recently published a full-length book called 'Meniere's Disease: What you need to know'.

World Recreation Association of the Deaf, Inc.

1550 San Leandro Boulevard, MS #196, San Leandro, CA 94577-4442, USA

Tel: 001 510 351 0397

Fax: 001 510 351 6036

E-mail: brucegross@aol.com

Website: www.wrad.org

Contact: Bruce Gross, President, International Division

           4642 Cocina Lane, Palmdale, CA 93551, USA

Venezuela

Federación Venezolana de Sordos

Apartado 50063, Sabana Grande, Caracas 1050, Venezuela

Tel: 00158 2 208 2961

Textphone: 001 582 208 2957

Fax: 00158 2 261 9952

Yugoslavia

Savez Gluvih Nagluvich Jugoslavije

Svetog Save 16-18, P O Box 911, YU-11000 Beograd, Jugoslavije

Zambia

Zambia National Association of the Deaf

P O Box 35821, Lusaka 10101, Zambia

Contact: McKenzie Mbewe

Zimbabwe

Association of the Deaf Zimbabwe

P O Box 6596, Harare, Zimbabwe

Contact: L Chivaura, Secretary

16

Deaf Schools

Comments from users of previous editions of the directory indicated that it would be useful to list schools for deaf children separately from schools with units or peripatetic teachers of the deaf. This section therefore contains details only of schools for deaf children, including those schools with sixth form colleges attached.

This section is listed alphabetically by the name of the school.

Aberdeen School for the Deaf

Regent Walk, Aberdeen, Grampian, AB2 1SX
Tel: 01224 480303
Textphone: 01224 480303
Fax: 01234 276075
E-mail: staff@abdnschdeaf.demon.co.uk
Contact: Mairi Macaulay, Head Teacher

ASD is a day school for pupils from nursery age through to secondary education. Its philosophy is total communication, and it is developing a programme of Sign Bilingualism. In the secondary department pupils are integrated into an adjoining mainstream school (supported by teachers of the deaf, according to their need). Funding: Education Authority.

Ashgrove School for the Deaf

Sully Road, Penarth, Vale of Glamorgan, The, CF64 2TP
Tel: 029 2070 4212
Textphone: 029 2070 4212/ 2070 4841
Fax: 029 2070 1945
Contact: Brian Brayford, Head of School and Service

Ashgrove School is a day/residential school for hearing impaired and autistic children. Hearing impaired children are educated in a purpose-built building with access to the most up-to-date hearing aid equipment. Pupils follow a curriculum which takes into account their linguistic, social and educational needs. The aim of the school is to prepare and equip pupils with the necessary skills for them to live a full and active life. Funding: Local Education Authority.

Beverley School for the Deaf

Beverley Road, Saltersgill, Middlesbrough, Cleveland, TS4 3LQ
Tel: 01642 277444
Fax: 01642 277453
Contact: E McBean, Head Teacher

Funding: Local Education Authority

Birkdale School for Hearing Impaired Children

40 Lancaster Road, Birkdale, Southport, Merseyside, PR8 2JY
Tel: 01704 567220
Textphone: 01704 567220
Fax: 01704 568342
E-mail: admin@bsfhic-ac.demon.co.uk
Website: www.birkdale-school.merseyside.org/
Contact: G Martin, Teacher of the Deaf

Birkdale School teaches deaf children to listen and talk, whilst providing access to a broad and balanced curriculum, enabling them to achieve their full potential. Pupils aged 5-19 are taught and supported by teachers of the deaf and have access to a fully equipped audiology and speech therapy department. Funding: non-maintained.

Braidwood School

Perry Common Road, Birmingham, West Midlands, B23 7AT
Tel: 0121 373 5558
Textphone: 0121 373 5558
Fax: 0121 382 5844
Contact: F. Ison-Jacques, Head Teacher

Braidwood School is a locally managed school for profoundly deaf children. All staff are qualified teachers of the deaf and use British Sign Language, Signed English and Sign Supported English. Braidwood adopts a 'child-centered' approach to the acquisition of good communication skills - the needs of the individual child are paramount.
Funding: Local Education Authority

Donaldsons College for the Deaf

West Coates, Edinburgh, Lothian, EH12 5JJ
Tel: 0131 337 9911
Textphone: 0131 337 9911
Fax: 0131 337 1654
Contact: Kathleen Clegg, Acting Principal

A grant-maintained school taking both residential and day pupils from nursery through to the end of secondary level education. It uses total communication.
Funding: Direct Grant

Elmfield School for the Deaf

Greystoke Avenue, Westbury-on-Trym, Bristol, Avon, BS10 6AY

Tel: 0117 950 1962
Textphone: 0117 950 1741
Fax: 0117 950 1962
Contact: Ros Way, Head Teacher

The school aims for each pupil to be a competent user of British Sign Language and English (through its written form). Both deaf and hearing staff are employed. The school has a new ICT Centre and promotes the use of ICT as an important communication and learning tool. Funding: Local Education Authority.

Frank Barnes Primary School for Deaf Children

Harley Road, London, NW3 3BN

Tel: 020 7586 4665
Textphone: 020 7586 4665
Videotel: 020 7722 7975
Fax: 020 7722 4415
Contact: Karen Simpson, Acting Head

Frank Barnes is a bilingual school with a growing reputation as a centre of excellence. We aim for fluency in both English and British Sign Language. We are committed to the same high standards of education as any quality mainstream primary school and believe that deaf children have the same potential to learn as hearing children. Funding: Local Education Authority

Garvel School for the Deaf

Chester Road, Larkfield, Greenock, Strathclyde, PA16 0TT

Tel: 01475 635477
Textphone: 01475 635477
Fax: 01475 637230
Contact: Margaret Keir, Head Teacher

Garvel Deaf Centre has a three-fold function, through the operation of Garvel School for pre-five and primary age deaf children, a secondary unit at Gourock High School, and a peripatetic service. We operate a bilingual provision which gives equal weight to British Sign Language and English. Funding: Education Authority

Gateside School

Craigielinn Avenue, Paisley, Renfrewshire, PA2 8RH

Tel: 0141 884 2090
Fax: 0141 884 6844
Contact: Elizabeth Quinn, Head Teacher

The well-established peripatetic service and specialist nursery, based at Gateside School, caters for pupils with a whole range of hearing loss, from mild to moderate through to severe and profound. Hearing impaired children in Renfrewshire share in educational opportunities enjoyed by their peers in local mainstream schools. The auditory-oral approach, combined with carefully managed integration, provides a rich educational experience for hearing impaired children and helps them to be a part of a wider world. Gateside School now has responsibility for visually impaired pupils, and for the development of a support service for pupils with sensory impairment. Funding: Education Authority.

Hamilton Lodge School for Deaf Children

Walpole Road, Brighton, East Sussex, BN2 2ET

Tel: 01273 682362
Textphone: 01273 682362
Fax: 01273 695742
E-mail: hamilton.lodge@ukonline.co.uk
Website: web.ukonline.co.uk/hamilton.lodge/
Contact: A Duffy, Principal

Hamilton Lodge School is a day and residential school for deaf children who require a flexible approach to communication using sign, speech and hearing. Through this Total Communication approach we seek to ensure that each child has full access to the National Curriculum from primary up to GCSE level. Funding: Independent.

Hamilton School for the Deaf

Wellhall Road, Hamilton, Lanarkshire, ML3 9JE

Tel: 01698 286618
Textphone: 01698 283095
Fax: 01698 425172
Contact: Jean Gorman, Head Teacher

Hamilton is a primary day school with a nursery facility. It uses Total Communication. Funding: Education Authority.

Hawkswood School

Antlers Hill, Chingford, London, E4 7RT

Tel: 020 8529 2561
Textphone: 020 8529 2561
Fax: 020 8529 2561
Contact: Katy Khan, Head of School and Service

Hawkswood is a special school providing education and support to children with a wide range of hearing difficulties across many boroughs in the East London area. In addition specialist teachers give advice and support to mainstream schools that have children with hearing difficulties.

Funding: Local Education Authority.

Heathlands School for Deaf Children

Heathlands Drive, St Albans, Hertfordshire, AL3 5AY

Tel: 01727 868596
Textphone: 01727 868596
Fax: 01727 860015
Contact: Mabel Davis, Head Teacher

Heathlands is an all-age school which caters for profoundly deaf children aged 3-16. The primary and secondary facilities are on separate sites. The school delivers the full National Curriculum through Total Communication and offers a large, stimulating nursery environment, speech and language therapy programmes delivered by qualified therapists, audiology clinic, radio aids, qualified teachers of the deaf with CACDP qualifications in sign language. There are opportunities for primary pupils to integrate with local mainstream schools supported by a teacher of the deaf. The secondary school is within a mainstream school where pupils get the best of both worlds. Weekly boarding facilities are available. Funding: Local Education Authority.

Jordanstown School for Children with Auditory or Visual Impairments

85 Jordanstown Road, Newtownabbey, County Antrim, BT37 0QE

Tel: 028 9086 3541
Textphone: 028 9086 3541
Fax: 028 9086 4356
Contact: Stephen Clarke, Headmaster of Deaf School

The Speech and Language Therapy Department provides a service to children with sensorineural hearing loss and/or a significant visual impairment which results in communication difficulty. The service is based in Jordanstown School and provides an outreach service to children with a hearing impairment within Homefirst Community Trust, including children on the Cochlear Implant Programme. The aim of the service is to maximise the communication ability of each child referred. Jordanstown is a voluntary maintained school using Total Communication, taking children aged 4-9 years. Funding: Voluntary Maintained.

Longwill School

Bell Hill, Birmingham, West Midlands, B31 1LD

Tel: 0121 475 3923
Fax: 0121 476 6362
E-mail: bday@rmplc.co.uk
Website: www.rmplc.co.uk/sites/bday
Contact: Peter Plant, Head Teacher

Longwill School is a primary day school for profoundly deaf sign language users. We offer a bilingual approach to the education of our children. We develop competence and confidence in British Sign Language as the children's first language before teaching English as a second language. British Sign Language provides access to communication and learning.
Funding: Local Education Authority

Mary Hare Grammar School for the Deaf

Arlington Manor, Snelsmore Common, Newbury, Berkshire, RG14 3BQ

Tel: 01635 244200
Textphone: 01635 244260
Fax: 01635 248019
E-mail: mhgsoxbr@rmplc.co.uk
Website: www.maryhare.org.uk
Contact: IG Tucker, Principal
Tel: 01635 248303

Mary Hare School educates children orally, believing, based on results, that academic success is best achieved by this method, and that the opportunity to speak and understand speech opens up the fullest social and work opportunities for deaf people. Speech and language therapists who provide assessment, treatment, advice and counselling in either group or individual sessions for pupils also work at Mill Hall Oral School for Deaf Children. Funding: non-maintained.

Mill Hall Oral School for Deaf Children

Pigeons Farm Road, Thatcham, Berkshire, RG19 8XA

Tel: 01635 573800
Textphone: 01635 573800
Fax: 01635 573802
Contact: Patricia Tufnell, Specialist Speech Therapist
Tel: 01444 454000

Mill Hall is a non-maintained primary school. It takes both day and residential pupils and uses natural auralism as its policy of communication. The two speech and language therapists provide a service consisting of assessment, treatment, advice and counselling of deaf or deafened children in either group or individual sessions.

17

The school aims to give all pupils the maximum opportunity to develop listening, speech and language skills, so that they can interact fully with all members of society. Funding: non-maintained.

Northern Counties School for the Deaf

Great North Road, Newcastle Upon Tyne, Tyne and Wear, NE2 3BB

Tel: 0191 281 5821
Textphone: 0191 281 5821
Fax: 0191 281 5060
E-mail: k.j.c.lewis@schools.ncl.ac.uk
Contact: K J C Lewis, Head Teacher

Northern Counties is a non-maintained school taking both residential and day pupils from nursery through to further education. It uses Total Communication. A specialist service is available for deaf children from pre-school up to 18, providing assessment, treatment, counselling, advice and a peripatetic service to schools. Work is done in groups and in individual sessions. Funding: non-maintained.

Oak Lodge School for the Deaf

101 Nightingale Lane, London, SW12 8NA

Tel: 020 8673 3453
Textphone: 020 8673 3453
Fax: 020 8673 9397
E-mail: info@oaklodge.wandsworth.sch.uk
Contact: Peter Merrifield, Head Teacher

Oak Lodge is a secondary school for deaf children, accepting both day and weekly boarding pupils aged 11-19. The school uses a bilingual approach to meet individuals' communication needs, with a mixed hearing and deaf staff team and specialist speech and language therapists. The 16+ department provides for students aged 16-19. Funding: Local Education Authority.

Ovingdean Hall School

Greenways, Brighton, East Sussex, BN2 7BJ

Tel: 01273 301929
Textphone: 01273 301929
Fax: 01273 305884
Contact: Malcolm Bown, Head Teacher

Ovingdean works to ensure that all pupils follow a full and varied curriculum which fits their profile of abilities. It seeks to involve pupils actively in their education and personal development and prepare them for a diverse and challenging society. The school uses a natural aural method of communication.
Funding: Non Maintained

Royal School for Deaf Children Margate and Westgate College for Deaf People

Victoria Road, Margate, Kent, CT9 1NB

Tel: 01843 227561
Textphone: 01843 227561
Fax: 01843 227637
E-mail: rsdmar@aol.com
Website: www.members.aol.com/rsdcmar/home.htm
Contact: David Bond, Principal

The Royal School for Deaf Children Margate and Westgate College for Deaf People provide education and training for pupils and students aged 4-16 (school) and 16-25 (college). Sign Supported English and British Sign Language communication are used. There are excellent resources including skilled, qualified and experienced staff. Some pupils are deafblind, or physically or learning disabled. Funding: non-maintained.

Royal School for the Deaf Derby

Ashbourne Road, Derby, DE22 3BH

Tel: 01332 362512
Textphone: 01332 362512
Videotel: 01332 363603
Fax: 01332 299708
E-mail: dcpb_staff@yahoo.com
Website: www.derbycollegedeaf@demon.co.uk
Contact: Tim Silvester, Principal

British Sign Language and English are used in the bilingual approach to the education of deaf children followed at RSD Derby. This gives access to the curriculum in the first language of most children who attend. Deaf staff work in all departments, providing access to deaf culture and positive role models. Funding: non-maintained.

Royal School for the Deaf Manchester

Stanley Road, Cheadle Hulme, Lancashire, SK8 6RF

Tel: 0161 610 0100
Fax: 0161 610 0101
Website: www:rsd.manchester.org
Contact: P Annear, Audiologist

Royal School for the Deaf Manchester provides learning opportunities suited to the needs of pupils/students who are deaf/hearing impaired with additional difficulties or complex special educational needs. Our primary aims are to realise the potential of every pupil/student by providing a communication-rich environment tailored to individual need. Funding: non-maintained.

17

Royal West of England Residential School for the Deaf

50 Topsham Road, Exeter, Devon, EX2 4NF
Tel: 01392 272692
Textphone: 01392 272692
Fax: 01392 431146
E-mail: rcd.exeter@eclipse.co.uk
Website: www.eclipse.co.uk/rsd.exeter
Contact: J Shaw, Principal

The Royal West of England Residential School for the Deaf is a non-maintained school and a registered charity. Pupils in school attend on a daily or weekly boarding basis. Students in further education are mainly 7-day boarders, but the college closes one weekend in each half-term. Pupils in school follow the National Curriculum and have the opportunity to sit a range of examinations at KS4 including GCSE, Certificate of Achievement, RSA and City and Guilds. The school adopts a Total Communication approach. Pupils in the secondary department are taught British Sign Language and before leaving school are entered for the CACDP Level I examination. Pupils are taught by teachers of the deaf, supported by classroom assistants. A range of professionals such as educational psychologists, educational audiologists, speech and language therapists, physiotherapists, and occupational therapists ensure that all the pupils' special educational needs are catered for. The school's swimming pool, gym, adventure playground, light stimulation room as well as local facilities provide the pupils with a range of experiences and challenges both in and out of school. Funding: non-maintained.

St Francis De Sales School for Children with Hearing, Speech and Language Difficulties

Beechmount Drive, Belfast, County Antrim, BT12 7LU
Tel: 028 9024 5599
Contact: Sister Maeliosa Byrne

St John's Catholic School for the Deaf

Church Street, Boston Spa, Leeds, West Yorkshire, LS23 6DF
Tel: 01937 842144
Fax: 01937 541471
Contact: T M Wrynne, Head Teacher

St John's is a residential and day school offering a first class oral education to pupils aged from 3 to 19. The broad, balanced curriculum offers GCSEs, Certificate of Achievement and many vocational courses. We have 20 teachers of the deaf, a full-time audiologist and speech and language therapists.

St Vincent's School for the Deafblind

Tel: 0141 778 2254
See entry under Deafblind Resources.

Tewin Water School for the Hearing Impaired

Knightsfield, Welwyn Garden City, Hertfordshire, AL8 7LW
Tel: 01707 376874
Textphone: 01707 376874
Fax: 01707 321738
Contact: Lucy Leith, Head Teacher

Tewin Water is a secondary school providing auditory/oral education for day and boarding pupils. It provides a special school environment with opportunities for integration in a mainstream school. This purpose-built new school has state-of-the-art facilities for hearing impaired pupils. Qualified teachers of the deaf deliver the full range of National Curriculum subjects. Funding: Local Education Authority.

The Mount School for the Deaf

Penkhull, Stoke on Trent, Staffordshire, ST4 7LU
Tel: 01782 236140
Textphone: 01782 236140
Fax: 01782 236140
Contact: B Richards, Head Teacher

A dedicated school for deaf children providing primary (including nursery), secondary and further education for deaf children. The method of communication used is Total Communication. Funding: Local Education Authority.

Thomasson Memorial School

Devonshire Road, Bolton, Lancashire, BL1 4PJ
Tel: 01204 843063
Fax: 01204 495675
Contact: Bill Wilson, Head Teacher

The school provides for pupils of nursery/primary school age who have a severe/profound hearing loss. The curriculum is delivered through an oral and or a sign supported approach depending on the pupil's individual communication needs. Funding: Local Education Authority.

Windsor Park School for the Deaf

Bantaskine Road, Falkirk, Stirlingshire, FK1 5HT
Tel: 01324 508640
Textphone: 01324 508640
Contact: M A Price, Acting Head Teacher

Windsor Park takes both primary and secondary pupils and uses the oral method of communication

Funding: Local Education Authority.

Yorkshire Residential School for Deaf Children

Leger Way, Doncaster, South Yorkshire, DN2 6AY

Tel:	01302 322822
Textphone:	01302 344524
Videotel:	01302 349207
Fax:	01302 342166
E-mail:	enquiries@yrsd-dcd.org.uk
Website:	www.yrsd-dcd.org.uk
Contact:	H Heard, Director

High-quality education, communication and care for deaf and hearing impaired young people up to the age of 16. We aim to provide a broad, balanced education to the highest standard, ensuring a safe, caring and supportive environment. We are keen to develop each pupil's language and communication by the most appropriate methods. Funding: non-maintained.

17

Education Authorities and Schools

This section lists mainstream schools with provision for deaf children from nursery level up to 18. Information is listed by UK country, then alphabetically by county. The entry for each county will begin with the name of the director of education followed by the names of any principal officer or special needs manager, followed by schools listed alphabetically. Units for deaf children attached to mainstream schools have different names in different areas. This can be confusing. For the purposes of this directory, 'Unit' denotes any specialist provision providing for a group of pupils with hearing loss operating within a mainstream school which is staffed by specialist teachers of the deaf.

This section is listed by country, then alphabetically by county, authority and unit.

England

➤ Avon

Education Services

Bath and North East Somerset Education Service

P O Box 75, Bristol, Avon, BS99 1RX

Tel: 01225 477000
Fax: 01225 394439
Contact: Peter Fudge, Head of Sensory
              Impairment Services
              Elmfield House, Greystoke Avenue,
              Bristol, Avon, BS10 6AY
Tel: 0117 950 6838
Textphone: 0117 950 6838
Fax: 0117 950 0779
Contact: Roy Jones, Director of Education,
              Cultural and Community Services
              P O Box 75, BRISTOL, BS99 1RX

Bristol Education Service

The Council House, College Green, Bristol, Avon, BS1 5TR

Tel: 0117 922 4402
Fax: 0117 922 2069

Family Centre for Deaf Children

Cranleigh Units, Frome House, Cranleigh Court Road, Yate, Avon, BS37 5DE

Tel: 01454 315404
Textphone: 01454 315405
Fax: 01454 315404

The Family Centre was formerly based at Elmfield School in Westbury-on-Trym in Bristol. The office is not normally staffed on a Tuesday.

North Somerset Education Service

P O Box 51, Town Hall, Weston-Super-Mare, Avon, BS23 1ZY

Tel: 01934 888888
Fax: 01934 888834
Contact: Peter Fudge, Head of Sensory
              Impaired Children's Services
              Elmfield House, Greystoke Avenue,
              Bristol, Avon, BS10 6AY
Tel: 0117 950 6838
Textphone: 0117 950 6838
Fax: 0117 950 0779

The Sensory Impaired Children's Service provides support for hearing impaired, visual impaired and multi needs sensory impaired children in Bristol, South Gloucestershire, Bath and North East Somerset and North Somerset. The service is jointly funded by these unitary authorities.

Units

Ashton Vale Infants School

Avebury Road, Ashton Vale, Bristol, Avon, BS3 2QG

Tel: 01272 664818

Henbury Comprehensive School

Marissal Road, Henbury, Bristol, Avon, BS10 7NJ

Tel: 0117 950 6624

Henbury uses the oral/aural method of communication.

Henbury Court Infants and Junior Mixed School

Trevelyan Walk, Henbury, Bristol, Avon, BS10 7NY

Tel: 0117 950 5191 Infants
              0117 950 5250 Junior

Henbury Court Infants use oral/aural communication method and sign, Henbury Junior use the oral/aural method.

18

King Edmund Community School

Sundridge Park, Yate, Bristol, Avon, BS17 4DY
Tel: 01454 312265
Fax: 01454 312307
Contact: J Dourneen, Headteacher

We are a Hearing Impaired Resource Base attached to a mainstream secondary school providing support for teachers and hearing impaired pupils in the school, so that full access to the National Curriculum is available to all hearing impaired students.

Mendip Green Infant School

Greenwood Road, Worle, Weston-Super-Mare, Avon, BS22 0EX
Tel: 01934 513791
Fax: 01934 522152
Contact: S Guildford, Teacher of the Deaf

The Hearing Impaired Resource Base attached to Mendip Green First School caters for children from reception to Year 3. It uses the oral/aural approach of communication. It aims to maximise successful integration for each individual child.

Petherton Road Infant School, Hearing Impaired Resource Base

Petherton Road, Hengrove, Bristol, Avon, BS14 9BX
Tel: 01275 832347
Contact: Claire Jacques, Teacher of the Deaf

The Hearing Impaired Resource Base caters for infant pupils with some degree of hearing loss in the south Bristol area.

Priory Comprehensive School

Queen's Way, St Georges, Weston-Super-Mare, Avon, BS22 0BP
Tel: 01934 511411
Fax: 01934 520199
Contact: Roger Bowerman, Teacher of the Deaf

Rodford Infant School

Barnwood Road, Yate, Avon, BS37 4JY
Tel: 01454 313939
Contact: Rebecca Hawkes, Teacher of the Deaf

Rodford Infants has an oral/aural communication policy.

Rodford Junior School

Barnwood Road, Yate, Avon, BS37 4JY
Tel: 01454 312516
Fax: 01454 312307

Rodford Junior School is a local education authority school with a Hearing Impaired Resource Base catering for approximately six children with moderate/severe hearing loss. The communication is currently oral/aural. From September 1999 this school will be amalgamated with its neighbouring infant school. The above information is therefore likely to change.

St Martin's Junior School

Spring Hill, Worle, Weston-Super-Mare, Avon, BS22 9BQ
Tel: 01934 628651
Fax: 01934 417522
Contact: Mrs McKellan, Teacher in Charge, Hearing Impaired Unit

Tyning Junior Mixed School

Walsh Avenue, Hengrove, Bristol, Avon, BS14 9SN
Tel: 01275 832728
Fax: 01275 832728
Contact: Sarah Diss, Teacher of the Deaf

Weston All Saints Primary School

Broadmoor Lane, Weston, Bath, Avon, BA1 4JR
Tel: 01225 427686
Fax: 01225 427699
Contact: A Sparks, Teacher of the Deaf
Tel: 01225 421786

We are a Hearing Impaired Resource Base (HIRB) currently supporting eight hearing impaired pupils at KS1 and KS2. Some of the pupils use an oral/aural approach but some use total communication. Three of our children have cochlear implants. At KS1 the pupils are supported in the base in the mornings for language and maths and integrate in the afternoon. During KS2 they are supported in the main in the classroom.

➤ Bath & NE Somerset
See Avon

18

➤ Bedfordshire

Education Services

Bedfordshire Education Service

County Hall, Cauldwell Street, Bedfordshire, MK42 9AP

Tel: 01234 228002
Fax: 01234 228249
Contact: Sue Briscoe, Senior Teacher in Charge of Work, Hearing Impaired Pupils

Child Development Centre, Hill Rise, Kempton, Bedfordshire, MK42 7EB

Tel: 01234 300710
Textphone: 01234 857575
Fax: 01234 854242

The Service for Sensory Impairment and Communication Difficulties meets the educational needs of hearing impaired pupils from birth to sixteen. Resource provisions in mainstream schools cover all three phases. The provisions have a total communication philosophy. The peripatetic team consists of three teachers of the deaf, one being an educational audiologist.

Luton Education Service

Unity House, 111 Stuart Street, Luton, Bedfordshire, LU1 5NP

Tel: 01582 546000
Fax: 01582 548454
Contact: Leslie Collett, Senior Teacher, Hearing Impairment, Education Support Services

Tel: 01582 548106
Textphone: 01582 548106

The Hearing Impaired Service supports hearing impaired/deaf children and their families from the point of diagnosis to leaving school. It aims to meet the communication needs of hearing impaired/deaf pupils.

Units

Five Springs School

Northwell Drive, Luton, Bedfordshire, LU3 3SP

Tel: 01582 572880
Fax: 01582 565506
Contact: Rosemary Agnew, Teacher of the Deaf

Five Springs School for children with moderate learning difficulties has a provision for the hearing impaired, 6 to 16 years. A teacher of the deaf and communicators use British Sign Language, if required, for children to fully access the modified National Curriculum. The school is to be redesignated to secondary provision taking pupils with moderate and severe learning difficulties.

Harlington Upper School

Goswell End Road, Harlington, Bedfordshire, LU5 6NX

Tel: 01525 755100
Fax: 01525 755101

Provision within mainstream school for hearing impaired students in the upper school (13 to18 years) phase.

Icknield High School

Riddy Lane, Luton, Bedfordshire, LU3 2AH

Tel: 01582 576561
Textphone: 01582 576562
Fax: 01582 561533
Contact: G Thomas, Teacher of the Deaf

The aim of the Hearing Impaired Department is to integrate hearing impaired pupils as fully as possible into the main school. The pupils are encouraged to develop sign language and to be socialised into deaf culture in order to accquire a sense of self-respect and self-worth.

Icknield Infant School

Birdsfoot Lane, Luton, Bedfordshire, LU3 2JB

Tel: 01582 591275
Contact: C Ingle, Teacher of the Deaf

A primary day school with nursery using Total Communication.

Icknield Junior School

Birdsfoot Lane, Luton, Bedfordshire, LU3 2JB

Tel: 01582 574687
Contact: L Collett, Senior Teacher, Hearing Impairment Service

Luton Hearing Impairement Service provides support for hearing impaired children and their families via pre-school visiting support in mainstream, support in special schools and provision within infant, junior, high and special schools. A few children attend schools for the deaf out of the borough. We meet a wide range of communication needs.

Parkfields Middle School

Park Road, Toddington, Bedfordshire, LU5 6AB

Tel: 01525 872555
Fax: 01525 875967
Contact: Imelda Taylor, Hearing Impaired Unit
Tel: 01525 876836

18

Stephenson Lower School and Nursery

Canvin Way, Bedford, MK42 0HL
Tel: 01234 261683
Contact: D Saunders, Head

Stephenson Lower School and Nursery caters for children 3 to 9 years old. Children with a hearing loss are fully integrated into the nursery at 3 years, transferring to the Lower School at 5 years. The children have communicator support using Total Communication. The children have time tabled sessions with a qualified teacher of the deaf.

Toddington St George Lower School

Manor Road, Toddington, Bedfordshire, LU5 6AJ
Tel: 01525 872360
Fax: 01525 872284
Contact: Imelda Taylor

➤ Berkshire
Education Services
Berkshire Education Service

Shire Hall, Shinfield Park, Reading, Berkshire, RG2 9XE
Tel: 0118 923 3625
Fax: 0118 975 0360
Contact: R Pither, Head of Sensory Consortium Service
           Town Hall, St Ives Road, Maidenhead, Berkshire, SL6 1RF
Tel: 01628 796787

A consortium service available to all families and schools within the six local education authorities (Bracknell Forest, Reading, Slough, West Berkshire, Royal Borough of Windsor and Maidenhead, and Wokingham). As a service we aim to respond effectively to the specific needs of each child and to link our work with that of Social Services and health authorities.

Central Berkshire Regional Hearing Teaching and Support Team

TASS Centre, East Hampstead Park Education Centre, Wokingham, Berkshire, RG40 3DF
Tel: 0118 989 0249

East Berkshire Regional Hearing Teaching and Support Team

TASS Centre, St Edmund's House, Ray Mill Road West, Maidenhead, Berkshire, SL6 8SB
Tel: 01628 679888
Fax: 01628 776971

Newbury Education Centre

Fir Tree Lane, Newbury, Berkshire, RG14 2QX
Tel: 01635 43351
Fax: 01635 529373

West Berkshire Regional Hearing Teaching and Support Team

TASS Centre, Reading Education Centre, Cranbury Road, Reading, Berkshire, RG30 2TS
Tel: 0118 950 9373

The peripatetic teaching and advisory service has specialist teachers for the hearing impaired available to work across the age range with schools and families through its early years and school age programmes. The team offers additional skills in educational audiology, specific learning difficulties, multi-sensory impairment, curriculum and inset.

Units
Denefield Secondary School

Long Lane, Tilehurst, Reading, Berkshire, RG31 6XY
Tel: 0118 941 3458
Fax: 0118 945 2847
E-mail: denefield@rmplc.co.uk
Website: www.denefield.org.uk
Contact: Michael Freeman, Teacher of the Deaf

Denefield Secondary has an oral/aural communication policy. A hearing impaired unit is based permanently on site.

Emmbrook Secondary School

Emmbrook Road, Wokingham, Berkshire, RG11 1JR
Tel: 0118 978 4406
Fax: 0118 989 2059
Contact: Gillian Woodley, Special Needs Coordinator

Foxborough Combined School

Common Road, Slough, Berkshire, SL3 8TX
Tel: 01753 546376
Fax: 01753 594111
Contact: Joanne Cooke, Teacher in Charge

18

Foxborough is a day primary school with a nursery attached. The communication method used is Total Communication.

Langleywood Secondary School
Langley Road, Slough, Berkshire, SL3 7EF
Tel: 01753 541549
Fax: 01753 593145
Contact: Jeff Richardson, Head Teacher

Newbridge Nursery School
Montague Street, Caversham, Reading, Berkshire, RG4 5AU
Tel: 0118 901 5538
Fax: 0118 901 5580
Contact: Brenda Grant, Headteacher

We are a 60-place nursery (LEA) whose policy is integration for all special educational needs children, to the best of their ability. The mainstream staff have attended signing courses and we use a Total Communication approach.

Park House School
Andover Road, Newbury, Berkshire, RG14 6NQ
Tel: 01635 240165
Fax: 01635 528884
E-mail: park_house_school@westberks.gov.uk
Contact: M Foster, Teacher of the Deaf

Park House is a secondary day school with an oral/aural communication policy.

Reading St Michael's County Primary School
Dee Road, Tilehurst, Reading, Berkshire, RG3 4AS
Tel: 0118 901 5550
Fax: 0118 901 5549
Contact: Lisa Miller, Teacher in Charge, Deaf Resource Base

St Michael's is a primary day school using Total Communication.

Wessex County Infant and Nursery School
St Adrian's Close, Cox Green, Maidenhead, Berkshire, SL6 3AT
Tel: 01628 629607
Fax: 01628 674731
Contact: Sally Robinson, Teacher in Charge, Infants
Tel: 01628 626724

Wessex County is a primary day school with nursery. It has an oral/aural communication policy.

Westwood Farm Infants School
Fullbrook Crescent, Tilehurst, Reading, Berkshire, RG3 6RY
Tel: 0118 942 6113
Contact: Alison Woodcock, Teacher in Charge

Westwood Farm Junior School
Fullbrook Crescent, Tilehurst, Reading, Berkshire, RG3 6RY
Tel: 0118 942 5182
Fax: 0118 945 4498
Contact: K Finigan, Teacher in Charge

➢ Blackburn
See Lancashire

➢ Blackpool
See Lancashire

➢ Bournemouth
See Dorset

➢ Bracknell Forest
See Berkshire

➢ Brighton and Hove
See East Sussex

➢ Bristol, City of
See Avon

18

➢ Buckinghamshire
Education Services
Buckinghamshire Education Service
County Hall, Aylesbury, Buckinghamshire, HP20 1UZ

Tel: 01296 395000
Contact: D McGahey, Director of Education
Tel: 01296 382204
Fax: 01296 383367
Contact: Margaret Williams, Senior Education Officer, Special Education
Tel: 01296 382674
Fax: 01296 382536

Milton Keynes Education Services
Saxon Court, 502 Avebury Boulevard, Central Milton Keynes, Milton Keynes, Buckinghamshire, MK9 3DS

Tel: 01908 253325
Fax: 01908 253556
Contact: Anne McGrath, Head of Hearing Impaired Service
           The Queensway Centre, Queensway, Bletchley, Milton Keynes, Buckinghamshire, MK2 2HB
Tel: 01908 375072
Fax: 01908 630280

The aim of our organisation is to help deaf and hearing impaired pupils access local educational provision effectively, providing support for children and staff in special and mainstream schools in Milton Keynes.

Units
Alex Campbell County Middle School
Buckingham Road, Bletchley, Milton Keynes, Buckinghamshire, MK3 5HT

Tel: 01908 373748
Contact: Julie Skinner

Bedgrove County First School
Ingram Avenue, Aylesbury, Buckinghamshire, HP21 9DJ

Tel: 01296 81353

Beech Green Nursery School
Totteridge Lane, High Wycombe, Buckinghamshire, HP13 7PG

Tel: 01296 82848

Castles County First School
Warwick Road, Bletchley, Milton Keynes, Buckinghamshire, MK3 6BA

Tel: 01908 372812
Contact: A Eynon, Teacher of the Deaf

Great Missenden Combined School
Church Street, Great Missenden, Buckinghamshire, HP16 0AX

Tel: 01494 862310
Fax: 01494 868300
Contact: Shirley Weston, Teacher of the Deaf

High Worth County Combined School
High Worth Close, High Wycombe, Buckinghamshire, HP13 7PH

Tel: 01494 525534
Contact: G Kilner, Headteacher
Fax: 01494 525534

Penn School
Church Road, Penn, High Wycombe, Buckinghamshire, HP10 8LZ

Tel: 01494 812139
Fax: 01494 817160
Contact: C A Jones, Headmaster

A coeducational day and boarding school for children with communication difficulties. All class groups are small and individual teaching is of major importance. Personal education plans are prepared for each child by the class teacher, speech and language therapist and special support assistants. A full life-skills programme with records of achievement and accreditation courses are available for all pupils. Penn School becomes non-maintained on 1 September 1999 and will be administered by The Rayners Special Educational Trust.

Stoke Mandeville Combined School
Lower Road, Stoke Mandeville, Aylesbury, Buckinghamshire, HP22 5XA

Tel: 01296 612371
Contact: Anne Netherwood, Hearing Impaired Department
Tel: 01296 614027

Stoke Mandeville is a mainstream primary school with a 12-place department for hearing impaired children from the Aylesbury Vale area. All children are statemented for a department place.

18

➤ Cambridgeshire
Education Services
Cambridgeshire Education Service
Shire Hall, Castle Hill, Cambridge, CB3 0AP
Tel: 01223 317990
Fax: 01223 718180
Contact: A Baxter, Director of Education,
            Libraries and Heritage
Fax: 01223 318180

Peterborough Professional Development Centre
Cottesmore Close, Peterborough, Cambridgeshire, PE3 9TP
Tel: 01733 268868
Fax: 01733 331526
Contact: J Dunn, Head of Service

To support hearing impaired pre-school children and their families, (assessments, home teaching, parent guidance, audiology support) and to support hearing impaired children in pre-school provisions. To support hearing impaired pupils in mainstream schools, in special schools and in schools with enhanced provisions for hearing impaired pupils.

Units
Bucklers Mead Community School
St John's, Thorpe, Peterborough, Cambridgeshire, PE3 6JG
Tel: 01935 24454 ext 243
Fax: 01935 31088
Contact: Karen Woollard, Tutor of Deaf Children

Secondary school, for pupils aged 11 to 16. We have an oral policy and hearing impaired children are fully integrated with their hearing peers as far as possible.

Burrowmoor County Primary School
Burrowmoor Road, March, Cambridgeshire, PE15 6RP
Tel: 01354 52330

Cottenham Village College
High Street, Cottenham, Cambridgeshire, CB4 4UA
Tel: 01954 51332
Contact: Kate Stocks
Tel: 01954 251332

Provides a broad and balanced curriculum for all hearing impaired students of secondary school age.

Fawcett County Primary School (and Cambridgeshire Hearing Support Service)
Alpha Terrace, Trumpington, Cambridge, CB2 2HS
Tel: 01223 568848
Fax: 01223 845622
Contact: D Dennis, Head of Cambridgeshire
            Hearing Support Services

To provide the best possible educational management of hearing impaired children throughout their pre-school and school years. This includes assessment, advice, parent guidance, teaching, support and liaison with other relevant professionals. A team of fully qualified teachers and assistants support a wide range of hearing impaired children on either a peripatetic or Unit basis.

Huntingdon Hearing Support Unit, Huntingdon County Junior, Infant and Nursery Schools
Ambury Road, Huntingdon, Cambridgeshire, PE18 7AD
Tel: 01480 457569
Fax: 01480 457569
Contact: J Morgan, Teacher of the Deaf

We support hearing impaired children from the local area in order to integrate them into a mainstream school setting, according to the needs of each individual child.

Jack Hunt Comprehensive School
Ledbury Road, Peterborough, Cambridgeshire, PE3 9PN
Tel: 01733 263526
Fax: 01733 330364
Contact: J Tutt, Teacher of the Deaf

Hearing support unit within a mainstream secondary school.

Longsand Community College
Longsands Road, St Neots, Cambridgeshire, PE19 1LQ
Tel: 01480 353535
Fax: 01480 350033
Contact: Lynn Donnelly, Teacher of the Deaf
Tel: 01480 568848

Mayfield County Primary School

Warwick Road, Cambridgeshire, CB4 3HN
Tel: 01223 712127
Contact: J Hill, Head Teacher, Hearing Impaired
            Unit for the School

Middleton Infant and Junior Schools

Bretton, Peterborough, Cambridgeshire, PE3 9XJ
Tel: 01733 260410

Neale Wade Community College

Wimblington Road, March, Cambridgeshire, PE15 9PX
Tel: 01354 653430
Fax: 01354 659429
Contact: Mrs Gibling, Hearing Impaired Unit

Sawston Village College

New Road, Sawston, Cambridgeshire, CB2 4BP
Tel: 01223 832217
Fax: 01223 836680
E-mail: 9055408.D4W@dialnet.co.uk
Contact: Nikky Parker, Special Educational
            Needs Coordinator

➢ Channel Islands
Education Services
Guernsey Education Service

The Grange, St Peter Port, Guernsey, Channel Islands, GY1 1RQ
Tel: 01481 710821
Fax: 01481 714475
Contact: Margaret Herquin, Teacher in Charge
            of Hearing Impaired Service
            Granville House, Mount Durand, St
            Peter Port, Guernsey, Channel Islands,
            GY1 1DZ
Tel: 01481 710721

Education of all children with hearing problem from dignosis to leaving full time education. Parental support sevices. General advice on 'hearing problems'.

Jersey Education Service

P O Box 142, Highlands, St Saviour, Jersey, Channel Islands, JE4 8QJ
Tel: 01534 509500
Fax: 01534 509800
Contact: Brian Grady, Director of Education

Units
Granville Secondary School

La Rue de Deloraine, St Saviour, Jersey, Channel Islands, JE2 7NN
Tel: 01534 35541
Fax: 01534 89347
Contact: Sue Frazer, Teacher of the Deaf,
            Hearing Impaired Unit

La Mare de Cartaret School

Rue de Galaad, Castel, Guernsey, Channel Islands, GY5 7FL
Tel: 01481 53530

➢ Cheshire
Education Services
Cheshire Education Services

County Hall, Chester, Cheshire, CH1 1SQ
Tel: 01244 602424
Fax: 01244 603821
Contact: D Cracknell, Group Director of
            Educational Services
Contact: Bill Wilson, Area Sensory Coordinator,
            Macclesfield and South Cheshire
            Stanley House, Bexton Road,
            Knutsford, Cheshire, WA16 0ED
Tel: 01625 534870
Contact: Jane Walton, Area Sensory
            Coordinator, Vale Royal, Chester and
            Ellesmere Port area
            The Professional Centre, Woodford
            Lodge, Woodford Lane West,
            Winsford, Cheshire, CW7 4EH
Tel: 01606 557328
Fax: 01606 862113
Contact: Joe Tunstall, Area Sensory
            Coordinator, Halton and Warrington
            Hallwood Park School, Hallwood Park
            Avenue, Southgate, Runcorn,
            Cheshire, WA7 2FL
Tel: 01928 719203

Service for the Sensory Impaired

Area Educational Office, Watling Street, Northwich, Cheshire, CW9 5ET
Tel: 01606 815706
Fax: 01606 815052
Contact: J Walton

The Service for Sensory Impaired is part of the Learning Support Service which exists to provide a coherent, flexible response to the needs of

18

children, families and professionals. Children with sensory impairment are placed within a range of educational establishments catering for all levels and types of hearing loss and visual acuity. Sensory impaired pupils are integrated into mainstream schools whenever it is appropriate for the child's special needs. The main forms of integrated provision being Hearing Impaired Units (HIUs) for hearing impaired pupils and Vision Impaired Resource Bases for visually impaired pupils. The funding for the HIUs have been delegated to the mainstream schools whilst the finance for the Vision Impaired Resource Bases is currently retained centrally.

Stockport Education Service

Stopford House, Stockport, Cheshire, SK1 3XE
Tel: 0161 480 4949
Fax: 0161 953 0012

The service supports deaf and visually impaired children up to 19 years of age, from the time of diagnosis through to the end of full-time education. In addition to support in schools, the service offers a wide range of additional services: youth club, parent support group, audiology clinics.

Trafford Education Service

P O Box 19, Town Hall, Tatton Road, Sale, Cheshire, M33 1YR
Tel: 0161 912 1212
Contact: A Lee, Chief Education Officer
Contact: Anne Reynolds, Sensory Impairment Support Service
            c/o Pictor School, Harboro Road, Sale, Cheshire, M33 5AH
Tel: 0161 973 0126
Textphone: 0161 973 0126
Fax: 0161 905 2051

Units
Ashton-on-Mersey Secondary School

Cecil Avenue, Sale, Cheshire, M33 5BP
Tel: 0161 972 0213
Textphone: 0161 972 0213
Fax: 0161 972 0213
Contact: P Borodenko, Teacher of the Deaf

Local education authority resourced unit for hearing impaired children in a grant maintained school. Aim is to fully intergrate hearing impaired children into mainstream school in order to maximise their potential educationally, socially and emotionally. The unit is a secure, safe place where hearing impaired children and their hearing

friends can come to chat, socialise and share any worries they may have.

Hazel Grove High School

Jacksons Lane, Hazel Grove, Stockport, Cheshire, SK7 5JX
Tel: 0161 456 4888
Contact: Sandra Crofts, Special Educational Needs Coordinator

A comprehensive school which receives some partially hearing students. The Stockport Sensory Impaired Service works alongside staff and gives between one and eight hours per week support for individual students, depending on need. Currently there is one profoundly deaf student and two who are partially hearing impaired.

Hyde Technology School

Hearing Impaired Resource Base, Old Road, Hyde, Cheshire, SK14 4SP
Tel: 0161 368 1353
Textphone: 0161 368 1353
Fax: 0161 368 5099
Contact: H Rockett, Head of Partial Hearing Unit

We are part of the Tameside Hearing Impaired Specialist Support Service. This Hearing Impaired Resource Base is in a secondary school and we support students aged 11 to 16 years. We use oral and Total Communication with our students, who are supported in mainstream and also work in small groups and on a one-to-one basis in the resource base.

Kingsley County Primary School

Middle Lane, Kingsley, Warrington, Cheshire, WA6 6TZ
Tel: 01928 788436
Fax: 01928 788436
Contact: A Rowe, Head Teacher

Lindow County Primary School

Upcast Lane, Wilmslow, Cheshire, SK9 6EH
Tel: 01625 582555
Contact: Gillian Simm, Head Teacher

Integrated Primary Education for pupils with a hearing impairment. A mainstream school with a Hearing Impaired Unit.

18

Middlewich County High School

King Edward Street, Middlewich, Cheshire, CW10 9BU
Tel: 01606 832013
Textphone: 01606 833170
Fax: 01606 738260
Contact: Claire Holmes, Head of Special Needs

Middlewich County Infant School

Park Road, Middlewich, Cheshire, CW10 9BS
Tel: 01606 832555
Contact: E Hughes, Head Teacher

Middlewich County Junior School

Park Road, Middlewich, Cheshire, CW10 9BS
Tel: 01606 833200
Fax: 01606 737979
Contact: D Watson, Head Teacher

The Russett School and Cheshire MSI Unit

Middlehurst Avenue, Weaverham, Northwich, Cheshire, CW8 3BW
Tel: 01606 853005
Contact: H Watts, Head Teacher

The Multi-sensory Impairment Unit, which shares the school transport, resources, facilities and governing body, is a recognised local education authority-funded provision. The pupils in the unit have varying degrees of visual and hearing loss, combined with a learning difficulty or physical difficulty, or both. The unit currently provides education for six pupils from the ages of 2 to 19 years. With the recent addition of a purpose-built classroom, opened in July 1997, the capacity of the primary and secondary unit has increased to 12 places. All pupils have a statement of special education needs. A Total Communication environment, combined with a multi-sensory approach, is the method used in the unit.

Thorn Grove Primary School

Cheadle Hulme, Stockport, Cheshire, SK8 7LD
Tel: 0161 485 1177
Fax: 0161 485 1233
Contact: Judith Jeddel, Teacher of the Deaf

A primary day school using bilingualism.

Upton County High School

St James' Avenue, Upton, Chester, Cheshire, CH2 1NN
Tel: 01244 313061
Fax: 01244 356564
Contact: C Mengal, Head of Hearing Impaired Unit

Wade Deacon County High School

Birchfield Road, Widnes, Cheshire, WA8 7TD
Tel: 0151 423 2721
Contact: J Jackson, Head Teacher

Westfield County Primary School

Clayton Crescent, Runcorn, Cheshire, WA7 4TR
Tel: 01928 572343
Fax: 01928 565099
Contact: M Sexton, Head Teacher

Wilmslow High School

Holly Road, Wilmslow, Cheshire, SK9 1LJ
Tel: 01625 526191
Fax: 01625 536858
Contact: R Lyon, Head Teacher

Woodlands County Infant School

Eddisbury Road, Ellesmere Port, Cheshire, L66 2JX
Tel: 0151 355 1714
Fax: 0151 357 4183
Contact: J P Jenkins, Head Teacher

➢ Cleveland

Education Services

Middlesbrough Education Service

P O Box 191, 2nd Floor, Civic Centre, Middlesbrough, Cleveland, TS1 2XS
Tel: 01642 245432
Fax: 01642 277453
Contact: Elaine McBean, Head of Beverley School for Deaf Children
Tel: 01642 277444

Special school for deaf children aged 4 to 17 years. Total Communication approach, strong links with mainstream schools and colleges. Qualified teachers, several deaf staff, speech and language therapist. Education to meet individual needs. Wide range of qualifications including GCSE. Outdoor and residential activities, dance, sign singing.

Redcar and Cleveland Education Service

P O Box 83, Kirkleatham Street, Redcar, Cleveland, TS10 1YA

Tel: 01642 444000
Fax: 01642 444122
E-mail: redcarsell@aol.com
Contact: Patrick Scott, Acting Director of Education

Redcar and Cleveland Local Education Authority (LEA) provides the full range of LEA services to schools including services for pupils with special educational needs. In partnership with the neighbouring LEAs in the Tees Valley, it maintains a Hearing Impaired Service which provides peripatetic support for young people in mainstream education. The LEA also has an agreement with Middlesbrough Local Education Authority for the admission of pupils to the Beverley School for the Deaf.

Stockton-on-Tees Education Services

P O Box 228, Municipal Buildings, Church Road, Stockton-On-Tees, Cleveland, TS18 1XE

Tel: 01642 393441
Fax: 01642 393479
E-mail: Education.Services@sbcss3.stockton-bc.gov.uk
Contact: Stanley Bradford, Director of Education

Units
Coulby Newham School

Manor Farm Way, Coulby Newham, Middlesbrough, Cleveland, TS8 0RJ

Tel: 01642 593113
Textphone: 01642 593113
Fax: 01642 598903
E-mail: coulbynewhamschool@onyxnet.co.uk
Contact: I Slater, Teacher of the Deaf, Hearing Impaired Service

Deaf children are integrated into mainstream as far as possible.

Sunnyside Primary School

Manor Farm Way, Coulby Newham, Middlesbrough, Cleveland, TS8 0RJ

Tel: 01642 596422
Fax: 01642 596422
E-mail: wbschneider@portablesl.ngfl.gov.uk
Contact: W Schneider, Teacher of the Deaf

A resource base for hearing impaired children run under joint arrangements between the boroughs of Stockton, Redcar and Cleveland, Hartlepool and Middlesbrough. We offer fully inclusive education within a supportive mainstream school, staffed by two qualified teachers of the deaf and three experienced special assistants.

The Avenue Primary School

The Avenue, Nunthorpe, Middlesbrough, Cleveland, TS7 0AG

Tel: 01642 324358
Fax: 01642 324358
Contact: Pauline Westgarth-Taylor, Head of Peripatetic Hearing Impaired Service

We provide educational support for hearing impaired children from diagnosis at pre-school level throughout their placement in school. We aim to minimise the effects of hearing loss through early intervention, on-going support and teaching and the provision of appropriate technical aids. Appropriate in-service training is included.

> ## Cornwall
Education Services
Cornwall Education Service

County Hall, Truro, Cornwall, TR1 3AY

Tel: 01872 322000
Textphone: 01872 322000
Fax: 01872 323818
Contact: J Harris, Director of Education

Units
Biscovey Infants and Junior School

Lamellyn Road, Par, Cornwall, PL24 2DB

Tel: 01726 812006
Contact: S Kelly, Head, Biscovey Junior

Biscovey Infants has nursery and primary sections. The Support Unit working with children with hearing loss has an oral policy.

Bodriggy Junior and Infant School

Humphry Davy Lane, Hayle, Cornwall, TR27 4AR

Tel: 01736 752808
Fax: 01736 755612
Contact: P Wilkinson, Teacher of the Deaf

Brunel Primary School

Callington Road, Saltash, Cornwall, PL12 6DX

Tel: 01752 848900
Fax: 01752 849749
Contact: H Williams, Teacher of the Deaf

Budehaven Community School

Valley Road, Bude, Cornwall, EX23 8DQ
Tel: 01288 353271
Fax: 01288 353733
Contact: Celia King, Teacher of the Deaf

Celia King runs a support base for the Bude/Camelford/North Wadesbridge area. There are four hearing aid wearers in school at present.

Camborne Nursery School

The Glebe, Camborne, Cornwall, TR14 7EP
Tel: 01209 713607

This is a local authority nursery for 3 and 4 year olds. There is an audiology assessment/teaching unit attached and we are able to accept children with disabilities including hearing impairment. Children are supported within the nursery as we are committed to inclusive education.

Doubletrees School

St Blazey Gate, St Blazey, Par, Cornwall, PL24 2DS
Tel: 01726 812757
Fax: 01726 812896
E-mail: double@claranet.co.uk
Contact: H Nott, Peripatetic, Children with
                  Severe Learning Difficulties

Doubletrees is a day school using a combination of sign language, Makaton and oral methods of communication, taking children from 2 to 19 years of age.

Pencalenick School

St Clement, Truro, Cornwall, TR1 1TE
Tel: 01872 520202
Textphone: 01872 520202
Fax: 01872 520729
E-mail: pencalenick.school@freeserve.co.uk
Contact: Margaret Bonner, Audiology
                  Department

Pencalenick is a secondary school taking both day and residential pupils, with an oral communication policy.

Poltair Community School

Trevarthian Road, St Austell, Cornwall, PL25 4BZ
Tel: 01726 75721
Contact: Jan Sproull, Teacher of the Deaf

Permanent Hearing Impaired Unit based at school.

Redruth Community School

Tolgus Vean, Redruth, Cornwall, TR15 1TA
Tel: 01209 314099
Fax: 01209 313604
Website: www.redruth.cjv.net
Contact: J Crozier, Head of Hearing Impaired
                  Unit

Roskear County Primary School

Camborne, Cornwall, TR14 8DJ
Tel: 01209 714346
Textphone: 01209 714346
Contact: G Hamilton, Teacher of the Deaf

Roskear is a primary school with an oral policy.

➢ County Durham
Education Services
Darlington Education Service

Town Hall, Darlington, County Durham, DL1 5YP
Tel: 01325 388802
Fax: 01325 388883
Contact: Rona Ford, Advisory Teacher for the
                  Hearing Impaired, Sensory Support
                  Services

                  Craig Lea, Uplands Road, Darlington,
                  County Durham, DL3 7SW
Tel: 01325 388192

The Sensory Support Service aims to provide relevant professional advice and educational support for children with significant sensory impairment from diagnosis through to their placement in an educational establishment. This support is to help minimise the effects of a sensory impairment.

18

Durham Education Service

Education Offices, County Hall, Durham, DH1 5UJ
Tel: 0191 386 4411
Fax: 0191 386 0487
Contact: Andrea Lyons, County Coordinator,
                  Sensory and Communication Support
                  Service

                  Broom Cottages Primary School,
                  Broom Road, Ferryhill, County
                  Durham, DL17 8AN
Tel: 01740 656998
Fax: 01740 657982
Contact: Keith Mitchell, Director of Education

Units

Belmont Comprehensive School
Belmont, Durham, DH1 2QP
Tel: 0191 386 5715
Fax: 0191 384 0538
Contact: Jan Seaman, Teacher of the Deaf

Broom Cottages Primary School
Broom Road, Ferryhill, County Durham, DL17 8AN
Tel: 01740 656998
Fax: 01740 657005
Contact: Susan Foulkes, Coordinator

Durham Gilesgate Primary School and Nursery Unit
Kepier Crescent, Durham, DH1 1PH
Tel: 0191 384 7284
Fax: 0191 375 0300
Contact: Cynthia Howarth, Teacher of the Deaf

Caters for all children from 3 to 11 years of age.

Sherburn Hill Primary School
Front Street, Sherburn Hill, Durham, DH6 1PA
Tel: 0191 372 0315
Textphone: 0191 372 1896
E-mail: shipsea@rmplc.co.uk
Contact: Trish Palmer, Teacher of the Deaf

We aim to provide specialist education support for children with a significant hearing impairment from diagnosis throughout their placement in an educational establishment. The purpose of such support is to help to minimise the effects of a sensory impairment through early intervention, continuing support and the provision of appropriate technical aids.

Woodham Comprehensive School
Washington Crescent, Newton Aycliffe, County Durham, DL5 4AZ
Tel: 01325 300328
Fax: 01325 301950
Contact: Julie Lang, Teacher of the Deaf

➤ Cumbria
Education Services
Cumbria Education Service
5 Portland Square, Carlisle, Cumbria CA1 1PU
Tel: 01228 606060
Fax: 01228 515189
Contact: Rose Foster, Advisory Teacher of the
            Deaf, Specialist Teaching Services
            The Gillford Centre, Upperby Road,
            Carlisle, Cumbria, CA2 4JE
Tel: 01228 606955

Cumbria Specialist Teaching Services employ 11 teachers of the deaf who support deaf children with a range of hearing losses, largely in their local mainstream school. A natural aural approach is used with most of the children. Those requiring sign support attend a primary-based unit or a residential school outside Cumbria.

Units
Bransty Primary School
Bransty, Mona Road, Whitehaven, Cumbria, CA28 6EG
Tel: 01946 693348
Fax: 01946 693348
Contact: Ruth Humpage, Teacher of the Deaf

At Bransty Hearing Impaired Unit we work with children who require intensive work with a teacher of the deaf. A number of children require sign supported English and/or British Sign Language - these are used according to need.

Greengate Infant School
Greengate Street, Barrow-in-Furness, Cumbria, LA13 9BY

Morton School
Wigton Road, Carlisle, Cumbria, CA2 6LB
Tel: 01228 607545
Fax: 01228 607546
Contact: Susan Neill, Teacher of the Deaf

Newlaithes Infant School
Langrigg Road, Carlisle, Cumbria, CA2 6DX
Tel: 01228 525023
Fax: 01228 525023
Contact: I Todd, Teacher of the Deaf

18

North Walney Primary School

Duddon Drive, Walney, Barrow-in-Furness,
Cumbria, LA14 3TN
Tel: 01229 471781
Textphone: 01229 471781
Fax: 01229 471781
E-mail: j.sharp@netcomuk.co.uk
Contact: John Sharples, Head

Victoria High School

Springfield Road, Ulverston, Cumbria, LA12 0EB
Tel: 01229 53005
Textphone: 01229 53164
Fax: 01229 53799

Whitehaven School

Cleator Moor Road, Whitehaven, Cumbria, CA28
8TY
Tel: 01946 852644
Fax: 01946 852650
Contact: Mr Thompson, Head of Learning
              Support

➢ Darlington
See County Durham

➢ Derby
See Derbyshire

➢ Derbyshire
Education Services
Derby Education Service

Middleton House, 27 St Mary's Gate, Derby, DE1
3NN
Tel: 01332 293111
Fax: 01332 716920
Contact: Rachel Oxley, Head of Special Needs
              Support Service
              Kingshead Centre, Bridge Street,
              Derby, DE1 3LB
Tel: 01332 716000
The special educational needs support team offers
support to children with special educational
needs. The sensory and pre-school team includes
a teacher for visually impaired children, who
supports children, schools and families.

Derbyshire Education Service

County Hall, Matlock, Derbyshire, DE4 3AG
Tel: 01629 580000
Fax: 01629 585401
Contact: Debbie Marston, Head of Service
              Service For Hearing Impaired, Aldercar
              Secondary School, Daltons Close,
              Langley Mill, Nottingham, NG16 4HL
Tel: 01773 718637
Textphone: 01773 713104
The service for the hearing impaired is part of
Derbyshire County Council Learner Support
Division. It aims to provide support, advice and
guidence to families and those providing for the
educational needs of hearing impaired people
from the point of diagnosis onwards.

Units
Aboretum Primary School

Corden Street, Derbyshire, DE23 8GP
Tel: 01332 291140
Fax: 01332 363478
Contact: J Clarke

An enhanced resource school in an inner city area,
providing specialist support for hearing impaired
children within mainstream classes. Many pupils
are from ethnic minorities families. Anjuman
Khavateen parents support group meets weekly at
the school.

Heanor Aldecar Infant School

Godkin Drive, Langley Mill, Derbyshire, NG16 4GL
Tel: 01773 713428
Fax: 01773 713428
Contact: Michelle Nicholls, Teacher of the Deaf

Heanor Langley Mill Junior School

Bailey Brook Crescent, Langley Mill, Derbyshire,
NG16 4FZ
Tel: 01773 712694
Fax: 01773 712964
Contact: Cathy Sergi, Teacher of the Deaf

Meadows Community Secondary School

Old Whittington, Chesterfield, Derbyshire, S41 9LG
Tel: 01246 450825
Fax: 01246 465014
Contact: E Williams, Teacher of the Deaf

This school has specialist teaching facilities and a
hearing impaired unit.

18

New Whittington Primary School

London Street, New Whittington, Chesterfield,
Derbyshire, S43 2AQ
Tel: 01246 450688
Fax: 01246 260042
E-mail: nwhittington@argonet.co.uk
Contact: A Cartledge, Head

Nursery and primary school for children aged 3 to
11 with integrated unit for hearing impaired
children.

Reigate Infant School

Reigate Drive, Derbyshire, DE3 4EQ
Tel: 01332 341272

This school has specialist teaching facilities.

Reigate Primary School

Reigate Drive, Derby, DE22 4EQ
Tel: 01332 298969
Textphone: 01332 298969
Contact: P Eaton, Head

Deaf children are integrated into the school as a
whole.

The Meadows School

High Street, Old Whittington, Chesterfield,
Derbyshire, S41 9LG
Tel: 01246 551921
Contact: Janet Blizard, Teacher of the Deaf

Woodlands Community School

Blenheim Drive, Allestree, Derbyshire, DE22 2LW
Tel: 01332 551921
Textphone: 01332 551921
Fax: 01332 553869
Contact: T Bate, Teacher of the Deaf

Woodlands is the enhanced resource school for
deaf children in Derby. It is an 11 to 18
comprehensive with 1,100 on roll and there are
currently 13 statemented deaf students as part of
the enhanced resource facility. The full range of
communication needs are catered for (oral, sign-
supported English, British Sign Language) and
students are fully integrated into mainstream
schools.

➢ Devon

Education Services

Devon Education Service

County Hall, Topsham Road, Exeter, Devon, EX2
4QG
Tel: 01392 382000
Contact: Graham Ingram, Team Manager,
            Sensory and ICT Advisory Service
            Summerway Middle School,
            Summerway, Exeter, Devon, EX4 8DF
Tel: 01392 461931
Textphone: 01392 462251
Fax: 01392 461026

A team of advisory teachers who specialise in the
provision of advice and support for young people
with visual and/or hearing problems, and those
who are specialists in the use of information
technology hardware and software for young
people with special educational needs.

Units

Bideford East-the-Water Primary School

Mines Road, Bideford, Devon, EX39 4BZ
Tel: 01237 475128
Fax: 01237 423439

A primary day school, Bideford uses the bilingual
system of communication.

Countess Weir Combined School

Glasshouse Lane, Exeter, Devon, EX2 7BS
Tel: 01392 873884
Fax: 01392 876983

Countess Weir is a primary school that mainly uses
the oral method of communication. It uses British
Sign Language and Signed English where
necessary.

Eggbuckland Community College

Westcott Close, Plymouth, Devon, PL6 5YB
Tel: 01752 779061
Textphone: 01752 779061 ext 250
Fax: 01752 766650
E-mail: mailbox@eggbuckland.plym.sch.uk
Website: www.eggbuckland.plym.sch.uk
Contact: G Packer, Teacher in Charge, Hearing
            Impaired Centre

18

Eggbuckland Vale Primary School

Charfield Drive, Eggbuckland, Plymouth, Devon, PL6 5PS

Tel: 01752 703656
Fax: 01752 769802
E-mail: 2703@eggbucklandvaleprimary.school
                .plymouth.gov.uk
Contact: Penny Wolfson, Hearing Support
                Coordinator

The Hearing Support Centre at Eggbuckland Vale Primary School is the provision for integrated education for pre-school and primary hearing impaired children from the City of Plymouth and the West of Devon. Children with moderate, severe and profound hearing impairment are supported by a team of qualified teachers of the deaf and experienced support assistants, using a Total Communication approach.

Honiton County Primary School

Clapper Lane, Honiton, Devon, EX14 8QF

Tel: 01404 42264
Fax: 01404 47431
Contact: Liz Aston, Teacher of the Deaf

The Hearing Support Centre provides integrated education for all types of deafness for children aged 3 to 11 years. We offer total communication to cater for every type of approach to language. The deaf children have access to all of the curriculum and all clubs including music tuition.

St Margaret's Primary School

Barewell Road, Torquay, Devon, TQ1 4PA

Tel: 01803 327090
Fax: 01803 322168
E-mail: 2456@st-
                margarets.school.torbay.gov.uk
Contact: P Roberts, Teacher of the Deaf

Westlands Upper School

Westlands Lane, Torquay, Devon, TQ1 3PE

Tel: 01803 327257
Fax: 01803 323210
Contact: Ian Theacker, Teacher of the Deaf

➤ Dorset
Education Services
Bournemouth Education Service

Dorset House, 20-22 Christchurch Road, Bournemouth, Dorset, BH1 3NL

Tel: 01202 456104
Fax: 01202 456105

Dorset Education Service

County Hall, Dorchester, Dorset, DT1 1XJ

Tel: 01305 251000
Fax: 01305 225057
Contact: Richard Ely, Director of Education, Arts
                and Libraries
Contact: M Smith, Director of County Services,
                Hearing and Visually Impaired Children

                Top O' Town House, Bridport Road,
                Dorchester, Dorset, DT1 1XT
Tel: 01305 224994
Fax: 01305 225098

Poole Education Services

Civic Centre, Poole, Dorset, BH15 2RU

Tel: 01202 633202
Fax: 01202 633899
Contact: M Smith, Director of County Services
                for Hearing Impaired and Visually
                Impaired Children

                Top O' Town House, Bridport Road,
                Dorchester, Dorset, DT1 1XT
Tel: 01305 224994
Fax: 01305 225098

The service for hearing impaired children operates county-wide under joint arrangements with Dorset, Bournemouth and Poole. The service manages the needs of hearing impaired children from diagnosis to school leaving age. In the east of the county there are special resource bases integrated into the three school phases.

Units
Branksome Heath Middle School

Livingstone Road, Poole, Dorset, BH12 3DX

Tel: 01202 743140
Contact: Anne Whittle, Teacher of the Deaf

18

Ferndown Upper School
Ferndown, Bournemouth, Dorset, BH22 9EY
Tel: 01202 871243
Fax: 01202 876661
E-mail: school@fernup.dorset.sch.uk
Contact: Mrs Bartlett, Special Needs Unit,
              Resource Base

St Edward's School
Dale Valley Road, Poole, Dorset, BH15 3HY
Tel: 01202 740950
Fax: 01202 733702
Contact: Martin Smith, Head of Hearing
              Impaired Unit

Sylvan Road First School
Livingstone Road, Poole, Dorset, BH12 3DX
Tel: 01202 743064
Fax: 01202 716360
Contact: Sue Barnsley, Hearing Impaired Unit
Textphone: 01202 747539

➤ East Riding of Yorkshire
See Humberside

➤ East Sussex
Education Services
Brighton and Hove Education Service
William Moon Lodge, The Linkway, Hollingdean,
Brighton, East Sussex, BN1 7EJ
Tel: 01273 290000
Fax: 01273 293456

East Sussex Education Service
County Hall, St Anne's Cresent, Lewes, East
Sussex, BN7 1SW
Tel: 01273 481000
Fax: 01273 481261
Part of the Special Teaching Support Services with
responsibility for hearing and visually impaired
children pre-school to further education including
the Hearing Support Facilities (Units) in
mainstream schools.

Units

Bevendean County Primary School
Heath Hill Avenue, Brighton, East Sussex, BN2 4JP
Tel: 01273 605211
Fax: 01273 622334
Contact: Anita Walker, Teacher of the Deaf

Claverham Community College
North Trade Road, Battle, East Sussex, TN33 0HT
Tel: 01424 772155
Contact: J Hotchkiss, Teacher of the Deaf,
              Hearing Support Facility

Support for hearing inmpaired pupils aged 11 to
16 years. Programmes of in-class support and one
to-one re-inforcement and extension within the
Hearing Support Facility.

Manor County Primary School
Downsview Crescent, Uckfield, East Sussex, TN22
1UB
Tel: 01825 760524
Fax: 01825 760524
Contact: C Risseouw, Teacher of the Deaf

Priory School
Mountfield Road, Lewes, East Sussex, BN7 2XD
Tel: 01273 481071
Fax: 01273 486922
E-mail: dfheppenstall@portables2.ngfl.gov.uk
Priory School is a secondary day school with a
policy of oral communication. It contains a
Hearing Support Facility provided by the East
Sussex Service for Children with Sensory Needs.

Robsackwood County Primary School
Whatlington Way, St-Leonards-on-Sea, Hastings,
East Sussex, TN38 9RB
Tel: 01424 853521
Fax: 01424 853038
Contact: J Benwell, Headteacher

Willingdon County Primary School
Rapsons Road, Willingdon, Eastbourne, East
Sussex, BN20 9RJ
Tel: 01323 482619
Contact: L Langlands, Teacher of the Deaf

We are a Hearing Support Facility that spans the
primary and secondary age range. We use Total
Communication with an emphasis on
spoken/signed English, as well as listening and
lipreading. There is an inclusive policy for all
children, and planned programmes of integration

are set according to individual need.

➤ Essex
Education Services
Barking and Dagenham Education Service
Town Hall, Barking, Essex, IG11 7LU
Tel: 020 8591 9236
Textphone: 020 8591 9236
Fax: 020 8591 9236
Contact: A Larbalastier, Chief Education Officer
Tel: 020 8592 4500
Contact: M Chandler, Head of Hearing Impaired Service
            Faircross School, Rosslyn Site, Rosslyn Road, Barking, Essex, IG11 9UH

Essex Education Service
P O Box 47, County Hall, Victoria Road South, Chelmsford, Essex, CM1 1LD
Tel: 01245 492211
Fax: 01245 492759
Contact: Paul Lincoln, Director of Education
Contact: Yvonne Ball, Specialist Coordinator for Hearing Impaired Children
            The Prittlewell Centre, Boston Avenue, Southend-On-Sea, Essex, SS2 6JH
Tel: 01702 431736
Textphone: 01702 431736
Fax: 01702 431739

Havering Special Educational Needs Support Service
Tel: 01708 773936
Fax: 01708 773892
Contact: Cathy Gray, Head of Special Needs Support Service

See entry under Communication Services.

Ilford Education Authority
Lynton House, 255-259 High Road, Ilford, Essex
Tel: 020 8478 3020
Contact: K Ratcliffe, Director of Education

Redbridge Primary Outreach Service for Hearing Impaired Children
Ding Primary School, Roding Lane North, Woodford Bridge, Essex, IG8 8NP
Tel: 020 8505 3706
Contact: Andrew Giles, Head of Primary Outreach Service

Romford Education Authority
Mercury House, Mercury Gardens, Romford, Essex, RM1 3DS
Tel: 01708 766999
Contact: C Hardy, Director of Education

Special Educational Needs Support Service
Broxhill Centre, Broxhill Road, Harold Hill, Romford, Essex, RM4 1XN
Tel: 01708 773936
E-mail: garlicks@havering.gov.uk
Contact: Lisa Harvey, Advisory Teacher for the Hearing Impaired

Our aim is to provide advice, support and monitoring to schools and families for children with a hearing impairment. This is done through pre-school support, working with primary, secondary schools and colleges. We also provide advice to the local education authority on issues relating to the children we see.

Units
Burnt Mill Comprehensive School
First Avenue, Harlow, Essex, CM20 2NR
Tel: 01279 300555
Fax: 01279 307234
Contact: C Gallacher, Head of Hearing Impaired Unit
Tel: 01279 307258
Textphone: 01279 307258

The unit offers both oral and Total Communication teaching to pupils, as required. Pupils work largely in the mainstream school, with support from unit staff. The unit provides a range of specialised resources in a modern setting. Staff include a teacher of the deaf, an educational communicator and specialist teaching assistants.

Caterham High School
Caterham Avenue, Ilford, Essex, IG5 0QW
Tel: 020 8551 4321
Fax: 020 8551 1933
Contact: Amanda Prenderville, Head of Hearing Impaired

Caterham's hearing impaired provision caters for secondary aged students who benefit from an aural/oral approach in an integrated setting with specialist support in the classroom. The outreach services are for students at other Redbridge Secondary School and secondary out-of-borough placements.

18

Eastbury Comprehensive School

Rosslyn Road, Barking, Essex, IG11 9UH

Tel:	020 8270 4001
Fax:	020 8270 4002
Contact:	Judith Bradey, Teacher of the Deaf

Five Elms Primary School

Wood Lane, Dagenham, Essex, RM9 5TB

Tel:	020 8593 3586
Contact:	Margaret Heaney, Hearing Impaired Base

Ghyllgrove Infant School

The Gore, Ghyllgrove, Basildon, Essex, SS14 1BG

Tel:	01268 521987
Fax:	01268 522113
Contact:	J Merrin, Teacher of the Deaf

We are an infant day school. We no longer have a nursery but provide inclusion within the school's, Early Years Class for children under 5. We have a Total Communication policy.

Glebe Infant School

Philbrick Crescent, Rayleigh, Essex, SS6 9HH

Tel:	01268 785414
Fax:	01268 781847
Contact:	M Dimmock, Teacher of the Deaf

Glebe Junior Mixed School

Creswick Avenue, Rayleigh, Essex, SS6 9HG

Tel:	01268 784253
Fax:	01268 786042
Contact:	M Coleman, Head Teacher

Great Baddow High School

Duffield Road, Chelmsford, Essex, CM2 0HA

Tel:	01245 265821
Fax:	01245 348614
Contact:	D Clark, Teacher of the Deaf

Local education authority secondary day school using Total Communication.

Hacton JMI School

Chepstow Avenue, Hornchurch, Essex, RM12 6AU

Tel:	01708 443991
Fax:	01708 443991

Unit for hearing impaired children attached to a mainstream school.

Lexden County Primary School

Trafalgar Road, Colchester, Essex, CO3 5AS

Tel:	01206 573519
Textphone:	01206 576555
Contact:	J Hieatt-Smith, Teacher of the Deaf

We are an 18-place unit offering Total Communication to children from nursery to aged 16. They are integrated into mainstream classes with support from a teacher of the deaf or signing assistant but also spend variable amounts of time working in the unit according to individual needs - they have full access to National Curriculum.

Mildmay County Junior

Robin Way, Chelmsford, Essex, CM2 8AU

Tel:	01245 265689
Contact:	J Pettas, Teacher of the Deaf

A primary day school with a policy of Total Communication.

Mildmay Infant Mixed School

Robin Way, Chelmsford, Essex, CM2 8AU

Tel:	01245 250021
Fax:	01245 250021
Contact:	A Wright, Teacher of the Deaf

Philip Morant Comprehensive School

Rembrandt Way, Gainsborough Road, Colchester, Essex, CO3 4QS

Tel:	01206 545222
Fax:	01206 577563
Contact:	David Croft, Head of Hearing Impaired Unit

We are a secondary school unit for hearing impaired pupils catering for children with a range of hearing losses from moderate to profound. We aim to integrate pupils as fully as possible into ordinary classes and activities. We provide British Sign Language support and interpretation for those pupils requiring this.

Sanders Draper Comprehensive School

Suttons Lane, Hornchurch, Essex, RM12 6RT

Tel:	01708 443068
Contact:	Julie Hewston

The Hearing Impaired Unit operates on a fully-integrational basis. The students (12 in total) are fully supported in lessons by teachers of the deaf and communicators using whatever communication method is appropriate.

Tany's Dell County Primary School

Tany's Dell, Harlow, Essex, CM20 2LS
Tel: 01279 866230
Fax: 01279 866231
Contact: Ruth Woodhouse, Teacher of the Deaf

The Sweyne Park School

Sir Walter Ralegh Drive, Rayleigh, Essex, SS6 9BZ
Tel: 01268 784721
Fax: 01268 780293
Contact: K Fisher, Head of Unit for Hearing
            Impaired
Tel: 01268 780299
Textphone: 01268 780299

A unit for hearing impaired children aged from 11 to 16 years within a mixed comprehensive school.

➤ Gillingham and Rochester
See Kent

➤ Gloucestershire
Education Services
Gloucestershire Education Service

Shire Hall, Gloucestershire, GL1 2TP
Tel: 01452 425300
Contact: K Anderson, Chief Education Officer
Tel: 01452 425301
Contact: M Geraghty, Head of Service
            Sensory and Language Impairment
            SENARC, Hucclecote Centre,
            Churchdown Lane, Gloucester, GL3
            3QN
Tel: 01452 427257
Textphone: 01452 427257
Fax: 01452 427259

The Sensory and Language Impairment Service uses both Total Communication and bilingualism as methods of communication.

South Gloucestershire Education Service

Bowling Hill, Chipping Sodbury, Gloucestershire, BS17 6JX
Tel: 01454 8633336
Fax: 01454 8632363

Units

Beaufort Community School

Windsor Drive, Tuffley, Gloucester, GL4 0RT
Tel: 01452 301381
Fax: 01452 380779
Contact: John Daniels, Teacher in Charge of Unit

The centre at Beaufort School provides special support for deaf children using the Total Communication approach. Children are integrated into mainstream as much as possible often with in-class signing support. Children enjoy proper membership of equal opportunities within the Beaufort School community.

Longlevens Infant School

Paygrove Lane, Longlevens, Gloucester, GL2 0AX
Tel: 01452 529464

Longlevens Junior School

Church Road, Longlevens, Gloucester, GL2 0AL
Tel: 01452 530177
Contact: Jane Parrish, Teacher in Charge

Longlevens Junior School has a special centre for severely and profoundly deaf children. We provide special teaching by a qualified teacher of the deaf, plus integration in mainstream classes with support from an assistant. We use a Total Communication approach.

Naunton Park Primary School

Naunton Lane, Cheltenham, Gloucestershire, GL53 7BW
Tel: 01242 513114
Fax: 01242 513114
Contact: S Gills, Teacher in Charge

➤ Halton
See Cheshire

18

➤ Hampshire
Education Services
Hampshire Education Service
The Castle, Winchester, Hampshire, SO23 8UQ
Tel: 01962 846400
Fax: 01926 845648
Contact: Paul Thomas, Special Educational
             Needs Adviser (Hearing Impairment)
             HIAS, Birch House, Barley Way, Fleet,
             Hampshire, GU13 8YB
Tel: 01252 814777
Textphone: 01252 814786

Support is provided for deaf and hearing impaired children up to 19 years of age. There is a peripatetic service and there are also specialist oral units and specialist units using signs.

Portsmouth Education Service
Civic Offices, Guildhall Square, Portsmouth, Hampshire, PO1 2EA
Tel: 023 9284 1200
Fax: 023 9284 1208

Southampton Education Service
Civic Centre, Southampton, Hampshire, SO14 7LY
Tel: 023 8083 2771
Contact: Maureen Richards, Specialist Teacher
             Adviser
             Frobisher House, Nelson Gate,
             Southampton, Hampshire, SO15 1GX
Tel: 023 8083 3392
Textphone: 023 80832798
Fax: 023 8083 3324

Peripatetic teaching service within the city of Southampton to deaf and hearing impaired children up to 19 years of age. Advising and training parents and teachers on strategies to help hearing impaired pupils. Providing assessment, teaching, support and equipment to help hearing impaired children's speech, language and communication development.

Units
Banister Infant School and Nursery
Banister Gardens, Southampton, Hampshire, SO15 2LX
Tel: 023 8039 3313

We are an infant school with a Hearing Impaired Unit. We use the oral/aural approach. We take children between the ages of 3 and 7.

Cove School
St John's Road, Cove, Farnborough, Hampshire, GU14 9RN
Tel: 01252 542397
Fax: 01252 524223
Contact: L Bowles, Teacher of the Deaf

At Cove Hearing Impaired Unit we aim to provide effective support in an integrated mainstream setting using a combination of in-class support and individual withdrawal. Programmes are tailored to meet the pupil's needs. We encourage pupils to strive towards full integration, independence and effective citizenship.

Henry Beaufort Secondary School
East Woodhay Road, Harestock, Winchester, Hampshire, SO22 6JJ
Tel: 01962 880073
Textphone: 01962 883667
Fax: 01962 883667
Contact: R Edwards, Teacher in Charge

The Hearing Impaired Unit was set up in 1995 to give access to secondary mainstream provision for students in the central division of Hampshire. The students' hearing losses range from moderate to profound. All students wear post-aural hearing aids in conjunction with a radio-aid system. The hearing impaired students are fully integrated into mainstream school life and have daily contact with the teacher of the deaf. They follow an aural/oral approach. Our ultimate aim is to help hearing impaired students achieve their academic and social potential.

Manor Junior School
Fernhill Road, Cove, Farnborough, Hampshire, GU14 9DX
Tel: 01252 521081
Fax: 01252 378954
Contact: Elizabeth Gwynn, Teacher in Charge

The unit for hearing impaired children is attached to Manor Infants and Junior Schools and caters for severely and profoundly deaf children from 4 to 11 years. Our aim is for the children to develop good spoken language and reach their highest potential academically.

Medstead Church of England Primary School
Medstead, Alton, Hampshire, GU34 5LG
Tel: 01420 562824
Fax: 01420 562451
Medstead Primary School has a unit for profoundly deaf children with an agreed number of five places. The school advocates a philosophy of

Total Communication. The teacher of the deaf there aims for all the deaf children to leave school able to read and write at National Curriculum levels ranging from 2 upwards and for all of them to have high self-esteem.

Neville Lovett Community School
St Anne's Grove, Fareham, Hampshire, PO14 1JJ
Tel: 01329 318003
A secondary day school with an oral/aural communication policy.

Northern Parade Junior School
Doyle Avenue, Portsmouth, Hampshire, PO2 9NE
Tel: 023 9266 2129
Fax: 023 9266 1376
E-mail: cjwatts@portablesi.ngfl.gov.uk
Contact: Chris Watts, Head Teacher

Park View County Infant School
Pinkerton Road, Basingstoke, Hampshire, RG22 6RT
Tel: 01256 322554
Fax: 01256 354229
Contact: P Sumner, Teacher in Charge

Park View County Junior School
Pinkerton Road, Basingstoke, Hampshire, RG22 6RT
Tel: 01256 322616
Fax: 01256 814279
Contact: A Fisher, Teacher in Charge

Penhale Infant School Nursery and Hearing Impaired Unit
Penhale Road, Portsmouth, Hampshire, PO1 5EF
Tel: 023 9282 1016
Fax: 023 9282 8738
Contact: A Larcombe, Head Teacher

A primary and nursery day school.

Richard Aldworth Community School
Western Way, Basingstoke, Hampshire, RG22 6HA
Tel: 01256 22691
Contact: R Shirliker, Teacher in Charge

Tanner's Brook Junior School
Elmes Drive, Southampton, Hampshire, SO15 4PF
Tel: 023 8077 4247
Fax: 023 8051 1226
Contact: E Roles
Tanner's Brook Junior School provides a specialist unit using the oral/aural approach to communication for hearing impaired children between the ages of 7 and 11years.

Wallisdean Junior School
Wallisdean Avenue, Fareham, Hampshire, PO14 1HU
Tel: 01329 232571
Fax: 01392 231822
Contact: B Dimmer, Teacher in Charge

Woodcote County Primary School
Tukes Avenue, Bridgemary, Gosport, Hampshire, PO13 0SG
Tel: 01329 234381
Textphone: 01329 827671
Fax: 01329 823911
E-mail: 2613F920@hants.gov.uk
Contact: Kate Meikie, Teacher of the Deaf

➢ Hartlepool
See Cleveland

➢ Herefordshire
Units
Beconside First and Middle School
Hazel Road, Rubery, Rednal, Herefordshire, B45 9DX
Tel: 0121 453 3801
Contact: R Moore, Teacher of the Deaf

Chase High School
Geraldine Road, Malvern, Herefordshire WR14 3NZ
Tel: 01684 893961
Fax: 01684 566642
Contact: C Burger, Team Leader, SCSI Hearing Impaired Resource Unit
               Geraldine Road, Malvern, Herefordshire, WR14 3NZ

A secondary day school using Total Communication. Specialist support is given by teachers of the deaf and specialist support assistants, usually on a one-to-one basis. The unit is acoustically adapted and individual tuition may

18

be provided on a withdrawal basis when needed. Each child has a radio hearing aid (where needed) to enable them to gain as much 'oral' input as possible, making use of residual hearing and encouraging speech. There is additional back-up support with a visiting speech therapist, specialist sign language coordinator and hearing aid technician, as well as additional links with other specialists such as a psychologist and careers officer.

Rushwick Church of England Primary School

Upper Wick Lane, Worcester, Herefordshire, WR2 2SU

Tel: 01905 422502
Contact: H Campbell, Head Teacher

St Mary's Roman Catholic High School

Lugwardine, Hereford, HR1 4DR

Tel: 01432 850416
Fax: 01432 851728
Contact: Paul Shannon, Acting Head Teacher

This is a resourced school. The Hearing Unit is no longer based there, but a part-time peripatetic teacher comes in for the hearing impaired students based there at present.

Waseley Hill High School

Rubery, Rednal, Herefordshire, B45 9EL

Tel: 0121 453 5211 ext 236
Fax: 0121 457 8850
Contact: D Conyers, Teacher of the Deaf

➢ Hertfordshire
Education Services
Advisory Teacher Service

The Woodside Centre, The Commons, Welwyn Garden City, Hertfordshire, AL7 4EN

Tel: 01707 320697
Fax: 01707 339151
Contact: Helen Porter, Visiting Teacher of the Deaf

The Advisory Teacher Service consists of teachers of the deaf who work on a peripatetic basis visiting hearing impaired children at home, playschool, nursery and schools where there is no teacher of the deaf on site. Support for language development is offered to parents, and teachers are advised on the children's access to the National Curriculum.

Hertfordshire Education Service

County Hall, Hertfordshire, SG13 8DF

Tel: 01992 555701
Fax: 01992 555719
Contact: Ray Shostack, Director of Education

Units
Barnwell School

Barnwell, Stevenage, Hertfordshire, SG2 9SR

Tel: 01438 351696
Contact: R Kenworthy, Teacher of the Deaf, Base for Sensory Impaired Pupils

A secondary day school using the oral method of communication.

Holywell Junior Middle and Infant School

Tolpits Lane, Watford, Hertfordshire, WD1 8NT

Tel: 01923 225188
Fax: 01923 440408
Contact: Marian Jordan, Teacher of the Deaf, Nursery and Infants

Maple Junior Mixed and Infant School

Hall Place Gardens, St Albans, Hertfordshire, AL1 3SW

Tel: 01727 859053
Fax: 01727 859053
Contact: Chris Ivory, Teacher of the Deaf

Our organisation aims to educate hearing impaired children alongside their hearing peers. We aim towards developing children's speech and language orally/aurally. Children integrate into the mainstream classes and are full members of those classes. At times children work in the unit on developing speech and language (individually) and on developing necessary basic skills to allow them access to the National Curriculum (with a small group of their hearing peers).

Marlborough Secondary School

Watling Street, St Albans, Hertfordshire, AL1 2QA

Tel: 01727 856874
Fax: 01727 855285
Contact: Angela Thompson, Head of Unit

Muriel Green Nursery

6 Lemsford Road, St Albans, Hertfordshire, AL1 3PB

Tel: 01727 851178
Fax: 01727 766000

A nursery assessment unit.

➢ Hull
See Humberside

➢ Humberside
Units
Andrew Marvell Secondary School
Barham Road, Bilton Grange Estate, Kingston upon Hull, Humberside, HU9 4EE

Tel: 01482 781975
Textphone: 01482 781975
Fax: 01482 786804
Contact: Martin Bell, Teacher in Charge

Supports hearing impaired pupils in the mainstream to access the National Curriculum and supports their needs to achieve their maximum potential.

Havelock Secondary School
Holyoake Road, Grimsby, Humberside, DN32 8JL

Tel: 01472 693946
Fax: 01472 693375
Contact: G Horsely, Head Teacher

St Anne's School
St Helens Drive, Welton, Brough, East Riding of Yorkshire, HU15 1NR

Tel: 01482 667379
Textphone: 01482 667379

School for children with severe learning difficulties with a unit for hearing impaired. Age range 3 to 16 years.

➢ Isle of Man
Education Services
Isle of Man Sensory Impairment Service
Cronk-y-Berry School, Hailwood Avenue, Douglas, Isle of Man, IM2 7PA

Tel: 01624 615995
Fax: 01624 615962
Contact: Theresa Vardill, Head of Sensory Impairment Service

Provides an educational service for all hearing impaired and visually impaired children on the Isle of Man. This includes pre-school children, primary, secondary and young people in the further education college. We are a team of qualified teachers of hearing impaired and visually impaired children. We have a primary and

secondary unit and a peripatetic service for mainstream children.

Units
Ballakermeen High School
St Catherine's Drive, Douglas, Isle of Man, IM1 4BE

Cronk-Y-Berry School
Hailwood Avenue, Douglas, Isle of Man, IM2 7PA

Tel: 01624 615995
Fax: 01624 615962
Contact: Theresa Vardill, Head of Sensory Impairment Service

The sensory impairment service provides advice to parents, and to pre-school centres, schools and colleges which have sensory impaired children integrated in mainstream. We are a team of qualified teachers of hearing and visually impaired units for children: Cronk-y-Berry Primary School and Ballakermeen Secondary School. We liaise with the Special Educational Needs and Psychology Service.

➢ Isle of Wight
Education Services
Hearing Impaired Service, Isle of Wight
14 Lower Pyle Street, Newport, Isle of Wight, PO30 1JW

Tel: 01983 823504

Isle of Wight Education Service
County Hall, Newport, Isle of Wight, PO30 1UD

Tel: 01983 823400

Units
Barton County Primary School
School Lane, Newport, Isle of Wight, PO30 2HL

Tel: 01983 522469/ 522880

Downside County Middle School
Furlongs Barton, Newport, Isle of Wight, PO30 2AX

Tel: 01983 524340
Fax: 01983 533467
E-mail: info@downsidems.iow.sch.uk
Contact: M James, Peripatetic Deaf Teacher

18

Medina County High School

Fairlee Road, Newport, Isle of Wight, PO30 2DX
Tel: 01983 526523
Fax: 01983 822821
E-mail: petra@tobanna.demon.co.uk
Contact: Petra Wilmott, Hearing Impaired
            Coordinator

A deaf unit in a mainstream secondary school with one teacher of the deaf and between 5 and 10 students with a range of losses (mild to profound). Communication is oral/aural, although the teacher of the deaf has BSL Stage II and would use sign language if appropriate.

➤ Isles of Scilly

Education Services

Isles of Scilly Education Service

Town Hall, St Mary's, Isles of Scilly, TR21 0LW
Tel: 01720 422537

➤ Kent

Education Services

Bexley Education Service

Hill View, Hill View Drive, Welling, Kent, DA16 3RY
Tel: 020 8303 7777
Fax: 020 8319 4302
Contact: M Moore, Advisory Service for Hearing
            Impaired Children
Tel: 020 8303 7777 ext 4463
Contact: A Reese, Educational Psychology and
            Assessment Service
Contact: P McGee, Director of Education

To promote support, teaching and advice to enable hearing impaired pupils to reach their full potential.

Bromley Peripatetic Services

Lovibonds Avenue, Orpington, Kent
Tel: 01689 59759
Contact: J P Hurd

Bromley Sensory Support Service

Widmore Centre, Nightingale Lane, Bromley, Kent, BR1 2SQ
Tel: 020 8313 3569
Contact: Sally Kirwan, Team Leader

Kent Education Service

County Hall, Maidstone, Kent, ME14 1XX
Tel: 01622 671411
Contact: Lindsey Rousseau, Head of Physical
            and Sensory Services
Tel: 01622 696034
Textphone: 01622 605720
Fax: 01622 605742

Educational services for children, students and their families with involvement from diagnosis of deafness through to further education.

Lewisham Sensory Support Team

New Woodlands Centre, 49 Shrossold Road, Bromley, Kent, BR1 5PD
Tel: 020 8695 0645
Contact: Margaret Morgan, Peripatetic Teacher
            of the Deaf

Units

Bexleyheath School

Graham Road, Bexleyheath, Kent, DA6 7DA
Tel: 020 8303 5696

Cheriton County Primary School

Church Road, Folkestone, Kent, CT20 3EP
Tel: 01303 276112
Fax: 01303 272305
Contact: Mary Johncock, Teacher in Charge

Provides high quality educational support for oral/aural hearing impaired pupils aged 2 years 6 months to 11 years, facilitating full access to curriculum and achievement of potential alongside hearing peers. Nursery assessment places are available if needed. Maintains close links with Total Communication Unit staff and pupils.

Christ Church High School

Milbank Road, Kingsnorth, Ashford, Kent, TN23 3HG
Tel: 01233 623465
Fax: 01233 636861
Contact: John Mulrenan, Headmaster

Christ Church School

Milbank Road, Kingsnorth, Ashford, Kent, TN23 3HG
Tel: 01233 623465
Fax: 01233 636181
Contact: Sandy Owen, Teacher of the Deaf

Darrick Wood School
(Infant/Junior/Secondary)

Lovibonds Avenue, Orpington, Kent, BR6 8ER
Tel: 01689 857271 Senior
               01689 859759 Junior
Textphone: 01689 857970
Fax: 01689 857257
E-mail: office@darrick_wood_bromley.sch.uk
Contact: Mrs Proudford, Head of Hearing
              Impairment Unit

Each school has its own hearing impairment unit.

Fairview County Primary School

Drewery Drive, Wigmore, Gillingham, Kent, ME8 0NV
Tel: 01634 373235

The Unit for Hearing Impaired Children has been established for many years and caters for children with hearing impairment. The unit offers oral/aural access to language for hearing impaired children with hearing losses ranging from moderate to profound. The children have personal hearing aids. Radio aid systems and auditory training units are in daily use. When withdrawn daily from mainstream, all hearing impaired children are taught by fully qualified teachers of the hearing impaired. The unit environment is conducive to hearing aid users. Each child has access to the National Curriculum via a carefully monitored individual integration programme.

Fleetdown Unit for Hearing Impaired Children, Fleetdown Primary Schools

Lunedale Road, Dartford, Kent, DA2 6JX
Tel: 01322 291001
Fax: 01322 224157
Contact: Sue Dane, Teacher in Charge

Specialist education for hearing impaired children in the north-west Kent area. Natural approach and Total Communication for nursery, infant and junior aged pupils, with integration into mainstream schools for social and some National Curriculum sessions.

George Spurgen County Primary School

Sidney Street, Folkestone, Kent, CT19 6HG
Tel: 01303 226363
Textphone: 01303 226363
Fax: 01303 226537
Contact: Bernagh Moseley, Teacher in Charge

The Unit for Hearing Impaired Children at George Spurgen County Primary School is attached to a mainstream primary school. We cater for

profoundly deaf children from 2 to 11 years who require Total Communication (sign language supports speech in all curriculum areas).

Hampton County Primary School

Fitzgerald Avenue, Herne Bay, Kent, CT6 8NB
Tel: 01227 369652
Fax: 01227 741549
Contact: K Tattersall, Head of Hearing Impaired
              Unit

All our hearing impaired children have full access to the National Curriculum and an individual programme of teaching and support enabling them to share as wide a range of learning experience as possible in an integrated setting. They have access to qualified teachers of the deaf and a speech therapist, and make use of the full range of audiological equipment.

Hartsdown School

George V Avenue, Margate, Kent, CT9 5RE
Tel: 01843 232144
Fax: 01843 299642
Contact: Valerie Hughes, Teacher in Charge
Tel: 01843 227957

Molehill Copse County Primary School

Hereford Road, Maidstone, Kent, ME15 7ND
Tel: 01622 661578
Fax: 01622 758016
Contact: Maureen Holland, Teacher in Charge

Pelham Primary School

Pelham Road, Bexleyheath, Kent, DA7 4HL
Tel: 020 8303 6556
Contact: A Williams, Head Teacher

Pelham Primary School has two units for hearing impaired children, one nursery infant and one junior. Each unit can take six children and offers either an oral/aural approach or Total Communication using sign-supported English.

Sittingbourne Community College

Swanstree Avenue, Sittingbourne, Kent, ME10 4NL
Tel: 01795 472449
Fax: 01795 470332
E-mail: ad805@dialpipex.com
Contact: Andrew Arden, Head of Unit

18

Slade County Primary School

The Slade, Tonbridge, Kent, TN9 1HR

Tel: 01732 350354
Fax: 01732 357521
Contact: Judith Marsden, Teacher in Charge

Slade Green Infant School

Slade Green Road, Erith, Kent, DA8 2HX

Tel: 01322 334689
Fax: 01332 334689
Contact: C Still, Head Teacher

Slade Green Junior School

Slade Green Road, Erith, Kent, DA8 2HX

Tel: 01322 330363
Contact: R Edwards, Head Teacher

Total Communication Hearing Impaired Unit taking a maximum of eight pupils, and one teacher of the deaf.

St George's School

Pembury Road, Tunbridge Wells, Kent, TN2 4NE

Tel: 01892 823096
Contact: Muriel McKenna

There is a teacher of the deaf based at the school.

St Mary's County Primary School

Gun Lane, Strood, Rochester, Kent, ME2 4UP

Tel: 01634 294133
Contact: Linda Baxter, Teacher in Charge

The Hugh Christie Secondary School

Norwich Avenue, Tonbridge, Kent, TN10 4QL

Tel: 01732 353544 ext 264
Fax: 01732 367833
Contact: Mike Kelleher, Teacher of the Deaf

The Maplesden Noakes School

Great Buckland, Maidstone, Kent, ME16 0TJ

Tel: 01622 754205
Textphone: 01622 754205
Fax: 01622 661707
Contact: Jane Bowles, Head of Unit

To assist the integrated education of the deaf at the Maplesden Noakes School by aural/oral support methods.

➢ Lancashire
Education Services
Bolton Education Service

P O Box 53, Paderborn House, Civic Centre, Bolton, Lancashire, BL1 1JW

Tel: 01204 522311
Fax: 01204 365492
Contact: Margaret Blenkinsop, Director of Education
Contact: Jean Mort, Head of Service for Sensory Impaired

Thomasson Memorial School, Devonshire Road, Bolton, Lancashire, BL1 4PJ

Tel: 01204 843063

Bury Education Service

Athenaeum House, Market Street, Bury, Lancashire, BL9 0BN

Tel: 0161 253 5000
Fax: 0161 253 5653
Contact: Janet Bentley, Sensory Support Service

c/o Radcliffe High School, Abden Street, Radcliffe, Bury, Lancashire, M26 0AW

Tel: 0161 724 8337

The Sensory Support Service works in partnership with the families and schools of hearing impaired children from the time of diagnosis until they complete their full time education. It aims to support the development of communication skills, maximise use of residual hearing, facilitate access to National Curriculum and develop awareness of implications of hearing impairment.

Lancashire Education Service

P O Box 61, County Hall, Preston, Lancashire, PR1 8RJ

Tel: 01772 254868
Fax: 01772 261630
Contact: C Trinick, Chief Education Officer

Manchester Education Service

Crown Square, Manchester, Lancashire, M60 3BB

Tel: 0161 234 7001
Contact: Susan Parsons, Head of Service

Newbrook, Newholme Road, West Didsbury, Manchester, M20 2XZ

Tel: 0161 445 5172
Textphone: 0161 445 5172
Fax: 0161 438 0058

Newbrook is the base for a large support service working with deaf/hearing impaired children, their families at home and pupils in Manchester schools, whether local mainstream, resourced or special. The service incorporates clerical staff, technicians, support workers, nursery nurses and teachers, including those with additional qualifications, such as audiology and sign language.

Oldham Education Service

Old Town Hall, Middleton Road, Chadderton, Oldham, Lancashire, OL9 6PP

Tel: 0161 678 4260
Fax: 0161 628 0443
Contact: Joseph Lally, Service Manager
           Park Dean School, St Martins Road, Fitton Hill, Oldham, OL8 2PY
Tel: 0161 627 0495
Fax: 0161 627 1147

The Service for Hearing Impairment is concerned with all aspects of education and support of deaf children, pupils and students and their families to give them every opportunity to achieve their full potential and to minimise the educational, social and emotional impact of hearing impairment.

Rochdale Education Service

PO Box 70, Municipal Offices, Rochdale, Lancashire, OL16 1YD

Tel: 01706 47474
Fax: 01706 58560

The Pupil Development Support Service aims to work in partnership with schools to implement the Local Education Authority's Special Educational Needs Policy, the stages of the Special Educational Needs Code of Practice. The Sensory Support Team supports hearing impaired children in working partnership with their parents/carers to provide a community response to the needs of hearing impaired children from the time of diagnosis. The philosophy of the Sensory Support Team (working with hearing impaired children) is to develop as far as possible each child's physical, intellectual, emotional and social competence towards an independent life, and to enable each child to communicate his/her needs, feelings, wants and desires to a level that can be understood by others.

Rochdale Pupils' Development Support Service

Albert Royds Street, Rochdale, Lancashire, OL16 2SU

Tel: 01706 633613
Textphone: 01706 631520
Fax: 01706 869275
Contact: V Stone, Team Leader, Sensory Support Team

Salford Education Service

Chapel Street, Salford, Lancashire, M3 5LT

Tel: 0161 832 9751
Fax: 0161 835 1561
Contact: David Johnston, Chief Education Officer
Contact: Christine Hayfield, Head of Hearing Impaired Service
           Halton House, 36 Eccles Old Road, Salford, M6 8RA
Tel: 0161 925 0530
Fax: 0161 925 0539

Tameside Education Service

Council Offices, Wellington Road, Ashton-under-Lyne, Lancashire, OL6 6DL

Tel: 0161 342 8355
Textphone: 0161 342 3260
Fax: 0161 342 3260
Contact: G Holt, Head of Service
           Education Development Centre, Lakes Road, Dukinfield, Lancashire, SK16 4TR
Tel: 0161 343 5932
Textphone: 0161 339 4599

We are a specialist support service for hearing impaired children and their families from birth to 16 plus. All teachers are qualified tutors of the hearing impaired and can sign. There are two audiologists within the team. A small group of nursery nurses (sign-qualified) assist the teachers.

18

Wigan Education Service

Gateway House, Standishgate, Wigan, Lancashire, WN1 1AE

Tel: 01942 828881
Contact: R Clark, Director of Education
Fax: 01942 828811
Contact: R Brett, Acting Head of Service

Jack Ashley Centre, Park Road, Hindley, Wigan, Lancashire, WN2 3RY

Tel: 01942 526312
Fax: 01942 742533

Units

Ashton High School

Aldwych Drive, Ashton on Ribble, Preston, Lancashire, PR2 1SL

Tel: 01772 513002
Contact: J Thurlwell, Teacher of the Deaf

The Deaf Support Department exists within a mainstream secondary school, providing for severely and profoundly deaf children using Total Communication.

Asmall Primary School

Tennyson Drive, Ormskirk, Lancashire, L39 3PJ

Tel: 01695 576654

Asmall Primary School is a local mainstream school run by Lancashire Education Authority with a Special Education Resource Facility (SERF) for a maximum of 12 severe or profoundly deaf children who can benefit from an integrated provision using a Natural Aural approach to language development.

Corpus Christi School

Longridge Road, Preston, Lancashire, PR2 5AY

Tel: 01772 716912
Fax: 01772 718779
Contact: M McDermott, Head of Advisory Teacher Service

Cross Hall High School

Wigan Road, Ormskirk, Lancashire, L39 2AT

Tel: 01695 572625
Fax: 01695 572348
Contact: Mr Ryder, Teacher of the Deaf

Elton High School

Walshaw Road, Bury, Lancashire, BL8 1RN

Tel: 0161 797 6542
Textphone: 0161 797 6542
Fax: 0161 761 3849
Contact: Denise Craven, Teacher of the Deaf

Elton Nursery and Primary School

Alston Street, Bury, Lancashire, BL8 1SB

Tel: 0161 764 4170

Hamer County Primary School

Albert Royds Street, Rochdale, Lancashire, OL16 2SU

Tel: 01706 631520
Fax: 01706 869275
Contact: Vanessa Stone, Acting Team Leader, Sensory Support Team, Hearing Impaired

Peripatetic teachers, trained as teachers of hearing impaired children, providing: specialist teaching and support in schools, nurseries and children and family centres; guidance and advice to families; advisory service to nurseries and schools; liaison with other organisations such as Healthcare Trust and Social Services; assessment of hearing impaired children's educational needs; in-service training to learning support assistants, care workers and other involved professionals. Bilingual teaching support to children and families (Urdu/Punjabi).

Heywood Community School

Heywood High, Sutherland Road, Heywood, Lancashire, OL10 3PL

Tel: 01706 360466
Fax: 01706 627280
Contact: C Harris, Teacher of the Deaf

The Hearing Support Centre at Heywood Community School supports hearing impaired students aged 11 to 16 years, offering dual provision. The centre uses both an oral/aural approach and sign-supported English as appropriate for the individual student. At present there are 21 who are supported by two teachers of the deaf and six educational communicators. The students are integrated and with support are able to access the full school curriculum, except for modern foreign language in some cases. These students are then offered sign language (Open College) as an alternative. Our aim is to enable each student to communicate their needs, feelings, wants, desires and thoughts to a level that can be understood by others by placing them

18

in a stimulating environment.

Holme Slack County School
Manor House Lane, Preston, Lancashire, PR1 6HP
Tel: 01772 795257
Fax: 01772 655257
Contact: Mrs Bradford, Teacher of the Deaf

Ivy Bank School
Byron Street, Burnley, Lancashire, BB12 6NU
Tel: 01282 775111
Fax: 01282 779350
Contact: Penny Rowbottom, Teacher of the Deaf

Lower Darwen County School
Milking Lane, Darwen, Lancashire, BB3 0PW
Tel: 01254 556394
Fax: 01254 668065
Contact: Susan Morton, Teacher of the Deaf

Moor Park High School
Moor Park Avenue, Preston, Lancashire, PR1 6DT
Tel: 01772 795428
Fax: 01772 653912
Contact: L Blackburn, Teacher of the Deaf

Moss Field County Primary School
West Starkey Street, Heywood, Lancashire, OL10 4TW
Tel: 01706 620628
Fax: 01706 620628

There are two units - one for infants and one for junior children. There are also reserved places in the nursery attached to the school. Basically an oral unit, but with provision for children reading signing. At present two teachers of the deaf and two special support assistants are on roll. Integration takes place as much as possible to ensure children have access to the National Curriculum and can socialise with their hearing peers.

Northlands High School
Moor Park Avenue, Preston, Lancashire, PR1 6DT

Royal Cross Primary School
Elswick Road, Ashton on Ribble, Preston, Lancashire, PR2 1NT
Tel: 01772 729705
Fax: 01772 729866
Contact: Ruth Boyle, Head Teacher

A specialist provision for pupils, communication needs enabling access to a first-class education; development of a positive view of deafness; fulfilment of potential in all areas and preparation for the future.

Sharples High School
Hill Cot Road, Bolton, Lancashire
Tel: 01204 308421
Fax: 01204 597689

The aim of the unit is to provide a secure environment in which all pupils have the opportunity to develop to their maximum potential academically, physically, spiritually and emotionally, and to enable pupils to make a full and rewarding contribution to the society in which they live.

Todmorden Road County Primary School
Todmorden Road, Burnley, Lancashire BB10 4EA
Tel: 01282 437277
Contact: Ann Tattersall, Teacher of the Deaf

We are an auditory/oral unit for deaf children aged 4 to 11 years. Where appropriate we integrate into mainstream curricular activities.

Waterloo School
Waterloo Road, Blackpool, Lancashire, FY4 3AG
Tel: 01253 315370
Fax: 01253 316493
Contact: Peter Rawcliffe, Head Teacher

➤ Leicester
See Leicestershire

➤ Leicestershire
Education Services
Leicester Education Service
Marlborough House, 38 Welford Road, Leicester, LE2 7AA
Tel: 0116 254 9922
Fax: 0116 233 9922
Contact: Rod Dyson, Team Leader, Hearing
           Impaired Service
           c/o STS, Western Annexe, County Hall,
           Glenfield, Leicester, LE3 8RF
Tel: 0116 232 0240
Fax: 0116 232 1195

Leicestershire Education Service

County Hall, Leicester Road, Glenfield, Leicester, LE3 8RF

Tel:	0116 232 3232
Fax:	0116 265 6332
Contact:	J Strong, Director of Education
Contact:	Hazel Baxter, Acting Hearing Impairment Team Leader, Specialist Teaching Service
Tel:	0116 265 6496

The Leicestershire Hearing Impairment Team provides a comprehensive teaching, educational, advisory and audiological support service for hearing impaired children and students of all ages, abilities and hearing loss, thus enabling them to have the same rights and opportunities as their hearing peers to ensure they achieve their full potential.

Rutland County Council Education Department

Catmose Street, Oakham, Leicestershire, LE15 6HP

Tel:	01572 722577
Fax:	01572 757713
Contact:	Clive Hadfield, Pupil and Client Services Officer

Rutland County Council supports educational provision in the 22 maintained schools in the county. Specialist provision for hearing impaired pupils is made via the Leicestershire Specialist Teaching Service.

Special Needs Teaching Service

Hearing Impaired Team, Leicester City Local Education Authority, New Parks House, Pindar Road, New Parks, Leicester, LE3 9RN

Tel:	01533 320240
Fax:	01533 321195
Contact:	Rob Dyson, Hearing Impairment Team Leader

The service meets the needs of all children with a permanent or long-term fluctuating hearing loss from diagnosis to school leaving. It aims to enhance the educational opportunities of these children, allowing them to take a full and active part in society.

Units
Beauchamp Upper School

Ridge Way, Oadby, Leicester, LE2 5TP

Tel:	0116 271 5809
Contact:	Susan Challacombe, Teacher of the Deaf

Buswells Lodge Primary School

Beauville Drive, Leicester, LE4 0PT

Tel:	0116 236 6769
Contact:	C Avard, Teacher of the Deaf

Crown Hills School and Community College

Gwendolen Road, Leicester, LE5 5FT

Tel:	0116 273 6893
Fax:	0116 273 0413
E-mail:	admin@crown-hills.freeserve.co.uk
Contact:	Paul Moran, Teacher of the Deaf

Gartree High School

Coombe Rise, Oadby, Leicestershire, LE2 5TQ

Tel:	0116 271 7421
Fax:	0116 272 0148
Contact:	D Loveday, Teacher of the Deaf

› Lincolnshire
Education Services
Lincolnshire Education Service

County Offices, Newland, Lincolnshire, LN1 1YQ

Tel:	01522 552222
Contact:	N Riches, Director of Education
Contact:	Geoff Platt, Head of Hearing Support Department
	Cherry Willingham Comprehensive School, Croft Lane, Cherry Willingham, Lincoln, LN3 4JP
Tel:	01522 750747
Fax:	01522 595021

The Sensory Impaired Service consists of 12 staff whose specialism includes the areas of hearing and vision. All staff hold additional specialist mandatory qualifications. Three teachers within the service are able to offer support involving total communication (signing). Members of the service are available to assist teachers and parents. The Sensory Impaired Service is mainly a specialist advisory service. A small amount of individual teaching is undertaken. There are five units for hearing impaired children with qualified teachers of the deaf on site. Peripatetic teachers offer individually tailored advice regarding special arrangements for hearing and vision impaired children's access to Key Stage tasks and tests, jointly with community audiology clinics.

18

Units

Cherry Willingham Comprehensive School
Croft Lane, Cherry Willingham, Lincolnshire, LN3 4JP
Tel: 01522 750747
Fax: 01522 595021
Contact: Geoff Platt, Head of Hearing Support Department

St Thomas' Primary School
Wyberton Low Road, Boston, Lincolnshire, PE21 7RZ
Tel: 01205 362860
Fax: 01205 362496
Contact: Barbara Prime, Teacher of the Deaf

Thomas Cowley Secondary School
School Lane, Donington, Spalding, Lincolnshire, PE11 4TF
Tel: 01775 820254
Contact: D Hale, Head of Hearing Impaired Unit
Tel: 01775 821231

➢ London
Education Services
Barnet Education Service
Town Hall, Friern Barnet Lane, London, N11 3DL
Tel: 020 8359 2000
Fax: 020 8359 3057
Contact: Valerie Standen, Sensory and Physical Support Service
Tel: 020 8359 3220
Contact: Michael Daubney, Chief Education Officer

Brent Education Service
P O Box 1, Chesterfield House, 9 Park Lane, Wembley, Middlesex, HA9 7RW
Tel: 020 8937 1234
Fax: 020 8830 4377
Contact: G Benham, Director of Education
Contact: Janet Gay, Special Needs Assessment and Pupils Service
Tel: 020 8937 3218

Camden Education Service
Crowndale Centre, 218-224 Eversholt Street, London, NW1 1BD
Tel: 020 7911 1525
Fax: 020 7911 1536
Contact: R Litchfield, Director of Education

Camden Learning Support Service
100 Stanhope Street, London, NW1 3JX
Tel: 020 7269 0975

Camden Peripatetic Service for Deaf/Hearing Impaired Children
c/o Frank Barnes School, Harley Road, London, NW3 3BN
Tel: 020 7722 1566
Contact: Jo Keyte, Advisory Teacher of the Deaf

City of London Education Service
P O Box 270, Guildhall, London, EC2P 2EJ
Tel: 020 7332 1750
Fax: 020 7332 1621
Contact: Stephen Denny, Assistant Education Officer for Special Needs

Local education authority for the City of London ('Square Mile').

Ealing Education Service
Perceval House, 14-16 Uxbridge Road, Ealing, London, W5 2HL
Tel: 020 8579 2424
Fax: 020 8566 2676
Contact: M Herman, Director Of Education

Greenwich Education Advisory Service for Deaf and Hearing Impaired Children and Students
Audiology Clinic, 32 Passey Place, Eltham, London, SE9 5DQ
Tel: 020 8850 6572
Contact: Carol Matthews, Coordinator

Greenwich Education Service
Riverside House, Woolwich High Street, Woolwich, London, SE18 6DF
Tel: 020 8854 8888
Fax: 020 8855 2427
Contact: J Kramer, Director of Education
Contact: Margaret Hart, Head of Special Needs

18

Hackney Education Service

Edith Cavell Building, Enfield Road, Hackney,
London, N1 5AZ

Tel: 020 7214 8400
Fax: 020 7214 8439
Contact: Linda Jordan, Head of Formal
            Assessment and Evaluation
Tel: 020 8356 7545
Contact: Penny Wiles, Peripatetic Service for
            Deaf/ Partially Hearing People
            New River Support Centre, Clissold
            Road, London, N16 9EX
Tel: 020 7249 9909

Hammersmith and Fulham Education Service

Cambridge House, Cambridge Grove, London, W6
0LE

Tel: 020 8576 5366
Fax: 020 8576 5501
Contact: Julia Johnston, Sensory and Language
            Impairment Team
            Gibbs Green School, Mund Street,
            North End Road, London, W14 9LY
Tel: 020 7610 3191
Fax: 020 7386 5163
Contact: Christine Whatford, Director of
            Education

Qualified and experienced teachers for pupils with
hearing impairment, visual impairment, or
language impairment who work with pre-school
children and their parents at home and with
pupils/students and their teachers in nursery,
primary and secondary schools.

Haringey Education Service

48 Station Road, Wood Green, London, N22 4TY
Tel: 020 8975 9700
Fax: 020 8862 3864
Contact: Jacky Tonge, Director of Education
            Services
            Weir Hall Road, London, N17 8LB
Tel: 020 8808 4191

Islington Education Authority

Laycock Street, Islington, London, N1 1TH
Tel: 020 7457 5874
Fax: 020 7457 5555
Contact: Andrew Roberts, Chief Education
            Officer
Contact: Jackie Blount, Head of Islington
            Learning Support Service
Tel: 020 7457 5711
Textphone: 020 7457 5711
Fax: 020 7457 5710

Advisory support to pupils with difficulties in
hearing, vision, language and communication,
multi-sensory impairment and specific learning
difficulties at school (5 to 16 years). Further
support is available for children under 5 with
sensory impairment and their families.

Kensington and Chelsea Education Service

Town Hall, Hornton Street, London, W8 7NX
Tel: 020 7937 5464
Fax: 020 7937 0038
Contact: D Dyer, Head of Service, Admission
            and Special Needs Education
            Department

Lambeth Education Service

234-244 Stockwell Road, London, SW19 9SP
Tel: 020 7926 1000
Fax: 020 7926 2633
Contact: J Simpson, Head of Service
            50 Acre Lane, London, SW2 5SD
Tel: 020 7926 2315
Contact: Heather Quesnay, Executive Director
            of Education
Tel: 020 7926 3013

Lambeth Service for Hearing Impaired Children

Braidwood Audiology Unit, 20 Elmcourt Road,
Tulse Hill, London, SE27 9BZ
Tel: 020 8670 8131
Contact: Sarah Pool, Teacher of the Deaf

Lewisham Education Service

Laurence House, 1 Catford Road, London, SE6 4SW
Tel: 020 8695 6000
Contact: A Efunshile, Director of Education

Newham Education Service

Broadway House, 322 High Street, London, E15 1AJ
Tel: 020 8555 5552
Fax: 020 8503 0014
Contact: Mary Clarke, Services for the Deaf and
            Partially Hearing Children
            New Tunmarsh Centre, Tunmarsh
            Lane, London, E13 9NB
Tel: 020 8557 6019
Textphone: 020 8557 6030
Fax: 020 8557 6031

Service for the deaf provides educational advice and support from diagnosis to 16 years in Newham mainstream schools. Service also runs a pre-school playgroup during term time. Service deaf instructor provides British Sign Language support to pre-school children in the home and at playgroup and to children and staff in Newham Schools. British Sign Language classes for personnel in education are run by the deaf instructors.

Southwark Education Service

1 Bradenham Close, Walworth, London, SE17 2QA
Tel: 020 7525 2674
Fax: 020 7525 2695
Contact: Gordon Mott, Director of Education

Southwark Support Service for the Hearing Impaired

2 Davey Street, London, SE15 6LH
Tel: 020 7701 1962
Contact: Monica Quinn, Head of Hearing
            Support Service

Tower Hamlets Education Service

Town Hall, Mulberry Place, 5 Clove Crescent, London E14 2BG
Tel: 020 7364 5000
Fax: 020 7364 6469
Contact: Mary Garside, Head of Service for
            Hearing Impaired People
            Special Educational Needs Centre, 85
            Harford Street, London, E1 4PY
Tel: 020 7364 6468

Education service for deaf and hearing impaired children. Two units for the hearing impaired, one nursery and primary and one secondary unit. Peripatetic service for pre-school and school-aged children in mainstream and junior schools, other than deaf, offering advice and support. Groups include English and singing classes for parents and families.

Waltham Forest Education Service

Municipal Offices, High Road, Leyton, London E10 5QJ
Tel: 020 8527 5544
Fax: 020 8556 8720
Contact: K Khan, Head of School Service
            Hawkswood School, Antlers Hill,
            Chingford, London, E4 7RT
Tel: 020 8529 2561

Hawkswood is a special school providing education and support to children with a wide range of hearing difficulties across many boroughs in the east London area. In addition, specialist teachers give advice and support to mainstream schools on children with hearing difficulties.

Wandsworth Education Service

Town Hall, Wandsworth High Street, London, SW18 2PU
Tel: 020 8871 7890
Contact: Paul Robinson, Director of Education

Westminster Education Service

P O Box 240, Westminster City Hall, 64 Victoria Street, London, SW1E 6QP
Tel: 020 7828 8087
Contact: D McGrath, Director of Education
Contact: Joy Gilson, Advisory Teacher for
            Hearing Impaired Children
            Essendine School, Essendine Road,
            London, W9 2LR
Tel: 020 7266 4225

Units
Blanche Nevile School and Service for Deaf and Hearing Impaired Children

1 Williams Grove, Wood Green, London, N22 5NR
Tel: 020 8352 2100
Fax: 020 8352 2101
Contact: Pete Makey, School and Service for
            the Hearing Impaired, Administrative
            Resource Centre

A school and service with departments based on the sites of three mainstream partnership schools offering a full range of support for deaf and hearing impaired pupils.

18

Culloden Primary School

Blair Street, London, E14 0NW

Tel: 020 7987 1020
Textphone: 020 7510 2231
Fax: 020 7538 2204
Contact: Karen Ingall, Coordinator for Deaf
           Children

Fortismere Secondary School

Tetherdown, Muswell Hill, London, N10 1NE

Tel: 020 8444 5124
Fax: 020 8444 9466
Contact: Mrs Lister, Teacher
Tel: 020 8374 3394

Gibbs Green School

Mund Street, North End Road, London, W14 9LY

Tel: 020 7610 3191
Fax: 020 7386 5163
Contact: Sarah Marshall, Team Leader, Sensory
         and Language Impairment Team

Grove House Primary School

Elmcourt Road, West Norwood, London, SE27 2DA

Tel: 020 8670 9429
Fax: 020 8655 7313
Contact: Pam Odlin, Head of Hearing Impaired
         Services

Haverstock School

Crogsland Road, Camden, London, NW1 8AS

Tel: 020 7267 0975
Fax: 020 7267 3807
E-mail: haverstock@rmplc.co.uk
Contact: Gill Gucklham, Teacher of the Deaf

Heathcote High School

Normanton Park, London, E4 6ES

Tel: 020 8529 5953
Fax: 020 8529 3935
Contact: Anne Shovelton, Teacher in Charge

Hendon School

Golders Rise, Hendon, London, NW4 2HP

Tel: 020 8202 9004
Fax: 020 8202 3341
Contact: Sally Pusgupta, Teacher of the Deaf

Highgate Primary School

North Hill, Highgate, London, N6 4AD

Tel: 020 8889 0171
Textphone: 020 8889 0171

James Wolfe Primary School

29 Randall Place, Greenwich, London, SE10 9LA

Tel: 020 8858 1882
Textphone: 020 8858 2472
Fax: 020 8305 2910
Contact: A Lockhart, Teacher of the Deaf

A unit for primary-aged children, 2 to 11 years, and severely or profoundly deaf. It is an integrating unit. Mode of communication: Total Communication. Unit rooms and some mainstream classrooms are acoustically treated. Children follow a curriculum which includes the National Curriculum.

Kingsbury Green Primary School

Old Kenton Lane, London, NW9 9ND

Tel: 020 8204 6423

The partial hearing unit caters for up to sixteen 4 to 11-year old deaf statemented children. Integration is determined according to the borough's criteria for levels of support. Mode of communication is according to the individual's need. The unit is well resourced and staffed, with good accommodation facilities.

Kingsbury High School

Princes Avenue, London, NW9 9JR

Tel: 020 8204 9814
Fax: 020 8206 0715

A unit with 24 places for hearing/visually impaired students. The students are fully integrated into the mainstream school with support. It uses English, sign-supported English and British Sign Language depending on the needs of the individual. There are seven full-time and five part-time staff as well as regular speech therapy.

Laycock Primary School

Laycock Street, Islington, London, N1 1SW

Tel: 020 7226 2927
Fax: 020 7704 2885
Contact: Sue Brownson, Teacher in Charge of
         Unit for Hearing Impaired Children

The unit caters for 50 children aged 3 to 11. It is attached to a mainstream primary school.

18

Lister Community School

St Mary's Road, London, E13 9AE
Tel: 020 8552 3839/ 8471 3311
Textphone: 020 8552 3839
Videotel: 020 8548 1043
Fax: 020 8472 1027
Contact: Jill Kirk, Teacher of the Deaf

Meridian Primary School

Meridian School, Old Woolwich Road, Greenwich, London, SE10 9NY
Tel: 020 8858 5574
Fax: 020 8858 5574

To educate deaf and hearing impaired primary aged children, in an integrated setting. To foster positive attitudes to hearing loss, by both hearing and deaf people.

New Kings Primary School

New Kings Road, Fulham, London, SW6 4LY
Tel: 020 7736 2414
Fax: 020 7371 0625
Contact: Pam Sandwell, Teacher of the Deaf

Rhodes Avenue Nursery and Primary School

Rhodes Avenue, Haringey, London, N22 4UT
Tel: 020 8889 2017
Textphone: 020 8889 2017
Contact: Pete Makey
            Blanche Nevile School, 1 Williams Grove, London, N22 5NR
Tel: 020 8352 2100

Rhodes Avenue Nursery and Primary are departments of Blanche Nevile School, which is a dispersed school on four sites. Rhodes Avenue is the Total Communication department.

Roding Primary School

Roding Lane North, Woodford Bridge, London, IG8 8NP
Tel: 020 8504 3706
Fax: 020 8506 1943
Contact: Zeta Saywell, Coordinator, In-school Provision

Roding is a 24-place unit. Children are integrated into mainstream classes. We are oral/aural, but are running a project of signed support in nursery and pre-school. We run the borough outreach service from the school.

Sedgehill School

Sedgehill Road, London, SE6 3QW
Tel: 020 8698 8911
Fax: 020 8461 4004
Contact: M Jefferson, Teacher of the Deaf

Hearing Impaired Unit attached to a mixed comprehensive. The pupils are integrated according to need and ability. The level of integration is flexible. All pupils have a statemnet and receive a radio aid for use in main school lessons. Teaching is also provided in the Hearing Impaired Unit.

Sellincourt Hearing Impaired Unit

Sellincourt Road, London, SW17 9SA
Tel: 020 8672 5982
Fax: 020 8672 6057

Sellincourt Hearing Impaired Unit caters for hearing impaired children aged 3 to 11 years. The communication method is aural/oral and qualified teachers of the deaf and/or specialist nursery nurses support the children in or out of mainstream classes.

Selwyn Primary School

Cecil Road, London, E13 0LX
Tel: 020 8471 6173
Fax: 020 8552 7609
E-mail: 1005927.mailbox@dialnet.co.uk
Contact: Ciaran Clerkin

Selwyn is the Newham resourced school for deaf pupils. Children are integrated into mainstream classes with teacher of the deaf, communicator and deaf instructor support.

Southfields Community Secondary School

333 Merton Road, Wandsworth, London, SW18 5JU
Tel: 020 8870 0171
Fax: 020 8874 9949
Contact: Elaine Elliot, Teacher of the Deaf

Southfields Hearing Impaired Unit (HIU) is a well established and integrated part of Southfields Community College. It caters for students with a range of hearing loss and offers an oral/aural approach to communication. The HIU provides students with a high level of specialist support in mainstream lessons, some small group teaching sessions in the HIU where appropriate, and access to a range of technology to facilitate access and develop literacy and communication skills.

St Johns and St Clements Primary School

Adys Road, Peckham, London, SE15 4DY

Tel:	020 7635 6999
Fax:	020 7635 6777

Provides primary education to some deaf/partially hearing children in mainstream and Partially Hearing Unit at primary school age.

St Paul's Way Community Secondary School

Shelmerdine Close, London, E3 4AN

Tel:	020 7987 1883
Fax:	020 7537 4529
Contact:	Bob Kingsley, Teacher of the Deaf

Secondary School Hearing Impaired Unit for pupils aged 11 to 16 years, with 20 to 24 pupils. Oral approach to learning, stressing independence for the individual while supporting them through GCSEs. Introduction to British Sign Language in Year 11 to broaden options for further education.

Summerside JMI School

Crossway, Finchley, London, N12 0QU

Tel:	020 8445 1192
Textphone:	020 8445 1192
Fax:	020 8445 5904
Contact:	Val Standen, Head of Hearing Impaired Services
Tel:	020 8359 2000

Woodside Community School

Woodside Road, London, E13 8RX

Tel:	020 7474 0121
Fax:	020 7511 4177
E-mail:	3164029.mailbox@dialnet.co.uk
Contact:	Valerie Dennis, Head of Inclusive Education

Woodside Community School is an inclusive secondary school with a resourced provision for 27 deaf and partially hearing students. The school is closing in July 1999. A new school, The Royal Docks Community School, opens in September 1999.

➢ Luton
See Bedfordshire

➢ Merseyside
Education Services
Knowsley Education Service

Education Office, Huyton Hey Road, Huyton, Merseyside, L36 5HY

Tel:	0151 433 3231
Contact:	H Ward, Head of Service for Hearing Impaired Children
	The Health Centre, Old Colliery Road, Whiston, Prescot, Merseyside, L35 3SX
Tel:	0151 430 6040
Contact:	P Wylie, Director of Education

Liverpool Education Service

14 Sir Thomas Street, Liverpool, Merseyside, L1 6BJ

Tel:	0151 227 3911
Fax:	0151 225 3029
Contact:	F Cogley, Director of Education
Contact:	Anton Florek, Head of Pupil Support Service

Sefton Education Service

Town Hall, Bootle, Merseyside, L20 7AE

Tel:	0151 933 6003
Contact:	G McGuinness, Head of Service Sensory and Special Educational Needs
	SENSS, Gores Lane, Formby, Merseyside, L37 3NY
Tel:	01704 879608
Fax:	0151 934 3185

SENSS (Special Educational Needs Support Service) is an assessment and teaching service for young people up to 19 years of age. It is a generic service covering learning difficulties, early years and pre-school, usual and hearing impairment services. It is staffed by advisory teachers and specialist support teachers.

St Helens Education Service

The Park Road Centre, Park Road, St. Helens, Merseyside, WA9 1HE

Tel:	01744 455321
Fax:	01744 455350
Contact:	J McGuffog, Head of Service for Hearing Impaired Children
Tel:	01744 617080

Audiological assessment of children's educational needs in schools and other establishments. Advice on educational placement for hearing impaired children. Teacher of the deaf support to hearing impaired children in mainstream. In-service training.

Wirral Education Service

Hamilton Building, Conway Street, Birkenhead, Merseyside, L41 4FD

Tel:	0151 666 2121
Fax:	0151 666 4207
Contact:	D Rigby, Director of Education
Contact:	C Peake, Head of Service

Units

Broadgreen Community Comprehensive School

Queens Drive, Liverpool, Merseyside, L13 5UQ

Tel:	0151 228 6800
Fax:	0151 220 9256
Contact:	S Stevens, Teacher of the Deaf

Ridgeway County High School

Noctorum Avenue, Birkenhead, Merseyside, L43 9EB

Tel:	0151 677 0013
Fax:	0151 678 6571
Contact:	Terri Burnet, Teacher of the Deaf
Tel:	0151 678 5641
Textphone:	0151 678 5641

Ridgeway Hearing Support Centre is a high-quality unit based in a mainstream secondary school. Deaf pupils may be supported in mainstream lessons or withdrawn for individual teaching by qualified and experienced teachers of the deaf. Pupils have access to on-site audiological services, speech therapy and up-to-date technology.

Rivington Primary School

Tennis Street North, St Helens, Merseyside, WA10 6TE

Tel:	01744 274904
Fax:	01744 615015
Contact:	Jenny Ashcroft, Hearing Impairment Unit

Townfield Primary School

Townfield Lane, Birkenhead, Merseyside, L43 2LH

Tel:	0151 652 8494
Textphone:	0151 652 8490

Woodlands County Junior School

Eddisbury Road, Whitby, South Wirral, Merseyside, L66 2JT

Tel:	0151 355 2857
Fax:	0151 355 1975
Contact:	Brian Gorman, Head Teacher

➤ Middlesbrough
See Cleveland

➤ Middlesex
Education Services
Barn Hill Care Training and Development Centre

Barnhill Lane, Hayes, Middlesex, UB4 9HD

Tel:	020 8842 1425
Fax:	020 8842 4411
Contact:	Clare Rule, Teacher in Charge, Hearing Impairment

The service provides support for sensory impaired children and young people (up to 18 years of age) from diagnosis throughout their placement in school. Specialist teachers in hearing or vision offer a range of support including a pre-school service and parent guidance; educational advice and assessment; curriculum support; information about and monitoring of equipment; professional training; liaison with health and other agencies and professionals.

Ealing Service for Sensory and Language Impairment

Room C20, Elthorne Education Centre, Westlea Road, Hanwell, Middlesex, W7 2AD

Tel:	020 8840 4050 ext 2153
Contact:	Ruth Macconville, Organisor of Sensory Impaired Service

Enfield Education Service

P O Box 56, Civic Centre, Enfield, Middlesex, EN1 3XQ

Tel:	020 8366 6565
Fax:	020 8982 7375
Contact:	Liz Graham, Director of Education

18

Harrow Education Service

P O Box 22, Civic Centre, Harrow, Middlesex, HA1 2UW

Tel: 020 8863 5611
Fax: 020 8427 0810
Contact: D Heath, Head of Service for Hearing Impaired Children

           Teacher's Centre, Tudor Road, Wealdstone, Harrow, Middlesex, HA3 5QD

Tel: 020 8424 3846/1
Contact: C Gilbert, Director of Education

Harrow Sensory and Communication Team (Hearing Impairment)

The Teachers Centre, Tudor Road, Wealdstone, Middlesex, HA3 5QD

Tel: 020 8424 3846
Contact: Doreen Natoff, Team Leader

Hillingdon Education Authority

Civic Centre, Uxbridge, Middlesex, UB8 1HA

Tel: 01895 50111
Contact: Graham Moss, Acting Group Director, Education Youth and Leisure Services

Hillingdon Sensory Impaired Service

Barn Hill Training and Development Centre, Barn Hill Lane, Hayes, Middlesex, UB4 9HD

Tel: 020 8842 1425
Contact: Clare Rule, Coordinator

Hounslow Education Services

Civic Centre, Lampton Road, Hounslow, Middlesex, TW3 4DN

Tel: 020 8570 7728
Fax: 020 8862 5249
Contact: J Trickett, Director of Education
Contact: Julia Driver, Head of Service

Richmond upon Thames Education Service

Regal House, London Road, Twickenham, Middlesex, TW1 3QB

Tel: 020 8891 7906
Fax: 020 8891 7714
E-mail: education@richmond.gov.uk
Website: www.richmond.gov.uk/education/
Contact: V McDonnell, Chief Education Officer
Tel: 020 8891 1411

Richmond upon Thames is a small, friendly education authority where close and collaborative relationships exist at all levels. Nursery education is provided at 1 nursery school and 16 nursery units. There are 39 primary schools and 8 comprehensive secondary schools (11 to 16 age range). There are also three special schools and six special units.

Richmond upon Thames Peripatetic Service for the Hearing Impaired

Curriculum and Teachers Centre, Clifden Road, Twickenham, Middlesex, TW1 4LT

Tel: 020 8891 4522
Contact: Cathy Routley, Advisory Teacher of the Deaf

The Teacher Centre

Tudor Road, Wealdstone, Harrow, Middlesex, HA3 5PQ

Tel: 020 8424 3846
Textphone: 020 8424 3846
Fax: 020 8427 2418
Contact: Doreen Natoff, Team Leader, Sensory and Communication Team (Hearing Impairment)

This team works with hearing impaired pupils from diagnosis to 19 years. Its aim is to ensure that they are fully included in school life. Teachers work in partnership with pupils, parents and colleagues in school. They provide INSET (in-service training) teaching support, sign language classes and a specialist toy library.

Units
Cedars First School Nursery

Whittlesea Road, Harrow Weald, Harrow, Middlesex

Tel: 020 8428 5825

Cedars Middle School

Whittlesea Road, Harrow Weald, Harrow, Middlesex

Tel: 020 8428 4525
Fax: 020 8420 1730
Contact: Mrs Jones, Teacher of the Deaf

Gifford Primary School

Greenhill Gardens, Northolt, Middlesex, UB5 6BU

Tel: 020 8845 4661

Gifford Primary School has a unit for deaf children attached. Pupils integrate into the mainstream according to their ability. Pupils are aged from 3 to 11 years. The unit meets the needs of children needing both oral and Total Communication approaches.

Glebe School
Sussex Road, Uxbridge, Middlesex, UB10 8PL
Tel: 01895 634169
Contact: Mrs Homer, Teacher of the Deaf

Hatch End High School
Headstone Lane, Harrow, Middlesex, HA3 6NR
Tel: 020 8428 4330
Fax: 020 8420 1932
Website: www.hatchend.harrow.sch.uk
Contact: Jennifer Webb, Deaf Resource Base

Heston Community School
Heston Road, Hounslow, Middlesex, TW5 0QR
Tel: 020 8572 1931/ 8577 1166
Fax: 020 8570 2647
This is a resource centre.

Norwood Green School (Infant/Junior)
Thorncliffe Road, Southall, Middlesex, UB2 5RN
Tel: 020 8574 6170 Infant
            020 8571 6082 Junior
Fax: 020 8571 6082
Contact: J Palmer, Head of Infant Centre
Tel: 020 8574 6170
Textphone: 020 8571 6082
Contact: Bernadette Molloy, Head of Junior
            Centre
Tel: 020 8571 6082
            020 8571 6082 Junior

Vyners School
Hearing Impaired Resource Base, Warren Road, Ickenham, Uxbridge, Middlesex, UB10 8AB
Tel: 01895 234342
Fax: 01895 237955
Contact: Paul Sewell, Teacher in charge
Hearing Impaired Unit, years 7 to 13. Oral/aural communication. Aim: 100 per cent integration into lessons. Number of places: 11. Accommodation: two-room unit base.

Walford High School
Bengarth Road, Northolt, Middlesex, UB5 5LH
Tel: 020 8845 4511

➢ Milton Keynes
See Bedfordshire

➢ Newbury
See Berkshire

➢ Norfolk
Education Services
County Sensory Support Service
c/o Heartsease High School, Marryat Road, Norwich, Norfolk, NR7 9DF
Tel: 01603 435709
Fax: 01603 432117
E-mail: ncsss@paston.co.uk.
Contact: D Pointon, Head of Service
Textphone: 01603 438677
Provides: hearing assessment, assessment of educational needs, advice on statutory assessment and on educational implications of sensory impairment, service training, support teaching up to 19 years of age, assistance with National Curriculum, SATS (Standard Assessment Tasks), GCSE/A-level and resources, support for parents, home visits, pre-school support, links with other agencies, multi-sensory impairment support.

Units
Clare School
South Park Avenue, Norwich, Norfolk, NR4 7AU
Tel: 01603 454199
Fax: 01603 250736
Contact: D Bowen, Centre Head

The Sensory Support Centre supports pupils within the school who are deaf, visually impaired or multi-sensory impaired.

Colman First School
Colman Road, Norwich, Norfolk, NR4 7AW
Tel: 01603 451010
Contact: Judith Nicholls, Teacher of the Deaf

18

Colman Middle School

South Park Avenue, Norwich, Norfolk, NR4 7AU

Tel: 01603 444201
Textphone: 01603 444209
Fax: 01603 444208
Contact: Yvonne Ball

This is a unit for deaf and partially hearing pupils, both signing and non-signing, aged between 8 and 12 years. Children are taught individually or in a small group by a teacher of the deaf and individual programmes of intergration into mainstream classes are planned and fully supported.

Thorpe St Andrew High School

Laundry Lane, Thorpe St Andrew, Norwich, Norfolk, NR7 0NB

Tel: 01603 497711
Fax: 01603 497712
E-mail: tfas@zetnet.co.uk
Contact: Carol Sowerby, Special Educational Needs Coordinator

➤ North East Lincolnshire
See Humberside

➤ North Humberside
Education Services
East Riding of Yorkshire Education Service

County Hall, Cross Street, Beverley, North Humberside, HU17 9BA

Tel: 01482 887700
Textphone: 01482 634794
Fax: 01482 884940
Contact: J Stallard, Head of Hearing Impaired Service

Lowfield Lane, Melton, North Ferriby, North Humberside, HU14 3HT

Tel: 01482 634738
Fax: 01482 634794

The Hearing Impaired Services serves the unitary authorities of Kingston upon Hull, East Riding of Yorkshire, North Lincolnshire and North East Lincolnshire. It has, over recent years, established a national reputation with its specialist staff, comprehensive support, both from teaching and non-teaching staff, as well as a professional administration service. The service works in close liaison with the four unitary health authorities, the careers service, social service, educational psychological service, schools for the deaf, hearing impaired adults and, most importantly, the parents of hearing impaired children. The

service headquarters, based in Melton, has a small toy library with toys and books available through a loan service to families with hearing impaired children. A range of information booklets and posters, covering all aspects of hearing impairment, is also available.

Humberside Service for the Hearing Impaired

Lowfield Lane, Melton, North Ferriby, North Humberside, HU14 3HT

Tel: 01482 634738
Textphone: 01482 634738
Fax: 01482 634794
Contact: Judith Fleming, Head of Service

Kingston upon Hull Education Services

Essex House, Manor Street, Kingston upon Hull, North Humberside, HU1 1YD

Tel: 01482 613161
Fax: 01482 613407
Contact: J Stallard, Head of Hearing Impaired Service

Lowfield Lane, Melton, North Ferriby, North Humberside, HU14 3HT

Tel: 01482 634738
Textphone: 01482 634794
Fax: 01482 634794

Details as for entry for East Riding of Yorkshire Education Service.

Units
Bethune Park Primary School

Pickering Road, Hull, North Humberside, HU4 7AD

Tel: 01482 505525
Textphone: 01482 505525
Contact: Helen Alphonus, Teacher of the Deaf

Kingston Secondary School

Pickering Road, Hull, North Humberside, HU4 7AD

Tel: 01482 644115
Textphone: 01482 644115

Tilbury Primary School

Tilbury Road, Hull, North Humberside, HU4 7EN

Tel: 01482 645174
Textphone: 01482 645174
Fax: 01482 640685
Contact: J Ibson, Teacher of the Deaf

The school provides a Total Communication approach to education for pupils aged 3 to 11 from the Old Humberside region. The school hosts adult classes in British Sign Language at all levels two evenings per week and one Saturday every month (Level III British Sign Language or equivalent).

Wansbeck Primary School
Wenning Grove, Hull, North Humberside, HU8 9SR
Tel: 01482 814172
Textphone: 01482 814172
Contact: Paul Leaver, Teacher of the Deaf

> North Lincolnshire
See Humberside

> North West Somerset
See Avon

> North Yorkshire
Education Services
North Yorkshire Education Service
County Hall, North Allerton, North Yorkshire, DL7 8AE
Tel: 01609 780780
Fax: 01609 778611
Contact: C Wellbourn, Director of Education
Contact: K Walker, Head of Service for Sensory Impaired

Units
Knavesmire County Primary School
Campleshon Road, York, YO23 1EY
Tel: 01904 652484
Fax: 01904 610287
Contact: L Costello, Teacher of the Deaf

Resource base for primary age hearing impaired pupils with statements. Part of York City Council Learning Support Services (Hearing Impairment). Staff have signing skills, but at present time an oral mode of communication is used with most pupils.

Le Cateau County Primary School
Le Cateau Road, Catterick Garrison, North Yorkshire, DL9 4ED
Tel: 01748 832292
Fax: 01748 836414
Contact: C Roberts, Teacher of the Deaf

Newby County Primary School
The Green, Highfield Estate, Scarborough, North Yorkshire, YO12 5JA
Tel: 01723 501279
Contact: A Smuk, Teacher of the Deaf, Hearing Impaired Unit

Aims: to give hearing impaired children full access to the National Curriculum; to support hearing impaired children in the mainstream classroom; to give them access to sound-proofed listening conditions with one-to-one and small groups input according to their individual needs; to ensure daily maintenance of the children's hearing aid equipment.

Scalby Secondary School
Fieldstead Crescent, Scarborough, North Yorkshire, YO12 6TH
Tel: 01723 362301
Fax: 01723 369226
Contact: L Coombes, Head of Hearing Impaired Unit

> Northamptonshire
Education Services
Northamptonshire Education Service
P O Box 149, County Hall, Guildford Road, Northampton, NN1 1AU
Tel: 01604 236250
Contact: D Lucas, Principal Educational Psychologist and Head of STEPS

STEPS (Support, Teaching and Educational Psychology Service) is the core service through which Northamptonshire meets its responsibilities towards children and young people with special educational needs. The service to pupils, parents and schools is delivered by educational psychologists and teachers with a wide range of specialist qualifications and experience.

18

Units

Avondale Infants School
Laburnum Crescent, Kettering, Northamptonshire, NN16 9PH
Tel: 01536 512040
Contact: Inga Walters, Teacher of the Deaf/ Teacher in Charge

Designated Special Provision (DSP) for children with hearing impairment. Children will have, or be in the process of having, a statement of Special Educational Need. The DSP offers a fully qualified teacher of the deaf and NNOB (nursery nurse) to support children using oral/aural communication. The DSP has excellent acoustic conditions and facilities for children with a hearing impairment.

Avondale Junior School
Laburnum Crescent, Kettering, Northamptonshire, NN16 9PH
Tel: 01536 316860
Contact: C Jervis, Head Master

Latimer School
Castle Way, Barton Seagrave, Northamptonshire, NN15 6SW
Tel: 01536 724219
Fax: 01536 725016
Contact: C Grimshaw, Head

Moulton County Primary School
Church Hill, Moulton, Northampton, NN3 7SW
Tel: 01604 643061
Fax: 01604 642328
Contact: Jenny O'Hey, Teacher of the Deaf

Northampton Middle School, St George's Campus
Barrack Road, Northampton, NN1 3RF
Tel: 01604 638855
Contact: J Evers, Teacher of the Deaf

We have Designated Special Provisions for hearing impaired children who communicate orally, aged 9 to 13 years. The provision includes a specially sound proof unit and resourced hearing impaired children's language needs. There is a full-time teacher of the deaf and three learning support staff.

Trinity Upper School
Trinity Avenue, Northampton, NN2 6JW
Tel: 01604 713621
Fax: 01604 792761
Contact: M Hart, Head of Unit

Hearing Impairment Unit on site.

Vernon Terrace Lower School
Vernon Terrace, Northampton, NN1 5HE
Tel: 01604 33894
Contact: M Starkey, Teacher of the Deaf

Severe and profoundly deaf pupils are included in mainstream classes throughout the school and supported through a Designated Special Provision with teachers of the deaf and nursery nurses.

Weston Favell Upper School
Booth Lane South, Northampton, NN3 3EZ
Tel: 01604 402121
Fax: 01604 410879
E-mail: wfus@western.rmplc.co.uk
Contact: J Howard, Head Teacher

➢ Northumberland
Education Services

Northumberland Education Services
County Hall, Morpeth, Northumberland, NE61 2EF
Tel: 01670 534314
Fax: 01670 533511
Contact: P Loftus, Head of Service, Education Development Centre
             Till House, Hepscott Park, Stannington, Morpeth, Northumberland, NE61 6NF

The educational support service for hearing impaired children across the county. It involves peripatetic and resource base provision utilising an auditory/oral approach.

Units

Belford County First School
West Street, Belford, Northumberland, NE70 7QD
Tel: 01668 213361
Contact: M Henry, Teacher of the Deaf

Belford Middle School
Williams Way, Belford, Northumberland, NE70 7NX
Tel: 01668 213361

Blyth Horton Grange County First School

Cowpen Road, Blyth, Northumberland, NE24 4RE
Tel: 01670 534350
Contact: P Loftus, Teacher of the Deaf

Cramlington County High School

Highburn, Cramlington, Northumberland, NE23 6BN
Tel: 01670 712311
Textphone: 01670 715011
Fax: 01670 730598

Hearing impaired support base using auditory/oral philosophy. Students are integrated into mainstream with support according to their individual needs. To allow them to maximise their potential they receive one-to-one in the support base to develop language and literacy skills.

Southlands County Middle School

Westloch Road, Southfield Lea, Cramlington, Northumberland, NE23 6LM
Tel: 01670 714475
Contact: Mrs Bohill, Teacher of the Deaf

➤ Nottinghamshire

Education Services

Nottinghamshire Education Service

County Hall, West Bridgford, Nottingham, NG2 7QP
Tel: 0115 982 3823
Textphone: 0115 977 3323
Fax: 0115 981 2824
Contact: R Skelton, Head of Sensory Support Service

            Glenbrook Management Centre, Wigman Road, Bilborough, Nottingham, NG8 4PD
Tel: 0115 929 9433
Fax: 0115 929 9767

The service aims to provide high-quality, effective and flexible support that enables the fullest possible social inclusion and individual development of deaf and visually impaired children in Nottinghamshire.

Units

Aldercar Infant School

Godkin Drive, Langley Mill, Nottinghamshire, NG16 4GL
Tel: 01773 713428
Fax: 01779 713428
Contact: Michelle Nichols, Teacher of the Deaf

Mainstream infant and nursery school with special teaching facility for the hearing impaired children.

Annie Holgate Infant and Junior School

High Leys Road, Hucknall, Nottingham, NG15 6EZ
Tel: 0115 963 2096 Infants
            0115 963 3880 Junior
Fax: 0115 956 8284
Contact: Lynne Evans, Individual Needs Centre

A primary day school using the oral/ bilingual method of communication.

Firbeck Primary School

Firbeck Road, Nottingham, NG8 2FB
Tel: 0115 928 3312
Textphone: 0115 985 4933
Fax: 0115 928 3312
Contact: Jean Redgate, Teacher of the Deaf, Individual Needs Centre

Langley Mill Junior School

Bailey Brook Cresent, Langley Mill, Nottinghamshire, NG16 4FZ
Tel: 01773 712694
Textphone: 01773 712694
Contact: J Thomas, Head Teacher

Portland Comprehensive School

Sparken Hill, Worksop, Nottinghamshire, S80 1AW
Tel: 01909 473656
Fax: 01909 530097
Contact: John Middleton, Teacher of the Deaf

St Augustine's Infant and Junior School

Longfellow Drive, Worksop, Nottinghamshire, S81 0DW
Tel: 01909 473473 Infants
            01909 473955 Juniors
Fax: 01909 530483
Contact: Elspeth Brien, Teacher of the Deaf, Individual Needs Centre
Tel: 01909 473473

The Individual Needs Centre serves the infant and junior schools (ages 3 to 11 years). It supports a

18

bilingual policy, and children integrate fully with support into the hearing classes. Staff with specialist qualifications work with the deaf children, enabling them to access the full curriculum.

William Sharp Comprehensive School

Bramhall Road, Nottingham, NG8 4HY
Tel: 0115 929 1492
Textphone: 0115 928 0786
Fax: 0115 942 5730
Contact: W Dickson, Teacher of the Deaf

Offers full access to National Curriculum plus lifeskills programme to achieve independence. Organised to offer supported integration in non-academic subjects. Small group teaching by specialist teachers of the deaf. Tutorial support.

➤ Oxfordshire
Education Services
Oxfordshire Education Service

Macclesfield House, New Road, Oxford, OX1 1NA
Tel: 01865 792422
Fax: 01865 791637
Contact: Graham Badman, Chief Education Officer
Contact: E Moore, Head of Service for Sensory Impairment
John Watson Resource Centre, Holton Park, Wheatley, Oxfordshire, OX33 1QJ
Tel: 01865 875165
Fax: 01865 875163

Southern Resource Base

Hendred Way, Abingdon, Oxfordshire, OX14 2AW
Tel: 01235 531070
Support service for hearing impaired students and children. Supporting from diagnosis into homes, nurseries, primary schools and secondary schools. A support service of teachers encouraging inclusion within a natural aural approach for the education of hearing impaired children.

Units
New Marston First School

Copse Lane, Oxford, OX3 0AY
Tel: 01865 761560
Fax: 01865 742944
Contact: J Kent, Head Teacher

Queensway County Primary School

Queensway, Banbury, Oxfordshire, OX16 9NE
Tel: 01295 251631
Fax: 01295 251550
Contact: Joy Willoughby, Head Teacher
Tel: 01295 275926

➤ Peterborough
See Cambridgeshire

➤ Plymouth
See Devon

➤ Poole
See Dorset

➤ Portsmouth
See Hampshire

➤ Reading
See Berkshire

➤ Redcar and Cleveland
See Cleveland

➤ Rutland
See Leicestershire

➤ Shropshire
Education Services
Shropshire Education Service

Shirehall Abbey, Foregate, Shrewbury, Shropshire, SY2 6ND
Tel: 01743 251000
Contact: C Adams, County Education Officer
Contact: Margaret Eatough, Educational Services for Hearing Impaired Children
Owen House, Radbrook Road, Shrewsbury, Shropshire, SY3 9BL
Tel: 01743 246997
Textphone: 01743 246997
Fax: 01743 255786

Telford and Wrekin Council, Education and Training
Owen House, Radbrook Centre, Shrewsbury, Shropshire, SY3 9BL
Tel: 01743 246997
Contact: Andrew Broughton, Team Leader, Educational Services for Hearing Impaired Children

➢ Slough
See Berkshire

➢ Somerset
Education Services
Hearing Support Service, Somerset
The Holway Centre, Keats Road, Taunton, Somerset, TA1 2JB
Tel: 01823 334475
Fax: 01823 323656
Contact: Anne Jackson, Acting Head of Hearing Support Service

Units
Bishop Fox's Community School
Bishop Fox Drive, Taunton, Somerset, TA1 3HQ
Tel: 01823 289211
Fax: 01823 334582
Bishop Fox is a secondary school for pupils aged 11 to 16.

Grass Royal Junior School
St Michael's Avenue, Yeovil, Somerset, BA21 4JW
Tel: 01935 423863
Fax: 01935 427099
Contact: Mrs Hurley, Teacher of the Deaf

Hugh Sexey Middle School
Sexeys Road, Blackford, Wedmore, Somerset, BS28 4ND
Tel: 01934 712211
Fax: 01934 712998
E-mail: h.s.blackford@argonet.co.uk
Contact: D Cameron, Head Teacher

Kings of Wessex Community School
Station Road, Cheddar, Somerset, BS27 3AQ
Tel: 01934 742608
Fax: 01934 742757

Ladymead Secondary School
Cheddar Road, Taunton, Somerset, TA2 7QP
Tel: 01823 331243
Fax: 01823 321450
Contact: Mrs Rolfe, Special Educational Needs

Oakfield Middle School
Oakfield Road, Frome, Somerset, BA11 4JF
Tel: 01373 462539
Fax: 01373 543370
Contact: Philip Hill, Head Teacher

Oakfield Middle School has a resource base for hearing impaired pupils. The children are integrated fully with their peers, supported where necessary, depending on their needs, and have some individual and small work sessions.

Pen Mill Infants School
St Michael's Avenue, Yeovil, Somerset, BA21 4LD
Tel: 01935 474224
Fax: 01935 414794
Contact: K Wollard, Teacher of the Deaf

Pen Mill also has a day nursery and has a mixed communication policy consisting of Total Communication, oralism and sign.

Trinity First School
Nunney Road, Frome, Somerset, BA11 4LB
Tel: 01373 461949
Contact: R Stillwell, Teacher of the Deaf

Trinity First is a primary day school using a natural aural method of communication.

Trinity Primary School
South Street, Taunton, Somerset, TA1 3AF
Tel: 01823 284128
Fax: 01823 334228
Contact: C Stephens, Teacher of the Deaf, Hearing Impaired Unit

Weare VC First School
Weare, Axbridge, Somerset, BS26 2JS
Tel: 01934 732270
Fax: 01934 732560
E-mail: dw@weare99.freeserve.co.uk
Contact: Helen Jackson, Teacher of the Deaf

18

See Avon

➤ South Humberside
Education Services
North East Lincolnshire Education Service
Eleanor Street, Grimsby, South Humberside, DN32 9DU
Tel: 01472 313131
Fax: 01472 323020
Contact: J Stallard, Head of Hearing Impaired Service

Lowfield Lane, Melton, North Ferriby, North Humberside, HU14 3HT
Tel: 01482 634738
Textphone: 01482 634794
Fax: 01482 634794

Details as for entry for East Riding of Yorkshire Education Service.

North Lincolnshire Directorate of Education and Personal Development
Hewson House, Station Road, Brigg, North Lincolnshire, DN20 8XJ
Tel: 01724 297010
Fax: 01724 297243
Contact: J Stallard, Head of Hearing Impaired Service

Lowfield Lane, Melton, North Ferriby, North Humberside, HU14 3HT
Tel: 01482 634738
Textphone: 01482 634794
Fax: 01482 634794

Details as for entry for East Riding of Yorkshire Education Service.

Units
Old Clee Primary School
Colin Avenue, Grimsby, South Humberside, DN32 8EN
Tel: 01472 697692
Textphone: 01472 697692
Contact: Linda Percival, Teacher of the Deaf

Westcliffe Primary School
Dryden Road, Scunthorpe, South Humberside, DN17 1PN
Tel: 01724 282243
Textphone: 01724 282243

A unit attached to a primary school, using an oral/aural approach. Accepts children from the north Lincolnshire area aged 3 to 11 years.

320

➤ South Yorkshire
Education Services
Barnsley Education Service
Berneslai Close, Barnsley, South Yorkshire, S70 2HL
Tel: 01226 770770
Fax: 01226 773599
Contact: John Gaskin, Head of Education

Shaw Lane, Barnsley, South Yorkshire, S70 6HY
Tel: 01226 733252
Contact: Ann Munro, Head of Service for Sensory Impairment, Special Educational Needs Support

Kirk Balk, Hoyland, Barnsley, South Yorkshire, S74 9HT
Tel: 01266 770770

Doncaster Education Services
PO Box 266, The Council House, College Road, Doncaster, South Yorkshire, DN1 3AD
Tel: 01302 737222
Fax: 01302 737223
Contact: A Taylor, Director of Education
Contact: D Houldsworth, Head of Teaching Support Service

Wilby Carr Middle School, Aldesworth Road, Doncaster, South Yorkshire, DN4 6LD
Tel: 01302 533444
Fax: 01302 530355

Rotherham Education Service
Norfolk House, Walker Place, Rotherham, South Yorkshire, S60 1QT
Tel: 01709 382121
Contact: Janetta Moore, Head of Service for Hearing Impaired Children

The Manor House, Church Street, Kimberworth, Rotherham, South Yorkshire, S61 1EP
Tel: 01709 561712

This local education authority-funded support service provides specialist staff and equipment in order to support children for whom there are educational implications due to hearing impairment. The service offers advice and support to parents and teachers, specialist teaching, assistance with technical aids, INSET (in-service training), liaison and formal assessments.

Sheffield Education Service

P O Box 67, Leopold Street, Sheffield, South Yorkshire, S1 1RJ

Tel: 0114 272 6341

Contact: H Bower, Director of Education

Tel: 0114 273 5726

Fax: 0114 273 6279

Contact: R Flowerday, Head of Service for Sensory Impaired Children

Hazlebarrow School, Hazlebarrow Crescent, Sheffield, South Yorkshire, S8 8AQ

Tel: 0114 237 4865

Fax: 0114 273 6279

This is a service covering the whole local education authority. Any child in either a unit school or mainstream school can be supported by qualified teachers of the deaf. There is also a service for pre-school children and close contact with both the Sheffield Health Authority and social services.

Units

Bramley Grange Junior and Infant School

Howard Road, Bramley, Rotherham, South Yorkshire, S66 0SY

Tel: 01709 543664

Contact: C Chettleburgh, Teacher of the Deaf

Tel: 01709 701746

This local education authority-funded provision supports pupils from 5 to 11 years to enable them to benefit fully from a mainstream primary curriculum. Specialist staff provide support throughout the school.

East Hill Primary and Secondary School

East Bank Road, Sheffield, South Yorkshire, S2 3PX

Tel: 0114 276 0245

Fax: 0114 272 8829

Visitor comes in to fix hearing aids. Ring for details.

Ecclesfield Comprehensive School

Barnsley Road, Sheffield, South Yorkshire, S35 9WD

Tel: 0114 246 1156

Fax: 0114 257 0998

Contact: Joe Tang, Teacher of the Deaf

Unit for hearing impaired children.

Greystones Primary School (Unit for Hearing Impaired Children)

Tullibardine Road, Sheffield, South Yorkshire, S11 7GL

Tel: 0114 266 3413

Fax: 0114 268 6235

An oral/aural unit that supports hearing impaired children as they integrate into the mainstream setting. Children's integration and support levels are planned according to individual need.

Hazlebarrow Primary School

Hazlebarrow Crescent, Sheffield, South Yorkshire, S8 8AQ

Tel: 0114 237 5778

Textphone: 0114 237 4865

Fax: 0114 237 4865

Contact: K Whyte, Unit Coordinator

This unit is for primary and nursery children from 3 to 11 years of age. All children use signing as a major means of communication. There is also a small group for deafblind children as part of this provision, which takes children from across the whole local education authority.

High Storrs Comprehensive School

Ringinglow Road, Sheffield, South Yorkshire, S11 7LH

Tel: 0114 267 0000

Fax: 0114 266 3624

Contact: Jenny Baxton, Coordinator, Integrated Resource for Hearing Impaired Unit

Ravenfield Primary School

Moor Lane North, Ravenfield, Rotherham, South Yorkshire, S65 4LZ

Tel: 01709 542678

This local education authority-funded provision supports pupils from 5 to 11 years to benefit from a mainstream primary curriculum. Specialist staff provide communication and learning support throughout the school as appropriate to each child

Scawsby and Ridgewood Comprehensive School

Barnsley Road, Doncaster, South Yorkshire, DN5 7UB

Tel: 01302 783939

Fax: 01302 390448

E-mail: ridgewd_j.sharpe@hotmail.com

Contact: J Sharpe, Head Teacher

18

Silverdale Comprehensive School

Bents Crescent, Sheffield, South Yorkshire, S11 9RT

Tel: 0114 236 9991

Unit for the deaf attached to a mainstream comprehensive school. Caters for profoundly deaf pupils in the 11 to 16 age range who need signing for communication. Integration with support, as appropriate for each individual. Other lessons delivered in the unit by qualified staff.

Talbot Secondary School

Norfolk Park Road, Sheffield, South Yorkshire, S2 3QE

Tel: 0114 250 7394
Fax: 0114 250 7857
Contact: Anne Sanderson, Teacher of the Deaf

Wickersley Comprehensive School

Bawtry Road, Wickersley, Rotherham, South Yorkshire, S66 0JL

Tel: 01709 542147

Support is provided for students aged 11 to 18 years. Each student follows a programme designed to meet their individual needs with a combination of in-class support and additional lessons taught by specialist staff.

Woolley Wood Primary School

Oaks Fold Road, Sheffield, South Yorkshire, S5 0TG

Tel: 0114 245 6885
Fax: 0114 257 0269
Contact: Marion Holley, Head Teacher

➤ Southampton
See Hampshire

➤ Southend
See Essex

➤ Staffordshire
Education Services

Staffordshire Education Authority

Education Offices, Tipping Street, Staffordshire, ST16 2DH

Tel: 01785 223121
Fax: 01785 278639
Contact: Malcolm Garner, Head of Services for Hearing Impaired
                Flash Ley Resource Centre, Hawksmoor Road, Stafford, ST17 9DR
Tel: 01785 356830
Textphone: 01785 356830
Fax: 01785 222086

The service for hearing impaired provides advice, guidance, assessment and practical, support for pupils and students with all levels of deafness and their families. This covers the whole age range from diagnosis through schooling and post-16 education and training. All staff are additionally qualified in this specialist area.

Stoke-on-Trent Education Service

Swan House, Boothen Road, Stoke-On-Trent, Staffordshire, ST4 4SY

Tel: 01782 234567
Fax: 01782 235996

Stoke-on-Trent Special Education Needs Support Service

Willfield Centre, Lauder Place North, Bentilee, Stoke-On-Trent, Staffordshire, ST2 0QL

Tel: 01782 598226
Fax: 01782 596470

Units
Sandford Hill Primary School and Hearing Impaired Unit
Clayfield Grove, Stoke-on-Trent, Staffordshire, ST3 5AQ

Tel: 01782 316340
Textphone: 01782 316340
Fax: 01782 316340
Contact: Andy Chapman, Teacher of the Deaf, Resource Coordinator
Textphone: 01782 595743

The unit offers opportunities for mainstream integration and aims to provide a comprehensive choice of support approaches, tailored to the preferred communication modes of individual pupils and/or their parents. A fundamental goal is to maximise pupils language development, communication and listening skills, whilst ensuring effective delivery of the National Curriculum.

Stoneydelph Infant School
Crowden Road, Tamworth, Staffordshire, B77 4LS

Tel: 01827 895836
Contact: V Massey, Teacher in Charge

To promote integration and equal access to the National Curriculum through support in mainstream and reinforcement in the unit. To improve communication skills through signing, lipreading and speech. To meet the needs of each individual and enable them to reach full potential.

Stoneydelph Junior School
Crowden Road, Tamworth, Staffordshire, B77 4LS

Tel: 01827 896666
Contact: J Ashford, Teacher in Charge, Hearing Impaired Unit

A junior day unit for the hearing impaired, attached to a mainstream junior school. The Hearing Impaired Unit uses Total Communication.

Thistley Hough High School
Newcastle Lane, Penkhull, Stoke-on-Trent, Staffordshire, ST4 5JJ

Tel: 01782 233733
Textphone: 01782 233733
Fax: 01782 233734
Contact: M Hawkins, Teacher of the Deaf

Torc High School
Silverlink Road, Tamworth, Staffordshire, B77 2HJ

Tel: 01827 286305

➢ Stockton-on-Tees
See Cleveland

➢ Stoke-on-Trent
See Staffordshire

➢ Suffolk
Education Services
Bury St Edmunds Service for Hearing Impaired Children
Shire Hall, Bury St Edmunds, Suffolk, IP33 1RX

Tel: 01284 722156
Fax: 01284 722106

Aims: to support children up to 5 years who have a hearing impairment, at home and in pre-school provision if appropriate; to support and monitor pupils who attend local schools; to support and monitor hearing impaired pupils with special schools; to liaise and work closely with health and social services.

Suffolk Education Service
County Hall, Grimwade Street, Ipswich, Suffolk, IP4 1LJ

Tel: 01473 230000
Contact: D Peachey, Chief Education Officer
Contact: Meenal Manning, Advisory Teacher of the Deaf
                Hearing Impaired Support Service Southern Area
                County Hall, Grimwade Street, Ipswich, Suffolk, IP4 3EJ
Tel: 01473 584791

Units
County Upper School
Beetons Way, Bury St Edmunds, Suffolk, IP32 6RF

Tel: 01284 754857
Fax: 01284 767313
Website: www.RMPLC.co.uk/eduweb/sites/cusb se/index.html
Contact: Jenkins, Teacher of the Deaf

18

Elm Tree Primary School

Ranworth Avenue, Lowestoft, Suffolk, NR33 9HN
Tel: 01502 562930
Fax: 01502 515769
Contact: Claire McNamara, Teacher of the Deaf

Kirkley High School

Kirkley Run, Lowestoft, Suffolk, NR33 0UQ
Tel: 01502 566321

A secondary day school using the oral method of communication.

Westbourne High School, Hearing Impaired Unit

Marlow Road, Ipswich, Suffolk, IP1 5JN
Tel: 01473 742315
Fax: 01473 464825
Contact: Sarah Norman, Teacher of the Deaf

Westbourne High School is a mixed 11 to 18 years comprehensive high school, part of Suffolk Education Authority. The Hearing Impaired Unit serves South Suffolk. It aims to provide any form of communication support needed, which currently includes British Sign Language, sign-supported English and oral support.

Westgate Primary School

Hospital Road, Bury St Edmunds, Suffolk, IP33 3JX
Tel: 01284 755988
Fax: 01284 704857
E-mail: westgateschool@compuserve.com
Contact: S Brierton, Teacher of the Deaf

Westley Middle School

Oliver Road, Bury St Edmunds, Suffolk, IP33 3JB
Tel: 01284 755144
Fax: 01284 703619
Contact: Karen Ludlow, Teacher of the Deaf

➤ Surrey

Education Services

Croydon Communication Support Service

Tel: 020 8683 4849/ 0554
Fax: 020 8683 4922
Contact: Jennifer Kidd, Head of Communication
            Support Services

See entry under Communication Services.

Croydon Education Service

Taberner House, Park Lane, Croydon, Surrey, CR9 1TP
Tel: 020 8686 4433
Fax: 020 8760 5447
Contact: Jennifer Kidd, Head of Communication
            Support Service
            Selhurst High School, The Crescent,
            Croydon, Surrey, CR0 2HN
Tel: 020 8686 4849
Contact: David Sands, Director of Education

Kingston Service for Hearing Impaired Children

North Kingston Centre, Audiology Unit, Richmond Road, Kingston, Surrey, KT2 5PN
Tel: 020 8547 6746
Contact: Lucy Cowdery, Head of Learning
            Support Services

Kingston Upon Thames Education Service

Guildhall 2, Kingston-upon-Thames, Surrey, KT1 1EU
Tel: 020 8546 2121
Fax: 020 8547 5296
Contact: D C Da Silva, Acting Head of Learning
            and Literacy
Tel: 020 8546 3389

The Learning and Literacy Support Service provides teacher support for children aged 2 to 16 plus years with special education needs at stages 3 to 5 CoP. There are three teachers for the hearing impaired within the sensory impairment team.

Merton Education Service

Civic Centre, London Road, Morden, Surrey, SM4 5DX
Tel: 020 8543 2222
Fax: 020 8545 3443
Contact: J Cairns, Director of Education

Surrey Education Service

County Hall, Kingston-upon-Thames, Surrey, KT1 2DJ

Tel: 020 8770 5000
Contact: Paul Grey, Chief Education Officer
Contact: Pauline Hughes, Coordinator for Hearing Impaired Services
             The Lodge, Glyn House, Church Street, Ewell, Surrey, KT17 2AP
Tel: 020 8393 2872
Textphone: 020 8393 2872
Fax: 020 8786 8045
Contact: Liz Barton, Further Education Coordinator
             The Lodge, Glyn House, Church Street, Ewell, Epsom, Surrey, KT17 2AR
Tel: 020 8393 2872
Textphone: 020 8393 2872

Sutton Education Services

The Grove, Carshalton Beaches, Surrey, SM5 3AL
Tel: 020 8770 6568
Contact: Helen Joseph, Coordinator of Hearing Impaired Service
             Abbey Primary School, Glastonbury Road, Morden, Surrey, SM4 6NZ
Tel: 020 8770 6741

Educational support services for hearing impaired. Two units in the borough; one primary and one secondary; both with loop systems. Total Communication - integrated set.

The Davidson Professional Centre

Davidson Road, Croydon, Surrey, CR0 6DD
Tel: 020 8655 3736
Fax: 020 8655 3418

Units

Abbey Primary School

Abbey Primary School, Glastonbury Road, Morden, Surrey, SM4 6NZ
Tel: 020 8770 6741
Fax: 020 8770 6743

Auriol County Junior School

Vale Road, Stoneleigh, Ewell, Surrey, KT19 0PJ
Tel: 020 8393 4721
Fax: 020 8786 8193

Auriol Junior School is a mixed school of approximately 400 pupils. An oral hearing-impaired unit is attached to the school. All the hearing impaired pupils are fully included into the mainstream with support from teachers of the deaf or learning support assistants.

Bishop David Brown School

Albert Drive, Sheerwater, Woking, Surrey, GU21 4RF
Tel: 01932 350191
Textphone: 01932 350191
Fax: 01932 349175
Contact: G Clegg, Teacher of the Deaf

We aim to enable each hearing impaired pupil to maximise their potential educationally, socially, and personally by providing a high-quality learning environment using a natural aural approach and specialist resources within an integrated mainstream setting.

Broadmere County Primary School

Devonshire Avenue, Sheerwater, Woking, Surrey, GU21 5QE
Tel: 01932 343747
Contact: G Brown, Teacher of the Deaf

Epsom and Ewell High School

Ruxley Lane, West Ewell, Surrey, KT19 9JW
Tel: 020 8397 0671
Fax: 020 8397 0724
E-mail: mlane@eehs.surrey.sch.uk
Contact: M Lane, Teacher of the Deaf

Hollyfield Secondary School

Surbiton Hill Road, Surbiton, Surrey, KT6 4TS
Tel: 020 8547 6800

Kingsley Schools

Primary Hearing Centre, Chapman Road, Croydon, Surrey, CR0 3NX
Tel: 020 8689 9038
Textphone: 020 8689 9038
Fax: 020 8689 9038
Contact: Cindy Paulding, Teacher in Charge

A Hearing Impaired Unit for primary age children 4 to 11, using sign-supported English and integrated into a mainstream school for some of each day, depending on need.

18

Knollmead Primary School

Knollmead, Tolworth, Surbiton, Surrey, KT5 9QP
Tel: 020 8337 3778
Textphone: 020 8337 3778
Fax: 020 8337 4650
Contact: Alex Rogers, Teacher of the Deaf

Knollmead is a mainstream primary school with an integrated Hearing Impaired Unit (HIU). The HIU has three experienced staff and can accommodate up to ten children. Its aim is to provide appropriate support to ensure that all its pupils have access to the curriculum and realise their full potential.

Overton Grange School

36 Stanley Road, Sutton, Surrey, SM2 6TQ
Tel: 020 8239 2383/ 6
Textphone: 020 8239 2386
Fax: 020 8239 2382
Contact: Karen Williams, Head of Hearing
            Support Department
Tel: 020 8239 2386

A secondary comprehensive school with a hearing support department catering for students with a statement for hearing impairment. The department uses a child-centred approach to Total Communication and students are integrated with support, for at least 50 per cent of the main school timetable.

Rushey Meadow Primary School

Rushey Meadow Lane, Fellowes Road, Carshalton, Surrey, SM5 2SG
Tel: 020 8669 7588
Fax: 020 8669 4335
Contact: J Davidson, Head Teacher

Rushey Meadow is a primary day school with nursery using the Total Communication method.

Shirley High School

Shirley Church Road, Croydon, Surrey, CR0 5EF
Tel: 020 8656 2987

This is a secondary resource base.

The Mead County First School

Newbury Gardens, Ewell, Surrey, KT19 0QG
Tel: 020 8786 7422
Contact: Pat Clasby, Head of Unit

The Mead Hearing Impaired Unit has 18 places for children with statements of special education needs for moderate to profound hearing losses. The teachers of the deaf use the oral/aural

approach to the acquisition of language. It welcomes children who have additional disabilities and it celebrates their abilities and achievements.

➢ Thamesdown
See Wiltshire

➢ Thurrock
See Essex

➢ Torbay
See Devon

➢ Tyne and Wear
Education Services
Dryden Professional Development Centre

Liaison Teacher Hearing Impaired, Evistones Road, Gateshead, Tyne and Wear, NE9 5UA
Tel: 0191 482 4133 ext 188

Gateshead Education Service

Civic Centre, Gateshead, Tyne and Wear, NE8 1HH
Tel: 0191 477 1011
Contact: J Arbon, Director of Education

Newcastle Education Authority

Silverhill Centre, Stocksfield Avenue, Newcastle-upon-Tyne, Tyne and Wear, NE5 2DX
Tel: 0191 274 7318
Fax: 0191 274 7284
E-mail: Silverlink@Onyxnet.co.uk
Contact: P Preston, Head of Service for Hearing
            Impaired Children

Work includes: initiating early educational intervention, particularly for severely or profoundly deaf children; working with parents to promote partnership in the education process using a communication approach which matches the needs of the child and family; providing on-going specialist educational support for the children, their parents, teachers and schools.

North Tyneside Education Service

Stephenson House, Stephenson Street, North Shields, Tyne and Wear, NE30 1QA

Tel: 0191 200 5151
Fax: 0191 200 6090
Contact: J Benneworth, Chief Education Officer
Contact: J Gallagher, Head of Hearing Impaired Service

Hadrian Education Centre, St Peter's Road, Wallsend, Tyne and Wear, NE28 7LQ

South Tyneside Education Service

Town Hall, South Shields, Tyne and Wear, NE33 2RL

Tel: 0191 427 1717
Fax: 0191 427 0584
Contact: Len Power, Community Education Officer

The Community Education Service exists to serve the community in adult education and training. Signing classes are promoted to provide training in courses leading to CACDP Stage I and II. This facility is open to both hearing and hearing impaired students.

South Tyneside Hearing Impaired Service

Chuter Ede Education Centre, Galsworthy Road, South Shields, Tyne and Wear, NE34 9UG

Tel: 0191 519 1909 ext 425
Fax: 0191 519 0600
Contact: Elaine Rayner, Teacher of the Deaf

An education service which provides support for deaf children and their families from pre-school to 16 years. There is a peripatetic teaching service and unit provision for pupils across the age range.

Sunderland Education Service

P O Box 101, Civic Centre, Sunderland, Tyne and Wear, SR2 7DN

Tel: 0191 417 4713
Fax: 0191 553 1400
Contact: M Gough, Hearing Impaired Support Team Leader

Sunderland Learning Support Service, Stannington Centre, Stannington Grove, Sunderland, Tyne and Wear, SR2 9JT

Tel: 0191 510 0808

The primary and secondary Partial Hearing Units in Sunderland are under the direct management of their parent schools. The Hearing Impairment Support Team within Sunderland Learning Support Service offers home and nursery support for pre-school children from diagnosis (including three afternoons of a specialist nursery provision) and supports in all mainstream and special schools.

Units
Benton Park Primary School

Corchester Walk, Newcastle-upon-Tyne, Tyne and Wear, NE7 7SS

Tel: 0191 266 5122
Fax: 0191 266 8206
Contact: J Bishop, Teacher of the Deaf

Resourced unit within mainstream primary school.

Broadwood Infants School

Broadwood Road, Newcastle-upon-Tyne, Tyne and Wear, NE15 7TB

Tel: 0191 274 6203
Contact: Marian Stornsoy, Teacher of the Deaf

Broadwood Junior School

Broadwood Road, Newcastle-upon-Tyne, Tyne and Wear, NE15 7TB

Tel: 0191 274 1684

There is a Hearing Impaired Unit attached to the school. The unit is part of Newcastle-upon-Tyne's service for hearing impaired children.

Heaton Manor School

Jesmond Park West, Newcastle-upon-Tyne, Tyne and Wear, NE7 7DP

Tel: 0191 281 8486
Fax: 0191 281 0381
Contact: John Dryden, Head Teacher

King Edward Primary School

Preston Avenue, North Shields, Tyne and Wear, NE30 2BD

Tel: 0191 257 0530
Contact: Kate Burgess
Tel: 0191 200 6337

The Deaf Support Centre (DSC) is situated within the nursery class of the primary school. There is a teacher of the deaf attached to the DSC and a special support assistant. Children attend the DSC from the age of 2 years 6 months to 3 years, thus gaining an extra year of nursery provision. The DSC provides a Total Communication environment within which the children gain language most appropriate to their needs.

18

Marden High School

Hartington Road, North Shields, Tyne and Wear, NE30 3RZ

Tel: 0191 257 4433
Contact: L Kindley, Teacher of the Deaf

Our Deaf Support Centre aims to integrate deaf pupils into mainstream lessons by offering support from a teacher of the deaf or special assistant. Our mode of communication is Total Communication, which we are all trained to deliver. Problematic subjects are delivered in the centre after withdrawal has been agreed with the relevant staff.

Monkhouse Primary School

Wallington Avenue, North Shields, Tyne and Wear, NE30 3SH

Tel: 0191 258 4462
Textphone: 0191 258 4462

We aim to provide a rich, balanced curriculum within a framework which allows each deaf child to reach full potential. This is done through a flexible, child-centred approach to communication and language development, offering the full spectrum of interaction from oral/aural, through Total Communication to British Sign Language. To achieve this speech and language therapists, teachers of the deaf and special assistants work in close cooperation.

Silverhill Centre

Stocksfield Avenue, Newcastle Upon Tyne, Tyne and Wear, NE5 2DX

Tel: 0191 274 7318
Fax: 0191 274 7284

Simonside County Primary School

Glasgow Road, Jarrow, Tyne and Wear, NE32 4AS

Tel: 0191 489 8315
Contact: Janet Scullion, Teacher of the Deaf
Tel: 0191 483 2938

The education of hearing impaired pupils in a mainstream setting.

Springfield Comprehensive School

Field Terrace, Jarrow, Tyne and Wear, NE32 5PR

Tel: 0191 489 3225
Fax: 0191 489 0088
Contact: P Bentley, Teacher of the Deaf

There is a Hearing Impaired Unit based at the school.

Thorney Close Primary School

Torquay Road, Sunderland, Tyne and Wear, SR3 4BB

Tel: 0191 553 6093
Fax: 0191 528 8199
Contact: L Smare, Teacher of the Deaf

Usworth Secondary School

Heworth Road, Washington, Tyne and Wear, NE38 2NF

Tel: 0191 416 7500
Fax: 0191 416 6014
Contact: Bill Roberts, Head of Learning Difficulties Unit

➤ Warrington
See Cheshire

➤ Warwickshire
Education Services
Warwickshire Education Service

22 Northgate Street, Warwick, CV34 4SR

Tel: 01926 410410
Fax: 01926 412746
Contact: P Cox, Education Officer
Contact: D Allan, Specialist Service Leader, Warwickshire SENSS

Cashmore Middle School, Baker Avenue, Leamington Spa, Warwickshire, CV31 3HB

Tel: 01926 470970

Units
Kenilworth School

Leyes Lane, Kenilworth, Warwickshire, CV8 2DA

Tel: 01926 859421
Fax: 01926 859426
E-mail: kenilsch@rmplc.co.uk
Contact: Christine Martin, Teacher of the Deaf

A primary day school using the oral/aural method of communication.

St John's Primary School

Mortimer Road, Kenilworth, Warwickshire, CV8 1FS

Tel: 01926 859883
Textphone: 01926 859833
Fax: 01926 859833
Contact: Robina Philips, Teacher of the Deaf
Tel: 01926 859833

This is a county-wide provision for profoundly deaf children who need signing to be educated within a mainstream primary school. The children are fully integrated, with full-time signed support, using sign-supported English. Key literacy lessons take place in the specialist unit. We have a deaf sign-language tutor. Speech therapy is also available.

St Nicholas Church of England Community School

Priory Road, Kenilworth, Warwickshire, CV8 2PE
Tel: 01926 853257
Contact: Mrs Naujokas, Special Educational
            Needs Coordinator

Weddington Primary School

Ramsey Avenue, Nuneaton, Warwickshire, CV10 0DR
Tel: 024 7634 0729
Textphone: 024 7638 2478
Fax: 024 7638 2478
Contact: M Moss, Teacher of the Deaf

➢ West Midlands
Education Services
Birmingham Education Service

Council House Extension, Margaret Street, Birmingham, West Midlands, B3 3BU
Tel: 0121 303 9944
Contact: Maggie Beech, Head of Service
            Visiting Teachers Service, Barrack
            Street, Nechells, Birmingham, West
            Midlands, B7 4HA
Tel: 0121 359 0883
Fax: 0121 333 4197

The Team for Children with Hearing Impairment is one of four teams in the service. Specialist teachers, support assistants, educational audiologists and technicians provide effective assessment, teaching and support to children and young people from birth to post-16. We work collaboratively with parents, health services, schools and many agencies to provide a high-quality service.

Coventry Education Service

New Council Offices, Earl Street, Coventry, West Midlands, CV1 5RS
Tel: 024 7683 3333
Textphone: 024 7647 1932
Fax: 024 7647 1932
E-mail: sss-cov@saqnet.co.uk
Contact: Eileen Robinson, Head of Sensory
            Support Service
            Cannon Park School Annexe,
            Bransford Avenue, Coventry, West
            Midlands, CV4 7PS
Tel: 024 7641 7415

The prime focus of our support is to ensure that children have maximum access to the educational system and are able to achieve their potential in academic, social, emotional and personal life. The service is staffed by qualified teachers of the deaf who support children and their families from diagnosis to leaving school.

Dudley Education Service

Westox House, 1 Trinity Road, Dudley, West Midlands, DY1 1JB
Tel: 01384 814225
Fax: 01384 452216
Contact: R Colligan, Chief Education Officer
Contact: Annette Hope, Physical and Sensory
            Service
            Church Street, Pensnett, Dudley, DY5
            4EY

Provides educational advice and support to schools and parents on all aspects of physical and sensory disability, including deafness, achieved through a team of visiting teachers of the deaf, primary and secondary resource base and extra-district support of pupils in special schools.

Sandwell Education Service

P O Box 41, Shaftsbury House, 402 High Street, West Bromwich, West Midlands, B70 9LT
Tel: 0121 525 7366
Fax: 0121 533 1528
Contact: S Gallagher, Director of Education
Fax: 0121 553 1528
Contact: C Warriner, Head of Service for
            Hearing Impaired Children
Tel: 0121 569 8528
Textphone: 0121 553 5933
Fax: 0121 569 8531

18

Solihull Education, Learning Support Service

P O Box 20, Council House, Solihull, West Midlands, B91 3QU

Tel: 0121 704 6000
Fax: 0121 704 6669
Contact: Peter McCann, Team Leader for Hearing Impaired Children

Reynalds Cross Centre, Kineton Green Road, Solihull, West Midlands, B92 7ER

Tel: 0121 706 0627
Textphone: 0121 706 0627
Fax: 0121 708 0198

A team of specialist teachers and assistants providing support to pre-school and school age hearing impaired children and their families. The service comprises a team of visiting teachers and three specialist units in mainstream school.

Walsall Education Service

Civic Centre, Darwall Street, Walsall, West Midlands, WS1 1DQ

Tel: 01922 650000
Fax: 01922 722322
Contact: M Quinn, Director of Education
Contact: W Brown, Head of Service, Education Development Centre

Field Road, Bloxwich, Walsall, West Midlands, WS3 3JF

Tel: 01922 711931
Fax: 01922 711932

Wolverhampton Education Service

Civic Centre, St Peter's Square, Wolverhampton, West Midlands, WV1 1RR

Tel: 01902 527811
Fax: 01902 314218
Contact: Ann Ryding, Team Leader, Services for Deaf and Hearing Impaired Children

Jennie Lee Centre, Lichfield Road, Wolverhampton, West Midlands, WV11 3HT

Tel: 01902 315936
Fax: 01902 315936

Service for hearing impaired and deaf children working to enable all children with hearing loss to reach their full potential. We provide advice and guidance to parents, carers and school staff. For some children in-class support is given. We also provide advice for statements of Special Educational Need.

Units

Ashwood Park Primary School

Bells Lane, Stourbridge, Dudley, West Midlands, DY8 5DQ

Tel: 01384 818545
Fax: 01384 818546

A primary day school with nursery using Total Communication.

Bartley Green School

Adams Hill, Birmingham, West Midlands, B32 3QJ

Tel: 0121 476 9246
Fax: 0121 478 1585
Contact: M Spalding, Teacher of the Deaf

Bellfield Infant and Junior Schools

Vineyard Road, Birmingham, West Midlands, B31 1PT

Tel: 0121 475 2406
Textphone: 0121 475 2406
Fax: 0121 475 4854
E-mail: jemorton@portables2.ngfl.gov.uk
Contact: Jean Morton, Teacher of the Deaf

A primary day school with nursery using the oral method of communication.

Calthorpe School for Children with Additional Disabilities

Darwin Street, Birmingham, West Midlands, B12 0TJ

Tel: 0121 733 4637

Churchfields High School

Church Vale, West Bromwich, West Midlands, B71 4DH

Tel: 0121 588 8452
Fax: 0121 588 8436
Contact: G Buckley, Teacher of the Deaf

We are a purpose-built Hearing Impaired Unit attached to Churchfields High School. There are three teachers of the deaf. Our main aims are to access the mainstream curriculum to our deaf students and to provide a safe and caring environment. We use a range of communication methods.

Dame Elizabeth Cadbury School

Woodbroke Road, Birmingham, West Midlands, B30 1UL

Tel: 0121 459 9919

Contact: Tom Patterson, Senior Adult Education Officer

Tel: 0121 459 9919/ 458 4058
0121 458 4058 Evening

Deansfield High School

Deans Road, Wolverhampton, West Midlands, WV1 2BH

Tel: 01902 556400

Fax: 01902 556401

Contact: P McLachlan, Teacher of the Deaf

East Park Junior School

Hollington Road, Wolverhampton, West Midlands, WV1 2DS

Tel: 01902 558735

Fax: 01902 558738

Contact: C Jones, Teacher of the Deaf

Tel: 01902 451667

Hargate Primary School

Hargate Lane, West Bromwich, West Midlands, B71 1PH

Tel: 0121 553 4178

Fax: 0121 553 3185

Contact: S Whitehouse, Teacher of the Deaf

Hawthorne Junior and Infant School

Hawthorne Road, Birmingham, West Midlands, B44 8QR

Tel: 0121 373 3891

Textphone: 0121 373 3891

Fax: 0121 350 9833

Contact: J Pollard, Teacher of the Deaf

We are a hearing resource base for primary-aged children (4 to 11 years). At present we have 19 pupils who have a variety of hearing losses. More and more children referred to us are profoundly deaf. We have six children who have cochlear implants. Mode of communication: Total Communication.

Howes Primary School

Palermo Avenue, Coventry, West Midlands, CV3 5EH

Tel: 024 7641 1711

Fax: 024 7669 3392

Contact: Mrs Rees, Teacher in Charge

Kingsthorne Pre-School Unit

Cranbourne Road, Birmingham, West Midlands, B44 0BX

Tel: 0121 373 3897

Fax: 0121 382 9637

Contact: Mrs Tursord, Teacher of the Deaf

Lyndon Hearing Impaired Unit

Daylesford Road, Solihull, West Midlands, B92 8EJ

Tel: 0121 742 5167

Fax: 0121 742 5167

Contact: J Kitson, Teacher of the Deaf

Lyndon Hearing Impaired Unit is a delegated unit which is a part of the local education authority-funded learning support service for Solihull. It aims to provide an integrated setting with a high level of specialist support according to need. It offers a broad-based curriculum, but with timetabled withdrawal time for extra language and speech work as appropriate.

Percy Shurmer Junior and Infant School

Longmore Street, Birmingham, West Midlands, B12 9ED

Tel: 0121 440 3431

Fax: 0121 440 3896

Contact: K Coates, Teacher of the Deaf

Peterbrook Primary School, Hearing Impaired Unit

High Street, Shirley, Solihull, West Midlands, B90 1HR

Tel: 0121 430 6733

Fax: 0121 474 6640

A specialist unit providing support for hearing impaired children of primary age, including nursery provision, using a Total Communication (signs to support English) approach.

18

Redhill School

Junction Road, Stourbridge, Dudley, West
Midlands, DY8 1JX
Tel: 01384 816355
Fax: 01384 816356
Contact: Simon Whitlow, Teacher of the Deaf

Shenley Court Secondary School

Shenley Lane, Birmingham, West Midlands, B29
4HE
Tel: 0121 475 5191
Fax: 0121 478 3711
Contact: Jackie Levett, Teacher of the Deaf

Stow Heath Infant School

Vaughan Road, Willenhall, Wolverhampton, West
Midlands, WV13 3UD
Tel: 01902 558815
Fax: 01902 558818
Contact: S Bonnick, Head Teacher

Provides inclusive education for profoundly deaf
pupils aged 3 to 7 years within a classroom-
integrated situation.

The College High School

395 College Road, Birmingham, West Midlands,
B44 0HF
Tel: 0121 373 1647
Fax: 0121 382 2707
E-mail: enquiry@collegeh.vham.school.uk
Contact: Miss Ainge, Hearing Impairment Unit

Windy Arbor Junior and Infant School

Chelmsley Wood, Woodlands Way, Birmingham,
West Midlands, B37 6RN
Tel: 0121 770 4964
Fax: 0121 779 3622
Contact: B Bowell, Head Teacher

➤ West Sussex
Education Services
West Sussex Education Service

County Hall, West Street, Chichester, West Sussex,
PO19 1RF
Tel: 01243 777100
Fax: 01243 777229
Contact: Annie Rees, Sensory Support Team
            Rydon Community School,
            Storrington, West Sussex, RH20 3AA

Units
Angmering School

Station Road, Angmering, Littlehampton, West
Sussex, BN16 4HH
Tel: 01903 772351
Contact: G Tisdall, Teacher of the Deaf

Arun Vale SSF (Infants)

York Road, Littlehampton, West Sussex, BN17 6EW
Tel: 01903 716550
A primary day school using the oral method of
communication.

Connaught County Junior School

York Road, Littlehampton, West Sussex, BN17 6EW
Tel: 01903 721677
Fax: 01903 731996
Contact: Julie Williams, Teacher in Charge of
            Special Support Facility

Northgate First School

Northgate Special Support Facility, Green Lane,
Northgate, Crawley, West Sussex, RH10 2DX
Tel: 01293 614878
Fax: 01293 419952
E-mail: ngssf@rmplc.co.uk
Contact: J Sewell-Rutter, Teacher in Charge

We are a special support facility for hearing
impaired pupils aged 4 to 12 years, attached to
First and Middle mainstream schools. Through an
individual integration programme and specific
auditory training and language work, we support
children in accessing as full an education as
possible.

Thomas Bennett Community College

Ashdown Drive, Tilgate, Crawley, West Sussex,
RH10 5AD
Tel: 01293 526255
Fax: 01293 527704
E-mail: tbcc@thomasbennett.n.direct.co.uk
Contact: Joan Newton

➢ West Yorkshire
Education Services
Bradford Education Service

Flockton House, Flockton Road, Bradford, West Yorkshire, BD4 7RY

Tel: 01274 752111
Contact: Diana Cavanagh, Director of Education

Calderdale Education Service

P O Box 33, Northgate House, Northgate, Halifax, West Yorkshire, HX1 1UN

Tel: 01422 252125
Textphone: 01422 364899
Fax: 01422 252133
E-mail: alss@alss.demon.co.uk
Contact: Linda Sutton, Head of Sensory Services

Heath Training and Development Centre, Free School Lane, Halifax, West Yorkshire, HX1 1UN

Tel: 01422 364899

The Hearing Impaired Service is part of a general service, the Assessment and Hearing Support Service. We function within a Total Communication philsophy. We have three resourced provisions in mainstream school.

Kirklees Education Authority

Oldgate House, Oldgate, Huddersfield, West Yorkshire, HD1 6QW

Tel: 01484 422133
Fax: 01484 446764
Contact: A Elson, Executive Director, Education and Social Services

Leeds Education Service

Selectapost, 17 Merrion House, Leeds, West Yorkshire, LS2 8DT

Tel: 0113 242 9111
Contact: J Rawlinson, Director of Education
Contact: Miranda Pickersgill, Head of Deaf & Hearing Impaired Service
Textphone: 0113 245 2240
Fax: 0113 243 8196

The Cropton Centre

Pontefract Road, Crofton, Wakefield, West Yorkshire, WF4 1LL

Tel: 01924 862739

Thorn Park School and Service for the Hearing Impaired

Thorn Lane, off Bingley Road, Bradford, West Yorkshire, BD9 6RY

Tel: 01274 773770
Textphone: 01274 773770
Fax: 01274 770387
E-mail: thornparks@aol.com
Contact: Malcolm Gordon, Head of Educational Services for the Hearing Impaired

West Yorkshire Education Authority

County Hall, Wakefield, West Yorkshire, WF1 2QL

Contact: A Lenney, Chief Education Officer
Tel: 01924 290900

Units
Allerton Grange High School

Talbot Avenue, Leeds, West Yorkshire, LS17 6SF

Tel: 0113 225 2002
Textphone: 0113 225 2002
Fax: 0113 225 2003
E-mail: dahiss@aghs.leeds.sch.uk
Contact: R Squire

Deaf and hearing impaired resourced provision. Five-day educational provision for deaf and hearing impaired students aged from 11 to 18 years from both within and outside Leeds. Deaf support team consists of teacher of the deaf, communication support workers and deaf instructors delivering a high school curriculum bilingually in British Sign Language and English.

Beckfoot Grammar School

Wagon Lane, Bingley, West Yorkshire, BD16 1EE

Tel: 01274 563803
This is a resourced school.

Brudenell Primary School

Welton Road, Leeds, West Yorkshire, SL6 1DT

Tel: 0113 278 5168
Contact: K Priestley, Teacher of the Deaf

Bruntcliffe High School

Bruntcliffe Lane, Morley, Leeds, West Yorkshire, LS27 0LZ

Tel: 0113 253 3803
Contact: A Gerhold

18

Cottingley Primary School

Dulverton Grove, Leeds, West Yorkshire, LS11 0HU

Tel: 0113 271 6666

Textphone: 0113 271 6666

Fax: 0113 277 6522

Contact: Annette Fletcher, Teacher of the Deaf

Fully integrated into classes. In a class we will have a deaf adult and child and a communication worker. We have induction loops in some rooms. Children are taxied in from all over Leeds.

Grafton Special School

Craven Road, Leeds, West Yorkshire, LS6 2ST

Tel: 0113 293 0323

Contact: C Rutherford, Teacher of the Deaf

Grafton School is a resourced special school for 80 children (aged 3 to 11 years). There are eight places for children who are deaf and hearing impaired. Other children have moderate, complex and severe difficulties. A teacher of the deaf and a deaf instructor support children using a bilingual approach. Staff and hearing children throughout the school are encouraged to use British Sign Language, and many pupils need a Total Communication approach.

Heaton Middle School

Haworth Road, Bradford, West Yorkshire, BD9 6LJ

Tel: 01274 548173

Contact: A Parker, Teacher of the Deaf

Holgate V Secondary School

Shaw Lane, Barnsley, West Yorkshire, S70 6HY

Tel: 01226 230720

We are a local education authority-funded hearing impaired resource. Based in a mainstream secondary school providing daily access to a qualified teacher of the deaf and classroom support from trained staff.

Horsforth West End Primary School

West End Lane, Horsforth, Leeds, West Yorkshire, LS18 5JP

Tel: 0113 258 2819

Contact: Miranda Pickersgill, Head of Resources

Blenheim Centre, Crowther Place, Leeds, LS6 2SJ

Longcar Junior and Infant School

Longcar Lane, Barnsley, West Yorkshire, S70 6BB

Tel: 01226 203387

Contact: John Barron

Educates deaf children. The resource base is orally led.

Lowerhouses Church of England Junior and Nursery Primary School

Lower Houses Lane, Almondbury, Huddersfield, West Yorkshire, HD5 8JY

Tel: 01484 226672

Textphone: 01484 226672

Fax: 01484 226673

E-mail: lowerhouses@ge02.poptel.org.uk

Contact: Sheila Whitworth, Teacher of the Deaf

Nab Wood Grammar School

Cottingley New Road, Bingley, Bradford, West Yorkshire, BD16 1TZ

Tel: 01274 567281

Fax: 01274 510688

Contact: P Kidd, Coordinator for the Hearing Impaired

Newsome Secondary School

Castle Avenue, Newsome, Huddersfield, West Yorkshire, HD4 6JN

Tel: 01484 226570

Textphone: 01484 226570

Videotel: 01484 223906

Fax: 01484 226572

E-mail: newsome-hs@GEOZ.Poptel.org.uk

Contact: Yvonne Roberts, Teacher of the Deaf

Park Road Primary School

Park Road, Batley, West Yorkshire, WF7 5LP

Tel: 01924 473862

Contact: Jan Cohen, Senior Teacher for Hearing Impaired Children

KESS Centre, off Ralthorpe Terrace, Huddersfield, HD5 9NY

Kirklees Education Service for hearing impaired children aims to help children with hearing impairment in Kirklees to achieve their potential and benefit from their education, and to help support families and school staff. KESHIC is a section of Kirklees Pupil Support Services which are managed by Graeme Sunderland. It supports all childen with special needs. It offers a range of provision and support to meet the individual needs of each child. KESHIC comprises three

18

resourced schools and a peripatetic team which supports the hearing impaired child and family from diagnosis to school-leaving age.

Parklands Girls High School

South Parkway, Leeds, West Yorkshire, LS14 6TY

Tel:	0113 273 1964
Fax:	0113 232 3591

Secondary girls comprehensive high school. The education of girls from the age of 11 to 18 years. Aims: to fulfil each pupil's academic potenial; to acquire knowledge and skill; to be aware of and respect shared values; to become self-confident young women.

Rawthorpe High School

Off Rawthorpe Terrace, Heathergrove Fold, Rawthorpe, Huddersfield, West Yorkshire, HD5 9NQ

Tel:	01484 226500
Fax:	01484 226515
E-mail:	sem-support@ge02.poptel.org.uk
Contact:	Jan Cohen, Head of Hearing Impaired Service

Shakespeare Primary School

Stoney Rock Lane, Leeds, West Yorkshire, LS9 9JF

Tel:	0113 248 2194
Contact:	Miranda Pickersgill, Head of Resources Blenheim Centre, Crowther Place, Leeds, LS6 2SJ

Swarcliffe Middle School

Swarcliffe Drive, Cove, Leeds, West Yorkshire, LS14 5JW

Tel:	0113 293 0275
Fax:	0113 293 0276
Contact:	N Martin, Head Teacher

➢ Wiltshire
Education Services
Swindon Education Service

Sanford House, Sanford Street, Swindon, Wiltshire, SN1 1QH

Tel:	01793 463902
Fax:	01793 488597
Contact:	Roger Thurlbeck, Senior Advisory Teacher for Hearing Impaired Children
Tel:	01793 463898
Textphone:	01793 463909

Educational provision for hearing impaired children in the Swindon Borough, from pre-school and school support to college.

Wiltshire Education Service

County Hall, Trowbridge, Wiltshire, BA14 8JB

Tel:	01225 713000
Fax:	01225 713982
Contact:	Lindsey Davies, Chief Education Officer
Tel:	01225 753641
Contact:	John McAuley, Senior Advisory Teacher of Hearing Impaired Children Avon Approach, Salisbury, Wiltshire, SP1 3SL
Tel:	01722 332046

Units
Downton Secondary School

Braemore Road, Salisbury, Wiltshire, SP5 3HN

Tel:	01725 510610
Fax:	01725 512841
Contact:	Jane Houdan, Head of Special Needs

Mountford Manor Infant School

Bothwell Road, Swindon, Wiltshire, SN3 3EZ

Tel:	01793 521665
Contact:	Val Weston, Teacher of the Deaf

Mountford Manor Junior School

Bothwell Road, Swindon, Wiltshire, SN3 3EZ

Tel:	01793 536494
Contact:	Marilyn Gough, Teacher of the Deaf

The school has a Hearing Impaired Unit which aims to enable all of the hearing impaired pupils to integrate into appropriate mainstream classes with Total Communication support as and when necessary. The children themselves choose whether they wish to sign or not.

Sarum St Paul's Church of England Primary School

Westminster Road, Salisbury, Wiltshire, SP2 7DG

Tel:	01722 336459
Contact:	Elizabeth McAuley, Teacher of the Deaf

Hearing Impaired Support Unit for children aged 4 to 11. Pupils are fully integrated and attend the unit on a withdrawal basis. They have classroom support.

18

The Clarenden School

Frome Road, Trowbridge, Wiltshire, BA14 0DU
Tel: 01225 762686
Fax: 01225 751034

The Clarenden is the designated secondary hearing impaired base for the Trowbridge area. However, at this time it does not have any hearing impaired students.

The Grove Primary School

Hazel Grove, Trowbridge, Wiltshire, BA14 0JG
Tel: 01225 755242
Fax: 01225 777988
Contact: Liz Poyser, Teacher of the Deaf

Hearing Impaired Unit on site.

The Ridgeway School

Inverary Road, Wroughton, Swindon, Wiltshire, SN4 9DJ
Tel: 01793 812824
Fax: 01793 815065
E-mail: arnolds@ridgeway.swindon.sch.uk
Contact: Stuart Arnold, Teacher of the Deaf

Ridgeway is a large comprehensive school with a unit providing support for children with severe or profound hearing impairment. There are usually 10 to 12 children from Swindon local education authority, but attendance would be considered from a wider area. The unit has close links with the local peripatetic service and audiology department at the hospital.

➤ Windsor and Maidenhead
See Berkshire

➤ Wokingham
See Berkshire

➤ Worcestershire
Education Services
Worcestershire Education Service

County Hall, Spetchley Road, Worcester, WR5 2NP
Tel: 01905 763763
Contact: R Broadbent, Head of Service for Children with Sensory Impairment
           17 Castle Street, Worcester, WR1 3AD
Tel: 01905 765630
Textphone: 01905 765626
Fax: 01905 765631

The Service for Children with Sensory Impairments provides educational advice and support for all children with a sensory impairment from diagnosis at pre-school throughout school and into further and higher education. The service also works with local health trusts to provide a screening and diagnostic programme to identify hearing problems.

Units
Arrowcrest First School

Wirehill Drive, Lodge Park, Redditch, Worcestershire, B98 7JU
Tel: 01527 528523
Fax: 01527 510153
Contact: C Illingworth, Head Teacher

The school aims to provide pupils with access to the mainstream curriculum and the opportunity of working and socialising with their hearing peers - in other words, full integration. Within the school there is a specially equipped resource room for auditory training. Staff include teachers of the deaf, communicators and speech and language therapists.

St Clement's Church of England Primary School

Hemwick Road, Worcester, WR2 5NS
Tel: 01905 423861
Fax: 01905 420562
E-mail: st.clements.pr@campus.bt.com
Contact: Jackie Pye, Teacher of the Deaf

➤ Wrekin
See Shropshire

➤ York
See North Yorkshire

➢ County Antrim
Education Services
Belfast Education and Library Board
40 Academy Street, Belfast, County Antrim, BT1 2NQ
Tel: 028 9032 9211
Fax: 028 9049 1972
Contact: Lillian Warnock, Head of Hearing
            Impaired Service
            Ulidia Resource Centre, Somerset
            Street, Belfast, County Antrim, BT7
Tel: 028 9049 1058
Contact: M Duke, Senior Peripatetic Teacher
            44 Ballylesson Road, Belfast, County
            Antrim, BT8 8JS
Tel: 028 9040 1246
Contact: A Lyle, Chief Executive/Advisory Officer
Tel: 028 9056 4000 ext 4066
Fax: 028 9033 1714

North Eastern Education and Library Board (NI), Educational Audiology Service
County Hall, 182 Galgorm Road, Ballymena, County Antrim, BT42 1HN
Tel: 028 2565 3333
Contact: Anne Ross, Head of Educational
            Audiology Service
Tel: 028 2566 2554
Fax: 028 2564 6071
Contact: G Topping, Chief Executive
Fax: 028 2564 6071

Service for the Sensory Impaired
Belvoir Drive, Belfast, County Antrim, BT8 4DL
Tel: 028 9049 1583
Contact: Irene Knox, Education Officer
            Grahamsbridge Road, Dundonald,
            Belfast, County Antrim, BT16 OHS
Tel: 028 9056 6200

The Service for the Sensory Impaired provides a peripatetic teaching service for children with sensory impairment throughout the South Eastern Education and Library Board. Advice and support is given to teaching staff and other agencies when requested.

South Eastern Education and Library Board, Northern Ireland
Grahamsbridge Road, Dundonald, Belfast, County Antrim, BT16 OHS
Tel: 028 9038 1188
Fax: 028 9038 3290
Contact: Irene Knox, Education Officer
Tel: 028 9056 6200

Units
Ballee Community School
Partially Hearing Unit, Ballee High School, Ballee Road West, Ballymena, County Antrim
Tel: 028 2564 9327
Fax: 028 2564 5136
Contact: B McKee, Teacher of the Deaf

Ballee Primary School
Ballee Antrim Road, Ballymena, County Antrim, BT42 3BD
Tel: 028 2564 4280

Ballygolan Primary School
41/83 Serpentine Road, Newtownabbey, County Antrim, BT36 7HB
Tel: 028 9037 0091
Contact: W Smyth, Teacher of the Deaf

Ballymoney High School
17 Garryduff Road, Ballymoney, County Antrim, BT53 7AN
Tel: 028 7066 2361
Fax: 028 7066 6792
Contact: A Offord, Teacher of the Deaf
Tel: 028 70662361

Ballymoney Primary School
North Road, Ballymoney, County Antrim, BT53 6BW
Tel: 028 7066 2340
Fax: 028 7066 7272
Contact: L Greehy, Teacher of the Deaf

Corpus Christi College
Ard-na-va Road, Belfast, County Antrim, BT12 6FF
Tel: 028 9024 5645
Fax: 028 9032 8388
Contact: Deirdre Ryan, Teacher of the Deaf

18

Cregagh Primary School

Mount Merrion Avenue, Belfast, County Antrim, BT6 0FL

Tel: 028 9040 1246
Fax: 028 9040 1246
Contact: Mary McCartan, Teacher of the Deaf

Deramore High School

Annadale Embankment, Belfast, County Antrim, BT7 3HE

Tel: 028 9069 2411

Holy Trinity Primary School

Monagh Road, Belfast, County Antrim, BT11 8EG

Tel: 028 9061 6465
Contact: P Mullan, Teacher of the Deaf

Holy Trinity Partial Hearing Unit is a coeducational unit for the education of hearing impaired children between the ages of 3 and 11 years. It is an oral unit situated in a mainstream primary school catering for the needs of children with a wide range of hearing losses. We consider one of our most positive features to be our ability to provide good integration for our pupils.

Orangefield High School

Cameronian Drive, Belfast, County Antrim, BT5 6AW

Tel: 028 9080 5040
Fax: 028 9080 5049
E-mail: headteacher.ohs@schools-class.ni.org.uk
Contact: M Nelson

The Hearing Impaired Department of the school pursues an oral/aural philosophy. Students range in age from 11 to 18 plus. All students have the opportunity to access the Northern Ireland Curriculum and follow GCSE, City & Guilds, RSA, AEB and GNVQ courses. There is a comprehensive programme of careers guidance for hearing impaired pupils.

St Rose's Girls Secondary School

Beechmont Avenue, Belfast, County Antrim, BT12 7NA

Tel: 028 9024 0937
Contact: Mary Gordon

This is a Hearing Impaired Unit for girls aged 11 to 18, who integrate as much as possible in mainstream subjects. They are educated orally making maximum use of residual hearing.

➤ County Armagh
Education Services
Southern Education and Library Board, Northern Ireland

3 Charlemont Place, The Mall, Armagh, BT61 9AX

Tel: 028 3751 2200
Fax: 028 3751 2491
Contact: J Kelly, Chief Executive
Textphone: 028 3751 2200
Fax: 028 3751 2490

Units
Brownlow High School

Tullygally Road, Craigavon, County Armagh, BT65 5BS

Tel: 028 3834 2121

Drumgor Primary School

Drumgor Road, Brownlow, Craigavon, County Armagh, BT65 5BP

Tel: 028 3834 1488
Fax: 028 3834 2319
Contact: Janice McKillop, Teacher of the Deaf

Facilities for up to eight deaf children. Teaching method is Total Communication.

Lismore Comprehensive School

Drumgask, Craigavon, County Armagh, BT65 5DU

Tel: 028 3834 2165
Fax: 028 3834 1504
Contact: Helen Moorehead, Teacher of the Deaf

➤ County Down
Units
Holy Family Primary School

1 Drumnaconagher Road, Teconnaught, Downpatrick, County Down, BT30 9AN

Tel: 028 4483 0319
Fax: 028 4483 1879
Contact: Rosemary Watts, Teacher of the Deaf

Newry Model Primary School

Catherine Street, Newry, County Down, BT35 6JG

Tel: 028 3024 046

18

St Colmcille's High School

Killyleagh Street, Crossgar, County Down, BT30 9DQ

Tel:	028 4483 0311
Fax:	028 4483 1383
E-mail:	staff@colmcill.co.uk
Contact:	Mrs Hamill, Teacher of the Deaf

➢ County Fermanagh
Education Services
Model School House - The Child Guidance Centre

24 Dublin Road, Enniskillen, County Fermanagh

Tel:	028 6634 3900
Fax:	028 6632 3493
Contact:	Winston Glass

➢ County Londonderry
Education Services
Child Guidance Centre

Bay View House, 4 Clooney Road, Londonderry, BT47 6TB

Tel:	028 7131 1939
Textphone:	028 7131 1213

Units
Drumachose Primary School

Alexander Road, Limavady, County Londonderry, BT49 0BS

Tel:	028 7172 2751
Fax:	028 7172 2751
E-mail:	drumachose_edu@m.s.n.com
Contact:	E Wallace, Teacher of the Deaf
Tel:	028 71722 751

A unit provides inclusive education at primary level for hearing impaired and blind children.

Limavady High School

Irish Green Street, Limavady, County Londonderry, BT49 9AN

Tel:	028 7176 2526
Fax:	028 7176 4102
Contact:	Alan Offord, Teacher of the Deaf

St Anne's Primary School

Upper Nassau Street, Londonderry, BT48 0EY

Tel:	028 7126 3046
Fax:	028 7137 4227
Contact:	Paula Mulholland, Teacher of the Deaf

➢ County Tyrone
Education Services
Western Education and Library Board

1 Hospital Road, Omagh, County Tyrone, BT79 0AW

Tel:	028 8241 1411
Fax:	028 8224 1442
Contact:	Margaret Harte, Special Education Department

Western Education and Library Board aims to promote an inclusive approach to the education of pupils with hearing difficulties. The Board has established a curriculum of provision to support such pupils within mainstream schools, or in units attached to mainstream schools. The Board works closely with other agencies to promote the optimal development of children and young people with hearing difficulties.

Units
Gibson Primary School

64 Old Mountfield Road, Omagh, County Tyrone, BT79 7EL

Tel:	028 8224 4552

St Conor's Primary School

109 Brookmount Road, Omagh, County Tyrone, BT78 5JQ

Tel:	028 8224 4683

There is a Partially Hearing Unit attached to the mainstream school. The pupils in the unit integrate in the school to varying degrees depending on the hearing loss of the pupil. The unit is staffed by two qualified teachers of the deaf and two classroom assistants.

St John's High School

37 Omagh Road, Dromore, County Tyrone, BT78 3AL

Tel:	028 8289 8284
Fax:	028 8289 8957
Contact:	Carmel McCarron, Teacher of the Deaf
Tel:	028 8289 8284

The school has a special unit for hearing impaired pupils designed for optimum listening conditions. Equipment (hearing aids and radio aids) is checked daily. Provison is made for individual

18

teaching/group teaching or integration into mainstream. Teaching and support from teachers of the deaf and two classroom assistants. Sign-supported English (Irish Sign Language lexicon) is available where necessary.

Scotland

➤ Aberdeenshire
Education Services
Aberdeenshire Education Service
Annexe, Woodhill House, Westburn Road, Aberdeen, AB16 5GB
Tel: 01224 665420
Contact: Dr J Banks, Senior Education Officer
Tel: 01224 664611

Grampian Hearing Impaired Service
Sinclair House, 619 King Street, Aberdeen, AB24 3BZ
Tel: 01224 481678

Summerhill Education Centre
Stronsay Drive, Aberdeen, AB15 6JA
Tel: 01224 208626
Contact: Isobel Gibson, Assistant Director of Education (Special Educational Needs)
Tel: 01224 346031

Educational support for hearing impaired children and young persons is provided on a city-wide basis by Services for the Hearing Impaired. These services comprise the following sections: Peripatetic Section, Partially Hearing Units (one primary, one secondary), Aberdeen School for the Deaf.

Units
Linksfield Academy
Stewart Crescent, Aberdeen, AB16 5SS
Tel: 01224 481343
Fax: 01224 276673
E-mail: acclink@rmplc.co.uk
Contact: Mrs Clouston, Partial Hearing Unit

Sunnybank Primary School
Sunnybank Road, Aberdeen, AB24 3NG
Tel: 01224 633363
Textphone: 01224 633363
Fax: 01224 621174
Contact: Mrs Bussell, Senior Teacher, Hearing Impaired Unit

➤ Angus
Education Services
Angus Education Service
Angus Council, County Buildings, Market Street, Forfar, Angus, DD8 3WE
Tel: 01307 461460
Fax: 01307 461848
Contact: Val Hayhow, Head of Hearing Impaired Service/Teacher of the Deaf (Peripatetic)
            Music Centre, Montrose Road, Forfar, Angus, DD8 2HT
Tel: 01307 464012

This is a service funded by Angus Education Authority and staffed by a teacher of the deaf. The aim is to provide support and advice to hearing impaired children, their teachers, parents and carers in order that the children have access to a broad and balanced curriculum and become fully integrated members of the community.

Dundee City Council Sensory Service
GDS, D86 Northern College, Gardyne Road, Dundee, Angus, DD5 1NY
Tel: 01382 454061/2
Fax: 01382 454024
Contact: Margaret Wilson, Head of Sensory Service

Covers Dundee city area. Unit provision for deaf and blind which are accessed by the whole region. Peripatetic service serves the visual and hearing impaired and pre-schools.

Units
Craigie High School
Garnet Terrace, Dundee, Angus, DD4 7QD
Tel: 01382 461587
Textphone: 01382 461587
Fax: 01382 461085
Contact: Christine Johnson, Teacher of the Deaf

We are a resource-based location situated in a mainstream secondary school. We cater for hearing impaired pupils requiring specialist support. Pupils are integrated into mainstream classes according to their needs.

McAlpine Primary School
Macalpine Road, Dundee, Angus, DD3 9HR
Tel: 01382 825425

Argyll

Education Services

Argyll and Bute Education Service

Argyll House, Alexandra Parade, Dunoon, Argyll, PA23 8AJ

Tel: 01369 704000
Fax: 01369 702614
Contact: Ronald Gould, Head of Support Service/Special Educational Needs

Offers an educational support service to staff working with hearing impaired children, to parents of hearing impaired children and to children who have a hearing impairment. Works with a team of professionals to support hearing impaired children throughout their educational career.

Ayrshire

Education Services

East Ayrshire Education Service

London Road Centre, London Road, Kilmarnock, Ayrshire, KA3 7JX

Tel: 01563 574057
Contact: J Mulgrew, Director of Education

Westpark School, Audiology and Peripatetic Unit

Playingfield Road, Crosshouse, Kilmarnock, Ayrshire, KA2 0JJ

Tel: 01563 536296
Contact: Helen Mitchell, Coordinator, Hearing Impaired Unit

Units

James Reid School

Primrose Place, Saltcoats, Ayrshire, KA21 6LH

Tel: 01294 467105

Towerlands Primary School

Heatherstane Way, Bourtree Hill, Irvine, Ayrshire, KA11 1DY

Tel: 01294 211265
Fax: 01294 223947

This is a unit for hearing impaired children within a mainstream school setting. It aims for all its children to access mainstream to their fullest potential. It is a Total Communication base.

Berwickshire

Units

Earlston Primary School, Resource Centre for Deaf Children

High Street, Earlston, Berwickshire, TD4 6HG

Tel: 01896 848977
Contact: Fiona Dove, Head

Peripatetic service. Caters for all deaf children from birth to 18 years.

Borders

Units

Tweedbank Primary School

Earlston Resource Centre for Deaf Children, Earlston Primary School, Earlston, Borders, TD4 6ED

Tel: 01896 848977
Contact: C Dove, Head of Hearing Impaired Service
Tel: 01896 754807

Central

Education Services

Claremont Unit for Hearing Impaired Children

Carse Terrace, Alloa, Central, FK10 2ED

Tel: 01259 215342

Dumfries and Galloway

Education Services

Dumfries and Galloway Education Service

30 Edinburgh Road, Dumfries, DG1 1NW

Tel: 01387 260427
Fax: 01387 260453
Contact: K McLeod, Director of Education

Units

Dumfries Academy

Academy Street, Great King Street, Dumfries, DG1 1BD

Tel: 01387 252846

Hecklegirth Primary School

Hecklegirth, Annan, Dumfriesshire, DG12 6HY

Tel: 01461 202606

18

> Dumfriesshire
Units
Moffat Academy
Academy Road, Moffat, Dumfriesshire, DG10 9DA
Tel: 01683 220114
Fax: 01683 221469
Contact: S Brown, Teacher of the Deaf

Wallace Hall Academy
Thornhill, Dumfriesshire, DG3 5DS
Tel: 01848 330294

> East Lothian
Education Services
Department of Education and Community Services
East Lothian Council, Council Buildings, Haddington, East Lothian, EH41 3HA
Tel: 01620 827562
Contact: Shannon Bigham, Pupil Support
Tel: 01620 827827

> Fife
Education Services
Fife Education Service
Fife House, North Street, Glenrothes, Fife, KY7 5LT
Tel: 01592 754411
Fax: 01592 416411
Contact: Anne Morris, Head of Hearing Impaired Services and Educational Audiologist
                   Auchterderran Centre, Woodend Road, Carenden, Fife, KY5 0NE
Tel: 01592 424708
Textphone: 01592 414713
Fax: 01592 414788
Contact: A McKay, Director of Education
                   Rothesay House, North Street, Glenrothes, Fife, KY7 5LT

Units
Auchmuty High School
Dovecot Road, Glenrothes, Fife, KY7 5JJ
Tel: 01592 415560
Contact: Jenny Gillon

The Resourced Base for the Hearing Impaired in Auchmuty High School is part of Fife's service for children and young people with sensory impairments. With a Total Communication philosophy, it aims to intergrate pupils socially and educationally in the school community. Pupils receive tutorial help and in-class support from a Teacher of the deaf.

Queen Anne High School
Broomhead, Dunfermline, Fife, KY12 0PQ
Tel: 01383 312672
Contact: Fiona Spowart, Teacher in Charge

Support for hearing impaired pupils in a high school, both by teachers of the deaf support in mainstream classes and individual/small group support work in specialist classroom.

South Parks Primary School
Napier Road, Glenrothes, Fife, KY6 1DS
Tel: 01592 415300
Contact: L Whitelaw, Head Teacher of the Deaf

> Highland
Education Services
Highland Education Service
Highland Council, Regional Buildings, Glenurquhart Road, Inverness, Highland, IV3 5NX
Tel: 01463 702804
Fax: 01463 702828
Contact: Hugh Fraser

Units
Mount Pleasant Primary School
Castletown Road, Thurso, Highland, KW14 8HL
Tel: 01847 893419
Fax: 01847 892601
Contact: Allan Lannon, Head Teacher of the Deaf

> Inverness-Shire
Units
Dalneigh Primary School
St Ninian Drive, Inverness, IV3 5AU
Tel: 01463 232636
Contact: Fiona Lyons, Speech & Language Tutor

➤ Isle of Lewis
Education Services
Western Isles Education Service
Council Offices, Sandwick Road, Stornaway, Isle of Lewis, HS1 3BQ
Tel: 01851 703773
Fax: 01851 705796
Contact: N Galbraith, Director of Education
Tel: 01851 703773 ext 431

Units
Stornoway Primary School
Jamieson Drive, Stornoway, Isle of Lewis, HS1 2LF
Tel: 01851 703418
Fax: 01851 706257
Contact: Jessica Steward, Senior Teacher of Hearing Impaired Unit

➤ Kirkcudbrightshire
Units
Dalbeattie Primary School
Southwick Road, Dalbeattie, Kirkcudbrightshire, DG5 4HR
Tel: 01556 610323

St Peter's Primary School
Maxwell Street, Dalbeattie, Kirkcudbrightshire, DG5 4AG
Tel: 01556 610294

➤ Lanarkshire
Education Services
Glasgow City Education Service
129 Bath Street, Glasgow, Lanarkshire, G2 2SY
Tel: 0141 227 6710
Contact: Margaret Orr, Senior Educational Officer Special Needs
Tel: 0141 287 6714

Glasgow City Council Education Department has a range of provisions. There is one school which follows a Total Communication approach and a primary and secondary aged unit which offer an oral approach. Children are also supported by a peripatetic service which serves both the primary and secondary sectors.

North Lanarkshire Education Service
Municipal Buildings, Kildonan Street, Coatbridge, Lanarkshire, ML5 3LF
Tel: 01236 441370
Contact: Jim McGuiness, Head of Support for Learning
Tel: 01236 812280

The Support for Learning Section within the Education Department overviews and manages the delivery of service from community education, and the Psychological Service to Early Years. It also overviews the provision for pupils with special educational needs, as well as school attendance and exclusion issues.

South Lanarkshire Education Resources
South Lanarkshire Council, Almada Street, Hamilton, Lanarkshire, ML3 0AE
Tel: 01698 454545
Contact: Anne Rooney, Specialist Services Manager

South Lanarkshire Education Resources aims to provide for and promote the interests of the people of South Lanarkshire and improve their quality of life by ensuring equality of opportunity, promoting access to education as a life-long process, and promoting partnerships with pupils, parents and the community.

Units
Dalziel High School, Hearing Impaired Department
Crawford Street, Motherwell, Lanarkshire, ML1 3AG
Tel: 01698 328628
Fax: 01698 328631
Contact: Ruby Davidson, Principal Teacher of the Deaf

The department serves hearing impaired pupils from all over North Lanarkshire and further afield. We use a natural oral approach and aim to achieve the fullest possible integration of pupils into mainstream curriculum. We provide individual/group support from trained teachers of the deaf in mainstream classes.

Earnock High School
Wellhall Road, Hamilton, Lanarkshire, ML3 9UE
Tel: 01698 285665
Fax: 01698 891948
E-mail: earnock@argonet.com
Contact: Sylvia Gordon, Principal Teacher, Deaf Education

18

The Department of Deaf Education, based within Earnock High School, was established in August 1993. The department caters for the needs of profoundly deaf children who communicate using sign language. Our deaf pupils reside in South Lanarkshire and surrounding areas. The deaf pupils attend mainstream classes with the support of a teacher of the deaf. In 1996 the South Lanarkshire Peripatetic Service for secondary-aged hearing impaired pupils also became part of the department. This service supports secondary age hearing impaired students in their local South Lanarkshire secondary school.

➤ Lothian
Units
Forrester High School
Broomhouse Road, Edinburgh, Lothian, EH12 9AD
Tel: 0131 334 9262
Fax: 0131 467 7134
Contact: Irene Beaver, Principal Teacher of Hearing Impaired Unit

➤ Midlothian
Education Services
City of Edinburgh Education Service
40 Torphichen Street, Edinburgh, Midlothian, EH3 8JB
Tel: 0131 229 9166
Contact: Alison Garbett, Head of Services
            St Giles Centre, Broomhouse Crescent, Edinburgh, EH11 3UB
Tel: 0131 443 0304

Support for children with sensory and communication impairments from diagnosis to school leaving. A wholly peripatetic service involved in teaching at home, nursery and school. Committed to early diagnosis and intervention. Children are included in their mainstream school and follow the nursery and 5 to 14 curriculum.

Greenhall Education Centre
Midlothian Council, Gowkshill, Gorebridge, Midlothian, EH23 4PE
Tel: 01875 823699
Fax: 01875 823603
Contact: Christine Knight, Education Officer, Pupils Support

A visiting teacher service to pupils is provided to schools in Midlothian through a service level agreement with the City of Edinburgh Council.

Midlothian Education Service
Greenhall Centre, Gowkshill, Gorebridge, Midlothian, EH23 4PE
Tel: 01875 823699
Fax: 01875 823603
Contact: D MacKay, Director of Education

Visiting Teaching and Support Services (Sensory, Communication and Special Educational Needs)
St Giles Centre, Broomhouse Crescent, Edinburgh, Midlothian, EH11 3UB
Tel: 0131 443 0304
Textphone: 0131 443 3206
Fax: 0131 444 2351
Contact: Alison Garbett, Head of Services

Support for children with sensory and communication impairment from diagnosis to school leaving. The service is a wholly peripatetic involved in teaching at home, nursery and school. Committed to early diagnosis and intervention. Children are included in their mainstream school and follow the nursery and 5 to 14 curriculum.

➤ Morayshire
Education Services
Moray Education Service
High Street, Elgin, Morayshire, IV30 1BX
Tel: 01343 543451
Fax: 01343 540183
Contact: Alex Leggatt

To service the educational needs of hearing impaired and deaf children in Moray. We operate a Peripatetic Hearing Impaired Service consisting of six FTE teachers of the deaf and 1.5 FTE communication assistants, one of whom is profoundly deaf. The purpose of these assistants is to help children in their own schools communicate through British Sign Language.

18

➢ Orkney Islands
Education Services
Orkney Children's Service

Council Offices, School Place, Kirkwall, Orkney Islands, KW15 1NY

Tel: 01856 873535
Contact: Nicky Palmer, Teacher of Hearing Impaired Children

           Children's Services, Papdale House, Berstane Road, Kirkwall, Orkney, KW15 1NA

Peripatetic service for pre-school, primary, secondary and college age range: up to 19 years. Hearing loss: mild to profound. Mode of communication: according to need.

➢ Renfrewshire
Education Services
Inverclyde Education Service

105 Dalrymple Street, Greenock, Renfrewshire, PA15 1HT

Tel: 01475 882700
Contact: Carol Jackson
Tel: 01475 712800

Inverclyde Department of Education Services provides peripatetic support to pupils with hearing impairment in mainstream schools on an outreach basis from Garvel Deaf Centre, which houses a specialist provision for school age and pre-school pupils. The head teacher of Garvel also manages the Deaf Unit, which is located within Gowack High School. The predominant philosophy of Garvel is one of bilingualism.

Renfrewshire Education Services

Cotton Street, South Building, Paisley, Renfrewshire, PA1 1LE

Tel: 0141 842 5606
Fax: 0141 842 5699

Provides a wide range of education and leisure services to the people of Renfrewshire.

Units
Garvel Deaf Centre

Chester Road, Greenock, Renfrewshire, PA16 0TT

Tel: 01475 635477
Fax: 01475 637230
Contact: Margaret Keir, Head Teacher

Garvel Deaf Centre is a provision for deaf children, incorporating a small school, a secondary unit and a peripatetic service. A bilingual policy is operated, which gives children the opportunity to acquire, where appropriate, both British Sign Language and English. It aims to encourage the development of each child's potential.

➢ Roxburghshire
Education Services
Borders Education Service

Council Headquarters, Newtown St Boswells, Melrose, Roxburghshire, TD6 0SA

Tel: 01835 824000
Fax: 01835 822145
Contact: J Christie, Director of Education

Scottish Borders Council Education Department aims to provide the most appropriate education to meet the needs of all children. These can be met in the local nursery, primary or secondary school, supported by teachers of the deaf, or in the specialist provision based in Earlston Primary School.

➢ Shetland Islands
Education Services
Shetland Islands Education

Shetland Island Council, Hayfield House, Lerwick, Shetland Islands, ZE1

Tel: 01595 744000
Fax: 01595 692810
Contact: J Halcrow, Director of Education

Education services are provided for children with all levels of hearing loss from the time of diagnosis through to school leaving age.

➢ Stirlingshire
Education Services
Falkirk Education Service

McLaren House, Marchmont Avenue, Polmont, Falkirk, Stirlingshire, FK2 0NZ

Tel: 01324 506600
Fax: 01324 506601
Contact: Gray Lambie , Communications and Information Coordinator
Tel: 01324 506602

Falkirk Council Education Services has overall responsibility for the management and day-to-day running of all educational establishments within the Falkirk Council area. This includes all schools management issues, early years, quality assurance, community education, finance, psychological services, curriculum, personnel and pupil-related issues.

18

➤ Strathclyde
Education Services
West Dunbartonshire Council SEN Support Service

Braehead Primary School, Meadow Road, Dumbarton, Strathclyde, G82 2DF

Tel: 01389 762166
Textphone: 01389 761936
Fax: 01389 761936
Contact: Moira Burger, Head Teacher

The service for hearing impaired children in West Dunbartonshire is an outreach service for approximately 40 children. It has three teachers of the deaf, one of whom heads the service, and a nursery nurse who liaises with staff in nurseries who have a hearing impaired child placed with them. The staff use an oral/aural approach with the majority of children in mainstream schools but can use signed English and British Sign Language as appropriate.

Units
Glencairn Primary School

Glencairn Street, Motherwell, Strathclyde, ML1 1TT

Tel: 01698 300281
Contact: Helen Bushe

Fully integrated nursery and primary provision for hearing-impaired pupils. Primary pupils taught in small deaf/hearing classes by teachers of the deaf. Also based in Glencairn is Visiting Services for Hearing Impaired (pre-school, primary and special).

Grange Academy

Beech Avenue, Kilmarnock, Strathclyde, KA1 2EW

Tel: 01563 543050
Fax: 01563 542648
Contact: Anne Barnaby, Teacher of the Deaf

Haysholm School

Bank Street, Irvine, Strathclyde, KA12 0NE

Tel: 01294 272481
Fax: 01294 276673
Contact: Mary McGlone, Head Teacher

Hearing Impaired Unit

39 Raglan Street, Glasgow, Strathclyde, G4 9QX

Tel: 0141 353 6136
Fax: 0141 353 6137
Contact: Marion Stewart, Unit Coordinator

The school is situated in a mainstream primary school and caters for pupils from Pr 1 to Pr 7. The children are taught by oral/aural methods and have links with the mainstream primary classes.

➤ Tayside
Units
Hillside Primary School

Denoon Terrace, Dundee, Tayside, DD2 2DH

Tel: 01382 69314
Contact: Morag Cooney

We have six hearing impaired pupils throughout the school who have a high level of integration with intensive language input from a teacher of the deaf in P1 and P2. After this the children are fully integrated into the mainstream classes with continued but less intensive help.

➤ West Lothian
Education Services
West Lothian Education Service

West Lothian Council, South Bridge Street, Bathgate, West Lothian, EH48 1TS

Tel: 01506 776107
Fax: 01506 776378
Contact: Carole Sturt, Coordinator, West
            Lothian Hearing Impaired Service
            Deams Primary School, Deams,
            Livingstone, West Lothian, EH54 8DB
Tel: 01506 418125

The Hearing Impaired Service teachers and nursery work closely with parents as soon as any difficulty has been identified by health professionals. The majority of deaf children and young people attend their local school and are visited by the specialist teachers who work closely with school staff and others involved with the child. Alternatively, children may attend Deans Primary School/Nursery or Deans Community High School if more specialist support is required. Staff liaise with an educational audiologist and colleagues in health to ensure that needs are monitored regularly.

➤ Wigtownshire
Education Services
Stranraer Area Learning Support Team

Foundry Lane, Stranraer, Wigtownshire, DG9 0DV

Tel: 01776 707193
Contact: E Grieve, Teacher of the Hearing
            Impaired

18

Wales

➤ Anglesey
See Gwynedd

➤ Blaenau Gwent
See Gwent

➤ Bridgend
See Mid Glamorgan

➤ Caerphilly
See Gwent

See Mid Glamorgan

➤ Cardiff
See South Glamorgan

➤ Carmarthenshire
See Dyfed

➤ Ceredigion
See Dyfed

➤ Clwyd
Education Services
Denbighshire Education Service
Council Offices, Whynnstay Road, Ruthin, Clwyd, LL15 1YN
Tel: 01824 706000
Fax: 01824 707446
Contact: Fred Williams, Head of Hearing Impaired Service
Tel: 01745 334153

Flintshire Education Service
County Hall, Mold, Clwyd, CH7 6NB
Tel: 01352 752121
Fax: 01352 758240
Contact: Elsbeth Parry, Advisory Teacher of the Deaf

Sensory Services, c/o Bryn Glas School for the Deaf, Clayton Road, Mold, CH7 1QX
Tel: 01352 755258
Textphone: 01352 758686

Hearing Impaired Service Mold
County Hall, Mold, Clwyd, CH7 6NB
Tel: 01352 755258
Contact: Elsbeth Parry, Teacher of the Deaf

Service for Sensory Impairment, c/o Bryn Glos School for the Deaf, Clayton Road, Mold, Clwyd, CH7 1SU

The service provides support for hearing impaired children in Flintshire schools.

Wrexham Education Service
Roxburg House, Hill Street, Wrexham, Clwyd, LL11 1SN
Tel: 01978 297500
Fax: 01978 297422
Contact: Anne Evans, Head of Sensory Services

Sensory Base, Erlas House, Brynestyn Lane, Wrexham, LL13 9TY

The Sensory Service Team in Wrexham County Borough Education Authority deals with education services for children with sensory difficulties. It deals with services for units, parents and schools.

Wrexham Special Education Centre
PO Box 1284, Guildhall, Wrexham, Clwyd, LL11 1WF
Tel: 01978 292000
Fax: 01978 292106
Contact: Terry Garner, Director of Education and Leisure Services
Tel: 01978 297421
Fax: 01978 297422

Units
Alun School
Wrexham Road, Mold, Clwyd, CH7 1EP
Tel: 01352 750755
Fax: 01382 758788
Contact: Sue Lewis, Teacher of the Deaf

18

Borras Park Infants School

Borras Park Road, Wrexham, Clwyd, LL12 7TH
Tel: 01978 352106
Contact: E Jones, Head Teacher

Borras Park Infants School in Wrexham incorporates a unit for partially hearing and profoundly deaf children. They are taught by a teacher of the deaf, and have access to all the specialist services they require, whilst having the opportunity to integrate into mainstream classes according to their individual needs.

Borras Park Junior School

Borras Park Road, Wrexham, Clwyd, LL12 7TH
Tel: 01978 359694
Fax: 01978 359694
Contact: G Jones , Head Teacher

Provides individual, small group and integrated mainstream education at Key Stage 2 and 13 pupils whose hearing losses range from mild/moderate to profound/total. A range of communication approaches is used, depending on the pupil. Staffing: one qualified teacher of the deaf (CACDP Stage II) and three full-time NNEBs.

Bryn Glas School

Clayton Road, Mold, Clwyd, CH7 1SU
Tel: 01352 758686
Textphone: 01352 758686
Fax: 01352 758313

The school provides a broad and balanced curriculum for pupils from nursery age to 19. The high level of support offered contributes to the success of the well-established programmes of integration into local primary and secondary schools and colleges of further education. Teaching is through the medium of Total Communication.

Christchurch County Primary School

Ernest Street, Rhyl, Denbighshire, LL18 2DS
Tel: 01745 337122
Contact: J Jones, Teacher of the Deaf

The Hearing Impaired Unit is based in a large primary school and the aim is to integrate the hearing impaired pupils as much as possible. It is mainly an oral/aural unit but uses sign-supported English with the profoundly deaf. We have a particular interest in cochlear implantation.

St David's High School

Rhosnesni Lane, Wrexham, Clwyd, LL13 9ET
Tel: 01978 265412
Fax: 01978 365678
Contact: Pat Hughes, Hearing Support Base

St David's is a mainstream comprehensive school which is resourced to cater for pupils with a hearing impairment. The pupils are integrated whenever possible with support from qualified teachers of the hearing impaired.

➤ Conwy
See Clwyd

➤ Denbighshire
See Clwyd

➤ Dyfed
Education Services
Carmarthenshire Education Service

County Hall, Carmarthen, Dyfed, SA31 1JP
Tel: 01267 234567
Fax: 01267 230848
Contact: Caril Mile, Head of Hearing Impaired
            Teachers
Tel: 01267 267803
Fax: 01267 267072

Ceredigion Education Service

County Office, Marine Terrace, Aberystwyth, Dyfed, SY23 2DE
Tel: 01545 570881
Fax: 01545 572009
Contact: Roger Williams, Director of Education
Tel: 01970 633601
Fax: 01970 633663
Contact: Fiona Evans, Teacher for the Hearing
            Impaired
Tel: 01970 633626
Fax: 01545 633663

To aid in the identification, assessment and subsequent coordination of provision for children with hearing impairment.

Ferryside Education Centre

Carmarthen Road, Ferryside, Dyfed, SA17 5TE
Tel: 01267 267803
Fax: 01267 267072

18

The Hearing Impairment Support Service is of a peripatetic nature and provides support in mainstream to all hearing impaired children, parents and support staff. This support consists of educational input, audiological management and a general heightening of awareness of a child's needs with the professionals involved.

Pembrokeshire Education Service

Cambria House, Haverfordwest, Dyfed, SA61 1TP
Tel: 01437 764551
Fax: 01437 775838
Contact: Sue James, Advisory Teacher for the Hearing Impaired
Tel: 01437 775295

Units
Ysgol Dewi Saint (Primary)

Bryndulais Avenue, Llanelli, Dyfed, SA14 8RS
Tel: 01745 351355
Contact: Fred Williams, Hearing Impaired Service
Tel: 01745 344390

➢ Flintshire
See Clwyd

➢ Gwent
Education Services
Blaenau Gwent Education Service

County Hall, Cwmbran, Torfaen, NP44 2XG
Tel: 01495 350555
Fax: 01495 301255
Contact: Anne Kelly, Speech, Hearing and Language Impairment Services
Tel: 01633 871226
Fax: 01633 873121

Monmouthshire Education Service

County Hall Civic Centre, Croesyceiliog, Cwmbran, Gwent, NP44 2XH
Tel: 01633 644644
Fax: 01633 644644
Contact: Anne Kelly, Speech, Hearing and Language Impairment Service
Tel: 01633 871226
Fax: 01633 873121

Newport Education Service

Civic Centre, Newport, Gwent, NP9 4UR
Tel: 01633 244491
Fax: 01633 244721
Contact: Anne Kelly, Head of Speech, Hearing and Language Impairment Services
Tel: 01633 871226
Fax: 01633 873121

Torfaen Education Service

County Hall Civic Centre, Croesyceiliog, Cwmbran, Gwent, NP44 2XH
Tel: 01495 838838
Contact: Ann Kelly, Head of Speech, Hearing and Language Impairment Service
           SHALIS, c/o Llantarnam Comprehensive School, Cwmbran, Torfaen, NP44 3XB
Tel: 01633 871226
Fax: 01633 873121

Speech, hearing and language impairment service. Working with parents and allied professionals, this service aims to provide effective educational support for hearing impaired and speech and language impaired children and young people, their families and schools. Support takes the form of on-going assessment, specialist information and support at home and school, the devising, monitoring and delivering of individual learning programmes, advice to schools on the differentiation of the National Curriculum, plus the supply and maintenance of specialist technical and teaching equipment needed by a pupil.

Units
Cross Keys College

Tel: 01495 333456
Textphone: 01495 333417
Fax: 01495 333386
Contact: Anne Carlson, Head

See entry under Further Education.

Hollybush Junior and Infant School

Ton Road, Cwmbran, Gwent, NP44 7LE
Tel: 01633 877501
Contact: S Dart, Teacher of the Deaf
Tel: 01633 877732

The department has a policy of integration and supports this with significant levels of small group work. Speech/language therapy targets are identified and incorporated into curriculum work. We have up to 24 primary-aged children with whom both speech and sign are offered. We have

18

eight implanted children and deaf adults are involved with the work of nine staff.

Llantarnam Comprehensive School
Cwmbran, Gwent, NP44 3XB
Tel: 01633 871226
Textphone: 01633 866711
Fax: 01633 873121/ 876652
Contact: R Godwin, Head of Hearing Impaired Unit

Newport Bettws Comprehensive School
Bettws Lane, Bettws, Newport, Gwent, NP9 6AB
Tel: 01633 856331

> Gwynedd
Education Services
Conwy Education Service
Bodlondeb, Conway, Gwynedd, LL32 8DU
Tel: 01492 575032
Fax: 01492 592114
Contact: J Doll, County Psychologist
Tel: 01492 575019

The Sensory Support Service, in partnership with others, aims to provide a quality service to all sensory impaired children and young people. The service aims to assist children, young people and their families or carers in assessing education that meets academic, personal and social needs, irrespective of the degree or complexity of sensory impairment. The service seeks to promote equality of opportunity which includes optimimum access to the National Curriculum.

Isle of Anglesey Education Service
Council Offices, Llangefni, Gwynedd, LL77 7TW
Tel: 01248 752900
Fax: 01248 752999
Contact: Val Owen, Teacher of the Deaf
Tel: 01286 679697

> Merthyr Tydfil
See Mid Glamorgan

> Mid Glamorgan
Education Services
Bridgend Education Service
Civic Offices, Angel Street, Bridgend, Mid Glamorgan, CF31 1LX
Tel: 01656 642200
Fax: 01656 668126
Contact: Mike Ridout, Head of Hearing Advisory Service
            Ysgol Peny Bont, Bridgend, Mid Glamorgan, CF31
Tel: 01656 667488
Fax: 01656 725230

Caerphilly Education Service
Ystrad Fawr, Ystrad Mynach, Hengoed, Mid Glamorgan, CF82 7SF
Tel: 01443 816016
Fax: 01443 816998
Contact: Anne Kelly, Speech, Hearing and Language Impairment Services
Tel: 01633 871226
Fax: 01633 873121

Education Service for Special Needs
Ysgol Penybont, Ewenny Road, Bridgend, Mid Glamorgan, CF31 3HT
Tel: 01656 667488

Merthyr Tydfil Education Service
Civic Centre, Castle Street, Merthyr Tydfil, CF47 8AN
Tel: 01685 725000
Fax: 01685 722146
Contact: Rosemary Taylor, Advisory Teacher, Hearing Impaired Education Directorate
            Ty Keir Hardie, Riverside Court, Avenue de Clichy, Merthyr Tydfil, Mid Glamorgan, CF47 8XD
Tel: 01685 724619

18

Units

Afon Taf Comprehensive
Yew Street, Troedyrhiw, Merthyr Tydfil, Mid Glamorgan, CF48 4ED
Tel: 01443 690401
Fax: 01443 693774
Contact: Carole Garrad, Teacher in Charge

We aim to integrate pupils as fully as possible into mainstream classes, thus developing true academic ability. We also aim to promote good communication skills, encourage normal socialisation within the peer group and build a healthy relationship between school and parents.

Blaengwawr Comprehensive School
Club Street, Aberdare, Mid Glamorgan, CF44 6TN
Tel: 01685 874341
Fax: 01685 883834
Contact: Peter Ford, Teacher of the Deaf

Bryn Celynnog Comprehensive School
Pencoedcae Road, Beddau, Pontypridd, Mid Glamorgan, CF38 2AE
Tel: 01443 203411/ 204642
Fax: 01443 217968
Contact: Paul Rowlands, Teacher of the Deaf

An integrated learning support centre based in and attached to Bryn Celynnog Comprehensive. All pupils are fully integrated into mainstream with support. The facility is purpose built for sensory and physically disabled students. Many other categories of special needs are also catered for.

Brynmenyn Primary School
Bryn Road, Brynmenyn, Bridgend, Mid Glamorgan, CR32 9LA
Tel: 01656 720280

Capcoch Primary School
School Street, Abercwinboi, Aberdare, Mid Glamorgan, CF44 6DF
Tel: 01443 472746
Contact: D Jones, Teacher of the Deaf

Hendre Infants and Junior School
St Cenydd Road, Caerphilly, Mid Glamorgan, CF83 2RP
Tel: 029 2085 2519 Infants
            029 20852518 Junior

Llwyn-Crwn Primary School
Llwyn-Crwn Road, Beddau, Pontypridd, Mid Glamorgan, CF38 2BE
Tel: 01443 203557
Fax: 01443 203557
Contact: Helen Weston, Teacher of the Deaf

School with a specialist deaf unit.

St Cenydd Comprehensive School
St Cenydd Road, Caerphilly, Mid Glamorgan, CF83 2RP
Tel: 029 2085 2504
Fax: 029 2088 9526
Contact: Mildred Hughes, Teacher of the Deaf

Hearing Impaired Unit aims for full integration into the mainstream school. Signing support and auditory/aural support are available. We teach all children aged 11 to 18 years and access to all courses, GCSE, GNVQ, A-Level is open to everyone. All learning needs are catered for.

Tonypandy Comprehensive School
Llewellyn Street, Penygraig, Rhondda, Mid Glamorgan
Tel: 01443 436171
Fax: 01443 430918
Contact: Mary Thomas, Teacher, Hearing
            Impaired Unit

Tonypandy Primary School
Primrose Street, Rhondda, Mid Glamorgan, CF40 1BQ
Tel: 01443 433006
Fax: 01443 433006
Contact: M Harrison, Head Teacher

Ynysawdre Comprehensive School
Heol yr Ysgol, Tondu, Bridgend, Mid Glamorgan, CF32 9EL
Tel: 01656 720643
Fax: 01656 722571
Contact: Jane Jones, Teacher of the Deaf

Ynysowen Junior School
Aberfan, Merthyr Tydfil, Mid Glamorgan, CF48 4NT
Tel: 01443 690478
Contact: Claire Harding, Hearing Impaired
            Support Teacher

18

➢ Monmouthshire
See Gwent

➢ Neath Port Talbot
See West Glamorgan

➢ Newport
See Gwent

➢ Pembrokeshire
See Dyfed

➢ Powys
Education Services
Powys Education Service

Southfields Annexe, Powys County Hall,
Llandrindad Wells, Powys, LD1 5LG
Tel: 01597 826000
Fax: 01597 826230
Contact: Keith Davies, Senior Teacher for the
            Hearing Impaired

            Area Education Offices, Old College,
            Newtown, Powys, SY16 1BE
Tel: 01686 626521
Fax: 01597 629626

Educational services for hearing impaired children.

Units
Brecon High School

Penlan, Brecon, Powys
Tel: 01874 622361
Contact: C Phillips, Teacher of the Deaf

Cefn Llys County Primary

Cefnllys Lane, Cefnllys, Llandrindod Wells, Powys,
LD1 5WA
Tel: 01597 822297
Fax: 01597 823781
Contact: Jill Thomas, Hearing Impaired Unit

Ladywell Green Nursery and Infant School

Newtown, Powys, SY16 4NU
Tel: 01686 626303
Contact: Keith Davis, Advisory Teacher for the
            Deaf

Llandrindod Wells County Primary School

Cefnyllys Lane, Llandrindod Wells, Powys, LD1 5WA
Tel: 01597 822297
Fax: 01597 823781
E-mail: cefnylls@powys.gov.uk
Contact: F Roberts, Head Teacher

Newtown High School

Newtown, Powys, SY16 1JE
Tel: 01686 626304
Fax: 01686 629956
Contact: Elizabeth Hughes, Teacher of the
            Hearing Impaired

A Partially Hearing Unit for children with profound
and severe hearing impairments integrated into
the mainstream. The unit is run by a qualified
teacher of the hearing impaired. Work in the unit
centres on speech and language development
auditory training and subject support.

➢ Rhondda, Cynon,Taff
See Mid Glamorgan

➢ South Glamorgan
Units
Coed Glas School

Ty Glas Avenue, Llanishen, Cardiff, South
Glamorgan, CF4 5DW
Tel: 029 2075 4862
Contact: Alison Cox, Teacher of the Deaf

Hearing Impaired Unit taking a maximum of 12
children, within a mainstream primary school.
Children have severe/profound losses.
Communication emphasis is on oralism.

Cogan Primary School

Pill Street, Cogan, Penarth, South Glamorgan, CF6
1JS
Tel: 029 2070 8497
Fax: 029 2070 6793
Contact: C Kell, Teacher of the Deaf

Llanishen High School

Heol Hir, Llanishen, Cardiff, South Glamorgan, CF4
5YL
Tel: 029 2075 3357
Textphone: 029 2075 2422
Contact: S Greenland, Teacher of the Deaf

18

A secondary unit for statemented deaf and hearing impaired pupils in a comprehensive school in Cardiff. The pupils integrate in mainstream classes with support from and withdrawal to the unit.

St Cyres Comprehensive School
St Cyres Road, Penarth, South Glamorgan, CF64 2XP
Tel: 029 2070 8708
Contact: Keith Howells, Teacher of the Deaf

St Cyres Comprehensive School provides an integrated education for its own hearing impaired pupils and also for pupils from Yrgol Erwr Delyn (school for physically handicapped children) and Arliprane School for Deaf Children.

➢ Swansea
See West Glamorgan

➢ Torfaen
See Gwent

➢ Vale of Glamorgan, The
See South Glamorgan

➢ West Glamorgan
Education Services
Neath Port Talbot Education Services
Civic Centre, Port Talbot, West Glamorgan, SA13 1PJ
Tel: 01639 763333
Fax: 01639 763000
Contact: Irene Lewis, Head of Hearing Impaired Service

             Glanymor Centre, Severn Crescent, Sandfields, Port Talbot
Tel: 01639 890108
Contact: Vivian Thomas, Director of Education, Leisure and Lifelong Learning
Tel: 01639 763298
Fax: 01639 763788
Contact: Derick Jones, Special Needs Manager
Tel: 01639 763350
Fax: 01639 890380

Swansea Education Services
County Hall, Oystermouth Road, Swansea, SA1 3SN
Tel: 01792 636000
Fax: 01792 636700
Contact: Phil Martin, Team Leader, Learning Disability Team

             Ty Llen, Sommerset Place, Swansea, SA1 1RR
Tel: 01792 405689

Units
Catwg Primary School
Neath Road, Crynant, Neath, West Glamorgan, SA10 8RS
Tel: 01639 642731
Fax: 01639 641831
Contact: D Rees, Head Teacher

Cwrt Sart Comprehensive School
Old Road, Briton Ferry, Neath, West Glamorgan, SA11 2ET
Tel: 01639 770088
Fax: 01639 770099
E-mail: mwilliams@cwrtsart.baglanit.org.uk
Contact: M Williams, Teacher of the Deaf

A comprehensive taking pupils aged 11 to 16 years, with all hearing impaired children being fully integrated. We have a strong caring tradition coupled with good academic opportunities and a range of enhanced learning opportunities.

Grange Primary School
West Cross Avenue, West Cross, Swansea, West Glamorgan
Tel: 01792 404766

We are a mainstream school with provision for 14 hearing impaired children, age range 3 to 11 years. Pupils are taught in two units by two qualified teachers of the deaf. The children are integrated with mainstream peers for a variety of subjects and sessions each week. This is organised on an individual need basis to make the maximum use of the experience for the individual. The school also incorporates a privately run nursery for two years upwards which can accommodate pupils with special educational needs. Before and after school childcare facilities are available. The school is set in extensive grounds with a pond and nature reserve, picnic and outdoor adventure play area, and facilities for dance and drama activities.

18

Olchfa Comprehensive School

Gower Road, Sketty, Swansea, West Glamorgan,
SA2 7AB

Tel:	01792 201222 ext 128
Textphone:	01792 201222
Fax:	01792 297174
Contact:	J Williams, Teacher of the Deaf

Sandfields Comprehensive School

Southdown View, Port Talbot, West Glamorgan,
SA12 7AH

Tel:	01639 884246
Fax:	01639 894951
Contact:	Susan Tetsill, Teacher of the Deaf

Sandfields Comprehensive School Unit for the
Hearing Impaired encompasses a Total
Communication philosophy. It provides for pupils
with profound hearing loss and/or additional
disabilities. Its aim is to promote a caring
environment where pupils reach their educational
and social potential through a policy of integration
and inclusion in the mainstream school.

> ## Wrexham
See Clwyd

18

Further Education

This section covers colleges offering further (and in some cases, higher) education courses. Services for students with a hearing loss are usually accessed through a Disability or Access Officer. Services usually include a mixture of human and technical communication support and there may also be textphones and radio aids available. For further details of what is available within each college, please contact individual colleges directly.

This section is listed alphabetically by college within country and county sections.

England

➢ Avon

City of Bristol College

Ashley Down Road, Bristol, Avon, BS7 9BU

Tel: 0117 904 5054

Textphone: 0117 904 5283

Videotel: 0117 942 0185/1/2

Fax: 0117 904 5186

E-mail: cbc@sbristol.tcom.co.uk

Website: www.cityofbristol.ac.uk

Contact: Nick Cowley, Coordinator, Deaf and Hearing Impaired Support Team

Tel: 0117 904 5200

The City of Bristol College has a dynamic and highly qualified staff of 20 professionals committed to delivering full or partial communication support to all deaf and hearing impaired students. These include teachers of the deaf, notetakers, CSW's and sign language teachers. The City of Bristol College has an inclusive policy and provides access for deaf students on to all courses subject to interview and assessment. Tutorials and regular reviews are an integral part of our service.

Trinity College

Stoke Hill, Bristol, Avon, BS9 1JP

Tel: 0117 968 2803

Fax: 0117 968 7470

E-mail: www.trinity-bris.ac.uk

Trinity College is an Anglican theological college training men and women for ordained and lay ministry in Anglican and other churches, in conjunction with Bristol Baptist College and Wesley College.

University College Bath Spa

Tel: 01225 875578

Fax: 01225 875525

E-mail: J.Kirkby@Bathspa.ac.uk

Website: www.bathspa.ac.uk

Contact: Julie Kirkby, Careers Adviser

See entry under Higher Education.

➢ Bath & NE Somerset
See Avon

➢ Bedfordshire

Barnfield College

Rotheram Avenue, Luton, Bedfordshire, LU1 5PP

Tel: 01582 569500

Fax: 01582 569731

Contact: Carol Doran, Programme Area Leader, Additional Support

Tel: 01582 569709

Textphone: 01582 569739

Vision 2000: To become the best provider of work-related training and education by delivering an exceptional level of service to all our customers and by promoting achievement in a quality, cost-effective and adult learning environment.

➢ Berkshire

Bracknell and Wokingham College

Church Road, Bracknell, Berkshire, RG12 1DJ

Tel: 01344 420411

Fax: 01344 860720

Contact: Nickola Foord
            Learning Resources Centre, Wick Hill Site, Bracknell, Berkshire, RG12 2JG

We are a College Learning Resource Centre, providing library and computer facilities, including CD-ROM, to full-and part-time students.

East Berkshire College of Further Education

Station Road, Langley, Slough, Berkshire, SL3 8BY

Tel: 01753 793207

Textphone: 01753 793226

Fax: 01753 793316

Contact: Kit Jillings, Team Leader, Learning Support

19

Reading Adult and Community College
Wilson Road, Reading, Berkshire, RG30 2RW
Tel: 0118 901 5251
Fax: 0118 901 5250
Contact: Maggie Walker, Head of Community
            Education
Tel: 0118 901 5255
The college provides general adult education covering 200+ subjects including arts and crafts, computing, lifestyles, languages and adult basic education. There are special courses and facilities for older people, and for students with disabilities. We also run a series of British Sign Language classes, starting throughout the year.

➢ Blackburn
See Lancashire

➢ Blackpool
See Lancashire

➢ Brighton and Hove
See East Sussex

➢ Bristol, City of
See Avon

➢ Buckinghamshire
Amersham and Wycombe College of Further Education, Art and Design
Stanley Hill, Amersham, Buckinghamshire, HP7 9HN
Tel: 01494 735555
Fax: 01494 735566
Contact: Liz Dawson, Programme Team Leader

The Chalfonts Community College
Narcot Lane, Chalfont St Peter, Gerrards Cross, Buckinghamshire, SL9 8TP
Tel: 01753 882032
Fax: 01753 890716
Contact: Gillian Walmsley, Head of Special
            Needs
The Chalfonts Community College provides full-time education for 1500 students who have special educational needs, particularly those who are partially deaf or hearing-impaired. All students

356

are fully integrated but are well supported.

➢ Cambridgeshire
Cambridge Regional College
Kings Hedges Road, Cambridge, CB4 2QT
Tel: 01223 418200
Fax: 01223 315957
Contact: Isobel Blakeley, Tutor for Hearing
            Impaired Students
Tel: 01223 418501
Textphone: 01223 418500
Appropriate communication is provided for deaf and hard of hearing students attending the college. Each student has an individual support programme.

Peterborough Regional College
Park Crescent, Peterborough, Cambridgeshire, PE1 4DZ
Tel: 01733 767366
Fax: 01733 767986
E-mail: margaretsolomon@peterborough.ac.u
            k
Contact: Margaret Solomon, Inclusive Learning

➢ Cheshire
Halton College
Kingsway, Widnes, Cheshire, WA8 7QQ
Tel: 0151 423 1391

The following are course centres in the Runcorn and Widnes area: Grange Comprehensive, Latham Avenue, Runcorn. Lipreading classes are held at Simms Cross Annexe, Widnes on Wednesday from 10am to 12 noon.

Macclesfield College
Park Lane, Macclesfield, Cheshire, SK11 8LF
Tel: 01625 614919

Mid Cheshire College of Further Education
Chester Road, Hartford, Northwich, Cheshire, CW8 1LJ
Tel: 01606 784344
Fax: 01606 75101

A further education college providing facilities for day students. Communication methods used are the oral/aural method and Total Communication.

Ridge Danyers College

Cheadle Road, Cheadle Hulme, Cheadle, Cheshire, SK8 5HA

Tel: 0161 485 4372

Fax: 0161 482 8129

Contact: Margaret Parker

Textphone: 0161 485 1772

Fax: 0161 482 8054

The college aims to support students who are hearing impaired and to develop lipreading as a skill in small groups with qualified staff. Students are encouraged to move into higher-level groups and to support other students outside the class. As of December 1998 there is no charge for this class. Accreditations may be available in 1999/2000. Lipreading classes are held in Stockport on Tuesday and Thursday in the morning, in the afternoons on Monday and Wednesday, and in the evenings on Tueday and Wednesday.

Ridges Danyers College

Hibbert Lane, Marple, Stockport, Cheshire, SK6 1AB

Tel: 0161 427 1111

Royal School for the Deaf Manchester

Tel: 0161 610 0100

Fax: 0161 610 0101

Website: www:rsd.manchester.org

Contact: Leighton Reed, Headteacher

See entry under Deaf Schools.

South Cheshire College

Danebank Avenue, Crewe, Cheshire, CW2 8AB

Tel: 01270 654654

Fax: 01270 651515

Contact: Chris Clark, Student Services

South Trafford College

Manchester Road, West Timperley, Altrincham, Cheshire, WA14 5PG

Tel: 0161 952 4755/ 4694

Stockport College of Further and Higher Education

Davenport Centre, Highfield Close, Stockport, Cheshire, SK3 8UB

Tel: 0161 958 3557

Fax: 0161 958 3554

Contact: Rachel Holmes, Department of Childhood Studies

From September 1999, the address for the Stockport College of Further and Higher Education will be: Wellington Road North, Stockport, Cheshire SK1 3UQ. Telephone: 0161 958 3100.

➢ Cleveland

Hartlepool College of Further Education

Stockton Street, Hartlepool, TS24 7NT

Tel: 01429 275453

Stockton and Billingham Technical College

The Causeway, Billingham, Cleveland, TS23 2DB

Tel: 01642 552101

Fax: 01642 360273

Contact: Dudley Staples, Coordinator for Hearing Impaired Students

The Hearing Impaired Support Service enables students of 16+ to access courses in Cleveland's 11 colleges.

➢ Cornwall

Cornwall College

Pool, Redruth, Cornwall, TR15 3RD

Tel: 01209 616172

Fax: 01209 611612

Contact: Kim Whitworth, Learning Disabilities Coordinator

Tel: 01209 611611

Students and prospective students are encouraged to contact the Learning Disabilities Coordinator to assess their specific needs and requirements.

Penwith College

St Clare Street, Penzance, Cornwall, TR18 2SA

Tel: 01736 335000

Fax: 01736 335100

Contact: R Andruszko, Principal

19

St Austell College
Trevarthian Road, St Austell, Cornwall, PL25 4BU
Tel: 01726 67911
Fax: 01726 68499

Truro College
Gloweth, Truro, Cornwall, TR1 3XX
Tel: 01872 264251
Fax: 01726 222360
Contact: P Stansfield, Learning Support
            Coordinator

Truro College has a contract with the County Audiology Service to provide support for students with a hearing loss. Services include a teacher of the deaf, equipment, reviews of needs, regular hearing tests and classroom support. Special exam needs can also be met such as separate rooms and invigilators.

➤ County Durham
Bishop Auckland Technical College
Woodhouse Lane, Bishop Auckland, County Durham, DL14 6JX
Tel: 01388 603052

Darlington College Of Technology
Cleveland Avenue, Darlington, County Durham, DL3 7BB
Tel: 01325 503050
Textphone: 01325 503252
Fax: 01325 503000
Website: www.darlington.ac.uk
Contact: George Hollis, Learning Development
            Services Manager

Durham Sixth Form Centre
Providence Row, The Sands, Durham, DH1 1SG
Tel: 0191 384 2217
Fax: 0191 386 3454
Contact: G Martin, Careers Department

Durham Sixth Form Centre is part of Gilesgate Comprehensive School and caters for 640 students in the 16-19 age range who come from a variety of schools in County Durham. Most students study A-Levels and proceed to further and higher education. A small number of students study Advanced Level GNVQ Business or Leisure and Tourism. Durham Sixth Form Centre is located close to the centre of Durham City.

New College
Framwellgate Moor Lane, Durham, DH1 5ES
Tel: 0191 375 4000
Fax: 0191 375 4222
Contact: Tina Garside, Special Needs
            Coordinator

➤ Cumbria
Carlisle College
Victoria Place, Carlisle, Cumbria, CA1 1HS
Tel: 01228 24464
Videotel: 01228 819000
Fax: 01228 514677
E-mail: jarmstrong@carlisle.ac.uk
Contact: Joan Armstrong, Learning Support
            Manager
Tel: 01228 819000 ext 2117

Carlisle College aims to offer equal access to premises and curriculum for its local community, including those with a disability, if possible. Students with additional support needs are invited to discuss their requirements prior to enrolment, to facilitate appropriate support, which may include providing communicators for deaf students.

➤ Derbyshire
Bradford and Ilkley Community College
121 Osmaston Road, Derby, DE1 2GA
Tel: 01274 753133
Textphone: 01274 753133
Fax: 01274 753446
E-mail: lisap@bilk.ac.uk
Website: www.bilk.ac.uk
Contact: Pauline Woolly, Central Health
            Services, Speech and Language
            Therapy Services
Tel: 01332 363371 ext 205

All courses are open to deaf students, the college also runs Wordpower/Numberpower (City and Guilds) courses for deaf students. Human and technical communication support is available in all areas of course work - textphones, radio aids, pagers, teachers of the deaf, communication support workers. Counselling is also available. Extra individual and group tutorials can be arranged as required. Approximately 20 deaf or hard of hearing students are admitted each year.

Broomfield College of Agriculture and Horticulture

Morley, Ilkestone, Derbyshire, DE7 6DN

Tel: 01332 831345

Contact: Ann Wilkinson, Learning Support
                Coordinator

A wide range of support for deaf and hard of hearing students. A package of support is agreed enabling students full and equal access to all courses. Resources on offer include: teachers of the deaf, sign language communicators, notetakers, lipspeakers, extra tutorials and specialist equipment, such as radio hearing aids.

Chesterfield College of Technology and Arts

Infirmary Road, Chesterfield, Derbyshire, S41 7NG

Tel: 01246 500500

Contact: John Turnbull, Advisory Lecturer for
                Hearing Impaired Students

Tel: 01246 500500 ext 651

Fax: 01246 500587

A wide range of support is available for deaf and hearing impaired students. A package of support is agreed, giving students full and equal access to all courses. Resources on offer include: teachers of the deaf, sign language communicators, notetakers, lipspeakers, extra tutorials and specialist equpiment such as radio hearing aids.

Derby College for Deaf People

Ashbourne Road, Derby, DE22 3BH

Tel: 01332 297550

Textphone: 01332 206642

Fax: 01332 206642

E-mail: dcdp_staff@yahoo.com

Website: www.derbycollegedeaf.demon.co.uk

Contact: Brenda Mullen, Principal

Residential college with approximately 110 students on roll, and 50 students admitted each year. A range of accommodation is offered to students both on site at Derby College for Deaf People and in nearby university halls of residence. Programmes offered include: GCSE A-Level, BTEC First and National Diploma; NVQ Levels 1-3, GNVQ Foundation, Intermediate and Advanced levels, City and Guilds; NEMAP; Asdan programmes; all available at local mainstream colleges. Access to FE and Vocational Credit Programme students have additional programmes on site which include: life skills, cookery, deafness studies and communication workshops. A comprehensive tutorial programme is available including one to one tutorials, group tutorials for GCSE mathematics and English, and a programme of

study skills, health education and British Sign Language. Equipment includes: radio aids, textphones, and back up from an audiologist providing new moulds and aids. Human support includes: lecturers for deaf people, communication support workers, speech therapist, deaf youth workers, deaf counsellors, access to careers advisors, and residential care workers. Comprehensive communication support is given in all areas of course work including work placement schemes.

Derby Tertiary College Wilmorton

London Road, Wilmorton, Derby, DE24 8UG

Tel: 01332 757570

Textphone: 01332 754466

Fax: 01332 576301

Contact: John Moakes, Support Services
                Manager, Learner Support

Tel: 01332 757570 ext 301

All courses run by the college are open to deaf students whether part-time, full-time or evening. An English course - English from Wordpower to GCSE - is run solely for deaf students. An accredited Study Skills course is offered for deaf students. Technical support includes radio aids and textphones. Human support includes notetakers, interpreters and communicators. Counselling and advice services are available to students. Communication support is available for all areas of coursework including work placements schemes. On average about 25 to 30 deaf students are admitted each year. Communication methods used are bilingual Total Communication.

High Peak College, Derbyshire

Harpur Hill, Buxton, Derbyshire, SK17 9JZ

Tel: 01298 71100

Textphone: 01298 28320

Contact: Carol Watkins, Advisory Lecturer for
                Hearing Impaired Students

A wide range of support is available for deaf and hearing impaired students. A package of support is agreed enabling students full and equal access to all courses. Resources on offer include: teachers of the deaf, sign language communicators, notetakers, lipspeakers, extra tutorials and specialist equipment such as radio hearing aids.

Mackworth College, Derby

Prince Charles Avenue, Mackworth, Derby, DE22 4LR

Tel: 01332 519951

Fax: 01332 510548

Contact: Carol Watkinson, Advisory Lecturer for Hearing Impaired Students

Tel: 01332 519951 ext 355

A wide range of support is available for deaf and hearing impaired students. A package of support is agreed enabling students full and equal access to all courses. Resources on offer include: teachers of the deaf, sign language communicators, notetakers, lipspeakers, extra tutorials and specialist equipment such as radio hearing aids.

North Derbyshire Tertiary College

Rectory Road, Clowne, Chesterfield, Derbyshire, S43 4BQ

Tel: 01246 810332

Contact: Jabba Datta, Learning Support Coordinator

A wide range of support is available for deaf and hearing impaired students. A package of support is agreed, giving students full and equal access to all courses. Resources on offer include: teachers of the deaf, sign language communicators, notetakers, lipspeakers, extra tutorials, and specialist equipment such as radio hearing aids.

South East Derbyshire College

Field Road, Ilkeston, Derbyshire, DE7 5RS

Tel: 01159 324212

Textphone: 0115 932 4212

Fax: 01773 717225

Contact: John Trevail, Student Services

Tel: 01159 324212 ext 335

A wide range of support is available for deaf and hearing impaired students. A package of support is agreed, giving students full and equal access to all courses. Resources on offer include: teachers of the deaf,sign language communicators, notetakers, lipspeakers, extra tutorials and specialist equipment such as radio hearing aids.

Woodlands Community School

Tel: 01332 551921

Textphone: 01332 551921

Fax: 01332 553869

Contact: T Bate, Teacher of the Deaf

See entry under Education.

➤ Devon

Bideford College

Hearing Support Unit, Bideford, Devon, EX39 3AR

Tel: 01237 477611

Fax: 01237 428114

Contact: Cynthia May, Teacher in Charge of Unit

Plymouth College of Further Education

The Library, Kings Road, Devonport, Plymouth, Devon, PL1 5QG

Tel: 01752 305368

Fax: 01752 305343

Contact: Annalisa Crawford

Royal West of England Residential School for the Deaf

Tel: 01392 272692

Textphone: 01392 272692

Fax: 01392 431146

E-mail: rcd.exeter@eclipse.co.uk

Website: www.eclipse.co.uk/rsd.exeter

Contact: J Shaw, Principal

See entry under Deaf Schools.

➤ East Riding of Yorkshire
See Humberside

➤ East Sussex

Eastbourne College of Art and Technology

St Annes Road, Eastbourne, East Sussex, BN21 2HP

Tel: 01323 644711

Fax: 01323 412239

Hastings College of Art and Technology

Archery Road, St Leonards On Sea, East Sussex, TN38 OHZ

Tel: 01424 442222/ 435619

Fax: 01424 445675

Ovingdean Hall School

Tel: 01273 301929
Textphone: 01273 301929
Fax: 01273 305884
Contact: Malcolm Bown, Head Teacher

See entry under Deaf Schools.

Plumpton College

Ditchling Road, Plumpton, Lewes, East Sussex, BN7 3AE

Tel: 01273 890454
Fax: 01273 890071
Contact: Paula Underwood, Learning Development Tutor

Plumpton College provides education and training for those interested in following careers in the land-based industries. Programmes are available which are either part-time or full-time and range from foundation level to HND. Specialist support for deaf students can be arranged for students who satisfy the appropriate entry criteria.

➢ Essex

Barking College

Dagenham Road, Romford, Essex, RM7 0XU

Tel: 01708 766841
Textphone: 01708 727033
Fax: 01708 731067
Contact: Pat Cridland

Basildon College

Nethermayne, Basildon, Essex, SS16 5NN

Tel: 01268 532015
Fax: 01268 522139
Contact: C J Robinson

A college helping students on child care courses.

Chelmsford College of Further Education

Moulsham Street, Chelmsford, Essex, CM2 0JQ

Tel: 01245 265611
Fax: 01245 266908
Contact: Phil Walden, Learning Support Manager

Chelmsford College aims to provide high quality education and training opportunities for individuals, groups and employers to enable them to achieve success. No disability or combination of disability should debar the individual from the right to further education.

Colchester Institute

Sheepen Road, Colchester, Essex, CO3 3LL

Tel: 01206 718000
Fax: 01206 763041
Contact: Julia Bivon, Inclusive Learning Coordinator
Tel: 01206 718741

Colchester Institute is a further education college with programmes ranging from entry to degree level. Services for hearing impaired students are offered in conjunction with Essex Education. Each student is individually assessed and offered support that (where possible) meets their needs.

Epping Forest College

Borders Lane, Loughton, Essex, IG10 3SA

Tel: 020 8508 8311
Fax: 020 8502 0186
Contact: Anne Winter, Manager, Learning Support Unit
Tel: 020 8508 8311 ext 887

Epping Forest College is a college of further education offering a wide range of academic/vocational programmes. Each year a number of young people and adults who are deaf study at the college. Early application is advised to ensure that appropriate support can be arranged.

Redbridge College

Little Heath, Romford, Essex, RM6 4XT

Tel: 020 8548 7400
Textphone: 020 8548 7400
Fax: 020 8599 8224
E-mail: college@redbridge.essex.sch.uk
Contact: Carolyn Hallahan, Senior Tutor

Redbridge College offers a wide range of GNVQ, NVQ, GCSE and A-level courses which are open to all students meeting the eligibility criteria. There is a full support mechanism including communicators and a teacher of the deaf in place, and technical support including radio aids and software packages available to help students in their studies. Specialist courses include: CACDP BSL courses in day/evening/block formats for Stage I and Stage II and the BTEC Communication Support Worker with Deaf People course (one year). The CACDP Deafblind communication course at Stage I is offered part-time.

19

South East Essex College

Carnarvon Road, Southend-On-Sea, Essex, SS2 6LS

Tel: 01702 220400

Fax: 01702 432320

E-mail: seessexcollege.ac.uk

Contact: Susan Coole, Head of Academic Support

E-mail: coolesue@seessexcollege.ac.uk

We aim to provide equal access for hearing impaired students to any course for which they are qualified. We offer support in the following areas: lipspeaking, notetaking, sign language; at interviews, classes, examinations and educational visits. This support is tailored to meet the specific needs of the individual student.

➢ Gillingham and Rochester
See Kent

➢ Gloucestershire
Gloucestershire College of Arts and Technology

73 The Park, Cheltenham, Gloucestershire, GL50 2RR

Tel: 01242 532154

Textphone: 01242 532050

Fax: 01242 532023

Contact: Jane Griffiths, Disability Support Coordinator

Tel: 01242 532417

GLOSCAT is a further education college offering a full range of vocational, academic and recreational courses at all levels, from basic to HND.

National Star Centre College of Further Education

Ullenwood, Cheltenham, Gloucestershire, GL53 9QU

Tel: 01242 527631

Fax: 01242 222234

E-mail: principal@natstar.ac.uk

Website: www.natstar.ac.uk/www.create-able.com

Contact: Allan White

The college aims to enable young people with physical disabilities to prepare for the best that adult life can offer through innovative programmes of education, training and independence.

Stroud College

Stratford Road, Stroud, Gloucestershire, GL5 4AL

Tel: 01453 763424

Textphone: 01453 761111 (9am to 1pm)

Fax: 01453 753543

Contact: Peter Windell

Stroud College is a further education establishment endeavouring to offer a flexible curriculum, providing individual learning programmes and promoting lifelong learning for all.

➢ Hampshire
Basingstoke College of Technology

Worting Road, Basingstoke, Hampshire, RG21 8TN

Tel: 01256 354141

Fax: 01256 306444

Contact: Kay Bird

Tel: 01256 306313

The college aims to meet the education and training needs of the whole community and to provide a culture of lifelong learning and equality of opportunity. It seeks to equip all college staff with the expertise, commitment and skills to meet successfully the needs of students and develop the quality of all college services. It continually evaluates the quality of the college's learning programme to ensure its continuous improvement.

Eastleigh College

Chestnut Avenue, Eastleigh, Hampshire, SO50 5BF

Tel: 023 8032 6326

Fax: 023 8032 2131

E-mail: goplaces@eastleigh.ac.uk

Contact: Pat Teague, Area Manager for Care

Fareham College

Bishopsfield Road, Fareham, Hampshire, PO14 1NH

Tel: 01329 815200

Fax: 01329 822483

Contact: Jennie Espiner, Learning Services Manager

The corporate ethos of Fareham College is dedicated to "the promotion of excellence in learning" for the whole of the community.

Farnborough College of Technology

Boundary Road, Farnborough, Hampshire, GU14 6SB

Tel: 01252 407004

Fax: 01252 404007

Contact: Sylvia Law, Course Coordinator

Farnborough College runs courses in lipspeaking and a newly accredited course in support work for deaf people. Students wishing to take the course in support work will need to have gained CACDP Stage I and will be required to complete a successful college interview. For further details of the courses please contact the college.

Lord Mayor Treloar College

London Road, Holybourne, Alton, Hampshire, GU34 4EN

Tel: 01420 547400/ 547425

Fax: 01420 542708

E-mail: Admissions@trelour.org.uk

Contact: Helen Burton, Admissions Department

The school and college provide high quality education, residential care, therapy, medical support and independence training for young people aged from 7 to 25 years with physical disabilities, speech and language impairments, and associated learning difficulties. Students at the school follow the National Curriculum to GCSE and courses at the College include NVQs/GNVQs, A-levels and ASDAN awards.

➢ Hartlepool
See Cleveland

➢ Herefordshire
Herefordshire College of Technology

Folly Lane, Hereford, HR1 1LS

Tel: 01432 352235

Textphone: 01432 365371

Fax: 01432 353449

➢ Hertfordshire
Barnet College

Wood Street, Barnet, Hertfordshire, EN5 4AZ

Tel: 020 8440 6321

Fax: 020 8441 5236

Contact: Geraldine Weston, Learning Support Coordinator

Tel: 020 8275 2810

Barnet College is a further education college which offers a wide range of additional learning support to help students meet the demands of their studies. The support provided is based on an assessment of individual need.

Dacorum College of Further Education

Marlowes, Hemel Hempstead, Hertfordshire, HP1 1HD

Tel: 01442 221557

Oaklands College

The Campus, Welwyn Garden City, Hertfordshire, AL8 6AH

Tel: 01707 326318

Textphone: 01707 326318

Fax: 01707 377544

Contact: Steven Nelson, Disability Learning Tutor

Tel: 01707 737000 ext 6528

West Herts College

Langley Road, Watford, Hertfordshire, WD1 3RH

Tel: 01923 812000

Fax: 01923 812480

Contact: Ruth Shadwell

Tel: 01923 812280

West Herts Collge is a further education college offering tuition in basic signing skills leading to BSL Stage I, and lipreading.

➢ Kent
Leigh City Technology College

Green Street Green Road, Dartford, Kent, DA1 1QE

Tel: 01322 620400

Fax: 01322 620401

E-mail: 9226900.d4w@dialnet.co.uk

Contact: Ron Hewett, Head of Department, Hearing Impaired Unit

Leigh CTC is primarily a secondary education facility for students in the age range 11 to 18, with a hearing impaired unit integrated into the facility. All courses are open to deaf students and communication support is available: radio aids, audiological support, teachers of the deaf and facilitators.

19

Mid Kent College

Maidstone Road, Chatham, Kent, ME4 6JD

Tel: 01634 830633

Contact: N Fenton-Smith, Advisory Teacher for the Deaf

Textphone: 01634 842339

Mid Kent College will either provide or coordinate learning support for students enrolling on further or higher education courses throughout the college.

Royal School for Deaf Children Margate and Westgate College for Deaf People

Tel: 01843 227561

Textphone: 01843 227561

Fax: 01843 227637

E-mail: rsdmar@aol.com

Website: www.members.aol.com/rsdcmar/home.htm

Contact: David Bond, Principal

See entry under Deaf Schools.

South Kent College

Shorncliffe Road, Folkestone, Kent, CT20 2NA

Tel: 01303 858200

Fax: 01303 858400

Website: www.southkent.ac.uk

South Kent College offers a full range of further and higher education courses. The college provides additional support for all students as necessary. It also offers courses for school leavers with learning difficulties and day and evening courses for adults with learning difficulties.

Thanet College

Ramsgate Road, Broadstairs, Kent, CT10 1PN

Tel: 01843 605040

Fax: 01843 605013

Contact: Cheryl Morgan, Integrated Learning Support Head

Tel: 01843 605040 ext 5563

Thanet College has worked successfully with hearing impaired students for eight years. We work closely with the Royal School for the Deaf in Margate and the Kent County Sensory Impaired Service. Students with hearing impairments may receive sign and notetaking support in their lectures. They are eligible for individual and small group tutorials to build confidence and assist in assignment and portfolio completion. An important part of tutorials is language extension work. A textphone service is being installed to ease communication between college and home. Exam modifications for students pursuing academic qualifications are provided as needed.

West Kent College

Brook Street, Tonbridge, Kent, TN9 2PW

Tel: 01732 358101

Textphone: 01732 350763

Fax: 01732 771415

Contact: Kenneth Culver, Coordinator of Support for Deaf Students

Tel: 01732 358101 ext 4115

West Kent College aims to develop confidence and independence in its students preparing for work/higher education. It seeks to provide equal opportunities for deaf and hearing impaired students by helping them to develop their language and communication skills. Support services provide the following: diagnostic assessment of hearing loss and support requirements; facilitating communication and learning through sign language, lipspeaking and notetaking; clarifying terminology and modifying language; individual tutorials and examination/assessment arrangements.

Westgate College

St Gabriel's House, 44 Elm Grove, Westgate-On-Sea, Kent, CT8 8LB

Tel: 01843 836300

Fax: 01843 836300

E-mail: westgate@aol.com

Contact: Freda Brown, Head of College

Westgate College is a national residential college for deaf people which focuses on inclusion and integration. It aims to develop students' potential for their future place within society. The college offers education and training within a Total Communication environment using a wide spectrum of mainstream and specialist provision.

Wye College

Tel: 01233 812401

Fax: 01233 812330

E-mail: Registry@wye.ac.uk

Contact: Caral Jovanovic

See entry under Higher Education.

➤ Lancashire

Accrington and Rossendale College
Sandy Lane, Accrington, Lancashire, BB5 2AW
Tel: 01254 389933

Blackburn College
Fielden Street, Blackburn, Lancashire, BB2 1LH
Tel: 01254 55144

Blackpool College
2 Ashfield Road, Blackpool, Lancashire, FY2 0HB
Tel: 01253 352352

Bolton College of Further Education
Manchester Road, Bolton, Lancashire, BL2 1ER
Tel: 01204 453479
Textphone: 01204 365067
Fax: 01204 365067
Contact: Guy Barnard, Support Unit for Deaf
            Students

A further education college providing facilities for day students and using Total Communication. Extensive provision and support is available for deaf students, including communicators, lipspeakers, notetakers, tutor for the deaf and extra tutorial support. Deaf awareness training and sign language classes are available as are classes for deaf people in numeracy, literacy and IT.

Burnley College
Ormerod Road, Burnley, Lancashire, BB11 2RX
Tel: 01282 436111

City College Manchester
Sale Road, Manchester, M23 0DD
Tel: 0161 957 1785
Textphone: 0161 945 5723
Videotel: 0161 946 0729 by appointment
Fax: 0161 945 3854
E-mail: roneill@manchester-city-coll.ac.uk
Website: www.manchester-city-coll.ac.uk/deaf/
Contact: Rachel O'Neill, Senior Lecturer,
            Learning Support 2
            Sale Road, Manchester, Lancashire,
            M23 0DD

All courses are open to deaf students. In addition, the following courses are offered for deaf students: CGLI 7307 Tutor Training, Advanced Diploma in Theraputic Counselling, Basic Counselling Skills, Wordpower entry Level I and Level 2 CGLI, Look After Yourself, Deaf Studies, Exploring Work, Make Your Experience Count, CLIAT IT, Maths, LINK School/College and Access to Further Education for Deaf Students. Communication support is available for all parts of a student's course. Around 50 to 65 deaf or hard of hearing students are admitted each year.

Hopwood Hall College
St Marys Gate, Rochdale, Lancashire, OL12 6RY
Tel: 01706 345346
Fax: 0161 643 2114
Contact: Andrea McEwen, Support Tutor for
            Sensory Impaired Students
            Rochdale Road, Middleton,
            Manchester, M24 6XH
Tel: 0161 643 7560 ext 3229

The college mission is to provide quality education and training at further education level and, through additional support, meets the needs of hearing impaired students in whichever programme they choose, whether vocational or academic. The support may be through a communicator, notetaker or technical resources.

Lancashire College
Southport Road, Chorley, Lancashire, PR7 1NB
Tel: 01257 276719
Fax: 01257 241370

Lancaster and Morecambe College
Morecambe Road, Lancaster, Lancashire, LA1 2TY
Tel: 01524 66215

North Trafford College
Talbot Road, Old Trafford, Manchester, Lancashire, M16 9AF
Tel: 0161 872 3731

Preston College
Learning Services, Room MG21, St Vincents Road, Fulwood, Preston, Lancashire, PR2 8UR
Tel: 01772 772277

19

Runshaw College

Langdale Road, Leyland, Preston, Lancashire, PR5 2DQ

Tel: 01772 622677
Fax: 01772 642009
Contact: M Phillips

Salford College

Windsor Evening Centre, Churchill Way, Salford, Lancashire, M5 5BH

Tel: 0161 736 4269

Skelmersdale College

Northway, Skelmersdale, Lancashire, WN8 6LU

Tel: 01695 728744

Tameside College

Beaufort Street, Ashton-under-Lyne, Lancashire, OL6 6NU

Tel: 0161 330 6911
Textphone: 0161 330 1830

University of Salford

The Crescent, Salford, Lancashire, M5 4WT

Tel: 0161 745 5065

Wigan and Leigh College

P O Box 53, Parsons Walk, Wigan, Lancashire, WN1 1RS

Tel: 01942 501604/ 5
Fax: 01942 501551
Contact: Jane Saldanha, Inclusive Learning
            Manager
Tel: 01942 761887/ 761849
Fax: 01942 761817

Wigan and Leigh College is a large further education college which offers a diverse range of programmes of study and has a national reputation for the support given to students with learning difficulties and/or disabilities. Students who require additional support are assessed on an individual basis in order that the provision made is effective and positively promotes the ethos of 'inclusive learning'.

➢ Leicester
See Leicestershire

➢ Leicestershire
Leicester South Fields College

Aylestone Road, Leicester, LE2 7RW

Tel: 0116 224 2000
Textphone: 0116 224 2004
Fax: 0116 224 2190
E-mail: info@lsfc.ac.uk
Website: www.lsfc.ac.uk
Contact: Matthew Pinches, School Manager,
            Continuing Studies/Additional Needs

Leicester South Fields is a further education college specialising in delivering a wide range of vocational and academic courses to students aged 16 and over. The college liaises closely with the Local Education Authority Hearing Impaired Service, and the Centre for Deaf People, to ensure appropriate specialist support is available to all students on all courses.

➢ Lincolnshire
North Lincolnshire College

Monks Road, Lincoln, LN2 5HQ

Tel: 01522 876000
Fax: 01522 876200
Contact: Barbara Plunkett, Guidance Services
Tel: 01522 876222
Textphone: 01522 876221

North Lincolnshire College integrates deaf and partially hearing students on mainstream programmes, providing support and guidance through a variety of specialist staff. Deaf awareness training is available to all staff. Hearing impaired students can make use of a sign language communicator, and one-to-one support, and can borrow relevant equipment.

➢ London
College of North West London

Dudden Hill Lane, London, NW10 2XD

Tel: 020 8208 5182
Textphone: 020 8208 5163
Fax: 020 8208 5151
Contact: Pat Brennan Barret
Tel: 020 8208 5192
Textphone: 020 8208 5182

Hackney Community College

Falkirk Street, London, N1 6HQ

Tel: 020 7613 9123

Textphone: 020 7613 9082

Fax: 020 7613 9016

Contact: Alan Murray

Tel: 020 7613 9083

Hackney Community College is committed to working in partnership to widen participation and achievement in education.

Kensington and Chelsea College

Wornington Road, London, W10 5QQ

Tel: 020 7573 5333

Kingsway College

Penton Rise, London, WC1X 9EL

Tel: 020 7278 0541 ext 282

Newham College of Further Education

High Street South, London, E6 6ER

Tel: 020 8257 4397

Textphone: 020 8257 4298

Fax: 020 8257 4307

Contact: Anita Harvey, Lecturer for Deaf Learners

People who are deaf can apply for any college course. Support includes tutors for deaf learners and communication support workers. Students share in the choice and ownership of their support.

Oak Lodge School for the Deaf

Tel: 020 8673 3453

Textphone: 020 8673 3453

Fax: 020 8673 9397

E-mail: info@oaklodge.wandsworth.sch.uk

Contact: Peter Merrifield, Head Teacher

See entry under Deaf Schools.

Southwark College

Waterloo Centre, The Cut, London SE1 8LE

Tel: 020 7815 1500

Fax: 020 7261 1301

Contact: Irene Hurley, Programme Manager
SLDD, Drummond Road, London, SE16 4EE

Tel: 020 7815 1510

Southwark College is one of the biggest providers of further education in south east London. We work closely with local schools and Southwark Council to encourage more young people to stay in education past the age of 16 and gain further qualifications. As well as encouraging school leavers to enter into further education, Southwark College is committed to encouraging lifelong learning and we are a key partner in the borough's Strategic Plan for Lifelong Learning.

The City Lit Centre for Deaf People

Keeley House, Keeley Street, London, WC2B 4BA

Tel: 020 7405 5118

Videotel: 020 7831 0736

Fax: 020 7831 6121

E-mail: CFDP@citylit.ac.uk

Contact: Karen Considine, Head of Centre

Textphone: 020 7405 5118

The City Lit Centre for Deaf People offers basic education courses for deaf adults, lipreading classes, sign language classes and a student support service. There are training courses for professionals working with deaf students. We also support further and higher education students in over 30 colleges in the London area.

Waltham Forest College

Forest Road, London, E17 4JB

Tel: 020 8527 2311

Fax: 020 8523 2376

Contact: Rob Waite, Learning Difficulties and Disabilities Manager

A further education college with a multi-ethnic clientelle. Its aim is a continuum towards greater inclusivity, to serve better the community; with strong emphasis on pre-Level II education and training.

➢ Merseyside

Birkdale Further Education Direct Support

40 Lancaster Road, Birkdale, Southport, Merseyside, PR8 2JY

Tel: 01704 567220

Textphone: 01704 567220

Fax: 01704 568342

Hugh Baird College
Balliol Road, Bootle, Merseyside, L20 7EW
Tel: 0151 922 6704
Fax: 0151 934 4469
Contact: Maureen Hughes, Coordinator, Special
            Educational Needs
Tel: 0151 934 3460

Liverpool Community College
Bankfield Road, Liverpool, Merseyside, L13 0BQ
Tel: 0151 252 3834
Textphone: 0151 252 3834
Fax: 0151 228 9055
Contact: Tony Forde, Departmental Head, Deaf
            Student Support

Deaf Student Support provides a service across all
college sites. Deaf students can have in-class
support, as well as tutorial support out of class
and teaching in key skills. Support and teaching
are reviewed regularly by support staff and
teaching staff together with the students.

Royal School for the Blind
Tel: 0151 733 1012
Fax: 0151 733 1703
Contact: J Byrne, Principal
See entry under Deafblind Resources.

Southport College
Mornington Road, Southport, Merseyside, PR9 0TT
Tel: 01704 500606
Fax: 01704 546240
Contact: Gina Steed, Senior Lecturer, Learning
            Support
Tel: 01704 500606 ext 2623

West Cheshire College
Regent Street, Ellesmere Port, Merseyside, L65
8EG
Tel: 0151 356 2300

Contact: Val Hill
West Cheshire College is a college of further
education with wide community links. We exist to
provide education and training for the community.

➢ **Middlesex**
Weald College
Brookshill, Harrow Weald, Middlesex, HA3 6RR
Tel: 020 8420 8895
Textphone: 020 8420 8894
Fax: 020 8420 8859
Contact: Paulette Grant, Lecturer for Hearing
            Impaired Students, Communication
            Support Unit

All mainstream courses (full-and part-time) are
available to deaf and hard of hearing students and
include A-level, GNVQ, City and Guilds, GCSE,
vocational and non-vocational courses. Some
courses are solely for deaf students and include
basic education and lipreading. An extensive
range of communication support services is
available and include radio aids and induction
loops on the technical side and communicators,
notetakers and lipspeakers. Sign language
classes are available for CACDP Stage I and II. The
Communication Support Unit also runs courses
leading to CACDP certificates in Deaf Awareness
and Deafblind Communicating and Guiding.

West Thames College
London Road, Isleworth, Middlesex, TW7 4HR
Tel: 020 8568 0244
Fax: 020 8569 7787

➢ **Milton Keynes**
See Bedfordshire

➢ **Newbury**
See Berkshire

➢ **Norfolk**
Great Yarmouth College of Further Education
Lichfield Road, Southtown, Great Yarmouth,
Norfolk, NR31 0ED
Tel: 01493 653423

Contact: Paul Bryne
Tel: 01493 655261
Special provision includes large screen IT facilities,
including LUNAR and HAL.

19

➤ North East Lincolnshire
See Humberside

➤ North West Somerset
See Avon

➤ North Yorkshire
Harrogate College
Hornbeam Park, Hookstone Road, Harrogate, North Yorkshire, HG2 8QT
Tel: 01423 879466/ 527524

Henshaw's College
Tel: 01423 886451
Fax: 01423 885095
Contact: Lynne Gilland, Marketing and Liaison Officer

See entry under Deafblind Resources.

Northallerton College
Grammar School Lane, Northallerton, North Yorkshire, DL6 1DD
Tel: 01609 774013
Fax: 01609 770265
E-mail: Conted@NorthallertonCollege.anyxnet.co.uk
Contact: Sandra McDougall, Continuing Education Department
Tel: 01609 773340

Norton College
Langton Road, Norton, Malton, North Yorkshire, YO17 9PT
Tel: 01653 693296
Fax: 01653 693338
E-mail: ntncoll@aol.com
Contact: C Roberts, Head of Careers Education and Guidance

Mainstream college with some use of radio hearing aids.

Selby College
Abbots Road, Selby, North Yorkshire, YO8 8AT
Tel: 01757 211040

York College of Further and Higher Education
Tadcaster Road, Dringhouses, York, YO2 1UA
Tel: 01904 770200/ 770303
Fax: 01904 770499
Contact: Jane Smedley, Learning Support Manager

Yorkshire Coast College of Further and Higher Education
Lady Ediths Drive, Scarborough, North Yorkshire, YO12 5RN
Tel: 01723 372105
Fax: 01723 501918
E-mail: ycoastco.ac.uk
Website: www.ycoastco.ac.uk
Contact: Margaret Copley, Admissions Officer

Further and higher education college including department for students with learning difficulties/disabilities.

➤ Northamptonshire
Tresham Institute of Further and Higher Education
St Mary's Road, Kettering, Northamptonshire, NN16 7BS
Tel: 01536 413123
Textphone: 01536 410252
Fax: 01536 522500
Contact: Pam Bairstow, Lecturer Responsible for Hearing Impaired Students
Tel: 01536 413074
Textphone: 01536 413074

Tresham Institute serves the needs of its local, national and international communities by offering the widest possible range of relevant education and training opportunities. Its Hearing Impaired Service serves to support deaf learners to access learning opportunities and achieve their learning potential.

19

➤ Nottinghamshire

Arnold and Carlton College

Digby Avenue, Nottingham, NG3 6DR

Tel: 0115 952 0052
Textphone: 0115 953 1222
Fax: 0115 953 1230
Contact: Joan Broughton, Head of Learning
            Development

The college aims to provide quality in education, opportunities for effective learning and a welcoming environment. It provides impartial and realistic information about options available in post 16 education and involves students in planning their learning programme. The college values previous learning and gives credit for achievement, also providing appropriate on-course academic and personal support. It supports local communities, business and the wider community in working towards national targets for education and training.

Basford Hall College

Stockhill Lane, Basford, Nottingham, NG6 ONB

Tel: 0115 916 2000
Textphone: 0115 960 7201

Hucknall College of Further Education

Portland Road, Hucknall, Nottingham, NG15 7SN

Tel: 0115 924 4123

Newark and Sherwood College

Friary Road, Newark, Nottinghamshire, NG24 1PB

Tel: 01636 680683
Fax: 01636 680681

North Nottinghamshire College of Further Education

Carlton Road, Worksop, Nottinghamshire, S81 7HP

Tel: 01909 473561
Fax: 01909 485564

A further education day college using a range of communication methods, namely sign language, oralism and Total Communication.

Nottinghamshire Service for Deaf Students

Wigman Road, Bilborough, Nottingham, NG8 4PD

Tel: 0115 929 9433
Textphone: 0115 929 9433

Portland College for People with Disabilities

Nottingham Road, Mansfield, Nottinghamshire, NG18 4TJ

Tel: 01623 499111
Fax: 01623 499133
Contact: Julie Wilkes, Admissions Officer

All courses are open to deaf students. Technical support for students is provided through the Speech and Language Therapy Department. Human communication support is available as required by students. On average around 2 to 3 deaf students are admitted each year.

South Nottingham College

Greythorn Drive, West Bridgford, Nottingham, NG2 7GA

Tel: 0115 914 6400
Textphone: 0115 914 6361
Fax: 0115 914 6444
Contact: Linda Jackson, Learning Support Tutor
Tel: 0115 914 6362

We provide various forms of support for deaf students, negotiated with the student. These include tutors for deaf students, qualified communication support workers, notetakers, interpreters and speech-to-text operators. The college runs British Sign Language, deaf awareness, notetaking, lipreading and deafblind qualifications and the BTEC Communication Support Workers course.

West Nottinghamshire College

Chesterfield Road South, Mansfield, Nottinghamshire, NG19 7BB

Tel: 01623 627191
Fax: 01623 429949
Contact: Peter Thompson, Sign Language
            Coordinator, Access (Continuing
            Education)
Tel: 01623 627191 ext 4446

19

Oxfordshire

North Oxfordshire College and School of Art

Broughton Road, Banbury, Oxfordshire, OX16 9QA

Tel: 01295 252221
Fax: 01295 250381
E-mail: gwharton@northox.ac.uk
Website: www.northox.ac.uk
Contact: Mairi Smith, Section Leader

North Oxfordshire College is a general college of further education located in Banbury. The college has approximately 6000 students, of which 1500 are full-time, 2500 part-time, and 2000 evening students. The college provides a wide range of courses, up to degree level, including many opportunities for students with learning and other difficulties including hearing impairment.

Oxford College of Further Education

Oxpens Road, Oxford, OX1 1SA

Tel: 01865 245871
Textphone: 01865 245871
Fax: 01865 248871
Contact: Susan Wheare, Coordinator, Hearing Support Centre
Tel: 01865 245871 ext 363
Textphone: 01865 245871 ext 363

A complete range of full time, part time and evening courses available, including GCSE, BTEC, City and Guilds and NVQs. Human support includes teachers of the deaf and communication support workers, for support in all areas of coursework including work experience and examinations. On average, 8 to 10 deaf students supported each year.

Westminster College

Harcourt Hill, Oxford, OX2 9AT

Tel: 01865 253319
Fax: 01865 247847
Contact: Ginny Madeley, Centre for the Study of Special Education

The Centre for the Study of Special Education, at Westminster College, came into being in 1994 to: promote quality education for learners of all ages with special educational needs in a range of educational contexts; engage in research to improve the quality of teaching and learning for people with special educational needs; provide opportunities for professional development through a large range of courses leading to degrees, certificates or diplomas in special education.

Peterborough

See Cambridgeshire

Redcar and Cleveland

See Cleveland

Shropshire

Shrewsbury College of Arts and Technology

Radbrook Road, Shrewsbury, Shropshire, SY3 9BL

Tel: 01743 232686
Fax: 01743 271563

Telford College of Arts and Technology

Haybridge Road, Wellington, Telford, Shropshire, TF1 2NP

Tel: 01952 642200
Fax: 01952 243657

Slough

See Berkshire

Somerset

Bridgwater College

Bath Road, Bridgwater, Somerset, TA6 4PZ

Tel: 01278 455464
Fax: 01278 444363
Contact: Emma Shelton, Tutor for Deaf Students
Tel: 01278 455464 ext 302
Textphone: 01278 455464 ext 302

We have a full-time tutor for deaf students. Students receive support according to their communications needs, for example a notetaker or a communications support worker. We run the Edexcel CSW Certificate in addition to BSL Stage I and II. This is a successful tertiary college that serves the needs of the local community.

Frome Community College

Tel: 01373 465353
Fax: 01373 452583

See entry under Education.

19

Yeovil College

Ilchester Road, Yeovil, Somerset, BA21 3BA
Tel: 01935 423921
Textphone: 01935 423921

Contact: Karen Fry, Learning Support
            Coordinator
            Mudford Road, Yeovil, Somerset, BA1
            4DR
Tel: 01935 423921 ext 354

The type of support available includes notetakers, loop systems, one-to-one tuition and special arrangements for exams.

> South Humberside
Technical College

North Lindsay, Kingsway, Scunthorpe, South Humberside, DN7 1AJ

> South Yorkshire
Doncaster College

Waterdale, Doncaster, South Yorkshire, DN1 3EX
Tel: 01302 553553
Fax: 01302 553511
Contact: Clive Edwards, Additional Student
            Support Coordinator
Tel: 01302 553721

We aim to support hearing impaired students to enable them to acheive their primary learning goal. Support is offered through signed communications, Braille translations and induction loop systems.

Sheffield College

Castle Centre, Granville Road, Sheffield, South Yorkshire, S2 2RL
Tel: 0114 260 3650
Textphone: 0114 260 3650
Fax: 0114 260 2101
Contact: Margaret Miller, Head of Service
            Service for Hearing Impaired Students

The service for hearing impaired students offers support to deaf and hard of hearing students on mainstream courses in Sheffield College and at Sheffield University. This includes equipment, communication and notetaking support and tutorials with lecturers for deaf students. Special classes in English, maths and lipreading are also offered and sign language for the general public.

> Staffordshire
Flash Ley Resource Centre

Tel: 01785 356830
Textphone: 01785 356830
Fax: 01785 356841
E-mail: hivipd.service@staffordshire.gov.uk
Contact: Malcolm Gardner, Head of Hearing
            Impaired Services

See entry under Resource Centres.

Leek College of Further Education

Stockwell Street, Leek, Staffordshire, ST13 6DP
Tel: 01538 398866
Fax: 01538 399506

Newcastle-under-Lyme College

Liverpool Road, Newcastle-Under-Lyme, Staffordshire, ST5 2DF
Tel: 01782 254231

Stafford College

Earl Street, Stafford, ST16 2QR
Tel: 01785 223800 ext 2499/ 2515
Fax: 01785 259953

Tamworth and Lichfield College

The Friary, Lichfield, Staffordshire, WS13 6QG
Tel: 01543 301100
Fax: 01543 301103

The Mount School for the Deaf

Tel: 01782 236140
Textphone: 01782 236140
Fax: 01782 236140
Contact: B Richards, Head Teacher

See entry under Deaf Schools.

> Suffolk
West Suffolk College

Out Risbygate, Bury St. Edmunds, Suffolk, IP33 3RL
Tel: 01284 701301
Fax: 01284 750561
Contact: Andy Carmichael, Unit Head for
            Learning Support and Development
Tel: 01284 716340

➤ Surrey

Brooklands College

Heath Road, Weybridge, Surrey, KT13 8TT

Tel:	01932 797700
Fax:	01932 797806
Website:	www.brooklands.ac.uk

Aims to serve the community by providing high quality, lifetime learning opportunities.

Guildford College of Further and Higher Education

Stoke Park, Guildford, Surrey, GUI 1EZ

Fax:	01483 63409
Contact:	Elaine Brace
Tel:	01483 448546
E-mail:	ebrace@guildford.ac.uk

The college mission statement is "to satisfy fully the needs of our customers and the community for individual and organisational development through lifelong education and training".

Merton College

Morden Park, London Road, Morden, Surrey, SM4 5QX

Tel:	020 8640 3001
Textphone:	020 8640 0428
Fax:	020 8640 0835
E-mail:	info@merton.ac.uk
Website:	www.merton.ac.uk
Contact:	Jan King, Learning Support Officer

Orchard Hill College of Further Education

6 Elm Avenue, Orchard Hill, Fountain Drive, Carshalton, Surrey, SM5 4NR

Tel:	020 8770 8125
Fax:	020 8642 3763
Contact:	Caroline Allen, Principal

Orchard Hill College of Further Education provides a wide range of courses designed to suit the needs of adult students with profound and multiple/severe learning difficulties. The college aims to provide a stimulating learning environment where adult students with a range of abilities can and do achieve. The college lecturers also offer training workshops and seminars "for practitioners, by practioners".

Queen Elizabeth Training College

Leatherhead Court, Woodlands Road, Leatherhead, Surrey, KT22 0BN

Tel:	01372 842204
Fax:	01372 844156
Contact:	Carol Bloxham, Office Manager

Queen Elizabeth Training College for disabled people is residential and provides vocational training, both industrial and commercial, to equip students with the skills and knowledge to take their rightful place in employment. NVQs are obtainable in all courses and assistance in finding employment is also available. Student intake is continuous. Applications through Disabled Employment Advisers.

RNIB Redhill College

Tel:	01737 768935
Fax:	01737 778776
Contact:	Peter Johnson, FEFC Coordinator

See entry under Deafblind Resources.

➤ Thurrock
See Essex

➤ Torbay
See Devon

➤ Tyne and Wear
Gateshead College

Durham Road, Gateshead, Tyne and Wear, NE9 5BN

Tel:	0191 490 0300
Videotel:	0191 490 1656
Fax:	0191 490 2313
Website:	www.gateshead.ac.uk
Contact:	John Gray, Learner Support Manager
Tel:	0191 490 2253

Gateshead College is particularly keen to offer opportunities for deaf students who wish to follow part-time or full-time college courses. Support arrangements can be discussed with the Learner Support Manager.

19

Newcastle College
Scotswood Road, Newcastle upon Tyne, Tyne and Wear, NE4 7SA
Tel: 0191 200 4000
Textphone: 0191 200 4403
Fax: 0191 200 4397
E-mail: ncl-coll.ac.uk
Contact: Lynne Farquharson, Sensory Support
            Coordinator
            Learning Support Service
Tel: 0191 200 4372
Textphone: 0191 200 4372
E-mail: lfarquhar@ncl-coll.ac.uk

Newcastle College is one of the largest further education colleges in the country. It has a long established support service for deaf students on discrete and/or mainstream courses. Students of any age from 16 upwards are welcome, and we aim to provide effective support to enable people to achieve their goals.

North Tyneside College
Spring Terrace, Newcastle Upon Tyne, Tyne and Wear, NE29 0HQ

Northern Counties School for the Deaf
Tel: 0191 281 5821
Textphone: 0191 281 5821
Fax: 0191 281 5060
E-mail: k.j.c.lewis@schools.ncl.ac.uk
Contact: K J C Lewis, Head Teacher

See entry under Deaf Schools.

➢ Warwickshire
North Warwickshire and Hinckley College
Hinckley Road, Nuneaton, Warwickshire, CV11 6BH
Tel: 024 7624 3154
Textphone: 024 7635 4981
Fax: 024 7632 9056

Rugby College of Further Education
Lower Hillmorton Road, Rugby, Warwickshire, CV21 3QS
Tel: 01788 338800
Textphone: 01788 338629
Fax: 01788 338575

Warwickshire College
Leamington Centre, Warwick New Road, Leamington Spa, Warwickshire, CV32 5JE
Tel: 01926 318000
Fax: 01926 318111
Contact: Kate Waddington, BSL Coordinator

The course is designed to enable students to acquire a basic ability to communicate in sign language. It aims to provide information about deaf people, the deaf community and deaf culture. The examination offered is the CACDP Stage I certificate in BSL. Stage II is offered as required.

➢ West Midlands
Bilston Community College
Westfield Road, Bilston, West Midlands, WV14 6ER
Tel: 01902 821000
Fax: 01902 821101
Contact: Julie Dodson-Brent

We offer CACDP stages I and II , British Sign Language and Deaf Awareness courses. We also run courses for deaf students in subjects ranging from catering to bricklaying.

Bournville College of Further Education
Bristol Road South, Northfield, Birmingham, West Midlands, B31 2AJ
Tel: 0121 411 1414
Textphone: 0121 411 2053
Fax: 0121 411 2231
E-mail: info@bournville.ac.uk
Website: www.bournville.ac.uk
Contact: Carrie MacHattie, Programme Area
            Head-Inclusion Support

Bournville College encourages everyone to access further education. Specialist staff and a range of equipment are available to enable students to reach their full potential. We believe that students should be able to join the course of their choice and follow it, with the individual support they need.

Dudley College
The Broadway, Dudley, West Midlands, DY1 4AS
Tel: 01384 455433
Fax: 01902 664316
E-mail: stephen.roper@dudleycol.ac.uk
Contact: Steve Roper

19

Dudley College is a further education establishment and has a long and successful tradition of providing sign language Stages I and II which is recognised by CACDP. Training is also provided in conjunction with Dudley Social Services at the Queens Cross Centre for the Deaf at Wellington Road, Dudley. Lipreading is provided at both beginner and intermediate stages.

East Birmingham College

Garretts Green Lane, Birmingham, West Midlands, B33 0TS

Tel: 0121 734 4471

Contact: Lynne Giles

Early Years Courses. Access to Child Care OCN qualifications. CACHE CCE DNN (NNEB), NVQ Level 3 equivalent. BTEC Diploma NVQ Level 3 equivalent. CACHE ADCE Level 4.

Great Barr Further Education Centre

Dagger Lane, West Bromwich, West Midlands, B71 2EB

Tel: 0121 357 4299 (termtime) 0121 525 2016 (summer)

Hereward College

Bramston Crescent, Tile Hill Lane, Coventry, West Midlands, CV4 9SW

Tel: 024 7646 1231

Fax: 024 7669 4305

E-mail: enquiries@hereward.demon.co.uk

Website: www.hereward.demon.co.uk

Contact: John Goodacre, Access Centre Manager

Tel: 024 7642 6100

E-mail: johng@hereward.demon.co.uk

The Access Centre offers its clients the opportunity to evaluate a range of enabling technologies relevant to their learning or training needs. Professionally trained staff undertake assessments independent of suppliers - an unbiased service which is used by students with physical and/or sensory disabilities in further/higher education and others as appropriate.

Matthew Boulton College

Sherlock Street, Birmingham, West Midlands, B5 7DB

Tel: 0121 446 4545

Fax: 0121 446 3105

E-mail: matthew-boulton.ac.uk

Contact: Sue Partridge, Faculty of Community, Art and Business Development

Matthew Boulton College aims to be an inclusive college. It provides courses at all levels; pre-foundation, NVQ, GCSE, A-Level, GNVQ, HND and certain degrees. It covers a wide range of vocational and academic areas. The college offers additional support to students with particular learning needs. It will employ communicators and signers as needed.

Queen Alexandra College For The Blind

Tel: 0121 428 5050

Fax: 0121 428 5047

E-mail: enquiries@qac.ac.uk

Website: www.qac.ac.uk

Contact: Sue Wright, Principal

See entry under Deafblind Resources.

Solihull College

Blossomfield Road, Solihull, West Midlands, B91 1SB

Tel: 0121 678 7001/ 2

Stourbridge College

Hagley Road, Stourbridge, West Midlands, DY8 1QU

Tel: 01384 344500

Fax: 01384 344345

Contact: Lorraine Robinson

Tel: 01384 344392

Further education college.

Tile Hill College of Further Education

Tile Hill Lane, Coventry, West Midlands, CV4 9SU

Tel: 024 7669 4200

Fax: 024 7646 4903

Contact: Liz Varnish

The college offers education and training covering a wide range of academic, vocational and leisure areas. Its major specialisms include: engineering, motor vehicle, health, media studies, business studies, information technology. In particular the college offers a wide range of provision for

19

students with learning difficulties and/or disabilities or students who are deaf or hard of hearing.

Walsall College of Arts and Technology
St Pauls Street, Walsall, West Midlands, WS1 1XN
Tel: 01922 657000
Textphone: 01922 657064
Videotel: 01922 720271
Fax: 01922 657040
E-mail: Deaf-base@walcot.ac.uk
Contact: Sue Spencer, Coordinator, Services for Deaf and Hearing Impaired Students

WALCAT aims for quality with equality. Deaf students are supported on mainstream courses as follows: educational interpreters (CACDP Stage III or equivalent, plus English qualifications) and student notetakers in lectures; one-to-one language support, weekly, in first language; specialist terminology BSL development; deaf counselling/guidance in student services; BSL base area; staff deaf awareness training.

Wulfrun College
Paget Road, Wolverhampton, West Midlands, WV6 ODU
Tel: 01902 317700
Textphone: 01902 312063
Fax: 01902 423070
E-mail: mail@wulfrun.ac.uk
Contact: Liz Horton
Tel: 01902 317700 ext 572
E-mail: hortone@wulfrun.ac.uk

Deaf and hearing impaired students may access any full-time, part-time or flexistudy course offered in the college, including GCSE, A-Levels and NVQ's. Individual learning programmes are devised to meet any additional support needs, including full in-class communicator support and English support.
BSL classes are taught daily by hearing impaired tutors.

➢ West Sussex

Bognor Regis Community College
Westloats Lane, Bognor Regis, West Sussex, PO21 5LH
Tel: 01243 827422/ 864401
Fax: 01243 841676
E-mail: BRCCOL@aol.com
Contact: Wendy Webb, Vocational Studies Department

Our aims are to educate students who wish to enter any of the caring professions (nursing, teaching, childcare, etc). Also to educate students of leisure and tourism about facilities available to all sectors of the community; to raise general awareness about physical disabilities.

Chichester College of Arts, Science and Technology
Westgate Fields, Chichester, West Sussex, PO19 3EZ
Tel: 01243 786321 ext 2209

➢ West Yorkshire
Bolton Royd College of Further Education
Manningham Lane, Bradford, West Yorkshire, BD8 7BB
Tel: 01274 546812

Bradford and Ilkley Community College
22-24 Easby Road, Bradford, West Yorkshire, BD7 1QX
Tel: 01274 753133
Textphone: 01274 753133
Fax: 01274 420441
Contact: Graham Wilson, Learning Support Organiser

We aim to make sure that deaf students have an equal chance of success on college courses with hearing students by providing assessment, sign language communicators, qualified teachers of the deaf, radio aids, loop systems and a range of other services.

Bradford and Ilkley Community College
Wells Road, Ilkley, West Yorkshire, LS29 9RD
Tel: 01943 609010 ext 348/ 9

19

Huddersfield Technical College

New North Road, Huddersfield, West Yorkshire, HD1 5JW

Tel: 01484 422133

Keighley College

Cavendish Street, Keighley, West Yorkshire, BD21 3DF

Tel: 01535 758500

Keighley College welcomes all potential students. Tutors are pleased to meet with students to discuss their individual needs prior to starting a course. Students negotiate learning programmes with their tutors. Additional support is available to help students succeed in their studies.

Park Lane College

Park Lane, Leeds, West Yorkshire, LS3 1AA

Tel: 0113 216 2000

Fax: 0113 216 2020

Contact: Brenda Harrison, Sector Leader, Special Needs

Shipley College

Exhibition Road, Shipley, West Yorkshire, BD18 3JW

Tel: 01274 757222

Contact: Kate Brown, Special Needs Coordinator

Vocational training, adult education.

Wakefield District College

Station Road, Hemsworth, Pontefract, West Yorkshire, WF9 4JP

Tel: 01977 610585

➤ Wiltshire
Swindon College

Regent Circus, Swindon, Wiltshire, SN1 1PT

Tel: 01793 498343

Textphone: 01793 498343

Fax: 01793 641794

Contact: John Michaux, Support Coordinator

A college of further and higher education offering a wide variety of courses. The college supports students with learning disbailities and difficulties. It uses Total Communication and has BSL support workers.

➤ Windsor and Maidenhead
See Berkshire

➤ Worcestershire
Kidderminster College

Hoo Road, Kidderminster, Worcestershire, DY10 1LX

Tel: 01562 820811

Fax: 01562 748504

Contact: Jackie Marshall, Special Needs and Learning Support

Kidderminster College aims to offer high quality education and training in a supportive, congenial environment. We aim to facilitate, within the context of Equal Opportunities, access and participation in all curriculum areas for students with learning difficulties and/or disabilities.

North East Worcestershire College

Blackwood Road, Bromsgrove, Worcestershire, B60 1PQ

Tel: 01527 570020

Textphone: 01527 572523

Fax: 01527 572900

Contact: Roy Sergent, Additional Support Coordinator

Worcester College of Technology

Deansway, Worcester, WR1 2JF

Tel: 01905 726002

Fax: 01905 721001

➤ York
See North Yorkshire

Northern Ireland

➤ County Antrim
Belfast Institute of Further and Higher Education, Brunswick Street Building

Brunswick Street, Belfast, County Antrim, BT2 7GX

Tel: 028 9026 5000

Fax: 028 9026 5101

Belfast Institute of Further and Higher Education, College Square East

College Square East, Belfast, County Antrim, BT1 6DJ
Tel: 028 9026 5000
Textphone: 028 9023 2564
Fax: 028 9026 5001
E-mail: dsu.bifhe@dnet.co.uk
Contact: Oonagh Gallagher, Deaf Support Unit
Tel: 028 9026 5040

The Deaf Support Unit works with the deaf community and with deaf organisations to achieve three main goals: to encourage and support deaf and hard of hearing students, to deliver sign language and deaf awareness, to provide a range of interpreting support services. BIFHE offers a number of BSL courses leading to CACDP exams. It can also design and deliver short courses for private, public and community organisations. These courses are tailor-made to meet the needs of the organisation and are delivered by Deaf Support Unit staff.

Belfast Institute of Further and Higher Education, Millfield Building

125-153 Millfield, Belfast, County Antrim, BT1 1HS
Tel: 028 9026 5000
Fax: 028 9026 5401

Belfast Institute of Further and Higher Education, Ormeau Building

Ravenhill Road, Belfast, County Antrim, BT6 8GH
Tel: 028 9026 5304

Belfast Institute of Further and Higher Education, Tower Street Building

Tower Street, Belfast, County Antrim, BT5 4FH
Tel: 028 9026 5268

Belfast Institute of Further and Higher Education, Whiterock Campus

Whiterock Road, Belfast, County Antrim, BT12 7PH
Tel: 028 9026 5000
Fax: 028 9026 5351

Castlereagh College of Further and Higher Education

Montgomery Road, Belfast, County Antrim, BT6 9JD
Tel: 028 9079 7144
Fax: 028 9040 1820
E-mail: castlereagh@tibus.com
Website: www.castlereagh.ac.uk
Contact: Mary Gallagher, Student Services Officer

A college of further and higher education offering a wide range of programmes to adult learners. Full-time and part-time courses are available, ranging from Basic Adult Education to Higher National Diploma level. Flexible study is offered to those who prefer it.

East Antrim Institute of Further and Higher Education, Larne Campus

Pound Street, Larne, County Antrim, BT40 1SQ
Tel: 028 2827 2268
Fax: 028 2827 23289
E-mail: eainst@campus.bt.com
Website: www.d-n-a.net/users/dnetaCfM

East Antrim Institute of Further and Higher Education, Newtownabbey Campus

400 Shore Road, Newtownabbey, County Antrim, BT37 9RS
Tel: 028 9085 5000
Textphone: 028 9085 5000
Fax: 028 9086 2076
E-mail: eainst@campus.bt.com
Website: www.d-n-a.net/users/dnetaCfM

Lisburn College of Further Education

Castle Street, Lisburn, County Antrim, BT27 4SU
Tel: 028 9267 7225

North East Institute of Further and Higher Education, Antrim Campus

Fountain Street, Antrim, BT41 4AL
Tel: 028 9446 3916
Fax: 028 9446 5132

North East Institute of Further and Higher Education, Ballymena Campus

Farm Lodge Avenue, Ballymena, County Antrim, BT43 7DF

Tel: 028 2565 2871

Fax: 028 2565 9245

Contact: Maggie Feeley, Community and Enterprise Development Manager

Tel: 028 2563 6262

North East Institute provides a wide range of vocational, leisure and academic courses both at outcentres and on each of its four campuses in Antrim, Ballymena and Magherafelt. We welcome enquiries from deaf people interested in courses and suggest that initial contact is made in writing so that appropriate communication provision can be made.

➤ County Down

East Down Institute of Further and Higher Education

Market Street, Downpatrick, County Down, BT30 6ND

Tel: 028 4461 5815

Fax: 028 4461 5817

E-mail: director@eastdown.prestel.co.uk

Contact: Marian Walsh, Careers Advisor

To provide education and training to all sections of the community. Our college offers GCSEs, A-levels, GNVQs, NVQs, HNCs as well as a wide range of hobby classes. Also professional qualifications in counselling, specific hearing difficulties, BA Degree, IATI, Communicating with the Deaf - Stages l and ll.

East Down Institute of Further and Higher Education

14 Blackhall Street, Kircubbin, Newtownards, County Down, BT22 2QU

Tel: 028 9173 8794

East Down Institute of Further and Higher Education

Donard Street, Newcastle, County Down, BT33 OAP

Tel: 028 4372 2451

Fax: 028 4372 6203

Kilkeel Institute of Further Education

Greencastle Street, Kilkeel, Newry, County Down, BT34 4BH

Tel: 028 3076 2582

Fax: 028 3076 5975

Contact: M McConville, Head of School of Care

Newry College of Further and Higher Education

Patrick Street, Newry, County Down, BT35 8DN

Tel: 028 3026 1071

North Down and Ards Institute of Further and Higher Education

Castle Park Road, Bangor, County Down, BT20 4TF

Tel: 028 9127 1254

Fax: 028 9127 0034

E-mail: 100633,2346@compuserve.com

Contact: Helen McKelvey, Health and Social Care Department

Tel: 028 9181 2116

➤ County Fermanagh

Fermanagh College

Fairview, 1 Dublin Road, Enniskillen, County Fermanagh, BT74 6AE

Tel: 028 6632 2431

Fax: 028 6632 6357

Contact: Mairead Millmore, Community Development Officer

Tel: 028 6632 2431 ext 223

The aims of this college are to serve all sections of the community regardless of religion or disability. The college offers classes in lipreading, deaf awareness and sign language. Accreditation is available.

Model School House

Tel: 028 6634 3900

Fax: 028 6632 3493

Contact: Winston Glass

See entry under Education.

19

> County Londonderry
Limavady College of Further Education
Main Street, Limavady, County Londonderry, BT49
0EX
Tel: 028 7176 2334

Magherafelt College of Further Education
22 Magherafelt Road, Magherafelt, County
Londonderry
Tel: 028 7963 2462
Fax: 028 7963 3501
Contact: Michael Clarke, Special Needs
            Department

North West Institute of Further and Higher Education
Duncreggan Road, Londonderry, BT48 0AA
Tel: 028 7137 4722

North West Institute of Further and Higher Education
Limavady Road, Londonderry, BT47 1LP
Tel: 028 7134 2617

> County Tyrone
East Tyrone College of Further Education
Circular Road, Dungannon, County Tyrone, BT71
6BQ
Tel: 028 8772 2323
Fax: 028 8775 2018

Omagh College of Further Education
Mountjoy Road, Omagh, County Tyrone, BT79 7AH
Tel: 028 8224 5433
Fax: 028 8224 1440
Contact: J Devlin, Principal

Scotland

> Aberdeenshire
Aberdeen College
Gordon Centre, Ellon Road, Bridge of Don,
Aberdeen, AB23 8LQ
Tel: 01224 612501
Fax: 01224 612500
Aberdeen College is Scotland's largest further
education establishment. The Sector of

Communication, Language and Media Studies
offers BSL Stages I and II classes on a part-time
day and evening basis.

> Angus
Dundee College
Old Glamis Road, Dundee, Angus, DD3 8LE
Tel: 01382 834834
Fax: 01382 458153
Contact: Marie McArthur
Tel: 01382 834834 ext 3139

> Ayrshire
Kilmarnock College
Holehouse Road, Kilmarnock, Ayrshire, KA3 7AT
Tel: 01563 523501
Fax: 01563 538182
E-mail: kilmarnock.ac.uk
Website: www.kilmarnock.ac.uk
Kilmarnock College offers beginners sign language
modules (over 200 students in 1997/8) and
courses leading to BSL Stage I and II. The college
is a registered CACDP centre and its success rate
for BSL Stage I was 93 per cent in 1998. All
classes are part-time and are offered during the
day and evenings.

> Dumbartonshire
Clydebank College
Kilbowie Road, Clydebank, Dunbartonshire, G81
2AA
Tel: 0141 952 7771
Fax: 0141 951 1574
Contact: Liz Greig
Deaf awareness and basic signing classes. CACDP
Stage I, two classes running. CACDP Stage II, one
class running.

> Fife
Auchterderran Centre
Post 16 SEN, Woodend Road, Cardenden,
Lochgelly, Fife, KY5 0NE
Tel: 01592 414771
Fax: 01592 414641

Glenrothes College

Stenton Road, Glenrothes, Fife, KY6 2RA

Tel:	01592 772233
Contact:	Joan Howell, Access and Support Coordinator

Glenrothes College aims to meet the aspirations of the community in respect of education and training by: identifying the needs of individuals, companies, trade unions, public bodies, community and voluntary organisations; satisfying these needs in a way which is responsive and flexible; placing the learner at the centre of its considerations.

➢ Lanarkshire

Coatbridge College

Kildonan Street, Coatbridge, Lanarkshire, ML5 3LS

Tel:	01236 422316
Fax:	01236 440266
E-mail:	mail@coatbridge.ac.uk
Website:	www.coatbridge.ac.uk
Contact:	Joe McCanney, Senior Lecturer, Support for Learning Section

Community Education

The Triangle, Kirkintilloch Road, Bishopbriggs, Lanarkshire, G64 2TR

Tel:	0141 762 6294
Fax:	0141 772 3269
Contact:	James Jack
Tel:	0141 578 0060

Glasgow College of Building and Printing

60 North Hanover Street, Glasgow, Lanarkshire, G1 2BP

Tel:	0141 332 9969
Fax:	0141 332 5170
Contact:	Nikki Stein, Careers Department

Glasgow College of Food Technology

230 Cathedral Street, Glasgow, Lanarkshire, G1 2TG

Tel:	0141 552 3751
Fax:	0141 553 2370
Contact:	Tommy Brunton, Learning Difficulties

Langside College

50 Prospecthill Road, Glasgow, Lanarkshire, G42 9LB

Tel:	0141 649 4991
Fax:	0141 632 5252
Contact:	George Ennis

Langside College provides quality educational services to post-16 learners across a range of needs and activities from non-advanced courses to Higher National Diplomas. The college offers ongoing support to students with learning needs and the services of a learning support officer are available.

Motherwell College

Dalzell Drive, Motherwell, Strathclyde, Lanarkshire, ML1 2DD

Tel:	01698 232323
Fax:	01698 275430
E-mail:	mcross@motherwell.co.uk
Website:	www.motherwell.co.uk
Contact:	Margaret Cross, Senior Lecturer, Sensory Impairment

South Lanarkshire College

86-88 Main Street, East Kilbride, Glasgow, Lanarkshire, G74 4JY

Tel:	01355 243018
Fax:	01355 231044
Website:	www.south-lanarkshire-college.ac.uk

➢ North Ayrshire

Focus Community Learning Centre

Primrose Place, Saltcoats, North Ayrshire, KA21 6LH

Tel:	01294 604612
Fax:	01294 468052
Contact:	Carol McHarg

Focus Community Learning Centre develops and provides life-long learning opportunities for people within the North Ayrshire area.

➢ Selkirkshire

Borders College

Melrose Road, Galashiels, Selkirkshire, TD1 2AF

Tel:	01896 757755
Fax:	01896 758179
E-mail:	info.bordcoll@scotborders.co.uk

19

➤ Stirlingshire
Falkirk College
Grangemouth Road, Falkirk, Stirlingshire, FK2 9AD

Tel: 01324 403000

Fax: 01324 403222

E-mail: 101544.3517@compuserve.com.

Contact: Margaret Strain, Senior Lecturer
            School of Continuing Education

Tel: 01324 403000 ext 3089

Currently, Falkirk College offers tutorial provision for deaf and hearing impaired students. Our school development plan states that increased support for hearing impaired students is planned for 1999/2000. Since January 1999, sign language and lipreading classes have been offered.

➤ Strathclyde
James Watt College of Further and Higher Education
Finnart Street, Greenock, Strathclyde, PA16 8HF

Tel: 01475 724433

Textphone: 01475 784292

Fax: 01475 888079

E-mail: susanmc@jameswatt.ac.uk

Contact: Ruth Gibson, Head of Sensory
            Impairment, Physical Disability

Tel: 01475 553108

On average 15 to 20 deaf or hard of hearing students are admitted each year. All courses are available for deaf students. In addition, the college offers the Deaf Unit Course, to provide an introduction to further education and to provide an opportunity, if required, for deaf students to gain qualifications to allow access to mainstream college courses. Radio aids and loop systems are available and human communication support is provided for all aspects of course work.

St Vincent's School for the Deafblind
Tel: 0141 778 2254

Contact: Alicia Crilly, Head

See entry under Deafblind Resources.

➤ West Lothian

Edinburgh's Telford College
Crewe Toll, Edinburgh, West Lothian, EH4 2NZ

Tel: 0131 332 2491

Textphone: 0131 551 2161

Videotel: 0131 315 2260/ 2305/ 4808

Fax: 0131 343 1218

E-mail: davidmch@ed-coll.ac.uk

Contact: David McHaffie, Tutor for Deaf
            Students

Edinburgh's Telford College is a large college (over 15,000 enrolments per year). Deaf students are taught in mainstream classes, with support as appropriate from the Learner Support Section of the School of Client Support Services. There are more tham 850 courses available at all levels up to HND.

West Lothian College
Marjoribanks Street, Bathgate, West Lothian, EH48 1QJ

Tel: 01506 634300

Contact: William Waugh

West Lothian College is a further education college covering a range of courses in technology, business, information technology, service industries, community studies and general education. Our delivery is aimed at a wide range of people including school links, community organisations and individuals and local companies. Our work can be accessed both day and evening and by flexible learning and is available at levels ranging from access (special needs clients) up to HND.

Wales

➤ Clwyd
Llandrillo College
Llandudno Road, Rhos on Sea, Colwyn Bay, Clwyd, LL28 4HZ

Tel: 01492 542338/9

Fax: 01492 543052

Contact: Alan Hale, Principal

➤ Dyfed
Ferryside Education Centre
Tel: 01267 267803

Fax: 01267 267072

Contact: Caril Miles, Hearing Impaired Service

See entry under Education.

19

➢ Gwent

Cross Keys College

Risca Road, Cross Keys, Newport, Gwent, NP1 7ZA

Tel: 01495 333456

Textphone: 01495 333417

Fax: 01495 333386

Contact: Julie Benger, Head of Unit

The support service for the hearing impaired aims to provide access for all students with hearing problems to mainstream courses. Services include: advice about courses, access to environmental aids, individual tuition, linguistic support, facilities for a communicator, interpreter, notetaker, lipspeaker.

➢ Mid Glamorgan

Bridgend College of Technology

Cowbridge Road, Bridgend, Mid Glamorgan, CF31 3DF

Tel: 01656 766588

Fax: 01656 647018

Contact: Judith Williams, Support Teacher for the Hearing Impaired

Help and assistance is given to hearing impaired students as they pursue their individual programmes in the college. Interpreters are assigned to those who need communication support. Equipment, such as conference folders, are available for student use. Additional one-to-one support is provided if required.

Pontypridd College

Ynys Terrace, Pontypridd, Mid Glamorgan, CF37 5RN

Tel: 01443 486121

Fax: 01443 409345

Contact: David Jones, Sensory Unit Course Tutor

Tel: 01443 663064

Pontypridd College provides a foundation course for all hearing impaired students who have yet to decide on a particular vocation, and an access course for those with a chosen vocation. A qualified teacher of the deaf and a team of sign language communicators enable hearing impaired students to be integrated into mainstream courses.

➢ Rhondda, Cynon,Taff

Rhondda College

Llwynypia, Tonypandy, Rhondda, Cynon,Taff, CF40 2TQ

Tel: 01443 432187

Fax: 01443 663228

Contact: Ruth Howlett, Tutor in Charge of Students with Learning Difficulties

➢ Vale of Glamorgan, The

Barry College

Colcot Road, Barry, Vale of Glamorgan, The, CF62 8YJ

Tel: 01446 743519

Textphone: 01446 743519

Fax: 01446 732667

Contact: Karen Avery-Clayton, Hearing Impairment, Earshot

EARSHOT

Barry College, Colcot Road, Barry, Vale of Glamorgan, The, CF62 8YJ

Tel: 01446 725004

Textphone: 01446 743519 (Use TDD)

Fax: 01446 732667

E-mail: earshot@barry.ac.uk

Contact: Karen Every-Clayton

Earshot is a support service for hearing impaired and visually impaired students in further and higher education in Cardiff and the Vale of Glamorgan. Mainstream support is provided in-class or through individual tutorials by specialist teachers, communicators or notetakers. We have a large resource base of specialist equipment for all sensory impairments.

19

> West Glamorgan

Neath Tertiary College

Dwr y Felin Road, Neath, West Glamorgan, SA10 7RF

Tel: 01639 634271

Fax: 01639 637453

Contact: Ian Cardy, Lecturer for the Hearing Impaired

Education of hearing impaired students in a setting most suitable to their needs. Courses include pre-vocational courses, NVQs, GNVQs, A-Levels. Support from teachers of the deaf, communicators and notetakers whenever necessary. Neath College offers a vast array of subjects at the above levels, enhancing student progression as required by the individual.

19

Higher Education

This section gives a list of universities offering courses in higher education. Services for students with a hearing loss are usually accessed through a Disability or Access Officer. Services usually include a mixture of human and technical communication support, and there may also be textphones and radio aids available. Some universities may have rooms in halls of residence especially adapted for deaf students. For further details of what is available within each college, please contact individual universities directly.

This section is listed alphabetically by college within country and county sections.

England

➢ Avon

University College Bath Spa

Newton Park, Newton St Loe, Bath, Avon, BA2 9BN

Tel: 01225 875578

Fax: 01225 875525

E-mail: J.Kirkby@Bathspa.ac.uk

Website: www.bathspa.ac.uk

Contact: Julie Kirkby, Careers Adviser

University of Bristol Centre for Deaf Studies

Social Sciences Complex, 8 Woodland Road, Bristol, Avon, BS8 1TN

Tel: 0117 954 6900

Textphone: 0117 954 6920

Fax: 0117 954 6921

E-mail: R.Carter@bristol.ac.uk

Website: www.bristol.ac.uk/Depts/DeafStudies

The Centre for Deaf Studies offers a range of programmes. BSc in Deaf Studies is a three year full-time undergraduate programme. It is suitable for deaf and hearing students. Students may opt to study interpreting units. The MSc in Deaf Studies is a one year full-time (up to five year part-time) programme. It is especially suitable for deaf and hearing professionals working with deaf people. CDS also offers a short course programme and has a range of information resources. Potential students are invited to contact the Centre by letter or telephone for further information.

University of the West of England

Room 1E22, Frenchay Campus, Coldharbour Lane, Bristol, Avon, BS16 1QY

Tel: 0117 976 2180

Textphone: 0117 976 2611

Videotel: 0117 976 2180

Fax: 0117 976 2193

E-mail: mike.wray@uew.ac.uk

Website: www.uew.uk/prospectus/disabledAccess.html

Contact: Mike Wray, Students Advisor (Disabilities)

All courses are open to deaf students, although no courses are run solely for deaf students. Technical support includes looped lecture theatres, a textphone and videophone. Human support should be purchased by the student using the Disabled Students Allowance. The university has a Disability Resource Centre where the Student Adviser (Disabilities) will offer advice on how to organise support. In examinations and admissions interviews the university will bear the cost of interpreters. There are currently 34 students with a hearing impairment at the university.

➢ Berkshire

University of Reading

Whiteknights, Reading, Berkshire, RG6 6AH

Tel: 0118 987 5123

Fax: 0118 987 4722

E-mail: k.h.dickinson@reading.ac.uk

Website: www.reading.ac.uk

Contact: K Dickenson, Special Needs Coordinator, Registrar's Department

A full range of undergraduate and postgraduate degree courses including the BA degree in Theatre Arts, Education and Deaf Studies are available for deaf students. Human communication support is provided upon request and usually funded from the Disabled Students Allowance. A radio microphone is available on loan, textphones are available on campus and flashing light alarm systems are installed in libraries and some halls of residence. Loop systems are in the major lecture theatres, with more being installed. The university has a Special Needs Advisory Committee and Coordinator. The Deafax Trust is based on the Bulmershe Campus and is able to arrange support.

20

University of Reading School of Education

Bulmershe Hall, Woodlands Avenue, Earley, Reading, Berkshire, RG6 1HY

Tel: 0118 931 8837

Textphone: 0118 926 6528

Fax: 0118 935 2080

Contact: Daphne Payne, Lecturer in Drama, Course Leader

University of Reading is an institute of Higher Education offering BA (Hons) in Theatre Arts, Education and Deaf Studies.

> Buckinghamshire

Open University

Office for Students With Disabilities, P O Box 79, Walton Hall, Milton Keynes, Buckinghamshire, MK7 6AR

Tel: 01908 653745

Textphone: 01908 655978

Fax: 01908 653744

E-mail: osd-wh@open.ac.uk

Website: www.open.ac.uk/ou/admin/access/services.html

The Open University aims to give deaf students equal access to all courses. The following are provided free of charge: communication support at tutorials and residential schools; subtitles and/or transcripts of audio-visual materials; the loan of personal radio aids; preparatory study skills courses.

> Cambridgeshire

Anglia Polytechnic University

East Road, Cambridge, CB1 1PT

Tel: 01223 363271

Fax: 01223 352973

Contact: Ed Barker, Senior Student Adviser-Learning Support

Tel: 01223 363271 ext 2578

E-mail: E.Barker@bridge.anglia.ac.uk

Student Support Services at Anglia Polytechnic University aims to support students with a disability/learning difficulty and to allow them, where possible, access to the curriculum. Prospective students are advised to contact a Student Adviser well in advance of applying for a course so that their learning support needs can be determined and advice on support and access given.

Newnham College Cambridge

Cambridge, CB3 9DF

Tel: 01223 335700

Fax: 01223 357898

E-mail: adm@newn.cam.ac.uk

Contact: Diana Lipton, Admission Tutor

Newnham is an all-women's college at which students may study for undergraduate and post-graduate degrees in any subject offered at Cambridge University. There are no deaf students at present, but we have admitted profoundly deaf students in the past. We would be happy to support deaf students through our personal supervision and tutorial systems.

University of Cambridge

Disabled Student Services, Bridget's, Tennis Court Road, Cambridge, CB2 1QF

Tel: 01223 332301

Fax: 01223 461324

E-mail: jdm35@cam.ac.uk

Website: www.cam.ac.uk

Contact: Jane McLarty, University Disability Adviser

The University Disability Adviser provides information, support and advice to people with a disability who are thinking of applying to Cambridge, and during their course. She can arrange informal visits to Colleges and Departments, and put you in touch with deaf people already at Cambridge.

> County Durham

Deaf Studies Research Unit

Department of Sociology and Social Policy, University of Durham, Elvet Riverside II, Durham, DH1 3JT

Tel: 0191 374 2304/ 2314/ 2306

Fax: 0191 374 4743

Website: www.vuw.ac.nz/~nzsldict/idslrorg/durham.html

Contact: David Brien

The Deaf Studies Research Unit (DSRU) provides a range of courses for deaf and hearing people in sign language and deaf studies at Certificate, Advanced Certificate, Advanced Diploma and MA levels. Courses may lead to qualifications in BSL/English interpreting, teaching of sign language, deaf studies and sign linguistics. Teaching is provided by a team of deaf and hearing staff. Courses are either delivered directly in BSL or bilingually in BSL and English. The DSRU also undertakes research in the areas of deaf community and culture, sign language studies and deaf studies.

University of Durham

Elvet Riverside II, New Elvet, County Durham, DH1 3JT
Tel: 0191 374 2304
Textphone: 0191 374 4743

➤ Derbyshire

University of Derby - Deafness Support Unit

Kedleston Road, Derby, DE22 1GB
Tel: 01332 622222
Textphone: 01332 622711
Fax: 01332 622742
E-mail: l.a.colebourne@derby.ac.uk
Contact: Louise Colebourne, Deafness Support Services Manager
Tel: 01332 622222 ext 1327

The University of Derby is committed to supporting deaf and hard of hearing students. An experienced and qualified team provide sign language, lipspeaking and notetaking support in formal taught sessions, and study skills sessions are also offered as an extra curricular activity. Deaf students are strongly advised to contact the Unit before making an application to the university to find out whether the team can offer the support they require.

➤ Devon

University College of St Mark and St John

Derriford Road, Plymouth, Devon, PL6 8BH
Tel: 01752 636700
Fax: 01752 636820
E-mail: priorl@marjon.ac.uk
Website: www.marjon.ac.uk
Contact: Nicki Wheeler

University of Exeter

Northcote House, Queens Drive, Exeter, Devon, EX4 4QJ
Tel: 01392 263263
Textphone: 01392 263263
Fax: 01392 263285
Website: gosh.ex.ac.uk/
Contact: Rodney Bridges, Advice Centre Manager
              Student Advice Centre, First Floor Devonshire House, Stocker Road, Exeter, Devon, EX4 4PZ
Tel: 01392 263520
Fax: 01392 263520
E-mail: r.e.e.bridges@exeter.ac.uk

All courses are open to deaf students. Loop systems have been installed in many buildings across campus. Portable microphones are available for lectures. Provision of support services is available when required, by arrangement, on an ad hoc basis. For further details, please contact the Student Advice Centre.

University of Plymouth

Babbage Building, Drake Circus, Plymouth, Devon, PL4 8AA
Tel: 01752 232278
Fax: 01752 232279
Contact: Steve Almy, Advisor to Deaf and Hard of Hearing Students, South West Regional Access Centre

Staff development, video networking, pool of notetakers, BSL Stage 1, special agency networking, external links. Induction programme and video, Windows 95, video for deaf students, code of practice for notetakers. Assessment of individual student needs. Internal environmental equipment -educational and on campus, for example, in accommodation.

20

➤ Dorset

University of Bournemouth

Talbot Campus, Fern Barrow, Poole, Dorset, BH12 5BB
Tel: 01202 524111
Fax: 01202 595025
E-mail: postmaster@bournemouth.ac.uk
Website: www.bournemouth.ac.uk
Contact: Valeria Morgan, Disability Coordinator

All courses are available to deaf students. The university will help students to purchase their own equipment. There are no loop systems. The university has three full-time counsellors and two full-time student welfare officers. Human support could be arranged for interviews, lectures, work placement schemes, tutorials and examinations. The provision of support is available full-time. On average five to six deaf students are admitted each year.

> East Sussex

University of Brighton

The Tithe Barn, Moulsecoomb Place, Lewes Road, Brighton, East Sussex, BN2 4GA

Tel: 01273 642887

Textphone: 01273 683552

Contact: Patricia Montaldo, Support Officer for Deaf/Hearing Impaired Students Student Services - Welfare

The University of Brighton Welfare Service aims to provide professional and impartial advice, assistance and information on a broad range of issues for current and prospective students. The service aims to offer up-to-date and unbiased information in an accessible format. The Welfare Service is available to all who need it regardless of racial origin, gender sexuality, nationality, disability, age or cultural/religious beliefs.

University of Sussex

Health Centre Building, Falmer, Brighton, East Sussex, BN1 9RH

Tel: 01273 606755

Website: www.sussex.ac.uk/

Contact: E A Draffan, Assistive Technology Centre

Health Centre Building, Falmer, East Sussex, BN1 9RH

Tel: 01273 678497

Fax: 01273 877241

E-mail: e.a.draffan@sussex.ac.uk

Website: www.sussex.ac.uk/Units/ATC

Offers advice, assessment and tuition for those who have been granted a Disabled Students Allowance by their Local Education Authority; guidance in the selection, acquisition and use of assistive technology; courses, workshops and training sessions for individuals and groups covering a variety of assistive technology topics, including internet, adapting the computer to suit individual needs, use of word processing; additional aids to help writing skills; advice on low and medium technology aids.

University of Sussex Research in Hearing

Falmer, Brighton, East Sussex, BN1 9RH

Tel: 01273 678502

Fax: 01273 678433

Website: www.biols.susx.ac.uk/Hearing_research.html

Hearing Research at Sussex is carried out by about 25 people in three groups with interests which range from auditory and speech perception to biophysics, molecular biology and organic chemistry. Multidisciplinary approach to the study of hearing both within groups and through cooperation between groups. Groups are mostly involved in basic research but also carry out clinical research in collaboration with the Royal Sussex Hospital (Ann Brown), molecular cloning (Guy Richardson and Richard Killick).There is also cooperation with the ENT department of the Royal Sussex Hospital through the provision of research training (Guy Richardson, Ian Russell).

> Essex

University of East London

Longbridge Road, Dagenham, Essex, RM8 2AS

Tel: 020 8590 7000

Textphone: 020 8849 3553

E-mail: vmparker@uel.ac.uk

Contact: Ros Gahan, Administrator for Students with Disabilities

Tel: 020 8590 7000 ext 6211

All courses are open to deaf students. Technical support and equipment includes: radio microphone available on loan, portable induction loop and loop fitted in some of the main lecture rooms. Human support includes: notetakers, communicators and interpreters at interviews and for classes, being funded by Disabled Students Allowance. On average between three and ten deaf students are admitted each year.

University of Essex

Wivenhoe Park, Colchester, Essex, CO4 3SQ

Tel: 01206 872365

Videotel: 01206 872365

Fax: 01206 873598

Website: www.essex.ac.uk

Contact: Angela Jones, Disability Coordinator, Student Support Officer

E-mail: angela@essex.ac.uk

The aim of the university is to promote excellence in research scholarship and education. All courses, undergraduate and postgraduate, are open to deaf students. Students are supported in

20

obtaining technical equipment, with the Disabled Students Allowance and with recruiting human communications support in the form of notetakers and interpreters. On average four deaf students are admitted each year.

➢ Hampshire
University of Portsmouth
Gun House, Ravelin Park, Hampshire Terrace, Portsmouth, Hampshire, P01 2QX

Tel:	023 9284 3159
Fax:	023 9284 3430
Website:	www.port.ac.uk
Contact:	Gail Hine, Disability Coordinator, Student Services Centre
E-mail:	gail.hine@port.ac.uk

It is the university's policy to judge applications from disabled students initially on academic criteria alone. However, it helps us to know of the level of hearing impairment in advance and to look at what support students will need. There are some loop systems installed within the university.

University of Southampton
University Road, Southampton, Hampshire, SO17 1BJ

Tel:	023 8059 5000
Fax:	023 8059 3939
Website:	www.soton.ac.uk

In principle all courses are open to applicants with the required academic grades. The university follows special procedures for all students who indicate a disability. After the academic decision has been made, the university will review the needs (technical and human) which a particular student may have. The university as such does not provide technical or human support. It does, however, endeavour to meet the needs of deaf students, for example notetaking on an ad hoc basis. Some lecture theatres have induction loops. Arrangements will be made for examinations. The university seeks to raise the consciousness of the community as a whole about the needs of all disabled students. They also have a group for children and adults, social activities and a newsletter.

University of Southampton Hearing and Balance Centre
Highfield, Southampton, Hampshire, SO17 1BJ

Tel:	023 8059 2288
Fax:	023 8059 4981
Website:	www.isvr.soton.ac.uk
Contact:	Mark Lutman

The Institute undertakes research, runs an MSc course in Audiology and provides a clinical service which includes the south of England Cochlear Implant Centre.

➢ Hertfordshire
University of Hertfordshire
College Lane, Hatfield, Hertfordshire, AL10 9AB

Tel:	01707 284000
Textphone:	01707 284000
Fax:	01707 284000
Website:	www.herts.ac.uk
Contact:	Sallie Cooper, Disabled Students Officer, Student Services
Tel:	01707 284454
Fax:	01707 284993

The university welcomes disabled students on all of its wide choice of study schemes. Adapted accommodation is available on the main campuses and each of the eight faculties has a named person who helps arrange technical and personal support. About 30 hard of hearing and deaf students are admitted each year.

➢ Humberside
University of Hull
Cottingham Road, Hull, Humberside, HU6 7RX

Tel:	01482 346311
Fax:	01482 466205
E-mail:	s.j.davies@admin.hull.ac.uk

All courses are available to deaf students. Counselling is available to all students, also advice from the Humberside County Council Service for the Hearing Impaired is sought. Human support is available for interviews, lectures, tutorials and examinations. Provision of support services is available part-time as required. Extra classes are provided for deaf students if required.

20

➢ Kent

Wye College

Wye, Ashford, Kent, TN25 5AH

Tel: 01233 812401

Fax: 01233 812330

E-mail: Registry@wye.ac.uk

Contact: Carol Jovanovic

Students graduating from Wye are awarded University of London BSc honours degrees. We offer degrees in a range of subject areas including biological sciences, business studies, management, the environment, agriculture and horticulture. Wye has a well established tradition of research and teaching. Almost all the college's academic staff are involved in their own research, and many have industrial and commercial experience. The college does not receive many applications from deaf people. However, all such applications are treated on a case-to-case basis and the college does its utmost to facilitate learning for students who are challenged with a hearing problem.

➢ Lancashire

Edge Hill University College

St Helens Road, Ormskirk, Lancashire, L39 4QP

Tel: 01695 575171

Contact: David Johnstone, Coordinator for Students with Disabilities

Tel: 01695 584277

Fax: 01695 584277

Edge Hill University College attempts to be an inclusive learning environment for all the students. The college provides undergraduate and postgraduate courses for approximately 10,000 students within the following schools: Health Studies, Humanities and Arts, Management and Social Sciences, Science and Technology, Education. Specialist facilities exist for disabled and deaf students.

Manchester Metropolitan University

All Saints Building, Oxford Road, Manchester, Lancashire, M15 6BH

Tel: 0161 247 3492

Textphone: 0161 247 3492

Fax: 0161 247 6852

Contact: Ann Barlow, Learning Support Coordinator

All courses are open to deaf students provided they qualify for a Disabled Students Allowance. If they do not then a student's place on a course will be negotiable, dependent upon resources, people required to support that person in their studies. The Access Summit Resource Centre for the four universities of Manchester provides technical support to disabled students, and there is a database of human support workers. Student Services will set up communication support workers for assignments. Communication support is available for most areas of academic study. Around six deaf or hard of hearing students enter the university each year.

Manchester Metropolitan University - Department of Psychology and Speech Pathology

Elizabeth Gaskell Campus, Hathersage Road, Manchester, Lancashire, M13 0JA

Tel: 0161 247 2585

Fax: 0161 247 6364

Contact: Anita Clokie, Course Coordinator

Tel: 0161 247 2112

Textphone: 0161 247 2112

The university runs a number of specialist courses enabling people to work with people who are hearing impaired or deaf. Anita Clokie is course coordinator for the Certificate of Higher Education in Teaching Speechreading (Lipreading) to Adults and the CACDP Level One (Intermediate) Lipspeaking Certificate. For further details of both courses please contact Ms Clokie. There is also a two-year distance learning Master of Arts in Social Work with Deaf People. Deaf students are encouraged to apply for the undergraduate and postgraduate professional social work courses. Placements with organisations for deaf people may be chosen. Contact Sue Jones, Department of Applied Community Studies, Manchester Metropolitan University, 799 Wilmslow Road, Didsbury, Manchester M20 2RR. Tel: 0161 247 21212 Textphone: 0161 247 2148

University of Central Lancashire

Preston, Lancashire, PR1 2HE

Tel: 01772 892594

Textphone: 01772 892594

Fax: 01772 892939

E-mail: l.barnes@uclan.ac.uk

Contact: Lynne Barnes, Course Leader-Deaf Studies
            Department of Education Studies

All courses and qualifications are open to deaf applicants, although no courses are organised solely for deaf students. A full range of technical and human support is available for academic and social activities. IT training and English classes are also available. On average, 25 deaf students per year are enrolled.

University of Lancaster
Bailrigg, Lancaster, Lancashire, LA1 4YW

Tel: 01524 592111

Textphone: 01524 592111

Fax: 01524 594294

Website: www.lancs.ac.uk/users/sp-needs/index.htm

Contact: Christine Quinn, Student Adviser, Special Needs Support Service

All degree courses at undergraduate and graduate level are open to deaf students. The university has a special needs technical officer who provides advice to students. There is also a small stock of technical aids for loan. Communication support is available and paid for through the Disabled Students Allowance. There is also a counselling service available to all students.

University of Manchester Centre for Human Communication and Deafness
Oxford Road, Manchester, Lancashire, M13 9PL

Tel: 0161 275 2000

Textphone: 0161 275 3364

Fax: 0161 275 3373

E-mail: chcd@man.ac.uk

Contact: Yvonne Aplin, Senior Lecturer in Education of the Deaf

The Centre offers a MEd (Hearing Impairment) by distance learning. This is a course designed for qualified teachers of the deaf who wish to extend their professional knowledge and skills.

➢ Leicestershire
University of Leicester
Study Support Centre, Fielding Johnson Building, University Road, Leicester, LE1 7RH

Tel: 0116 252 5002

Fax: 0116 252 5513

E-mail: pbd1@le.ac.uk

Contact: Linda Kirkham, Study Support Officer

All courses are open to deaf and hard of hearing students. Technical support and equipment provided includes: radio microphones, portable loops; fitted loops in some teaching areas; one-to-one human support; a notetaker service and Disabled Students Allowance advice. The Disability Statement details details the university's policy on disabled students.

University of Leicester De Montfort
The Gateway, Leicester, LE1 9BH

Tel: 0116 255 1551

University of Loughborough
Loughborough, Leicestershire, LE11 3TU

Tel: 01509 222770

Textphone: 01509 222770

Fax: 01509 223912

E-mail: dans@lboro.ac.uk

Contact: David Jackson, Head of Services, Disability and Additional Needs

Tel: 01509 222769

Staff in the Disability and Additional Needs Service provide support to students on any course at the university who have a disability. They also offer advice on the support available at the university to prospective students who have a disability. This includes students who are deaf or hard of hearing.

➢ London
Birkbeck College
1 Malet Street, London, WC1E 7HX

Tel: 020 7631 6207

Contact: P J Barber, Psychology Department

The Human Performance Laboratory of Birkbeck's Psychology Department is currently investigating the effects of visual factors on the reception and understanding of face-to-face video-linked communication.

Imperial College of Science, Technology and Medicine, London
Exhibition Road, London, SW7 2AZ

Tel: 020 7589 5111

Textphone: 020 7589 5111

Fax: 020 7594 9050

Contact: Loretto O'Callaghan, Disabilities Officer

Tel: 020 7594 8935

E-mail: l.ocallaghan@ic.ac.uk

Imperial College welcomes applications from students with special needs who are encouraged to write in as early as possible before submitting their application form, indicating the courses they are interested in and their disability. It is important that the college has awareness about the degree of disability in advance because access to and physical arrangements within some of its buildings may present difficulties. Also, the college considers it important to advise students

20

of what facilities are available before submitting an application. The college is continuing in its efforts to improve access.

London College of Music

St Marys Road, London, W5 5RF

Tel: 020 8231 2573

Fax: 020 8231 2587

Contact: David Grant, Advice and Counselling Team, Special Needs

All courses are available to deaf students. Technical and human support is available for lectures and examinations. Technical support is available for tutorials. Provision of support could be provided full-time, part-time and evenings.

London School of Economics and Political Science

Houghton Street, London, WC2A 2AE

Tel: 020 7405 7686

Fax: 020 7242 0392

Website: www.lse.ac.uk

All full time and part-time LSE courses are open to deaf students. Equipment includes radio microphones and induction loops. Interpreter support is not provided.

University College London

Gower Street, London, WC1E 6BT

Tel: 020 7391 1343

Textphone: 020 7391 1343

Fax: 020 7380 7327

Website: www.phon.ucl.ac.uk/educ/ug1996.html

Contact: Patrick Mulcahy, Disability Coordinator

E-mail: p.mulcahy@ucl.ac.uk

All courses at UCL are open to deaf students. A number of the lecture theatres at the college are fitted with induction loop systems. There is at present a postgraduate bursary scheme for hearing impaired students. College videos have been subtitled and FM radio microphones are provided (subject to availability). There is no specialist human support for deaf students, but UCL has Occupational Health and Counselling services which can offer advice and support. Around five deaf students are admitted each year.

University of City of London

Northampton Square, London, EC1V OHB

Tel: 020 7477 8000

City offers a MSc in Human Communication. This is the first MSc in the South East designed to meet the needs of teachers of the deaf within a multi-professional approach. The course is part-time (one day a week over two years).

University of London Guildhall

Calcutta House, Old Castle Street, London, E1 7NT

Tel: 020 7320 1137

Fax: 020 7320 1237

Contact: Bryan Jones, Equal Opportunities Adviser, Student Affairs

University of North London

166-220 Holloway Road, London, N7 8DB

Tel: 020 7607 2789

E-mail: disabilities@unl.ac.uk

Website: www.unl.ac.uk/student_services

Contact: Victoria Pettipher, Disabilities Officer

Tel: 020 7753 3323

Textphone: 020 7753 5145

Fax: 020 7753 5788

The University of North London is committed to providing a high-quality educational experience that meets the needs of disabled students. Further information about Disabilities Services can be found on our web page which also includes the university's Disability Statement.

University of the South Bank

103 Borough Road, London, SE1 0AA

Tel: 020 7928 8989

Fax: 020 7815 8155

Contact: John Beaumont, Disability Support Coordinator, Student Advisory Centre

All courses are open to deaf students who meet the academic requirements of the course. Technical and human support is provided through the City Lit Institute's FHE Support Unit.

University of Westminster

74 Great Portland Street, London, W1N 5AL

Tel: 020 7911 5161

Textphone: 020 7911 5163

Fax: 020 7911 5162

E-mail: dblaycock@wmin.ac.uk

All courses are open to deaf students. Computer related technical support is available from the Computer Centre for People with Disabilities (see entry under Resource Centres), as is human support supplied by the City Lit Institute for Deaf

People. CCPD supports disabled students generally but works with a range of specialist agencies for deaf people on a range of projects.

➢ Merseyside
University of Liverpool
150 Mount Pleasant, Liverpool, Merseyside, L69 3GD

Tel:	0151 794 4717
Fax:	0151 794 4718
E-mail:	s.a.jones@liv.ac.uk
Website:	www.liv.ac.uk
Contact:	Sarah Jones, Student Welfare Adviser, Student Services Centre

Textphone: 0151 794 4713

All courses and qualifications are open to deaf students. Support is arranged on an individual basis (including Disabled Students Allowance claims).

University of Liverpool John Moores
The Mews via Egerton Court, 2 Rodney Street, Liverpool, Merseyside, L3 5UX

Tel:	0151 231 3188
Textphone:	0151 231 3360
Fax:	0151 231 3152
E-mail:	eounit@livjm.ac.uk
Contact:	Joanna Smith, Disability Welfare Advisor, Equal Opportunities Unit

All courses are open to deaf students. Communication support services at the University are provided by the Hearing Impaired Unit at City of Liverpool Community College and are paid for through the Disabled Students Allowance. Some rooms in university halls of residence are specifically adapted to meet the requirements of hearing impaired students. Few lecture rooms have loop systems installed. Information on facilities and services for hearing impaired students is available from the Disability Welfare Advisor. On average, around 75-80 deaf or hard of hearing students are admitted each year.

➢ Norfolk
University of East Anglia
Norwich, Norfolk, NR4 7TJ

Tel:	01603 592493
Fax:	01603 593454
Website:	www.uea.ac.uk
Contact:	Linda Shepherd, Deputy Dean of Students, Dean of Students' Office

All courses are open to deaf students. Some technical support is available; lecture theatres and some teaching rooms are looped. Human support can be provided through the Dean of Students' Office and paid for by Disabled Students Allowance. The Dean of Students' Office is happy to handle the payment side for the student. The Learning Support Unit provides study skills sessions on an individual and group basis as well as printed and computer-based study skills materials. Residential accommodation for students with a significant hearing loss is fitted with appropriate alarm equipment. On average around five deaf or hard of hearing students are admitted each year.

➢ North Yorkshire
University of York
Heslington, York, YO1 5DD

Tel:	01904 430000
Fax:	01904 433433

All courses are open to deaf students. Some lecture theatres are looped and flashing light fire alarms have been installed. Interpreter support can be provided, paid for through the Disabled Students Allowance.

York College of Further and Higher Education
Tadcaster Road, Dringhouses, York, YO2 1UA

Tel:	01904 770200/ 770303
Fax:	01904 770499
Contact:	Jane Smedley, Learning Support Manager

The College aims to enable people to access, participate and progress within, to and from learning programme. We are working towards providing an inclusive learning environment and learning programmes that ensure the learning needs of all individuals are met. This includes people who are deaf, partially hearing or hard of hearing. Our programmes range from entry level to HND. We also provide classes in British Sign Language, deaf awareness and lipreading.

➢ Northumberland
Northumberland College
College Road, Ashington, Northumberland, NE63 9RG

Tel:	01670 841200
Fax:	01670 841201

The college aims to provide inclusive education. The Certificate in Learning Support Course aims to develop candidates' skills in planning,

20

implementing and evaluating learning support.

➤ Nottinghamshire

The Nottingham Trent University

Burton Street, Nottingham, NG1 4BU

Tel: 0115 941 8418

Textphone: 0115 948 6163

Fax: 0115 948 6014

Website: www.ntu.ac.uk

Contact: Chris Baxter, Deaf Adviser, Disabilities Office

Tel: 0115 948 6395

Textphone: 0115 948 6357

E-mail: chris.baxter@ntu.ac.uk

The university's Student Support Services have a range of support for deaf and disabled students. Disability Support offers advice for individual students, both current and prospective, on the support that is available, and liaises with university departments and outside agencies where appropriate.

University of Nottingham

University Park, Nottingham, NG7 2RD

Tel: 0115 951 4377

Textphone: 0115 951 4378

Fax: 0115 951 4376

E-mail: mary.foley@nottingham.ac.uk

Contact: Mary Foley, Student Services Office, Registrar's Department

All courses are open to deaf students. Some technical support is provided by the university in the form of loops in lecture theatres and flashing fire alarms and textphones in halls of residence. There is a part-time support tutor for deaf students who runs a support group and provides help in obtaining notetakers.

➤ Oxfordshire

University of Oxford

University Offices, Wellington Square, Oxford, OX1 2JD

Tel: 01865 270000

Fax: 01865 270708

Website: www.ox.ac.uk

Contact: Deborah Poppam, University Equal Opportunities Officer

Tel: 01865 270083

Textphone: 01865 280300

All courses are available to deaf students. Some lecture theatres have induction loops. Equipment can be provided for the indvidual as appropriate. Notetakers are provided for lectures. Technical and human support is provided for interviews and lectures. Human support is provided for tutorials and technical support is provided for examinations. Provision for support services is available full-time, part-time or evenings. The university has a fund for the support of disabled students and disabled candidates for admission, including students with hearing impairment.

University of Oxford Brookes

Gipsy Lane, Headington, Oxford, OX3 OBP

Tel: 01865 741111

Fax: 01865 483073

E-mail: enquiries@brookes.ac.uk

Website: www.brookes.ac.uk

Contact: Keith Cooper, Head of Student Services

Provision of equipment includes radio microphones. General counselling and special examinations can be arranged if required. Support is given at interviews, during the course and examinations. Oxford Brookes offers a mixed mode course with a substantial taught element for candidates wishing to train as teachers of the deaf. The course is of two years (part-time) duration and open to qualified teachers. For further details contact the course secretary at the School of Education.

➤ South Gloucestershire

See Avon

➤ South Yorkshire

University of Sheffield

Firth Court, Western Bank, Sheffield, South Yorkshire, S10 2TN

Tel: 0114 222 1265

Fax: 0114 222 1304

E-mail: rebecca.proctor@sheffield.ac.uk

Website: www.shef.ac.uk/

The University of Sheffield is committed to respond effectively and appropriately to the additional support needs of disabled students. Admissions tutors look at academic suitability; discussions regarding additional support remain separate. The central support and welfare section of the Student Services Department coordinates the support of disabled students.

20

University of Sheffield Hallam

City Campus, Pond Street, Sheffield, South Yorkshire, S1 1WB

Tel:	0114 253 3813
Textphone:	0114 2253964
Fax:	0114 2252161
E-mail:	l.spriggs@shu.ac.uk/guidance@shv.ac.uk
Contact:	Alec Archer, Education Advisor - Disability
Fax:	0114 225 2161

All courses at the university are open to deaf students. Induction loops are fitted in the main lecture theatres, textphones are placed in key locations, radio microphones are available for loan, and some rooms in halls of residence are specifically adapted to meet the requirements of deaf students. Notetakers and communicators are readily available and many staff throughout the University have sign language skills to Stage 2. Support is given by academic staff and extra tutorials are provided if required by the student. Communication support is provided in all areas of course work from interview stage to examinations and including work placement schemes. Approximately 15-20 deaf or hard of hearing students are admitted each year.

➢ Staffordshire

University of Keele

Keele, Staffordshire, ST5 5BG

Tel:	01782 621111
Contact:	Toni Middling, Student Learning Support Tutor, Department of Academic Affairs
Tel:	01782 584105

All undergraduate and postgraduate courses are available to deaf students. Technical support includes: induction loop in large lecture theatre, portable induction loops and textphones in Students Union. Counselling services are available to all students and there is an Adviser to students with multiple disablities.

University of Staffordshire

4-5 Winton Square, Station Road, Stoke-on-Trent, Staffordshire, ST4 2AD

Tel:	01782 294977
Textphone:	01782 294977
Fax:	01782 746517
E-mail:	l.lewis@staffs.ac.uk
Website:	www.staffs.ac.uk
Contact:	Liz Lewis, Disability Support Services Manager

All courses are open to deaf students. Technical support is available in the form of a technology assessment unit to help students decide what equipment meets their needs, technology support, loop systems, flashing/vibrating alarms in student residences and a textphone in the admissions office. Human communication support is also available and can be obtained for all academic situations including work placements. Extra classes are available for deaf students if required. On average between three and six deaf students are admitted each year.

➢ Surrey

Guildford College of Further and Higher Education

Tel:	01483 448500
Fax:	01483 63409
Contact:	Elaine Brace
Tel:	01483 448546
E-mail:	ebrace@guildford.ac.uk

See entry under Further Education.

Royal Holloway College, London

Egham Hill, Egham, Surrey, TW20 0EX

Tel:	01784 434455
Fax:	01784 437520
Contact:	Rebecca Harrison , Dean of Students Office/Student Support Services Manager
Tel:	01784 443393/ 4

Royal Holloway is one of the eight larger colleges of the University of London but is situated at Egham in Surrey. In 1998 there were around 5,700 undergraduate and postgraduate students in 19 departments covering the Humanities, Performing Arts, Social Sciences and Sciences. Applications from students with disabilities are welcome.

20

University of Surrey

Wey Flat, Guildford, Surrey, GU2 5XH

Tel: 01483 259261

E-mail: p.kerin@surrey.ac.uk

Contact: Philippa Kerin, Special Needs
              Coordinator

Support is given to students who have a disability or specific difficulty. We give them advice on finance, daily living and academic assistance.

➤ Tyne and Wear

University of Northumbria at Newcastle

Library Building, Sandiford Road, Newcastle upon Tyne, Tyne and Wear, NE1 8ST

Tel: 0191 237 3385

Contact: Sandra Chilton, Disabilities Adviser,
              Student Services

Textphone: 0191 222 1051

Fax: 0191 227 4553

All courses are open to deaf and hearing impaired students. Some lecture theatres have loop systems and each faculty office has a textphone. Support for individual students is arranged by the adviser and help is given in arranging assessments and claiming the Disabled Students Allowance. The adviser gives on-going support and advice and works closely with the RNID in Darlington. On average there are 10 to 15 new deaf/hearing impaired students each year.

University of Sunderland

Chester Road, Sunderland, Tyne and Wear, SR1 3SD

Tel: 0191 515 2952

Textphone: 0191 515 2107

Fax: 0191 515 2949

Website: www.sunderland.ac.uk

Contact: Margery Surtees, Disability Support
              Adviser, Student Services Centre

The majority of courses are open to deaf and hard of hearing students. Technical support to students is supplied via the Disability Support Team and NERAC (North East Regional Access Centre) which is part of the National Federation of Access Centres. Advice is given on developing an individual package of support to match each student's needs. On average, around 20-35 deaf or hard of hearing students are admitted each year.

➤ West Midlands

Birmingham Institute of Art and Design

Linden Road, Birmingham, West Midlands, B30 1JX

Tel: 0121 331 5777

Fax: 0121 331 5779

Contact: Tom Jones, Professor/Head of
              Department, Foundation and
              Community Studies Department

University of Aston

The Aston Triangle, Birmingham, West Midlands, B4 7ET

Tel: 0121 359 3611

Fax: 0121 359 4664

Website: www.aston.ac.uk

Contact: Pamela Bell-Ashe, Assistant Registrar

All courses are available for deaf and hard of hearing students. Technical and human support is provided according to individual needs. Extra tutorials can be arranged if necessary. On average four deaf or hard of hearing students are admitted each year.

University of Birmingham

Edgbaston, Birmingham, West Midlands, B15 2TT

Tel: 0121 414 4866

University of Central England

Perry Barr, Birmingham, West Midlands, B42 2SU

Tel: 0121 331 5000

University of Coventry

Priory Hall, Priory Street, Coventry, West Midlands, CV1 5FB

Tel: 024 7683 8029

Textphone: 024 7683 8029

Fax: 024 7683 8074

E-mail: ssx019@cov.ac.uk

Contact: Denise Connors, Disabilities Welfare
              Assistant, Student Services
              Disabilities Office

Coventry University welcomes students with disabilities and recognises that education is a right for all who can benefit from it. The Disabilities Office runs a study support scheme and has close links with the Student Access and Support Unit (SASU), who provide professional sign language interpreters, communicators and notetakers.

20

University of Warwick

Gibbet Hill Road, Coventry, West Midlands, CV4 7AL

Tel: 024 7652 3761

Textphone: 024 7652 8177

Fax: 024 7652 2433

E-mail: t.j.stone@warwick.ac.uk

Contact: Tom Stone, University Senior Tutor

We welcome students with any disability. We work closely with 'Student Access Support Unit' at Coventry Technical College who support our deaf and partially hearing students by providing notebooks, lipspeakers and signed communication.

University of Wolverhampton

Stafford Street, Wolverhampton, West Midlands, WV1 1SB

Tel: 01902 321000

Fax: 01902 322739

E-mail: sles@wlv.ac.uk

Website: www.wlv.ac.uk

Contact: Kristiaan Dekesel, Course Leader, Deaf Studies

Tel: 01902 322664

Textphone: 01902 322531

All courses are open to deaf students. The Visual Language Centre (VLC) gives help and advice about disability grants and allowances, communication support and technical aids. Potential students are assessed for their individual communication needs prior to entry into the University. The VLC also runs four undergraduate courses: BA Hons in Deaf Studies combined with other subjects; BA Hons in Interpreting (BSL/English); Foundation in Interpreting (one year course) solely focusing on sign language skills; Certificate in Higher Education for Technical Officers. On average, approximately 70 to 80 deaf or hard of hearing students are admitted each year.

➤ West Yorkshire

University of Bradford

Disability Office, Room K22, Richmond Building, Richmond Road, Bradford, West Yorkshire, BD7 1DP

Tel: 01274 383736

Textphone: 01274 385094

Fax: 01274 235340

Contact: Liz Clarke, Coordinator for Disabled People

Tel: 01274 235156

Textphone: 01274 235094

The University of Bradford welcomes disabled students and support is available through the university's Disability Office. Students who are deaf or partially hearing will be assessed by Disability Office staff so that their educational and technological support needs can be met whilst they are studying at the university.

University of Huddersfield

Queensgate, Huddersfield, West Yorkshire, HD1 3DH

Tel: 01484 472675

Textphone: 01484 473121

Fax: 01484 473120

Contact: Carol Moran, Student Support Officer Student Services

Students with disabilities are asked to contact the university prior to application to discuss individual needs, support available and to arrange a visit if required. Access guides are available that outline the services on offer.

University of Leeds

ULIS Building, 177 Woodhouse Lane, Leeds, West Yorkshire, LS2 3AR

Tel: 0113 233 2616

Textphone: 0113 233 2616

Fax: 0113 233 3927

Contact: Judith Russell, Disabilities Officer

Fax: 0113 233 3926

E-mail: j.russell@adm.leeds.ac.uk

Disability Services aims to provide information, guidance and support to disabled and dyslexic people who work and study at the University. The Service works with departments and external partners in order to ensure the specific requirements of disabled people are incorporated in all practices and procedures.

20

University of Leeds Metropolitan

Room D211, Calverley Street, Leeds, West Yorkshire, LS1 3HE

Tel: 01132 832600

Textphone: 01132 425733

Contact: Jackie Watson, Disability Support Coordinator

Disability Support offers support to disabled students at the university to enable them to access their studies effectively. Coordinating a network of support and processing Disabled Students Allowance applications to Local Education Authorities. Providing upport in lectures and adapted accommodation. Offering a range of services to enable students to participate fully in the life of the university.

➤ Wiltshire

Swindon College

Tel: 01793 498343

Textphone: 01793 498343

Fax: 01793 641794

Contact: John Michaux, Support Coordinator

See entry under Further Education.

Northern Ireland

➤ County Antrim

Belfast Institute of Further and Higher Education

Tel: 028 9026 5000

Textphone: 028 9023 2564

Fax: 028 9026 5001

E-mail: dsu.bifhe@dnet.co.uk

Contact: Oonagh Gallagher, Deaf Support Unit

Tel: 028 9026 5040

See entry under Further Education.

Castlereagh College of Further and Higher Education

Tel: 028 9079 7144

Fax: 028 9040 1820

E-mail: castlereagh@tibus.com

Website: www.castlereagh.ac.uk

Contact: Bertie Allen, Student Services Officer

See entry under Further Education.

North East Institute of Further and Higher Education

Tel: 028 2565 2871

Fax: 028 2565 9245

Contact: Maggie Feeley, Community and Enterprise Development Manager

Tel: 028 2563 6262

See entry under Further Education.

Queen's University

University Road, Belfast, County Antrim, BT7 1NA

Tel: 028 9024 5133

Fax: 028 9024 7895

Website: www.qub.ac.uk

Contact: Evelyn McFarland, Joint Universities Deaf Education Centre, Room 101, Central Teaching Facility

Tel: 028 9027 3918

Textphone: 028 9033 5511

University of Ulster at Jordanstown

Shore Road, Newtownabbey, County Antrim, BT37 0QB

Tel: 028 9036 8252

Textphone: 028 9036 8252

Fax: 028 9036 8551

Website: www.ulst.ac.uk/studaffairs/jude

Contact: Hazel Wilson, Signing Development Officer, JUDE Centre

            Room 9F14, The Mall, Shore Road, Newtownabbey, County Antrim, BT37 0QB

E-mail: H.Wilson@ulst.ac.uk

The Joint Universities Deaf Education Centre (JUDE), is a joint support unit based at the universities of Ulster and Queens, to facilitate access to Higher Education and entry to employment for deaf and hard of hearing students. JUDE aims to ensure that the necessary support is available at the onset of a course, by coordinating and providing communication and/or techincal support: providing deaf awareness training and basic sign language classes to staff and peer students.

➢ County Down
North Down and Ards Institute of Further and Higher Education

Tel: 028 9127 1254

Fax: 028 9127 0034

E-mail: 100633,2346@compuserve.com

See entry under Further Education.

➢ County Londonderry
University of Ulster

Cromore Road, Coleraine, Londonderry, BT52 1SA

Tel: 028 9032 8515

Fax: 028 7032 3005

Website: www.ulst.ac.uk/studaffairs/jude

Contact: Brian Caul, Director of Student
            Services (all campuses)

Tel: 028 9032 4397

All courses are open to deaf and hearing impaired students. The Guidance and Welfare Officer carries out an initial assessment of students' special needs and endeavours to provide assistance in a number of ways: liaising with Education Authorities for special equipment grants and funds for communication support; coordinating academic support; and providing personal support should any problems arise. Technical support can be provided through audio-visual services, and some lecture theatres will have induction loop systems. Portable loop systems will also be available and both Jordanstown and Coleraine campuses have textphones in the student services reception areas.

University of Ulster at Magee

Northland Road, Londonderry, BT48 7JL

Tel: 028 7137 5271

➢ Co Cork
Higher Education Equality Unit

54 College Road, University College Cork, Cork

Tel: 00353 21902167

Fax: 00353 21271349

E-mail: heeu@ucc.ie

Contact: Olive Broderick, Information Worker

The HEEU is a national unit funded by the Higher Education Authority. It is hosted by University College, Cork. The HEEU works to reduce inequality in Higher Education institutions by promoting and encouraging good policy and practice. We have a broad focus, being concerned with a wide range of inequalities, for example socio-economic/class background, gender, race, disability, age, sexual orientation, family status and religion or political belief - which might be faced by staff (academic, administrative and ancillary) and students within Irish higher education institutions.

➢ Aberdeenshire
University of Aberdeen

University Office, Regent Walk, Aberdeen, AB24 3FX

Tel: 01224 273505

Fax: 01224 272039

Website: www.abdn.ac.uk

Contact: John Powell, University Regent,
            Regent's Office

E-mail: ejpowell@admin.abdn.ac.uk

The University of Aberdeen aims to create, develop, apply and transmit through the work of all its members, knowledge, skills and understanding at the highest levels of excellence. Applications are welcomed from students with disabilities. It is our policy to consider such applications on the same academic grounds as apply to all other applications.

➢ Angus
University of Dundee

Park Wynd, Dundee, Angus, DD1 4HN

Tel: 01382 344 145

Fax: 01382 345 509

➢ Fife
Fife College

St. Brycedale Avenue, Kirkcaldy, Fife, KY1 1EX

Tel: 01592 268591

Textphone: 01592 268591

Fax: 01592 640225

Website: www.fife.ac.uk

Contact: Cath Cunningham, Lifelong Learning

20

➤ Lanarkshire

Glasgow Dental Hospital and School

378 Sauchiehall Street, Glasgow, Lanarkshire, G2 3JZ

Tel: 0141 211 9600
Fax: 0141 211 9800
E-mail: show.scot.nhs.uk
Contact: Andrew Lamb

University of Paisley

High Street, Paisley, Lanarkshire, PA1 2BE

Tel: 0141 848 3000
Fax: 0141 848 3804
Contact: Margaret Cassidy, Special Needs Advisory
Tel: 0141 848 3923
E-mail: cass-sao@paisley.ac.uk

To support hearing impaired/deaf students to access all activities/lectures/seminars. To offer guidance in relation to Disabled Students Allowance application, to offer technical support and guidance as and when required, to provide a weekly informal drop-in session as a special needs support group.

➤ Midlothian

University of Edinburgh

34 Buccleuch Place, Edinburgh, Midlothian, EH8 9JS

Tel: 0131 650 6828
Textphone: 0131 650 4108

Contact: Pat Butson, Coordinator for Students with Special Needs

All courses are open to deaf students. Provision of equipment includes phonic ear and inductive loop if required. Human support includes: photocopying lecture notes, interpreters, counselling, extra tuition according to individual needs. Support is given during the course, tutorials and examinations. Extra classes are also given. There are currently 14 students at the university who have some hearing impairment.

University of Heriot-Watt

Administration 2, Edinburgh, Midlothian, EH14 4AS

Tel: 0131 451 3509
Fax: 0131 449 5153
Contact: Sandra Sabiston, Adviser to Students with Special Needs, Student Welfare Services
E-mail: s.sabiston@hw.ac.uk

All courses are available for deaf and hard of hearing students. There are loop systems in all lecture theatres and radio microphones are available for use in seminar rooms. Interpreting support can be provided. A counselling service is also provided. Support services are available for interviews, lectures, tutorials and examinations.

➤ Stirlingshire

University of Stirling

Geddes Court, Stirling, FK9 4LA

Tel: 01786 467080
Fax: 01786 466806
E-mail: siss7.@stir.ac.uk
Website: www.stir.ac.uk
Contact: Alison Beggs, Student Support Officer, Student Information and Support Office

Students can apply for a broad variety of courses detailed in the undergraduate and postgraduate prospectuses. Some technical support is available; there are some infra-red systems installed and a programme to buy more of these is ongoing.

➤ Strathclyde

University of Strathclyde

Level 4, The Graham Hills Building, 50 George Street, Glasgow, Strathclyde, G1 1QE

Tel: 0141 548 3402
Textphone: 0141 548 4739
Fax: 0141 553 4132
E-mail: a.simpson@mis.strath.ac.uk
Contact: Anne Simpson, Special Needs Advisor, Student Advisory and Counselling Service

Most courses are suitable for students who are deaf or hard of hearing. Technical support is available from the Special Needs Service, and the RNID, who will also organise communication support. The Special Needs Service welcomes enquiries from potential students who are wondering whether the University of Strathclyde can meet their needs.

Wales

➤ Dyfed
University College Aberystwyth
Old College, King Street, Aberystwyth, Dyfed, SY23 2AX

Tel:	01970 623111
Fax:	01970 622007
E-mail:	gaj@aber.ac.uk
Contact:	Gareth Jones, Director of Welfare and Senior Tutor
Tel:	01970 233111

Textphone: 01970 611446

All courses in the prospectus are open to deaf students. Equipment can be provided by arrangement with the local education authorities. The college has purchased radio-microphone equipment for student use which can be borrowed on a short- or long-term basis. Some assistance is given through the college Access Funds, each case is assessed individually. No specific counselling service is available for deaf students but they can obtain counselling from the General Service. The services of the local Audiology Department is available to students. Approximately two deaf students are admitted each year.

➤ Mid Glamorgan
University of Glamorgan
Treforest, Pontypridd, Rhondda, Cynon,Taff, CF37 1DL

Tel:	01443 482494
Textphone:	01443 482494
Fax:	01443 482084
Website:	www.glam.ac.uk

All courses are available to deaf students. The Adviser for Special Needs can assist with approprite course requirements, advice on appropriate equipment, benefits and accessing the resources provided to disabled students at Glamorgan. Induction loops are installed in the large lecture theatres and there are textphones in some departments. Communication support is available through the university. There are Learning Resources Centres (LRC) at both the main site and Glyntaff.

➤ South Glamorgan
University of Cardiff
Dean of Students' Office, 47 Park Place, Cardiff, South Glamorgan, CF1 3AT

Tel:	029 20874610
Fax:	029 2087 4947
Website:	www.cf.ac.uk
Contact:	Caryl Davies, Student Adviser, Disabilities/Special Needs, Dean of Students' Office
Tel:	029 2087 4610
E-mail:	daviesc@cardiff.ac.uk

All courses are open to deaf students subject to appropriate academic qualifications. Technical aids include radio aids and flashing/vibrating alarm systems for residences. The university can help students to identify suitable support and put them in touch with appropriate organisations locally. The university counselling service is open to all students.

➤ West Glamorgan
University of Swansea
Singleton Park, Swansea, West Glamorgan, SA2 8PP

Tel:	01792 205678
Textphone:	01792 295089
Fax:	01792 295336
Website:	www.swan.ac.uk
Contact:	R Edwards, Disability/Special Needs

The only equipment available is the loop system in the large lecture theatre. Counselling service and students union welfare service are available. Interpreter support is available. Extra classes have been made available in the past.

20

Employment and Training

Deaf and hard of hearing people face particular problems when trying to find a job or training opportunities and this section gives some ideas as to where to look.

The staff in the RNID Employment and Learning Projects will be able to assist deaf and hard of hearing people with information, advice, guidance, and support to help them in gaining employment and/or training or increase their promotion prospects at work.

The RNID also advises employers and training providers on how to make their work places and training centres suitable for deaf and hard of hearing people. It has also set up a scheme where professional deaf people act as mentors to other deaf people who are looking for work.

This section lists RNID contacts, then other organisations providing help and support specifically to deaf and hard of hearing people looking for employment and/or training. It then lists other more general organisations involved in employment, careers and training and finally a comprehensive list of Training and Enterprise Councils in the UK.

RNID Employment and Learning Contacts

RNID Employment and Learning Project Colwyn Bay

Suite 3, Penrhos Manor, Oak Drive, Colwyn Bay, Clwyd, LL29 7YW

Tel:	01745 585589
Textphone:	01745 585541
Fax:	01745 585052
Contact:	Sian Hutchinson, RNID Employment Adviser
Textphone:	01492 536142

RNID Employment and Learning Project Cymru

3rd Floor, 33-35 Cathedral Road, Cardiff, CF1 9HB

Tel:	029 2033 3034
Textphone:	029 2033 3036
Fax:	029 2033 3035
Contact:	Robert Langford, RNID Employment Adviser

RNID Employment and Learning Project Manchester

Royal Schools for the Deaf Manchester, Stanley Road, Cheadle Hulme, Cheadle, Cheshire, SK8 6RQ

Tel:	0161 610 0159
Textphone:	0161 610 0161
Fax:	0161 610 0160
Contact:	Ian Tremayne, RNID Employment Adviser

RNID Employment and Learning Project Northern Ireland

Wilton House, 5 College Square North, Belfast, County Antrim, BT1 6AR

Tel:	028 9032 1733
Textphone:	028 9024 9462
Videotel:	028 9043 8354
Fax:	028 9023 3868
Contact:	Alan McClure, RNID Employment Adviser
Contact:	Martin MacMurtie, RNID Employment Adviser

RNID Employment and Learning Project Scotland

9 Clairmont Gardens, Glasgow, Lanarkshire, G3 7LW

Tel:	0141 332 0343
Textphone:	0141 332 5023
Fax:	0141 331 2640
Contact:	Lynn Williams, RNID Employment Adviser
Contact:	Gillian McLeish, RNID Employment Adviser

RNID Employment Project Bath

13b Church Farm Business Park, Corston, Bath, Avon, BA2 9AP

Tel:	01225 874460
Textphone:	01225 874460 ext 19
Fax:	01225 874246
Contact:	Mal Crookes, Employment Worker
Contact:	Trish Vallance, Employment Link Worker

21

About the RNID Employment and Learning Project

There is a pilot mentoring project called Recruitment and Career Progression for Deaf People. The contact is Trish Vallance, Employment Link Worker (see above for contact details).

Please note that the role of all the RNID Guidance Officers is advisory. This means that they assist deaf and hard of hearing people with their job/training search, but they do not actually have job vacancies to match people up with.

Please note: if you live in one of these areas and want to meet a Guidance Officer, you need to textphone/fax/write first to make an appointment.

We regret that we cannot offer an employment service outside Manchester, Belfast, Glasgow and Cardiff, Colwyn Bay and Bath, and are unable to meet up with you in London or other areas. Should you require further information, please contact the RNID HelpLine on:

Tel: 0870 60 50 123
Textphone: 0870 60 33 007
Fax: 020 7296 8199

Other organisations around the country for deaf and hard of hearing people looking for employment and/or training

If you live in the Avon area:

The Disability Unit at the University of Bristol and the Centre for Deaf Studies at the University of Bristol are both well worth your time contacting. They both have training courses and programmes that are aimed at unemployed deaf and hard of hearing people. Some of these courses are for those seeking employment.

ADSI - Access for Deaf Students' Initiative

Union Building, Queens Road, Clifton, Bristol, Avon, BS8 1LN

Website: www.bris.ac.uk/Depts/ADSI
Contact: Christine Chubb, Disability Officer
Tel: 0117 954 5710
Textphone: 0117 954 5730
Fax: 0117 954 5715

University of Bristol Centre for Deaf Studies
22 Berkeley Square, Avon, BS8 1HP

E-mail: R.Carter@bristol.ac.uk
Website: www.bristol.ac.uk/Depts/DeafStudies
Contact: Dr Mary Griggs, Administration Tutor
                  University of Bristol, 8 Woodland
                  Road, Bristol, BS8 1TN
Tel: 0117 954 6900
Textphone: 0117 954 6920
Fax: 0117 954 6921

If you live in the Berkshire area:

Deafax Trust

Technology Centre, Bulmershe Court, The University, Earley, Reading, Berkshire, RG6 1HY
Tel: 0118 926 0259
Textphone: 0118 926 0257
Videotel: 0118 935 3574
Fax: 0118 926 0258
E-mail: 101331.1044@compuserve.com
Website: www.deafax.org
Contact: Yvonne Momber, Senior Trainer
Contact: Sue Walsh, Training and Development
                  Manager

If you live in the Clwyd area:

Deaf Access Wales

3 Maesgwyn Road, Wrexham, Clwyd, LL11 2AP
Tel: 01352 751201
Textphone: 01352 751660
Fax: 01352 751201
Contact: Gary Jones, Community Development
                  Officer, Community Work and
                  Education

If you live in the Hampshire area:

21

Hampshire Deaf Association

Fairbairn Centre, 18 Augustine Road,
Southampton, Hampshire, SO14 0PL

Tel: 023 8022 6803
Textphone: 023 8033 9872
Fax: 023 8023 2848
E-mail: hantsdeafass@compuserve.com
Website: www.info-quest.com./deafsociety
Contact: Susan Balfour, Employment Officer

If you live in the Kent area:

Access Centre

Beckenham Hospital, Trapnell Wing, Croydon
Road, Beckenham, Kent, BR3 3QL

Tel: 020 8289 8050
Textphone: 020 8289 8090
Fax: 020 8289 8060
Contact: Brenda Farmer, Job Club Coordinator

If you live in the London area:

Camden Deaf Job Club

1st Floor, 108-110 Camden High Street, London,
NW1 0LU

Tel: 020 7284 2908
Textphone: 020 7284 2873
Fax: 020 7284 2905
Contact: Arif Guijarro, Job Club Manager

Camden Deaf Job Club is exclusively for deaf and
hard of hearing people. Our aim is to assist
members in gaining lasting and fulfilling
employment. We offer professional help with
CVs, letters, application forms and free job search
facilities. There are two permanent staff, together
with volunteer British Sign Language students.

DeaFinIT

96 Normanton Park, London, E4 6ES

Tel: 020 8523 9113
Textphone: 020 8523 9613
Videotel: 020 8523 9113
Fax: 020 8523 9613
E-mail: deafinituk@hotmail.com
Contact: Stuart Alexander, Project Manager

Works with young deaf people to train and
support them to get jobs in the IT sector.

Deafworks

3rd Floor, 6-12 Emerald Street, Bloomsbury,
London, WC1N 3QA

Tel: 020 7405 4735
Textphone: 020 7405 4745
Fax: 020 7405 4796
E-mail: deafwork@aol.com
Contact: Nicholas Callow, Information Manager

A Deaf-led business, Deafworks aims to advance
equality for Deaf people either by working directly
with any organisation through in-house training,
researching views of services, writing leaflets, and
acting as consultants, or by offering a variety of
specialised workshops and courses (including
British Sign Language) for both Deaf and hearing
people.

Small Creative Solutions

The Lodge, 64 Pinner Road, Harrow, Middlesex,
HA1 4HZ

Tel: 020 8427 5569
Textphone: 020 8427 0515
Fax: 020 8861 5528
Contact: Sarah Jennings, Training and
                Enterprise Officer

Small Creative Solutions is not a job club and it is
not just for deaf people. It is an organisation that
supports disabled people with work placements,
jobs and to set up business. It is included here
because Sarah Jennings is deaf herself and signs.

Westminster Job Club for Deaf People

42 Westbourne Park Road, London, W2 5PH

Tel: 020 7641 5710
Textphone: 020 7641 5711
Fax: 020 7641 5712
E-mail: pdbu@westphyfdis.demon.co.uk
Contact: Sally Pamment, Senior Project Worker

The Job Club can provide help with stationery,
computers, textphones, newspapers and
compiling a CV and advice and help. The Job Club
is now running a social afternoon on the last
Saturday of every month with refreshments
provided.

21

If you live in the Nottinghamshire area:

Nottinghamshire Deaf Society

22 Forest Road West, Nottingham, NG7 4EQ

Tel:	0115 970 0516
Textphone:	0115 970 0516
Fax:	0115 942 3096
Contact:	Sharon Bramwell, Employment Development Officer

If you live in the West Midlands:

Birmingham Institute for the Deaf

Ladywood Road, Birmingham, West Midlands, B16 8SZ

Tel:	0121 246 6100
Textphone:	0121 246 6101
Fax:	0121 246 6125
E-mail:	bid@bid.org.uk
Website:	www.bid.org.uk
Contact:	Gail Conway, Employment Officer
Contact:	Zana Little, Senior Employment Officer

See entry under Regional Organisations.

Other places you can go for help...

1. Job Search

To search for a job you should be going to the Job Centre and looking in newspapers, but also most deaf and hard of hearing people seek work nationally by looking at "Read Hear" on Ceefax on the TV: BBC 2, page 640.

2. Local Job Centre

Inside each job centre there is a person called a "Disability Employment Adviser" (DEA). You need to meet the DEA and register with him/her to get onto the "Access to Work" (AtW) Scheme. This means that when you have a job interview, a notetaker, lipspeaker or interpreter can be booked. Once you start work, equipment, such as fire alarms, pagers, textphones and/or human aids, such as notetakers, lipspeakers or interpreters will also be able to be booked (for examples, for meetings and the induction period).

As well as being the link to the "Access to Work"

scheme, the DEA can also give you advice and guidance on local employment and learning opportunities.

The DEA can sort out work placements, support you in finding a job/training and perform assessments.

If you need an interpreter for your meeting with the DEA, you need to tell the DEA beforehand, so that one can be booked.

3. Local Careers Service/Careers Partnership

This is another very good place to go to look for suitable training or employment opportunities. You need to make an appointment with the careers adviser and if you need an interpreter for your meeting, you need to tell the careers adviser beforehand, so that one can be booked.

4. Local Social Services/Social Work Department

Contact your local Social Services to see if they have any specific provision for deaf people. If they do, contact them because they might know of someone who specifically supports deaf people in finding employment and training in your local area.

5. Local Deaf Club

You should also contact your local deaf club and ask the people if they know of anybody locally who supports deaf people in finding employment and training.

Employment and Training - General

Listed below is a miscellaneous list of organisations involved in employment, careers and training work. They are not specifically deafness related but may be useful to contact.

21

Abbey Training Services

314 Antrim Road, Newtownabbey, County Antrim, BT36 8EG

Tel:	028 9084 0527
Fax:	028 9083 8290
E-mail:	c.gibson@unite.co.uk
Contact:	Clare Little

Antrim Training and Employment Agency
25-27 Church Street, Antrim, BT41 4BE
Tel: 028 9446 2834
Fax: 028 9442 8355
Contact: Walter Scott, Disablement
                  Employment Adviser

Armagh Training and Employment Agency
5 Thomas Street Centre, Dungannon, County Tyrone, BT70 1HN
Tel: 028 8772 2525
Fax: 028 7976 1231
Contact: Tommy Mitchell, Disablement
                  Advisory Officer

Covers Western area.

Ballymena Training and Employment Agency
35-39 Bridge Street, Ballymena, County Antrim, BT43 5EL
Tel: 028 2566 0777
Fax: 028 2566 0766
Contact: Walter Scott, Disablement
                  Employment Adviser

Areas covered: Ballymena, Ballymoney.

Banbridge Training and Employment Agency
50 Newry Street, Banbridge, County Down, BT32 3HA
Tel: 028 4066 2149
Fax: 028 4062 6872

Bangor Training and Employment Agency
65 High Street, Bangor, County Down, BT20 5BE
Tel: 028 9127 9999
Fax: 028 9146 5747
Contact: Romine Dufsin, Temporary
                  Disablement Employment Adviser

Bankvale Training and Development Services
26 Derby Street, Glossop, Derbyshire, SK13 8LP

Batley Worklink
28 Alfreds Way, Batley, West Yorkshire, WF17 5DR
Tel: 01924 422416
Textphone: 01924 422416
Fax: 01924 422050

An employment service for people with a disability.

Bedford Careers Centre
Eagle Court, Dame Alice Street, Bedford, MK40 2SR
Tel: 01234 210000
Fax: 01234 246260

Belfast Training and Employment Agency
Gloucester House, Chichester Street, Belfast, BT1 4RA
Tel: 028 9025 2201

The Disablement Advisory Service (DAS) operates through a network of training and employment agency offices. DAS opens up jobs and training opportunities to disabled people. DAS is committed to helping employers recruit and retain disabled employees. It also offers a range of practical and financial help to assist disabled people and employers as well as a professional assessment service.

Business in the Community Cymru
6th Floor, Empire House, Mount Stuart Square, Cardiff, South Glamorgan, CF1 6DN
Tel: 029 2048 3348
Fax: 029 2046 1513
E-mail: paulrowson@bitc.org.uk
Contact: Paul Rowson, Director

Business in the Community Cymru works with businesses to develop corporate social responsibility. Project areas include: education, economic development and employee involvement. Equality is integrated throughout our work. Links with the voluntary sector are important and we seek to introduce sustained links with business.

Cambridge Careers Centre
62 Burleigh Street, Cambridge, CB1 1DJ

Cambridgeshire Careers Guidance
7, The Meadow, Meadow Lane, St. Ives, Huntingdon, Cambridgeshire, PE17 4LG
Tel: 01480 375827

Career Path for Adults
Kent House, 30 Billing Road, Northampton, NN1 5DQ

Careerdecisions Ltd

Daniel House, Ground Floor, Trinity Road, Bootle, Merseyside, L20 3RG

Tel: 0151 955 6300
Fax: 0151 934 2463
Contact: Chris Green

Careerdecisions Ltd provides an all-age guidance service and a placing service for young people and has an equal opportunities policy of service provision and access to services. There is a careers adviser with a company-wide responsibility for clients with sensory impairments based at Old Swan Careers Centre. (Contact: Neil Alecock 0151 228 2285)

Careers and Education Business Partnership

Sutton Coldfield Careers Centre, Lichfield Road, Sutton Coldfield, West Midlands, B74 2NP

Tel: 0121 355 1021
Fax: 0121 354 6962
Website: www.cebp.co.uk.
Contact: Brian Roddis

Careers and Education Business partnership delivers quality careers advice and guidance, and supports and develops world of work activities, for people of all ages in Birmingham via a citywide network of five careers centres and eight local education business partnerships.

Careers Information Unit

Suffolk Careers Limited, St Helens Court, St Helens Street, Ipswich, Suffolk, IP4 2JZ

Tel: 01473 581449
Fax: 01473 581429
Contact: Joy Squirrell, Information Assistant

Suffolk Careers provides careers advice, information and guidance to the people of Suffolk. In addition to our services to schools and colleges, young people and their parents, we offer a range of services to adults and employers.

Careers Partnership

Salford Careers Office, The Coach House, 25 Bolton Road, Salford, Lancashire, M6 7HL

Tel: 0161 743 0163
Fax: 0161 745 9427

Charterhouse Partnership

Morrell House, 98 Curtain Road, London, EC2A 3AA

Tel: 020 7613 1156
Fax: 020 7739 5482
E-mail: johncurtis@charterhouse-
            partnership.co.uk
Website: www.charterhouse-partnership.co.uk
Contact: John Curtis

Charterhouse Partnership (Principals: Jean Brading and John Curtis) is an employment consultancy with expertise in employment and disability, graduate employment and career management. A major function of the partnership is the Employment Disability Assessment Service, which prepares reports for the courts about employment prospects of individual disabled people for use in the courts in connection with claims for compensation.

Cookstown Training and Employment Agency

17 Oldtown Street, Cookstown, County Tyrone, BT80 8EE

Tel: 028 7976 6950
Fax: 028 7976 1231
Contact: Kate McElroy, Disablement
            Employment Adviser

DART

The Friary Centre, The Friary, Cardiff, CF1 4AA

Tel: 029 2064 4696
Textphone: 029 2023 2913
Fax: 029 2039 7138
Contact: Jacqui Moore, Assistant Community
            Education Officer

Derby Career Office

8 Curzon Street, Derby, DE1 1LL

Tel: 01332 200033

Dewsbury Worklink

Town Hall Way, Dewsbury, West Yorkshire, WF17 5DR

Tel: 01924 459442
Textphone: 01924 459442
Fax: 01924 459486

An employment service for people with a disability.

21

Disability Matters

The Old Dairy, Tiebridge Farm, North Houghton, Stockbridge, Hampshire, SO20 6LQ

Tel:	01264 811120
Fax:	01264 810889
Contact:	Mike Freeney

Dorset Careers

Lansdowne House, Christchurch Road, Bournemouth, Dorset, BH1 3JP

East Ayrshire Employment Initiative

65 King Street, Kilmarnock, Ayrshire, KA1 1PT

Tel:	01563 544554
Fax:	01563 573780
E-mail:	eaei.2432@compuserve.com
Contact:	Sharon McRoberts

Employment Opportunities for People with Disabilities

74 Great Portland Street, London, W1N 5AL

Tel:	020 7580 7545
Videotel:	020 7637 8061

Fife Careers Information Services

Albany House, Albany Gate, Glenrothes, Fife, KY7 5NP

Tel:	01592 415196
Fax:	01592 415199
E-mail:	fifecareers@sol.co.uk

Fife Careers provides information and advice for young people. Clients with hearing impairments are given specialist professional support to ensure their needs are met.

Guideline Careers Service

Mansfield Careers Centre, 30-32 Regent Street, Mansfield, Nottinghamshire, NG18 1SS

Handsworth Careers Centre

11 Soho Road, Birmingham, B21 9SN

Harrogate Careers Centre

15-17 Station Bridge, Harrogate, North Yorkshire, HG1 1SP

Tel:	01423 871722
Fax:	01423 705273
Contact:	Catherine Wellings
	Harrogate Careers Centre, 21 Hornbeam Square South, Harrogate, North Yorkshire, HG2 8NB

York and North Yorkshire Guidance Service is contracted by the Department of Education and Employment to deliver careers education and guidance in North Yorkshire and the city of York. We work in schools, colleges and with businesses and the wider community to provide high quality and impartial careers guidance services.

Hertfordshire Careers Services Limited

Hertfordshire House, Civic Centre, St Peter's Street, St Albans, Hertfordshire, AL1 3JZ

Tel:	01727 816944
Fax:	01727 846659

Hertfordshire Careers Services Limited

Careers Centre, Marlowes, Hemel Hempstead, Hertfordshire, HP1 1HQ

Tel:	01442 61511
Fax:	01442 69458

Huddersfield Worklink

5 Silver Court, Silver Street, Aspley, Huddersfield, West Yorkshire, HD5 9AG

Tel:	01484 223500
Textphone:	01484 518809
Fax:	01484 547929

An employment service for people with a disability.

Huntingdon Careers Centre

Walden House, Market Hill, Huntingdon, Cambridgeshire, PE18 6NR

Ilkeston Careers Office

Field Road, Ilkeston, Derbyshire, DE7 5RS

Tel:	01559 302636
Fax:	01559 300080

Johnstone Area Careers Office

12 Laighcartside Street, Johnstone, Renfrewshire, PA5 8BY

Kilwinning Careers Office

Claremont Crescent, Kilwinning, Ayrshire, KA13 7HF

Leicestershire Careers and Guidance Services

1 Pocklingtons Walk, Leicester, LE1 6BT

Tel: 0116 262 7254
Fax: 0116 262 0682
E-mail: info@leicester-careers.co.uk
Website: www.leicester-careers.co.uk

We aim to provide first-class careers information, guidance and placing services to our clients and to act as a link between clients and providers of education, employment and training.

Lifetime Careers - Bolton, Bury, Rochdale

Chatsworth House, Bold Street, Bolton, Lancashire, BL1 1LS

Tel: 01204 840789
Fax: 01204 599029
Contact: Bill Hutchings

Lifetime Careers is a statutory careers service provider and provides impartial information, guidance and help to enter appropriate education, training and employment. In doing so it promotes equality of opportunity and raises aspirations.

Lisburn Training and Employment Agency

71 Bow Street, Lisburn, County Antrim, BT28 1BJ

Tel: 028 9262 3378
Fax: 028 9262 3401
Contact: Gina Burns, Disablement Employment Adviser

Magherafelt Training and Employment Agency

28 Queen Street, Magherafelt, County Londonderry, BT45 6AB

Tel: 028 7963 3804
Fax: 028 7963 4218
Contact: Vincent Donnelly, Disablement Advisory Officer

Covers Eastern area.

Margate Careers Centre

3rd Floor Mill House, Mill Lane, Margate, Kent, CT9 1LB

Newry Training and Employment Agency

5-13 Marcus Street, Newry, County Down, BT34 1ET

Tel: 028 3026 1222
Fax: 028 3026 2675
Contact: Patricia Boyle, Disablement Employment Adviser

There is a Disablement Employment Advisor covering the areas of Newry, Kilkeel and Newcastle.

Newtownabbey Training and Employment Agency

41 Church Road, Newtownabbey, County Antrim, BT36 7LH

Tel: 028 9054 8125
Textphone: 028 9054 8134
Fax: 028 9054 8110
Contact: Marina Smyth, Disablement Employment Adviser

Omagh Training and Employment Agency

Kevlin Building, Kevlin Avenue, Omagh, County Tyrone, BT78 1ER

Tel: 028 8225 5500
Fax: 028 8225 5511
Contact: Pat Mullan, Disabilities Officer

Orkney Opportunities Centre

The Brig, 2 Albert Street, Kirkwall, Orkney, KW15 1HP

Peterborough Careers Centre

Cavell Court, 9-11 Lincoln Road, Peterborough, Cambridgeshire, PE1 2PQ

Prospects Careers Service

2nd Floor, 151 High Street, London, N14 6BP

21

Prospects Careers Services

Walsall Careers Centre, 30-30a Station Street, Walsall, West Midlands, WS2 9JZ

Tel: 01922 636333
Fax: 01922 636222

REMPLOY

Merrington Lane Industrial Estate, Spennymoor, County Durham, DL16 7EY

Tel: 01388 814511
Fax: 01388 420509
Contact: Mrs Burns, Production Clerk

Rothesay Careers Office

7 Castle Street, Glasgow, Argyll, PA20 9HA

Tel: 01700 503600
Fax: 01700 503130

Seetec Training and Job Search Centre

267 Cranbrook Road, Ilford, Essex, IG1 4TG

Tel: 020 8491 1188
Fax: 020 8491 2303
E-mail: info@seetec.co.uk
Website: www.seetec.co.uk
Contact: Beth Chalmers

Selly Oak Careers Centre

778 Bristol Road, Selly Oak, Birmingham, West Midlands, B29 6NA

Shaw Trust

Regional Office for Central and Wales, De Salis Drive, Hampton Lovett, Droitwich, Worcestershire, WR9 0QE

Tel: 01905 795194
Textphone: 0345 697288
Fax: 01905 796884
Contact: Elaine Wellings

The trust provides a range of employment-related services including: supported placements; programmes for people who have experienced mental health problems; training towards vocational qualifications; employment rehabilitation; training for work; work preparation; vocational guidance. Projects in operation throughout the country.

Sheffield Careers Guidance Services

AEEU House, 43 Furnival Gate, Sheffield, South Yorkshire, S1 3SL

Tel: 0114 273 5461
Fax: 0114 273 5190
E-mail: enquiries@scgs.org.uk

Sheffield Careers Guidance Services provides careers information and advice to a wide range of clients living, working or seeking to work in Sheffield, including young people and their parents in schools and colleges, those in training, the unemployed and adults. We adopt our range of skills to suit individual needs. The same is true of our services to employers - whether it is a vacancy to be filled or an entire recruitment and training strategy to be devised, we can advise and assist.

Sheffield Employment Services

DS3 Level 3, Rockingham House, 123 West Street, Sheffield, South Yorkshire, S1 4ER

Tel: 0114 275 6146
Textphone: 0114 275 5879
Fax: 0114 259 6262

All policy queries relating to mainstream job brokering, external relations including overseas placing and national vacancies, new and existing jobsearch programmes.

Shetland Careers Service

Careers Office, Toll Clock Centre, Lerwick, Shetland Islands, ZE1 0DE

Tel: 01595 695791
Fax: 01595 694011
Contact: A J Carter, Careers Services Manager

Shetland Careers Services exists to provide effective careers guidance, information services and guidance to enter appropriate education, training and work; the help provided is unbiased, centred on the individual and available to all ages from trained careers advisers.

Solihull Careers Centre

P O Box 1701, Solihull, West Midlands, B91 3BN

Tel: 0121 605 3444
Fax: 0121 605 3434
Contact: Alan Thomas, Senior Careers Advisor
           28g Bosworth Drive, Chelmsley Wood, Birmingham, B37 5DP
Tel: 0121 770 1861
Fax: 0121 779 7351

Solihull Careers Centre provides an information, advice and vocational guidance service to both young people and adults. Additional support is provided for individuals with special needs and disabilities including those with hearing impairment. The support commences in school at Year 9 and extends through further education and training, unemployment and employment.

South East London PACT

92-94 Borough High Street, London, SE1 1LJ

Tel: 020 7805 3650

Textphone: 020 7805 3652

Fax: 020 7805 3651

Contact: Moira Beddoe, Manager, PACT

The Disability Service (DS) is an organisation set up in 1992. The aim of the PACT within the DS is to offer people with disabilities help and advice in finding and retaining work or appropriate training; and to help and encourage employers to make work and training opportunities available to them.

Stevenage Careers Centre

Six Hills Way, Stevenage, Hertfordshire, SG1 1LB

Tel: 01438 351582

Fax: 01438 743959

Stirling Careers Office

6 Viewfield Place, Stirling, FK8 1NQ

Tel: 01786 462036

Fax: 01786 448360

Suffolk Careers Ltd

43 St Andrews Street South, Bury St Edmunds, Suffolk, IP33 3PH

Tel: 01284 768493

Fax: 01284 704199

Telford and Wrekin Training and Development Centre

Madeley Court, Court Street, Madeley, Telford, Shropshire, TF7 5DZ

The Careers Office

Manse Brae, Lochgilphead, Argyll, PA31 8RA

Tel: 01546 602725

Fax: 01546 602750

Contact: Norma Ross, Special Needs Careers Advisor

Argyll and Bute Careers Service aims to provide an impartial, unbiased and confidential careers guidance service, enabling its clients to make individual, well-informed and realistic career decisions which will contribute to their own personal development and the well-being of their economic community.

Toucan

Tanzaro House, Ardwick Green North, Manchester, Lancashire, M12 6FZ

Tel: 0161 273 5122

Fax: 0161 273 5122

E-mail: ToucanEurope@compuserve.com

Website: www.toucan-europe.co.uk

Contact: Alex McDonald, Project Worker

Toucan is a non-profit cooperative working in the area of research and development, providing technical assistance, management and training and development for organisations within the European Union. The focus of activities is work with people experiencing social exclusion and innovative actions and development that offer opportunities for economic and social integration.

Training and Employment Agency Newry

5 Marcus Street, Newry, County Down, BT34 1ET

Tel: 028 3026 1222

Fax: 028 3026 2675

Training and Employment Agency, HQ

Adelaide House, 39-49 Adelaide Street, Belfast, County Antrim, BT2 8FD

Tel: 028 9025 7466

Fax: 028 9025 7468

Contact: Irene Murphy

The Disablement Advisory Service is the part of the Training and Employment Agency which helps people with disabilities find suitable employment and training opportunities. DAS offers a broad range of help including Access to Work (NI), the Job Introduction Scheme and Employment Support. It also supports special training and employment schemes run by disability organisations.

21

Training and Employment Agency, Londonderry

5 Waterloo Place, Londonderry, BT48 6BT

Tel: 028 7126 4294

Fax: 028 7127 3704

Contact: Margaret McCloskey, Disability Advisor

Covers Londonderry and Limavady.

Training and Employment Grants

East End Partnership (TEGs) Ltd, East End Enterprise Centre, 78-80 Tollcross Road, Glasgow, Lanarkshire, G31 4XA

Tel: 0141 556 2222

Fax: 0141 556 1977

Contact: Jane Adamson

East End Partnership (TEGs) was established in 1996 to manage and administer the training and employment grants (TEGs) programme in Glasgow and on behalf of the Glasgow Development Agency.

Waltham Forest Careers Guidance

398a Hoe Street, London, E17 9AA

Tel: 020 8521 9020

Fax: 020 8520 7466

Contact: Nirvani Ramsawak, Careers Information Officer

Tel: 020 8521 9020 ext 111

We offer careers guidance to young people up to 21 years old and to adults. We also offer services to schools, colleges, local employers and training providers.

West Country Training and Consultancy Services

Central House, New North Road, Exeter, Devon, EX4 4HF

Tel: 01392 496717

Fax: 01392 496717

West Didsbury Careers Office

141 Barlow Moor Road, Manchester, Lancashire, M20 2PQ

Western Isles Guidance Service

Adult Guidance Centre, Town Hall, South Beach, Stornoway, Western Isles, HS1 2BE

Tel: 01851 705200

Fax: 01851 705289

Wisbech Careers Centre

2 Stermyn Street, Wisbech, Cambridgeshire, PE13 1EQ

AZTEC

Manorgate House, 2 Manorgate Road, Kingston upon Thames, Surrey, KT2 7AL

Tel: 020 8547 3934

Fax: 020 8547 3884

E-mail: info@aztec-iip.co.uk

Website: www.aztec-iip.co.uk

AZTEC is the Training and Enterprise Council for South West London. They provide a range of services to businesses and organisations, adding value by improving performance, competeiveness and profitability. They provide opportunities to individuals to develop their skills and talents and also to further their employment.

Barnsley and Doncaster TEC

Conference Centre, Eldon Street, Barnsley, South Yorkshire, S70 2JL

Tel: 01226 248088

Fax: 01226 291625

E-mail: steve.wragg@bdtec.co.uk

Website: www.bdtec.co.uk

Bedfordshire and Luton CCTE and Business Link Bedfordshire

Woburn Court, 2 Railton Road, Woburn Road Industrial Estate, Kempston, Bedford, MK42 7PN

Tel: 01234 843100

Fax: 01234 843211

E-mail: training@bed-tec.org.

Website: www.beds-chamber.co.uk

21

Birmingham and Solihull TEC

Chaplin Court, 80 Hurst Street, Birmingham, West Midlands, B5 4TG

Tel: 0121 622 4419
Fax: 0121 622 1600
E-mail: l.whitten@bstec.co.uk

We promote a high skill economy, create a climate of training and enterprise throughout the community, stimulate the growth and development of business in Birmingham and Solihull as the key to wider social and economic prosperity, and encourage the development of all people in Birmingham and Solihull.

Bolton and Bury CCTE

Clive House, Clive Street, Bolton, Lancashire, BL1 1ET

Tel: 01204 397350
Fax: 01204 363212
E-mail: bbtecinfo@dial.pipex.com

Bradford and District TEC

Mercury House, 4 Manchester Road, Bradford, West Yorkshire, BD5 0QL

Tel: 01274 751333
Fax: 01274 751344
E-mail: info@bradtec.co.uk

Access to hundreds of job and training vacancies throughout Bradford and district. Training designed to get young people and adults into work (aged 16-63). Support to help new businesses set up, and existing businesses grow. Programmes designed to help school-aged children learn about the world of work, and much more support available.

Calderdale and Kirklees TEC

Park View House, Woodvale Office Park, Woodvale Road, Brighouse, West Yorkshire, HD6 4AB

Tel: 01484 400770
Videotel: 01924 423173
Fax: 01484 400672
E-mail: info@cktec.co.uk
Website: www.cald-kirk.businesslink.co.uk

Cambridgeshire TEC and BL Limited (Central and South Cambridgeshire)

Unit 2-3 Trust Court, Chivers Way, The Vision Park, Histon, Cambridge, CB4 4PW

Tel: 01223 235635
Fax: 01223 235631/ 632
E-mail: knorman@cambs.tec.org.uk

CELTEC North Wales TEC

St Asaph Business Park, Glascoed Road, St Asaph, Clwyd, LL17 0LJ

Tel: 01745 538500
Textphone: 01745 538707
Fax: 01745 538501
E-mail: celtec@celtec.co.uk
Website: www.celtec.celtec.co.uk

CEWTEC (Chester, Ellesmere Port and Wirral)

Egerton House, 2 Tower Road, Birkenhead, Merseyside, L41 1FN

Tel: 0151 650 0555/ 0800 132762
Fax: 0151 650 0777
E-mail: it@cewtec.co.uk

CEWTEC is the Training and Enterprise Council for Chester, Ellesmere Port and Wirral. Its mission is "to build a strong and sustainable local economy by developing business, people and partnerships."

County Durham TEC

Horndale Avenue, Aycliffe Industrial Park, Newton Aycliffe, County Durham, DL5 6XS

Tel: 01325 351166
Fax: 01325 381362
E-mail: ask@cdtec.co.uk

County Durham TEC exists to help maximise the potential of business and individuals within the county by offering training and development opportunities and business support.

Coventry and Warwickshire CCTE

Oak Tree Court, Binley Business Park, Harry Weston Road, Coventry, West Midlands, CV3 2UN

Tel: 024 7665 4321/ 0800 252198
Fax: 024 7645 0242
E-mail: stuartc@cw-chamber.co.uk

Working in partnership to enhance the economy of Coventry and Warwickshire, to improve the competitiveness of Coventry and Warwickshire businesses. Encourages members and potential members of the workforce to acquire and develop

21

the range and level of skills and capabilities needed for employment and self employment. To be recognised as the "voice of business" for Coventry and Warwickshire.

Dorset TEC

Provincial House, 25 Oxford Road, Bournemouth, Dorset, BH8 8EY

Tel: 01202 466400

Fax: 01202 299457

E-mail: enquiries@dorset-tec.com

To improve the local economy by helping to increase the competiveness of businesses and people in Dorset.

Dudley TEC

Dudley Court South, East Waterfront, Level Street, Brierley Hill, Dudley, West Midlands, DY5 1XN

Tel: 01384 485000

Fax: 01384 483399

E-mail: j.gray@dudley.org.uk

Website: www.dudley-tec.co.uk

Contact: J Gray, Information Officer

ELTEC (East Lancashire)

Red Rose Court, Clayton Business Park, Clayton le Moors, Accrington, Lancashire, BB5 5JR

Tel: 01254 301333/ 0800 696696

Fax: 01254 399090

E-mail: marketing@eltec.co.uk

Website: www.eltec.co.uk

Enterprise Cumbria

Venture House, Regents Court, Guard Street, Workington, Cumbria, CA14 4EW

Tel: 01900 66991/ 0800 667755

Fax: 01900 604027

E-mail: amcbridge@cumbriaenterprise.co.uk

Website: www.cumbriatec.co.uk

Essex TEC

Redwing House, Hedgerows Business Park, Colchester Road, Chelmsford, Essex, CM2 5PB

Tel: 01245 450123

Fax: 01245 451874

E-mail: information@essex.tec.org.uk

Website: www.essex.tec.org.uk

FOCUS Central London TEC

Centre Point, 103 New Oxford Street, London, WC1A 1DR

Tel: 020 7896 8484

Fax: 020 7896 8686

E-mail: focus-central-london.co.uk

Website: www.focus-central-london.co.uk

Focus Central London is the new Training and Enterprise Council for Central London. Covering Camden, Hackney, Islington, the City of London, the City of Westminster, Kensington and Chelsea, Hammersmith and Fulham, Southwark and Lambeth. Training and Enterprise Councils (TECs) are independent companies led by business people. Various courses are available covering vast aspects of training leading to NVQs to gain and maximise career potential.

Greater Nottingham TEC

Marina Road, Nottingham, NG7 1TN

Tel: 0115 941 3313

Textphone: 0115 958 3368

Fax: 0115 948 4589

E-mail: jminton@gntec.co.uk

Website: www.gntec.co.uk

Greater Peterborough CCTE

Stuart House, City Road, Peterborough, Cambridgeshire, PE1 1QF

Tel: 01733 890808

Fax: 01733 890809

E-mail: gpccte@gpccte.co.uk

Hampshire TEC

25 Thackeray Mall, Fareham, Hampshire, PO16 0PQ

Tel: 01329 230099

Fax: 01329 237733

E-mail: beryl.court@hampshiretec.co.uk

Richard Hastilow is managing director of Hampshire Training and Enterprise Council Limited. The company serves the businesses and people of the Hampshire area through a range of business support services and skills development programmes. It also works with private and public sector partners on development projects to boost the local economy.

21

Heart of England TEC (Oxfordshire)

26-27 The Quadrant, Abingdon Science Park, off
Barton Lane, Abingdon, Oxfordshire, OX14 3YS

Tel: 01235 553249/ 0800 888500

Fax: 01235 555706

E-mail: enquiry@hoe.tec.co.uk

Herefordshire and Worcestershire CCTE

Chamber Court, Castle Street, Worcester, WR1 3AD

Tel: 01905 723200

Textphone: 0800 959598

Fax: 01905 613338

E-mail: margaretR@HWCCTE.co.uk

Website: www.hwccte.co.uk

Hertfordshire TEC

45 Grosvenor Road, St Albans, Hertfordshire, AL1
3AW

Tel: 01727 813600/ 0800 919000

Fax: 01727 813443

E-mail: stewart.sega@herts.tec.co.uk

Hertfordshire TEC provides a wide range of
services to businesses and training services to
individuals in Hertfordshire. The TEC promotes
the principle of lifelong learning as the key to
economic prosperity for businesses and the
people who work in them.

Humberside TEC

The Maltings, Silvester Square, Silvester Street,
Hull, North Humberside, HU1 3HL

Tel: 01482 226491

Fax: 01482 213206

E-mail: info@humbersidetec.co.uk

Humberside Training and Enterprise Council is
funded by the government primarily to deliver
training and enterprise programmes. Our purpose
is to contribute to increased competitiveness and
growth within the Humberside economy, by
helping businesses grow and people learn. This
will lead to greater opportunities, raised
achievement and an improved quality of life.

LAWTEC (Lancashire Area West)

Caxton Road, Fulwood, Preston, Lancashire, PR2
9ZB

Tel: 01772 792111

Fax: 01772 792777

E-mail: lawtec@compuserve.com

LAWTEC works with businesses, schools, colleges
and eight local authorities to improve the skills of
local people and the competiveness of local
businesses throughout western Lancashire.
LAWTEC offers a wide range of support for
businesses and individuals including Investors in
People, modern apprenticeships, management
development, recruitment and training grants,
Business Start-Up, Graduate Workstart and adult
careers guidance.

Leeds TEC

Belgrave Hall, Belgrave Street, Leeds, West
Yorkshire, LS2 8DD

Tel: 0113 234 7666

Fax: 0113 245 1243

E-mail: tecinfo@leedstec.co.uk

Leicestershire TEC

Meridian East, Meridian Business Park, Leicester,
LE3 2WZ

Tel: 0116 265 1515

Fax: 0116 265 1501

Leicestershire TEC's mission is to work in
partnership with others to secure long-term
prosperity for our local economy by encouraging a
lifelong learning culture, developing a world class
workforce, improving business performance and
assisting in the regeneration of local community.

Lincolnshire TEC

Beech House, Witham Park, Waterside South,
Lincoln, LN5 7JH

Tel: 01522 567765

Fax: 01522 510534

E-mail: admin@lincs-tecgroup.org.uk

Lincolnshire TEC's mission is to bring about
economic regeneration, business growth and the
development of a highly skilled workforce in
Lincolnshire. One of its five strategic objectives is
"In partnership, to work towards developing a
fairer society in Lincolnshire which addresses
social exclusion and where those individuals who
face disadvantage are empowered to achieve their
full potential".

21

London East TEC

Boardman House, 64 Broadway, Stratford, London, E15 1NT

Tel: 020 8432 0000
Fax: 020 8432 0399
E-mail: jill.simpson@letec.co.uk

Manchester TEC

Lee House, 90 Great Bridgewater Street, Manchester, Lancashire, M1 5JW

Tel: 0161 236 7222
Fax: 0161 236 8878
E-mail: reception@mccitecbl.org.uk

Merseyside TEC

3rd Floor Tithebarn House, Tithebarn Street, Liverpool, Merseyside, L2 2NZ

Tel: 0151 236 0026/ 0800 317857
Fax: 0151 236 4013
E-mail: info@merstec.u.net.com
Website: www.info@merstec.u.net.com

Mid Wales TEC

1st Floor, St David's House, New Road, Newtown, Powys, SY16 1RB

Tel: 01686 622494/ 0800 252903
Fax: 01686 622716
E-mail: enquiry@powys.tec.org.uk

Milton Keynes and North Buckinghamshire CCTE

Tempus, 249 Midsummer Boulevard, Milton Keynes, Buckinghamshire, MK9 1EU

Tel: 01908 259000
Fax: 01908 230130
E-mail: tempus@mk-chamber.co.uk
Website: www.mk-chamber.co.uk

Norfolk and Waveney TEC

St Andrews House, St Andrews Street, Norwich, Norfolk, NR2 4TP

Tel: 01603 763812
Fax: 01603 763813
E-mail: susanne.mills@nwtec.co.uk

The TEC is a strategic body which acts as a catalyst in the development of the local economy, promotes enterprise and provides support to business and develops skills. The TEC's mission is "to help increase the wealth and improve the

prospects and quality of life for the business and people of Norfolk and Waveney."

North and Mid Cheshire TEC

Spencer House, Dewhurst Road, Birchwood, Warrington, Cheshire, WA3 7PP

Tel: 01925 826515/ 0800 282020
Fax: 01925 820215
E-mail: general@normid.u-net.com

North Derbyshire TEC

Block C, St Mary's Court, St Mary's Gate, Chesterfield, Derbyshire, S41 7TD

Tel: 01246 551158
Fax: 01246 544688
Website: www.nderbytec.co.uk

North London TEC

Dumayne House, 1 Fox Lane, Palmers Green, London, N13 4AB

Tel: 020 8447 9422
Fax: 020 8882 5931
E-mail: post@nltec.co.uk

Training and Enterprise Council. Aims to enable local business and people to succeed through business competiveness and workforce strategies. Covers London boroughs of Enfield, Haringey and Barnet.

North Nottinghamshire TEC

1st Floor, Block C, Edwinstowe House, High Street, Edwinstowe, Mansfield, Nottinghamshire, NG21 9PR

Tel: 01623 824624
Fax: 01623 824070
E-mail: enquiries@nntec.co.uk
Website: www.nntec-co.uk

North West London TEC

Kirkfield House, 118-120 Station Road, Harrow, Middlesex, HA1 2RL

Tel: 020 8901 5000
Fax: 020 8901 5100
E-mail: brendon.walsh@nwltec.co.uk

North Yorkshire TEC

TEC House, 7 Pioneer Business Park, Amy Johnson
Way, York, YO30 4TN

Tel: 01904 691939

Fax: 01904 690411

E-mail: info@nyorks-tec.co.uk

Website: www.nyorks-tec.co.uk

Northamptonshire TEC

Royal Pavilion, Summerhouse Road, Moulton Park
Industrial Estate, Northampton, NN3 6BJ

Tel: 01604 671200

Videotel: 01604 490444

Fax: 01604 670362

E-mail: email@chamber-nptn.co.uk

Northumberland TEC

Suite 2, Craster Court, Manor Walks Shopping
Centre, Cramlington, Northumberland, NE23 6XX

Tel: 01670 713303

Fax: 01670 713323

E-mail: stephen_cowell@ntec.co.uk

Website: www.northumberland_tec@ntec.co.uk

Oldham Chamber of Commerce, Training and Enterprise

Meridian Centre, King Street, Oldham, Lancashire,
OL8 1EZ

Tel: 0161 620 0006

Fax: 0161 620 0030

E-mail: jenniewilliams@oldhamchamber.co.uk

Website: www.oldhamchamber.co.uk

Provides one-stop shop of business advice and
training for individuals.

PROSPER

Prosper House, Budshead Road, Plymouth, Devon,
PL6 5XR

Tel: 01752 785785/ 0800 252713

Fax: 01752 770925

E-mail: help@prosper-group.co.uk

PROSPER provides business support, advice and
information through its Business Link Devon and
Cornwall Service. PROSPER's Individual Solutions
service provides advice and information on
training and development programmes for
individuals of all ages.

Rochdale Borough CCTE

St James Place, 160-162 Yorkshire Street,
Rochdale, Lancashire, OL16 2DL

Tel: 01706 644909

Fax: 01706 649979

E-mail: info@rbccte.co.uk

Website: www.rbte.co.uk

Rotherham CCTE

Moorgate House, 23 Moorgate Road, Rotherham,
South Yorkshire, S60 2EN

Tel: 01709 830511

Fax: 01709 362519

E-mail: c.duff@rccte.org.uk

Website: www.rccte.org.uk

Sandwell TEC

1st Floor, Black Country House, Rounds Green
Road, Oldbury, West Midlands, B69 2DG

Tel: 0121 543 2222

Fax: 0121 543 4444

E-mail: sandtec.demon.co.uk

Website: www.sandwelltec.co.uk

Sheffield TEC

St Mary's Court, 55 St Mary's Road, Sheffield,
South Yorkshire, S2 4AQ

Tel: 0114 270 1911

Fax: 0114 275 2634

E-mail: snewton@sheffieldtec.co.uk

Shropshire CCTE

Trevithick House, Stafford Park 4, Telford,
Shropshire, TF3 3BA

Tel: 01952 208200

Fax: 01952 208208

E-mail: enquiries@shropshire-chamber.co.uk

Website: www.shropshire-chamber.co.uk

To be the foremost voice of Shropshire business,
providing information and advice, exceeding the
expectations of our customers, increasing and
sustaining our membership and building a strong
national profile.

21

SOLOTEC

Lancaster House, 7 Elmfield Road, Bromley, Kent, BR1 1LT

Tel: 020 8313 9232
Fax: 020 8313 9245
E-mail: advice.centre@solotec.co.uk

SOLOTEC's mission is "to contribute to sustainable economic growth in South London by addressing the combined challenges of business competitiveness, job creation, skills enhancement and exclusion from opportunties."

Somerset TEC

East Reach House, East Reach, Taunton, Somerset, TA1 3EN

Tel: 01823 321188
Fax: 01823 256174
E-mail: email@somerset.tec.org.uk

Somerset TEC is funded by government to satisfy training programmes for young people and adults and works with its many partners to help improve and sustain economic success and competiveness in Somerset through the development of all its people and the stimulation of enterprise.

South and East Cheshire TEC

P O Box 37, Middlewich Business and Industrial Park, Dalton Way, Middlewich, Cheshire, CW10 0HU

Tel: 01606 737009
Fax: 01606 737022
E-mail: user38172@aol.com

South East Wales TEC

Technocentre, Beignon Close, Ocean Way, Cardiff, South Glamorgan, CF1 5HF

Tel: 029 2031 1400
Fax: 029 2031 141
E-mail: sewtec@enablis.co.uk

Southern Derbyshire CCTE

St Helens Court, St Helens Street, Derby, DE1 3GY

Tel: 01332 290550
Fax: 01332 292188
E-mail: info@sdccte.com

Southern Derbyshire Chamber works towards the development of the Southern Derbyshire economy, business community and local people. Development of our local workforce through our Training Enterprise Council role has been delivered through our youth and adult training

418

programmes and is underpinned by our support of a lifelong learning culture.

St Helens CCTE

7 Waterside Court, St Helens, Merseyside, WA9 1UE

Tel: 01744 742000
Fax: 01744 742040
E-mail: julie.felton@st-helens-ccte.co.uk

Staffordshire TEC

The Glades, Festival Way, Festival Park, Stoke-on-Trent, Staffordshire, ST1 5TQ

Tel: 01782 202733
Fax: 01782 286215
E-mail: info@staffstec.org.uk

Staffordshire TEC exists to help local people and employers to improve their skills through training, education and development. Working with a variety of partners we offer a broad range of initiatives to help employers, young people and adults to realise their full potential.

Stockport and High Peak TEC

1 St Peters Square, Stockport, Cheshire, SK1 1NN

Tel: 0161 477 8830
Videotel: 0161 477 4036
Fax: 0161 480 7243
E-mail: trevorj@shptec.co.uk
Website: www.blstockport.co.uk

Suffolk TEC

2nd Floor, Crown House, Crown Street, Ipswich, Suffolk, IP1 3HS

Tel: 01473 218951/ 0800 181915
Fax: 01473 231776
E-mail: epayne@suffolk.tec.org.uk

Sunderland City TEC

Business and Innovation Centre, Sunderland Enterprise Park, Wearfield, Sunderland, Tyne and Wear, SR5 2TA

Tel: 0191 516 6000
Fax: 0191 516 6161
E-mail: Jules.Preston@sunderland.TEC.org.uk

Sunderland City TEC provides training programmes for the unemployed, particularly young people, through modern apprenticeships. The TEC also manages a Business and Innovation Centre, Business Link Sunderland and Pathways, which is an adult guidance unit.

Surrey TEC
Technology House, 48-54 Goldsworth Road,
Woking, Surrey, GU21 1LE
Tel: 01483 728190
Fax: 01483 755259
E-mail: info@surrey.tec.co.uk

Surrey TEC is committed to promoting growth and prosperity through effective training and enterprise throughout the country. One of Surrey TEC's principal goals is to create a world class workforce in Surrey to ensure that local businesses can compete successfully in the national and global markets.

Sussex Enterprise
Greenacre Court, Station Road, Burgess Hill, West Sussex, RH15 9DS
Tel: 01444 259259
Fax: 01444 259190
E-mail: mette.payne@sussexenterprise.co.uk
Website: www.sussexenterprise.co.uk

Tees Valley TEC
Training and Enterprise House, 2 Queens Square, Middlesbrough, Cleveland, TS2 1AA
Tel: 01642 231023
Fax: 01642 232480
E-mail: teesvalley@tec.co.uk
Website: www.teesvalleytec.co.uk

Tees Valley TEC's role is to promote economic development across the five council boroughs of Darlington, Hartlepool, Middlesbrough, Redcar and Cleveland and Stockton-on-Tees. Our services include job training course for school leavers and the unemployed. We also provide a range of business support services, including a business start-up package.

Thames Valley Enterprise
Pacific House, Imperial Way, Reading, Berkshire, RG2 0TF
Tel: 0118 921 4000/ 0800 775566
Fax: 0118 975 3054
E-mail: knowhow@tve.co.uk
Website: www.tec.co.uk/tve

The Learning and Business Link Company
26 Kings Hill Avenue, Kings Hill, West Malling, Kent, ME19 4TA
Tel: 01732 220000
Fax: 01732 841641
E-mail: inform@kenttec.demon.co.uk

The Link Group Gloucestershire
Conway House, 33-35 Worcester Street, Gloucester, GL1 3AJ
Tel: 01452 524488/ 0800 220262
Fax: 01452 509678
E-mail: info@linkgroup.co.uk

Tyneside TEC
Moongate House, Fifth Avenue Business Park, Team Valley, Gateshead, Tyne and Wear, NE11 0HF
Tel: 0191 491 6000
Fax: 0191 491 6159
E-mail: enquiries@tynesidetec.co.uk

Wakefield TEC
Grove Hall, 60 College Grove Road, Wakefield, West Yorkshire, WF1 3RN
Tel: 01924 299907
Fax: 01924 201062
E-mail: christy.sullivan@wakefield-tec.co.uk
Website: www.wakefield-tec.co.uk

Wakefield TEC is committed to creating, through partnership, prosperity in the local area, in terms of both employment and economic growth. A wide range of business support, and training and development services are available for businesses and individuals. These include: youth and adult training programmes, Investors in People, management development initiatives, Prospect Corner career and guidance service, and education/business partnerships.

21

Walsall TEC
5th Floor, Townend House, Townend Square, Walsall, West Midlands, WS1 1NS
Tel: 01922 424242
Fax: 01922 424243
E-mail: waltec@dial.pipex.com

All Walsall TEC's services are geared, directly or indirectly, to making Walsall companies more competitive. Better performance leads to greater competitiveness. So do better quality, better management and better productitivity. And they all depend, ultimately, on people, and therefore their skills, knowledge and abilities. The TEC continues to focus strongly on services that drive up skill levels among individuals, and on persuading companies of the crucial importance of investing in people.

West London TEC

West London Centre, 15-21 Staines Road, Hounslow, Middlesex, TW3 3HA

Tel: 020 8577 1010

Fax: 020 8570 9969

E-mail: info@wltec.co.uk

Website: www.wltec.co.uk

During our six years of operation we have focused on discovering what our customers want to be successful, and targeting our services accordingly. Innovative and effective partnerships are helping to coordinate the delivery of services genuinely matched to the needs and ambitions of West London.

West Wales TEC

3rd Floor Orchard House, Orchard Street, Swansea, West Glamorgan, SA1 5DJ

Tel: 01792 354000

Textphone: 01792 354053

Fax: 01792 354001

E-mail: mailbox@westwales.tec.org.uk

Website: www.westwales.tec.org.uk

WESTEC

St Lawrence House, 29-31 Broad Street, Bristol, Avon, BS99 7HR

Tel: 0117 927 7116

Fax: 0117 922 6664

E-mail: enquiries@westec.co.uk

WESTEC'S role is to help improve the overall prosperity of the area. We do this by helping business to be more competitive, managing training to improve skills in the workforce and removing barriers for people who are excluded from the workforce. We support various partners: Business Link West; Learning Partnership West; The Western Development Partnership and the Equality Foundation.

Wigan CCTE

Wigan Investment Centre, Waterside Drive, Wigan, Lancashire, WN3 5BA

Tel: 01942 705705

Fax: 01942 705272

E-mail: info@wbp.org.uk

Website: www.wbp.org.uk

Wight Training and Enterprise

Mill Court, Furrlongs, Newport, Isle of Wight, PO30 2AA

Tel: 01983 822818

Fax: 01983 527063

E-mail: tbutler@wightenterprise.co.uk

Wiltshire and Swindon TEC

The Bora Building, Westlea Campus, Chelmsford Road, Westlea Down, Eastleaze, Swindon, Wiltshire, SN5 7EZ

Tel: 01793 501500

Fax: 01793 501555

E-mail: mkt@trainingpays.com

Wiltshire and Swindon TEC is an independent company formed in 1991 by local people using government funds to improve national competitiveness at a local level. It does this through supporting the development both of individuals and of business within the county.

Wolverhampton CCTE

Pendeford Business Park, Wobaston Road, Wolverhampton, West Midlands, WV9 5HA

Tel: 01902 445500

Fax: 01902 445200

E-mail: enquiries@wton-chamber.co.uk

Providing information services to businesses in Wolverhampton and South Staffordshire. Services provided include: general business-related information enquiries, in-depth research services, and access to database labels and listings and to credit-checking facilities.

Information, Advice and Legal Services

Grouped here is a range of organisations which provide advice, counselling or legal services for deaf and hard of hearing people or who are aware of the special communication needs of deaf people. Details are given on the range of services an organisation can provide. Organisations range from the general such as Citizens Advice Bureaux to the specific such as the Terrence Higgins Trust.

Organisations are listed alphabetically under the following headings: information, advice, counselling, grants and legal services.

Information

Association of Disabled Parents in the Norfolk Area

145 Main Road, Clenchwarton, King's Lynn, Norfolk, PE34 4DT

Tel: 01553 768193

Specialises in information on disabled parenting.

Association of Voluntary Organisations in Wrexham

Ty Avow, 21 Egerton Street, Wrexham, Clwyd, LL11 1ND

Tel: 01978 312556
Fax: 01978 263980
E-mail: avow@dial.pipex.com
Website: www.dspace.dial.pipex.com/town/plaza/ylk58/

AVOW is the County Voluntary Council for Wrexham County Borough. It provides information, advice and practical services to the voluntary sector, including payroll services, legal advice, employment advice, a volunteer bureau, photocopying, room hire, training and advice on Charity Commission issues.

Bedfordshire Advocacy Alliance

41 Mill Street, Bedford, MK40 3EU

Tel: 01234 262080
Fax: 01234 359999

Provides information and advocacy services to people with learning disabilities.

Birmingham Deaf Youth Enquiry Advice

641 Bristol Road, Selly Oak, Birmingham, West Midlands, B29 6AE

Tel: 0121 471 4745
Textphone: 0121 471 4745

Bridgend Association of Voluntary Organisations

10 Park Street, Bridgend, Mid Glamorgan, CF31 4AX

Tel: 01656 647255
Fax: 01656 647312
Contact: Amanda Peters, Director

British Deaf Association Health and Counselling Service

17 Macon Way, Herald Drive, Crewe, Cheshire, CW1 6EE

Tel: 01270 250736
Textphone: 01270 250743
Fax: 01270 250742
Contact: Michelle Simpson, Health and Counselling Services Manager

British Deaf Association Health and Counselling Service provides health information, advice and counselling to any member of the deaf community. Counselling can be by textphone or face to face. Referrals from GPs or social services are welcome, as are self-referrals. All BDA registered counsellors follow a strict confidentiality policy and receive regular supervision.

Bromsgrove and Redditch Citizen Advocacy

17-21 Worcester Road, Bromsgrove, Worcestershire, B61 7DL

Tel: 01527 575239

Provides short-term advocacy and citizen advocacy to older people and people with disabilities.

Buckinghamshire Chiltern Disability Information Network

Amersham Health Centre, Chiltern Avenue, Amersham, Buckinghamshire, HP6 5AY

Tel: 01494 434460
Textphone: 01494 434472

CALL Citizen Advocacy
1a Newland, Lincoln, LN1 1UX
Tel: 01522 511114
Fax: 01522 510215

Carmarthen Association of Voluntary Services (CAVS)
11-12 King Street, Carmarthen, Dyfed, SA31 1BH
Tel: 01267 236367
Fax: 01267 221972
E-mail: pawb@cavs.prestel.co.uk
Website: www.homeusers.prestel.co.uk/cavs/
Contact: Ieuan Williams, Director

Carmarthenshire Association of Voluntary Services is an independent charity which provides support, advice, information and training to voluntary and community groups in Carmarthenshire.

Ceredigion Association of Voluntary Organisations
First Floor, Werndriw Lodge, 23 High Street, Lampeter, Ceredigion, SA48 7BH
Tel: 01570 423232
Fax: 01570 422427
E-mail: cavo.cmgc@virgin.net
Contact: Sandra Morgan, Director

We are a County Voluntary Council: promoting, supporting and coordinating the work of voluntary organisation in Ceredigion and acting as a link between the voluntary and statutory sectors. We help voluntary organisations with support, information and advice on a whole range of matters, and publish a regular newsletter.

Citizen Advocacy Southern Cambridgeshire
Centre 4a, Gonville Place, Cambridge, CB1 1LY
Tel: 01223 516637

Conwy Voluntary Services Council
8 Rivieres Avenue, Colwyn Bay, LL29 7DP
Tel: 01492 534091
Fax: 01492 535397
E-mail: cvsc@dial.pipex.com
Website: www.marketsite.co.uk/cvsc
Contact: Jan Smith, Information Officer

Conwy Voluntary Services Council is a registered charity (No. 1061697) which aims to support voluntary and community action in Conwy by helping new projects, bringing groups together, providing training and practical help, producing a regular newsletter and offering information and advice on funding, volunteering, how groups can work effectively and legal matters.

Cumbria Youth Enquiry Service
155 Stricklandgate, Kendal, Cumbria, LA9 4RF
Tel: 01539 734820
Fax: 01539 734820
Contact: Diane Walker

The Youth Enquiry Service (YES) is part of Cumbria Youth Service which is staffed by qualified and experienced youth workers. YES provides resources, practical help, support and information on a wide range of concerns. There is access to a counselling service. Staff are also qualified in British Sign Language stages I and II.

Denbighshire Voluntary Services Council
Station Road, Ruthin, Clwyd, LL15 1BP
Tel: 01824 702441/ 703805
Fax: 01824 705412
Contact: Eirwen Godden, Chief Officer

DVSC is an independent body working with and on behalf of voluntary organisations, community groups and volunteers. We offer practical help and provide a representative voice to decision-makers. We aim to promote and develop a vibrant voluntary sector that encourages community activities and enriches people's lives.

Directions Plus
72-74 Newmarket Road, Cambridge, CB5 8DZ
Tel: 01223 569600
Textphone: 01223 569600
Fax: 01223 506470

Free, independent and impartial information and advice for disabled people and carers who live in Cambridge, South Cambridgeshire and East Cambridgeshire.

Disability Direct
Rosehill Business Centre, Normanton Road, Derby, DE23 6RH
Tel: 01332 299499
Textphone: 01332 365055
Fax: 01332 365055

Provides information on any subject to people with disabilities.

Disability Information and Advocacy Service

Old Municipal Buildings, Corporation Street, Taunton, Somerset, TA1 4AJ

Tel: 01823 327453

Fax: 01823 332760

Contact: Linda Porter

The service aims to provide information on a variety of subjects including: holidays, equipment, employment, finance, accommodation, welfare, consumer services, mobility, caring services, leisure pursuits and access. We also have a fully qualified advocate who is able to give advice over the phone and represent clients at tribunal.

Disability Information Centre

Middlesbrough General Hospital, Ayresome Green Lane, Middlesbrough, Cleveland, TS5 5AZ

Tel: 01624 827471

Fax: 01624 817825

E-mail: jane@mbro_disinfo.demon.co.uk

Contact: Jane Mason, Information Officer

Information Service on disability equipment, support groups, medical conditions, etc. (Not a benefit advice service.)

Disability Information Service

Living Options, Shaftesbury Centre, Percy Street, Swindon, Wiltshire, SN2 2AZ

Tel: 01793 514055 ext 145

Disability Information Service Huntingdonshire

Disability Resource Centre, Ermine Street North, Papworth Everard, Cambridgeshire, CB3 8RH

Tel: 01480 830833

Textphone: 01480 831024

Provides information, advice and advocacy to disabled people, carers and professionals.

Disability Information Service Surrey

Harrowlands, Harrowlands Park, Dorking, Surrey, RH4 2RA

Disability Information Trust

Mary Marlborough Centre, Nuffield Orthopaedic Centre, Old Road, Headington, Oxford, OX3 7LD

Tel: 01865 227592/ 227596

Fax: 01865 742348

Disability Initiatives Unit

Leicestershire County Council, Chief Executive's Department, County Hall, Glenfield, Leicester, LE3 8RA

Tel: 0116 265 6081

Textphone: 0116 265 6160

Fax: 0116 265 6160

Disability Resource Team

Pelmark House, 11 Amwell End, Ware, Hertfordshire, SG12 9HP

Tel: 01920 466005

Textphone: 01920 466005

Fax: 01920 466031

Contact: Pamela Daley, Customer Services

Quality through equality: providing a range of services to help all organisations meet the needs of disabled people as employees, clients and customers. To ensure good-practice policies and assist compliance with the Disability Discrimination Act 1995, and all up-coming enactments.

Disability West Midlands

Prospect Hall, College Walk, Selly Oak, Birmingham, West Midlands, B29 6LE

Tel: 0121 414 1616

Textphone: 0121 414 1188

Fax: 0121 414 0077

E-mail: diswm@disabilitywm.co.uk

Run 'Outlook', a mentoring service for young people with physical and/or sensory disabilities.

Disabled Advice and Information Centre

107 Bannister Drive, Leyland, Preston, Lancashire, PR5 1GD

Disabled Persons Housing Service

Walbrook Housing Association Ltd, 66-68 Curzon Street, Derby, DE1 1LP

Tel: 01332 372141

Fax: 01332 293051

Disjointed Ltd

1a Garendon Street, Leicester, LE2 0AH

Tel: 0116 253 6299

Fax: 0116 251 0225

Ethnic Minority Advocacy Partnership

27 Barry Road, East Dulwich, London, SE22 0HX

Tel: 020 8693 6088

Fax: 020 8299 4818

Offers advocacy services to people with learning difficulties from the ethnic minority community.

Flintshire Local Voluntary Council

P O Box 19, St David's Park, Ewloe, Deeside, Flintshire, CH5 3WA

Tel: 01352 703334

Fax: 01352 703478

Contact: Kieran Duff, Manager
            P O Box 19, St David's Park, Ewloe, Deeside, Clwyd, CH5 3WA

Aims to work in partnership with others to support and develop voluntary activity and voluntary groups in Flintshire. Main activities: providing information and advice to voluntary and community organisations; helping groups to access funding and other resources; providing training; developing new projects; promoting volunteering; representing the views of voluntary organisations. Produces 'Voluntary Voices' newsletter.

Forest Bookshop

8 St John Street, Coleford, Gloucestershire, GL16 8AR

Tel: 01594 833858

Textphone: 01594 833858

Videotel: 01594 810637 Bookshop

Fax: 01594 833446

E-mail: deafbooks@forestbk.demon.co.uk

Website: www.forestbk.demon.co.uk

Contact: Doug McLean, Managing Director

Videotel: 01594 832712

Specialists in books, videos, CD-roms etc on deafness and deaf issues. Forest Bookshop provides a fast and efficient mail order service and produces a free 64-page catalogue. All orders are dealt with the day they are received for next-day delivery wherever possible. Well over 1,000 titles are always in stock.

Greater London Association of Disabled People

336 Brixton Road, London, SW9 7AA

Tel: 020 7346 5800

Textphone: 020 7346 5811

Fax: 020 7346 5810

E-mail: glad@btinternet.com

Website: www.disabilitynet.co.uk/groups/glad

Contact: Steven Knopf

GLAD covers the Greater London area. Most of its members are other organisations, but a small number are individuals. GLAD is in touch with deaf and hard of hearing people through its member groups. It does not provide any specific advice on or about deafness. Publishes 'London Disability News' (10 times a year), 'Disability Update' (25 times a year) and 'Boadicea' - for disabled women (6 times a year).

Gwent Association for Voluntary Organisations

8 Pentonville, Newport, Gwent, NP9 5HB

Tel: 01633 213229

Fax: 01633 221812

Contact: Byron Grubb

Aims: to support mainstream organisations, offers training, advice and information; to recruit volunteers and offer a comprehensive service to voluntary organisations in Gwent; to provide opportunity for voluntary organisations to work together through participation; to encourage the planning of new services; to identify the needs and wants of the services; to support town and community services.

Havering Housing Aid and Information Service

Mercury House, Mercury Garden, Romford, Essex, RM1 3DT

Tel: 01708 772817

Fax: 01708 772813

Contact: Jane Hare, Senior Housing Aid and Information Officer

Tel: 01708 772827

Provides advice and assistance, where possible, on housing difficulties, homelessness and debt counselling, for which casework can be undertaken, if requested. Advice is given on a wide range of housing issues including council, private and rented housing.

Health Information Centre Loughborough

Baxter Gate, Loughborough, Leicestershire, LE11 1TT

Tel: 01509 611600

Health Information In The Weald

Sevenoaks Hospital, Hospital Road, Sevenoaks, Kent, TN13 3PG

Tel: 01732 455155

Health Information Service Lincolnshire

Ermine Library, Ravendale Drive, Lincoln, LN2 2BT

Tel: 01522 568990
Fax: 01522 513066

Health Information Service Nottingham

Victoria Health Centre, Glasshouse Street, Nottingham, NG1 3LW

Tel: 0115 924 3328
              0800 665544 Helpline
Fax: 0115 941 3371

A free and confidential service covering Nottinghamshire, Leicestershire and Derbyshire, providing information on diseases, conditions and treatments; local health services and self-help groups; how to complain about NHS services; how to improve health; Patients' Charter standards, and hospital waiting times. Open Monday-Friday, 9.30am-5pm, plus answerphone. Textphone available on freephone line.

Health Promotion Aberdeen

181 Union Street, Aberdeen, AB11 6BB

Health Promotion for Older People

Overdale Hospital, Westmount Road, Jersey, Channel Islands, JE1 3UH

Tel: 01534 622028

Health Promotion Milton Keynes

Shipley Court, Marsh End Road, Newport Pagnell, Milton Keynes, MK16 8EA

Tel: 01908 217121
Fax: 01908 216748

Health Promotion Service Bristol

Central Health Clinic, Tower Hill, Bristol, Avon, BS2 0JD

Tel: 0117 929 1010 ext 6477
Fax: 0117 975 0607

Healthbox

Springhill, Brindley Way, Wakefield 41 Business Park, Wakefield, West Yorkshire, WF2 0XQ

Tel: 01924 889883
              0800 665544 Helpline
Fax: 01924 889810

The service is free to all, completely confidential and available every week day from 9am to 7pm. The range of health information includes: medical conditions and treatments, how and where to get treatment, hospital waiting times, medical procedures, self-help and support groups, complaints procedures, NHS services, Patients' Charter standards. The NHS Health Information Service is part of a national service providing information about health and the NHS. North, East, West Yorkshire, Cumbria and the North East areas are covered. There are also tapes available for individuals to listen to on a variety of health conditions.

Healthwise Helpline

Tel: 0800 665544 Freephone
Textphone: 0800 7315092
Fax: 0151 227 4019
E-mail: mmurray@healthwise.co.uk
Website: www.healthwise.org.uk

Healthwise is the NHS Health Information Service for the North West of England, Cambridge and Huntingdon. Healthwise also provides the National Drugs Helpline, the National HIV/AIDS Helpline, and the National Alcohol Helpline.

22

Help for Health Trust

Health Information Service, Freepost, Winchester, Hampshire, SO22 5DH

Independent Advocacy Service

Cambridge House, 131 Camberwell Road, London, SE5 0HF

Tel: 020 7703 0261

Fax: 020 7703 2903

Provides an advocacy service for people who use or wish to use community care service.

Information Link

Tresawls Road, Truro, Cornwall, TR1 3LG

Tel: 01872 253545

Textphone: 01872 253545

Fax: 01872 253232

Contact: Pam Vickery, Manager

Information Link is a central point of contact where patients, relatives and carers and health professionals across Cornwall can find information about health and treatment, healthy lifestyles, national and local support, and illness and disability. Contact is either in person or by telephone or fax. We have an individual and room loop system and wheelchair accessible toilet.

Interlink

Maritime Offices, Woodland Terrace, Maesycoed, Pontypridd, Mid Glamorgan, CF37 1DZ

Tel: 01443 485337

Fax: 01443 486107

Contact: Steve Kent

Information and advice on funding sources and applications, employing people, legal matters and charitable law. Opportunities for training and volunteering and access to practical facilities and resources.

Kent Information Federation

Ground Floor, Cygnet, Windmill Street, Gravesend, Kent, DA12 1BQ

King's Fund Library

11-13 Cavendish Square, London, W1M 0AN

Tel: 020 7307 2568/9

Fax: 020 7307 2805

E-mail: libenq2@kingsfund.org.uk

Website: www.kingsfund.org.uk

The King's Fund Library holds information on health and social care issues. It is the only specialist health and social care library to allow public access. It can provide literature searches, statistical information, contact details of other organisations and referrals to other colleagues within the King's Fund. There is a fee for photocopying and also for any searches undertaken on commercial databases.

Mantell Gwynedd

24-26 High Street, Caernarfon, Gwynedd, LL55 IRH

Tel: 01286 672626

Fax: 01286 678430

E-mail: mantellg@globalnet.co.uk

Contact: Saran Thomas, Chief Officer

Support and advice for voluntary and community groups in Gwynedd. We also provide training and resources for voluntary organisations and promote the concerns of the local voluntary sector. Our project - the Gywnedd Consumer Unit - ensures a voice for the service user in the planning process of services for people with a physical or sensory disability.

National Library for the Handicapped Child

Reach Advice Centre, California County Park, Nine Mile Ride, Finchhamstead, Berkshire, RG40 4HT

Tel: 0118 973 7575

Fax: 0118 973 7105

Contact: Desmond Spiers, Librarian and Information Officer

The library exists to give assistance to all children who have difficulties with reading, language and communication. It provides information, advice and runs workshops. It will also exchange information with other organisations. The newsletter of the library is issued three times a year.

National Music and Disability Information

Foxhole, Dartington, Totnes, Devon, TQ9 6EB

Tel: 01803 866701

Neath and Port Talbot Library and Information Services

Reginald Street, Velindre, Port Talbot, SA13 1YY

Tel: 01639 899829
Fax: 01639 899152
E-mail: j.l.ellis@neath-porttalbot.gov.uk.
Contact: J Ellis, Administrator Officer

To provide a public library service that meets the educational, information, recreational and cultural needs of individuals and groups. A network of library buildings provides in each community a focal point for lifelong learning, and promotes active citizenship and social inclusion by the use of traditional and electronic means.

Neath Port Talbot CVS

2 Alfred Street, Neath, SA11 1EF

Tel: 01639 631246
Fax: 01639 646947
Contact: Richard Jones, Information Officer

To support and develop the participation of community groups, voluntary organisations and individuals in the voluntary sector throughout the Neath Port County Borough area.

NHS Direct Health Information Service

Tel: 0800 665544 Freephone

Anyone can call the freephone number at any time from 10am to 5pm, Monday to Friday. Staff will either be able to give an immediate reply, direct you to another source for the information you need, call you back, send information through the post or do further research. The Health Information Service is purely an information service. Its staff are not doctors and cannot diagnose illnesses or give personal counselling. They can, however, tell you how to contact clinics, counselling services or self-help groups which may be able to help. The Service operates on a local basis. Calls are automatically routed to the nearest office so that information about hospital services, self-help groups, and many other matters is relevant to your own area.

North Birmingham Advocacy Group

The Underwood Centre, Underwood Close, Erdington, Birmingham, West Midlands, B23 7HD

Tel: 0121 382 3222
Fax: 0121 373 8988

Pembrokeshire Association of Voluntary Services

1st Floor, 19a Bridge Street, Haverford West, Dyfed, SA61 2AL

Tel: 01437 769422
Fax: 01437 769431
Contact: Ann Moazzin, Director

This is the association of voluntary and community groups in Pembrokeshire, and aims to promote and strengthen voluntary effort and community activity throughout the county.

Portsmouth Volunteer Bureau and Voluntary Sector Support Centre

338 Commercial Road, Portsmouth, Hampshire, PO1 4BT

Tel: 023 9282 0954
Fax: 023 9287 3785
E-mail: xccspohn@hants.gov.uk
Contact: Amanda Morris, Information Officer

Powys Association of Voluntary Organisations

Davies Memorial Gallery, The Park, Newtown, Powys, SY16 2NZ

Tel: 01686 626220
Fax: 01686 621537
Contact: Linda Pepa, Chairperson

We are the coordinating body for voluntary action in Powys and are a registered charity. We work to eight aims: to support voluntary organisations and encourage good practice; to support and promote volunteering; to encourage cooperation and collaboration between voluntary organisations; to encourage partnership between the voluntary sector and statutory agencies; to develop and support new initiatives to meet unmet needs; to empower local communities by encouraging participation in development; to identify and articulate the concerns of the voluntary sector; to enhance intermediary services.

22

RNID Helpline

19-23 Featherstone Street, London, EC1Y 8SL
Tel: 0870 60 50 123
Textphone: 0870 60 33 007
Fax: 020 7296 8199
E-mail: helpline@rnid.org.uk
Website: www.rnid.org.uk

RNID Information and Environmental Equipment Service, Buckinghamshire

Tel: 01296 434839 information only
Textphone: 01296 436722
Fax: 01296 436358
Contact: Linda Croton, Information Officer
See entry under Resource Centres.

RNID Library

The Institute of Laryngology and Otology, 330-332 Gray's Inn Road, London, WC1X 8EE
Tel: 020 7915 1553
Textphone: 020 7915 1553
Fax: 020 7915 1443
E-mail: rnidlib@ucl.ac.uk
Website: www.ucl.ac.uk/Library/RNID
Contact: Mary Plackett, RNID Librarian

The Library can provide reading lists on all aspects of deafness and related topics. Although the Library does not lend directly to individuals, it can be accessed as a reference library, books can be borrowed on inter-library loan, and photocopies of extracts from books and journals can be supplied at a charge. For details of opening hours, photocopying costs etc, contact the Librarian at the above address. The library is owned by RNID and the library service is run by University College London.

RNID Tinnitus Helpline

Tel: 0345 090210 Helpline
Textphone: 0845 601 0821
Fax: 0115 978 5012
E-mail: tinnitushelpline@btinternet.com
Website: www.rnid.org.uk
Contact: Kathie Price, Manager
Tel: 0115 942 1525
Textphone: 0115 942 1525
See entry under Tinnitus.

Sandwell Citizen Advocacy

28 Wood Street, Tipton, West Midlands, DY4 9BQ
Tel: 0121 520 8070
Textphone: 0121 520 0006
Fax: 0121 557 0721

Provides advocacy services to anyone in the Sandwell area.

South Warwickshire Advocacy Alliance

Park House, 17 Avenue Road, Leamington Spa, Warwickshire, CV31 3PG
Tel: 01926 887990
Fax: 01926 427127

Southwark Disablement Association

Aylesbury Day Centre, 2 Bradenham Close, London, SE17 2QB
Tel: 020 7701 1391
Textphone: 020 7703 6901
Fax: 020 7277 0481
E-mail: sda@dircon.co.uk
Website: www.sda.dircon.co.uk
Contact: Steve Gold

SDA is an organisation of and for disabled people, providing community care support services to people with physical and sensory disability, aged 18 to 64 years.

Southwark Phoenix Women's Health Organisation

55 Nigel Road, Peckham, London, SE15 4NP
Tel: 020 7732 8844
Textphone: 020 7732 5130
Fax: 020 7635 6115

Offers basic counselling skills for deaf women. Various courses/workshops on different aspects of health ie. sexual health, Sickle Cell Anaemia, Lupus, aromatherapy, fibroids, hysterectomy, organised on a monthly basis. Please contact the organisation for more details. Can provide sign language interpreter. Women with disabilities are welcome.

22

Sutton Disability Information

c/o SCILL, 3 Robin Hood Lane, Sutton, Surrey, SM1 2RJ

Tel: 020 8770 4065
Textphone: 020 8770 4068
Fax: 020 8770 4067
E-mail: sutton.disability.information@dial.pip ex.com
Website: www.dspace.dial.pipex.com/Sutton.di sability.information
Contact: Romey Criswick, Office Coordinator

An independent advice centre providing free information on all aspects of disability.

Umbrella

Ronnie MacKeith Child Development Centre, Derbyshire Royal Infirmary, London Road, Derby, DE1 2QY

Tel: 01332 254930
Fax: 01332 254930

Provides information on various subjects to disabled people but in particular to families with children with special needs.

Vale Council for Voluntary Services

Barry Community Enterprise Centre, Skomer Road, Barry, Vale of Glamorgan, The, CF62 9DA

Tel: 01446 741706
Fax: 01446 421442
E-mail: valecvs@pop3.poptel.org.uk
Contact: David Maggs, Executive Director

The Vale Council for Voluntary Services is an independent charity with a flourishing membership of voluntary and community organisations active in the Vale of Glamorgan. It helps to improve the quality of life of individuals and communities by supporting voluntary groups, developing and co-ordinating voluntary action and challenging discrimination.

Voluntary Action Cardiff

Shand House, 2 Fitzalan Place, Cardiff, South Glamorgan, CF2 1BD

Tel: 029 2048 5722
Fax: 029 2046 4196
E-mail: voluntary.action@btinternet.co.
Contact: Alan Bull, Chief Officer

Voluntary Action Lewis

30 Francis Street, Stornoway, Isle of Lewis, HS1 2ND

Tel: 01851 702632
Videotel: 01851 701447
Fax: 01851 703035
E-mail: valewis@cali.co.uk

Voluntary Action Merthyr Tydfil

4th Floor, Oldway, Castle Street, Merthyr Tydfil, Mid Glamorgan, CF47 8UX

Tel: 01685 350116
Textphone: 01685 350116
Fax: 01685 373822
Contact: Ian Davy, Coordinator

We are an independent association whose members are voluntary groups working to improve the community. We aim to support voluntary and community action in the County Borough of Merthyr Tydfil by: helping new projects; bringing groups together; offering information and advice on funding, legal matters, volunteering, how your group can work effectively; producing a regular newsletter; providing training and practical help.

Voluntary Action Rutland

Rutland Volunteer Centre, Oakham, Leicestershire, LE15 6QH

Tel: 01572 722622

Voluntary Action Stoke-on-Trent

The Dudson Centre, Hope Street, Hanley, Stoke-on Trent, Staffordshire, ST1 5DD

Tel: 01782 683030
Fax: 01782 683199
Contact: Maureen Atkinson

Voluntary Services, Lisburn

52a Bachelors Walk, Lisburn, County Antrim

Contact: Hilary Menary
Tel: 028 9267 1979
Fax: 028 9260 5412

Voluntary Service Lisburn provides many services to our local community. These include the Volunteer Bureau, elderly and disabled, eg Homecare, home from hospital, minibus, etc, training, parents and children, community development, conversation, recycle and reuse.

22

Wales Council for Voluntary Action

Ty Tyldesley, Ffordd Clarence, Llandudno, Gwynedd, LL30 1DT

Wales Council for Voluntary Action (WCVA) is the voice of the voluntary sector in Wales. It represents and campaigns for voluntary organisations, volunteers and communities in Wales. WCVA leads the sector in providing advice, information and training; lobbying decision-makers at all levels; safeguarding and increasing resources for the sector; and responding positively to new challenges.

Walsall Advocacy Scheme

c/o Service Users Council, Whitehall School, Weston Street, Walsall, West Midlands, WS1 4SQ

Tel: 01922 644983

Fax: 01922 644983

Provides advocacy to disabled people, including people with sensory disabilities.

Women's Health Information and Support Service

Jordan House, 7a St Benedict's Street, Norwich, Norfolk, NR2 4PE

Tel: 01603 623835

Fax: 01603 623835

Wren Centre

7 Wren Avenue, Ipswich, Suffolk, IP2 0TJ

Tel: 01473 686804

Textphone: 01473 686804

Wyre Forest Citizen Advocacy

Burgage Lodge, 184 Franche Road, Kidderminster, Worcestershire, DY11 5AD

Tel: 01562 820078

Fax: 01562 829704

Ynys Mon Voluntary Services

Room 20, Mon Training, Pen yr Orsedd Industrial Estate, Llangefni, Gwynedd, LL77 7JA

Contact: John Jones, Principal Officer

The aim of Ynys Mon Voluntary Services is to support, strengthen and develop voluntary and community groups on the island by providing advice and information.

Youth Information Project

Caia Park Children and Young People's Centre, 101 Prince Charles Road, Wrexham, Clwyd, LL13 8TH

Tel: 01978 311992

Fax: 01978 364162

Contact: Anne Pritchard, Team Leader

Advice

Barton Hill Advice Centre

c/o Barton Hill Settlement, 43 Ducie Road, Barton Hill, Bristol, BS5 0AX

Tel: 01272 557993

Contact: Christine Bridges

We are an independent advice centre which specialises in providing free information, advice and advocacy on social security benefits to residents of East Bristol (DSS area). We run several drop-in advice sessions per week (telephone the Advice Centre for times), and provide free representation at social services and disability appeals tribunals.

Bassetlaw Disability Link

East Gate Centre, Albion Close, Worksop, Nottinghamshire, S80 1RA

Tel: 0800 378066 Freephone

Textphone: 01909 501664

Bedford GateOpener

The Old School, Cardington, Bedford, MK44 3SX

Tel: 01234 838792

Fax: 01234 838149

Affiliated to SCOPE. Provides information, advice and advocacy (with specialist knowledge of cerebral palsy) to people with disabilities.

Blackfriars Advice Centre

199 Walworth Road, London, SE17 1RL

Tel: 020 7701 3999

Blenheim Project

321 Portobello Road, London, W10 5SY

Tel: 020 8960 5599

Fax: 020 8960 0508

The Blenheim Project provides a drop-in open daily from 1 to 4pm (Wednesday is for women only). The drop-in offers counselling, needle exchange, detox etc. Our day programme is for crack/cocaine users wanting to recover from intensive use.

Camberwell Advocacy Office
Cambridge House, 131 Camberwell Road, London, SE5 0HF

Tel:	020 7708 1408
Fax:	020 7252 4720

CARES
The Carers Centre, 2 Bearwood Road, Smethwick, West Midlands, B66 4HH

Tel: 0121 558 7003

Supports carers and their sick, elderly or disabled clients.

Centre 81
Tarworks Road, Great Yarmouth, Norfolk, NR30 1QR

Tel:	01493 852573
Fax:	01493 331541

Citizen Advocacy Information and Training
164 Lee Valley Technopark, Ashley Road, Tottenham Hale, London, N17 9LN

Tel: 020 8880 4545

Community Drug Project
146 Camberwell Road, London, SE5 0EE

Textphone: 020 7701 3527

Drop-in service available Monday to Friday from 2 to 5pm, please note that Tuesday is for women only. The Community Drug Project offers information, advice and support to people living in Southwark, experiencing problems associated with their drug use. It has four main services: opiate service, criminal justice service, crack team and day programme. It will be happy to arrange interpreters if deaf clients require their services.

Consumer and Money Advice Centre
376 Walworth Road, London, SE17 2NG

Tel:	020 7703 5049
Fax:	020 7701 3314

A whole range of consumer advice, and money advice - debt, bills, loans or credit agreements, rent, mortage or council tax, checking your benefits or tax. Help is given with complaints, filling in forms and preparing tribunals and other cases.

Contact a Family
170 Tottenham Court Road, London, W1P 0HA

Tel:	020 7383 3555
Fax:	020 7383 0259
E-mail:	info@cafamily.org.uk
Website:	www.cafamily.org.uk

Contact a Family is a national charity working to support families who have a child with any type of disability or special need. Offers advice and information to parents and professionals, particularly in relation to rare disorders. Supports parents who may want to develop a group nationally or locally.

Council of Disabled People Warwickshire
Independent Options, Rugby, Fawsley House, 25 Hillmorton Road, Rugby, Warwickshire, CV22 5AB

Tel:	01788 575846
Textphone:	01788 575846
Fax:	01788 575853

Coventry Council of Disabled People
26a Starley Road, Coventry, West Midlands, CV1 3JU

Tel: 024 7622 6747

Daventry Area Council for the Disabled
1 The Rowans, Daventry, Northamptonshire, NN11 5QA

Tel: 01327 704704

Deaf Advice Service Sheffield
173 Arundel Gate, Sheffield, South Yorkshire, S1 2LQ

Tel:	0114 278 0595
Textphone:	0114 278 0410
Fax:	0114 279 8090

DASS aims to provide information on any aspect of deafness. There is a selection of environmental aids for demonstration and there is information on welfare rights issues including benefits. DASS can offer advice on any aspect of welfare rights, family and relationship problems, consumer rights, employment, legal issues, etc. It can also provide advice on deaf issues and equipment. DASS can be contacted for information about sign language classes in the Sheffield area.

22

DIAL UK

Park Lodge, Tickhill Road, Doncaster, South
Yorkshire, DN4 8QN

Tel: 01302 310123
Textphone: 01302 310123
Fax: 01302 310404
E-mail: dialuk@aol.com
Website: www.members.aol.com/dialuk
Contact: Jo Sampson, Information Services
             Manager

A membership network covering the UK, giving
advice on any aspect of disability. It consists of
over 100 local DIALs with their own funding and
management committees and a national focus and
support centre, DIAL UK, which provides
information and assistance on training,
management and information technology to its
members. Please call for details of the nearest
DIAL in your area.

Disability Alliance Educational and Research Association

Universal House, Wentworth Street, London, E1
7SA

Tel: 020 7247 8776

Disability Lincolnshire

Ancaster Day Centre, Boundary Street, Lincoln,
LN5 8NJ

Tel: 01522 510759

Disability Wales

Llys Ifor, Crescent Road, Caerphilly, CF83 1XL

Tel: 029 2088 7325
Fax: 029 2088 8702

Drink Crisis Centre

Crisis and Assessment Centre, 124 Brook Drive,
London, SE11 4TQ

Fairdeal

Magazine Business Centre, 11 Newmarket Street,
Leicester, LE1 5SS

Tel: 0116 255 9711
Textphone: 0116 255 9991
Fax: 0116 255 9991

Federation of Independent Advice Centres

4 Dean's Court, St Paul's Churchyard, London,
EC4V 5AA

Tel: 020 7489 1800
Fax: 020 7489 1804

FIAC provides services to member centres, giving
advice on setting up and running advisory
services, disseminating information, promoting
training, and so on. It promotes the provision of
independent advice services across the UK and
supports member centres delivering independent
advice to the public. FIAC can give details of the
nearest independent advice centre in your area.

Gainsborough Hearing Helpline

21 Garfield Street, Gainsborough, Lincolnshire,
DN21 2LA

Tel: 01427 614514

Contact: Ruth Good, Secretary

We hold a social club for deaf and hard of hearing
people to get together in a social and friendly
atmosphere, also a clinic once a week for tune-ups
for hearing aids and to present any updates of
new equipment and any news concerning
deafness.

Greater Manchester Deaf Asian Community Group

Tel: 0161 273 3415
Textphone: 0161 273 3415
Fax: 0161 273 6698
Contact: Naina Mehta, Coordinator
Tel: 0161 428 9153

See entry under Deaf Clubs.

Independent Panel for Special Education Advice

22 Warren Hill Road, Woodbridge, Suffolk, IP12
4DU

Tel: 01394 382814
Fax: 01394 380518
Contact: John Wright

This is a registered charity, providing free advice
and support for parents with children who have
special educational needs. Has a network of
professional panel members who also give free
independent second opinions.

Independent Panel for Special Education Advice, NI

c/o DSA, Belfast Branch, Graham House, Knockbracken Healthcare Park, Saintfield Road, Belfast, BT8 8EH

Tel: 028 9070 4606

Fax: 028 9070 5633

Contact: Geraldine MacEvoy

An independent charity providing free advice and support for parents of children with special educational needs.

Ipswich Disabled Advice Bureau

Room 11, 19 Tower Street, Ipswich, Suffolk, IP1 3BE

Tel: 01473 217313

Fax: 01473 286548

Islay and Jura Advice Centre

Highfield, High Street, Bowmore, Isle of Islay, PA43 7JE

Tel: 01496 810669

Fax: 01496 810669

Provides free, independent, impartial and confidential advice on any matter to any group or individual. Affiliated member of Citizen Advice Scotland.

Kingston Women's Centre

169 Canbury Park Road, Kingston upon Thames, Surrey, KT2 6LG

Tel: 020 8541 1964

Textphone: 020 8541 1941

Contact: Cathy Kelly, Coordinator

To provide an effective, easily accessible and affordable counselling information and support service for all women, particularly those who have experienced abuse, violence or social isolation.

Leicestershire Guild of the Disabled

The Guild Hall, Colton Street, Leicester, LE1 1QB

Tel: 0116 251 5565

Fax: 0116 251 9969

London Ethnic Minority Deaf Association

c/o Stratford Advice Arcade, 107-109 The Grove, London, E15 1HP

Tel: 020 8522 1700

Textphone: 020 8522 1958

Fax: 020 8522 1842

London Ethnic Minority Deaf Association aims to provide culturally specific services to deaf people from ethnic minority communities. It works to provide equal access to services, information, training and education for ethnic minority deaf people living in London, many of whom are isolated and discriminated against.

London Women's Aid

P O Box 14041, London, E1 6NY

Tel: 020 7392 2092

LWA provides practical help and emotional support to women and children experiencing domestic violence. It refers women to refuges (safe houses) in the London area, as well as to other specialist advice agencies. Women who don't speak English can communicate with us through Language Line; there are refuges for women from different ethnic backgrounds, and for women with learning difficulties.

Lordship Lane Welfare Rights Unit

Lordship Lane Advice Centre, 121 Lordship Lane, East Dulwich, London, SE22 8JF

Tel: 020 8299 1515
            020 8299 1516 Appointments

The Unit is open on Monday and Thursday in the afternoon from 2.30 to 5pm. Please telephone for an appointment.

Meadows Advice Group

Queens Walk Community Centre, Queens Walk, Nottingham, NG2 2DF

Tel: 0115 986 0197

Fax: 0115 955 0152

Contact: Tim Price

Milton Keynes Centre for Integrated Living

330 Saxon Gate West, Central Milton Keynes, Milton Keynes, Buckinghamshire, MK9 2ES

Tel: 01908 231344

Textphone: 01908 231505

Fax: 01908 231335

Provides tribunal representation.

22

National Association of Citizens Advice Bureaux

115-123 Pentonville Road, London, N1 9LZ

Tel: 020 7833 2181

Fax: 020 7883 4371

NACAB exists to provide free, impartial and confidential advice and help, through a network of local bureaux, to anyone on any subject. NACAB at a national level seeks to exercise a responsible influence on the development of social policies and services, both locally and nationally.

REACH: National Advice Centre for Children with Reading Difficulties

California Country Park, Nine Mile Ride, Finchampstead, Wokingham, Berkshire, RG40 4HT

Tel: 0118 973 7575
            0345 973 7020 Helpline

Textphone: 0118 973 7575

Fax: 0118 973 7105

E-mail: reach@reach-reading.demon.co.uk

Contact: Desmond Spiers, Information Officer

Provides a resource and information/advice centre for those who work with children whose disability, illness or learning problem affects their reading, language or communication. The centre contains both printed books and books on sound tape and video plus equipment and software. The collections are for reference only. REACH produces a range of publications and provides in-service training courses.

RNID Cymru Community Project

3rd Floor, 33-35 Cathedral Road, Cardiff, CF1 9HB

Tel: 029 2033 3034

Textphone: 029 2033 3036

Fax: 029 2033 3035

Website: www.rnid.org.uk

Contact: Karen Jones, Community Project Officer

Textphone: 029 2033 3042

Shelter

Kingsbourne House, 229-231 High Holborn, London, WC1V 7DA

Tel: 020 7404 7447
            0808 800 4444 Freephone

Textphone: 0808 800 4444 Freephone

Contact: Les Burrows, Regional Information
            Coordinator
            Information Department

Shelter believes that homelessness is the result of a failed housing system. We believe that homelessness will be eliminated only by the creation of a housing system that meets people's needs, is affordable, is fair to all sections of society, and is socially and economically sustainable. Shelter aims to provide a lead in developing this vision by: translating our values into realisable proposals for a new national housing policy, convincing decision-makers and the wider public that such ideas are feasible and desirable, and demonstrating by practical projects and models of good practice that change is possible.

Shropshire Disability Consortium

The Disability Resource Centre, Lancaster Road, Shrewsbury, Shropshire, SY1 3NJ

Tel: 01743 440972

Textphone: 01743 444569

Fax: 01743 461349

Suffolk Coastal Disability Advice Service

Cedar House, Pytches Road, Woodbridge, Suffolk, IP12 1EP

Tel: 01394 387070

Thetford and District GateOpener

c/o The Riversdale Centre, Tanner Street, Thetford, Norfolk, IP24 2BQ

Tel: 01842 763973

Fax: 01842 763973

Affiliated to SCOPE, GateOpener provides information on any subject, with specialist knowledge of cerebral palsy.

Wellingborough Council for the Disabled

18 Broadway, Wellingborough, Northamptonshire, NN8 2DA

Tel: 01933 225209

Counselling

Bath Centre for Psychotherapy and Counselling

1 Walcot Terrace, London Road, Bath, Avon, BA1 6AB

Tel: 01225 466635
Fax: 01225 429720
Contact: Judy Ryde

Provision of counselling and psychotherapy (£12-£34 per session). Suitable referral found. A few counsellors who work with deaf people. Also a low-cost service (£15 per session) for those unable to afford a full fee. Training in counselling and psychotherapy. Hope to install hearing loop.

Croydon Youth Information and Counselling Service

132 Church Street, Croydon, Surrey, CR0 1RF

Tel: 020 8680 0404
Fax: 020 8681 0494

Free and confidential information, advice and counselling for young people aged 13 to 25. Phone/fax for an appointment or simply call in during drop-in hours: Monday 12 noon to 1pm, Tuesday to Friday 4 to 8pm. A mobile information project can visit services for young people free of charge, providing an on-site informal service.

Hackney Young People's Counselling Service

25-27 Hackney Grove, London, E8 3NR

Tel: 020 8986 4016
Fax: 020 8985 0044
E-mail: ocentre@aol.com

Offers crisis, short- and long-term counselling, creative therapy and group work for young people aged 13-25. Also offers advice and information on issues that affect young people, including housing, homelessness and benefits.

London Rape Crisis Centre

P O Box 69, London, WC1X 9NJ

Tel: 020 7837 1600 Helpline
           020 7916 5466 Office Line
Fax: 020 7916 5519
E-mail: lrcc@freeserve.co.uk

A free, confidential telephone helpline run by women and girls who have been raped or sexually assaulted at some time in their lives. It is also open to relatives, friends and workers for information and support about related issues.

Michael Davis Counselling

Don Cottage, 102 Old Town, Peebles, EH45 8JE

Tel: 01721 721909
Textphone: 01721 721284
Fax: 01721 721909

Mr Davis provides counselling for deaf, deafened or hard of hearing people, their families, friends, relatives or others. He is himself deaf from birth and uses a hearing aid. He is happy to use speech, to lipread or to use sign (either British Sign Language or signed supported English). He holds the Diploma in Person-Centred Counselling, a method of counselling based on the belief that the client and not the counsellor knows best what is troubling him or her. The overall aim of the counsellor is to listen carefully, to show understanding and to help make clear any thoughts or feelings. Fees are £10 to £25 an hour. The first session may be free to help the client decide if Person-Centred Therapy is the right approach for them.

Rape and Sexual Abuse Support Centre

P O Box 383, Croydon, London, CR9 2AW

Tel: 020 8293 1122
Textphone: 020 8239 1124
Fax: 020 8239 0101
E-mail: rasasc@cableinet.co.uk
Contact: Briony Hallam, Manager
Tel: 020 8293 0099

RASASC is a charity run by and for women and girls who have experienced rape or sexual abuse either recently or in the past. Our objectives are: to provide a free, confidential helpline which is open 365 days a year, Monday to Friday 12noon to 2.30pm, 7 to 9.30pm, weekends and public holidays 2.30 to 5pm, (an answerphone is available at all times) to provide information, advice and appropriate referrals to friends, partners, work colleagues and other organisations; to treat male survivors sympathetically and to refer them to more appropriate services.

Sandwell Rape Crisis Centre

P O Box 2223, West Bromwich, West Midlands, B70 8AH

Tel: 0121 525 9981 Helpline
           0121 525 9835 Office
Fax: 0121 525 9913
Contact: J Watson

We provide face-to-face and telephone counselling for women and girls who have experienced rape, sexual abuse or assault. We are at present coordinating a counselling and support service for deaf women survivors of rape, sexual abuse or assault.

Waterloo Community Counselling

Barley Mow Clinic, Frazier Street, London, SE1 7BD

Tel: 020 7928 3462

Fax: 020 7928 3464

WCC was set up to provide counselling to people who have limited access to counselling because of the demand on existing NHS-provided resources, and the cost of funding counselling privately. This service is available to people living in Southwark, Lambeth and Lewisham. People living outside these areas can be seen but there will be a charge for the service to be met by themselves, or can be seen by referral (GP, or social worker for example.)

Westminster Pastoral Foundation

23 Kensington Square, London, W8 5HN

Tel: 020 7937 9355

WPF is a counselling centre with affiliated centres all over the country. It offers special courses for deaf people, taught in British Sign Language, with both deaf and hearing tutors. It produces a factsheet on counselling for deaf people.

Grants

Help for Acquired Deafness Fund

61 Middlebridge Street, Romsey, Hampshire, SO51 8HJ

Tel: 01794 517636

James Powell UK Trust

c/o Disability Scotland, Princess House, 5 Shandwick Place, Edinburgh, Midlothian, EH2 4RG

Tel: 0131 228 8800

Help with provision of communication aids, equipment and related services to disabled people.

Peter Greenwood Memorial Trust

18 Braithwaite, Keighley, West Yorkshire, BD22 6PX

Tel: 01535 605065

Fax: 01535 605065

E-mail: andre.okdia@dial.pipex.com

The Trust has been established to assist hearing impaired individuals to further their education and/or training. Consideration is given to those of post-school age who are applying for, have been

accepted on, or are following a recognised course of further or higher education or training. Applications must be received on the official form by July each year and accompanied by a letter from a sponsor who is not a member of the applicant's family. Awards are tenable for one year only and on the evidence of official acceptance upon an approved course. Typical grant £100-£500.

Rinati Cambell Trust

116 Firs Avenue, Colnay Hatch Lane, London, N11 3NQ

Snowdon Award Scheme

22 Horsham Court, 6 Brighton Road, Horsham, West Sussex, RH13 5BA

Tel: 01403 211252

Fax: 01403 271553

Veale Wasbrough Charitable Trust

Orchard Court, Orchard Lane, Bristol, Avon, BS1 5DS

Tel: 0117 925 2020

Fax: 0117 925 2025

Contact: Julie Exton

Donations are made to registered charities in the Bristol area only and range between £20 and £200 on average. Applications from individuals welcomed but emphasis will be on those causes supported by individual staff or the firm as a whole.

Legal Services

ACC Legal Services

32 St Marks Road, London, W10 6JN

Tel: 0800 9567049 Freephone
           020 8964 3879

Contact: Anthony Pitt

Preparation of wills; estate work. Advice and assistance on personal injury and medical negligence, property and company law.

Amery-Parkes Solicitors

169 Edmund Street, Birmingham, West Midlands, B3 2TE

Tel: 0121 236 0076

Textphone: 0121 233 2314

Fax: 0121 200 1041

Contact: Tony Thomas, Solicitor

Legal advice and assistance in all areas of law but particularly in the fields of litigation. Both Tony Thomas and one of his colleagues have passed Stage I (Basic) examinations in British Sign Language.

Angell and Company

5 Pierrepont Street, Bath, Avon, BA1 1LB

Tel: 01225 484244

Fax: 01225 461055

Contact: Sarah Angell, Principal Solicitor

Angell and Company deal with domestic disputes, family breakdown, children cases, divorce and injunctions. They cover the West of England. An interpreter service is available with notice. A textphone has been installed for direct telephone contact with clients. The first half-hour consultation is free (although interpreter fee would have to be charged for if the client were ineligible for Legal Aid).

Bookkeeping Services

P O Box 19, Stanmore, Middlesex, HA7 4YL

Textphone: 020 8954 5695

Fax: 020 8954 5695

E-mail: 786shahabreza@msn.com

Shahab Services aims to provide a fast, friendly and highly cost-effective accounting and bookkeeping service to all our clients. Shahab specialises in services to deaf and disabled people, to charitable and community group organisations.

Cartwright and Lewis Solicitors

100 Hagley Road, Birmingham, West Midlands, B16 8LT

Tel: 0121 452 1989

Fax: 0121 456 3977

Contact: Fiona Debney, Solicitor

Deaf Legal Access Group

Zermansky & Partners, 10 Butts Court, Leeds, West Yorkshire, LS1 5JS

Tel: 0113 245 9766

Textphone: 0113 245 9766

Fax: 0113 246 7465

Contact: Jessica Penrose, Coordinator

The Deaf Legal Access Group is a newly established, voluntary, non-profit-making organisation, made up of solicitors and other legal service providers, as well as interpreters, support workers and other interested parties. All members of the group share a common interest in working with deaf clients, as well as others interested in looking at the whole area of the provision of legal services to deaf clients. The aim of the Deaf Legal Access Group is to improve the provision of legal services to deaf people. The Group intends to achieve its aim by pursuing a number of objectives: to establish a network and register of legal service providers; to act as a central resource for information on the provision of legal service providers; to facilitate deaf awareness training for legal service providers, and other agencies dealing with the rights of deaf people; to facilitate training on procedures relating to the justice system for interpreters and other human aids to communication; to help establish projects relating to deaf issues; to set standards for the provision of legal services; to establish regional networks. Membership is £5 for an individual, £10 for a charity or organisation and £30 for others. Cheques should be made payable to Deaf Legal Action Group and sent to Jessica Penrose at the address above.

Deaf Legal Access Group South London and North Kent

Justin House, 6 West Street, Bromley, Kent, BR1 1JN

Tel: 020 8290 0333

Textphone: 020 8290 7364

Fax: 020 8464 3332

Contact: Susan Oliver, Solicitor, Joint Coordinator South London and North Kent

Lesley Perry and Susan Oliver are joint coordinators for the Deaf Legal Access Group working to improve the provision of legal services to deaf people in this region.

Deafwill

32 St Marks Road, London, W10 6JN

Tel: 0800 9567049 Freephone
              020 8964 3879

Contact: Anthony Pitt

Support and advice to deaf people wanting to make a will.

Disability Law Service

2nd Floor, High Holborn House, 52-54 High Holborn, London, WC1V 6RL

Tel: 020 7831 8031
Textphone: 020 7831 8031
Fax: 020 7831 5582

Provides free legal advice and information for disabled people throughout Britain.

Judge and Priestley

Justin House, 6 West Street, Bromley, Kent, BR1 1JN

Tel: 020 8290 0333
Textphone: 020 8290 7364
Fax: 020 8464 3332
E-mail: soliver@judge-priestley.co.uk
Contact: Susan Oliver, Solicitor

We have a specialist family and child law solicitor, and are local coordinators for the Deaf Legal Access Group to improve the provision of legal services to deaf people. A free advice evening is offered for family and welfare benefits advice once a month: call 0800 634 6444 for details.

Langleys Solicitors

Queens House, Micklegate, York, YO1 1JH

Tel: 01904 610886
Fax: 01904 611086
Website: www.langleys.co.uk
Contact: Margaret Rogers, Solicitor

Langleys is happy to assist hard of hearing people with will-making and general inheritance and tax advice.

Law Centres Federation

Duchess House, 18-19 Warren Street, London, W1P 5DB

The Federation exists to support and advise law centres throughout the UK through the provision of secure funding. It encourages the setting up of centres in areas where free legal advice is needed. The Federation publicises the services and present funding situation of law centres and works with other national advice groups in areas of mutual concern.

Legal Aid Board (Head Office)

85 Gray's Inn Road, London, WC1X 8AA

Tel: 020 7813 1000
Fax: 020 7813 8631
Contact: Caroline O'Dwyer, Press Officer

The Legal Aid Board administers legal aid in England and Wales for advice and assistance work and for civil proceedings. We operate under guidelines set down by Parliament and under the general guidance of the Lord Chancellor.

McCormacks Solicitors

122 Mile End Road, London, E1 4UN

Tel: 020 7790 4339
Fax: 020 7790 5846
Contact: L Miller

Pitt and Co

32 St Marks Road, London, W10 6JN

Tel: 020 8964 3879

The solicitors have an arrangement with a registered trainee interpreter, who is qualified in law interpreting.

Southwark Law Centre

14-16 Hanover Park, Peckham, London, SE15 5HG

Tel: 020 7732 2008
Fax: 020 7732 3034

Southwark Mediation Centre

92 Camberwell Road, London, SE5 0EG

Tel: 020 7708 4959
Fax: 020 7798 5568

Offers a service of disputes resolution to people in Southwark. The Centre mainly works with neighbours disputes, but can also assist with such things as landlord/tenant disputes, joint tenants' conflict, small business disputes, disputes within groups. The Centre resolves 70 per cent of all referrals.

22

Broadcasting

At present the BBC, ITV and Channel 4 are legally required to subtitle at least 50 per cent of their programmes and this percentage will rise over the next few years. Channel 5 is currently required to subtitle less, but again this percentage will rise. Cable and satellite channels are not required to subtitle their programmes. This section lists broadcasting companies together with details of their subtitling and programming for deaf viewers. Also listed are some of the subtitling companies themselves and the Deaf Broadcasting Council, the deaf viewers' broadcasting watchdog. Companies are listed alphabetically.

Anglia Television Limited

Anglia House, Prince of Wales Road, Norwich, Norfolk, NR1 3JG

Tel: 01603 615151
Textphone: 01603 663258
Fax: 01603 631032
E-mail: angliatv@anglia.tv.co.uk
Website: www.anglia.tv.co.uk
Contact: Tina Ball, Press & Public Relations

Anglia subtitles three and a half hours of local news per week and plans to subtitle 40 hours of local programmes over the next year (this will double the figure for 1998).

BBC Belfast

Room 259, Broadcasting House, Ormeau Avenue, Belfast, County Antrim, BT2 8HQ

Tel: 028 9033 8000
Fax: 028 9033 8806
Contact: Eddie Fleming, Editor, Text Services

BBC Subtitling

Wood Lane, London, W12 7TS

Tel: 020 8752 7054
Textphone: 020 8752 7069
Fax: 020 8752 7059

Comments on subtitled programmes can be sent to this adress or Room 4169, Broadcasting House, Queen Margaret Drive, Glasgow G12 8DG.

BBC Television Centre

Wood Lane, London, W12 7TS

Tel: 020 8743 8000
Textphone: 020 8740 6890
Fax: 020 8749 8258

BBC Wales

Broadcasting House, Llantrisent Road, Llandaff, Cardiff, CF5 2YQ

Tel: 029 2032 2000
Fax: 029 2055 2973
Contact: Geraint Davies, Controller

Border Television

The Television Centre, Carlisle, Cumbria, CA1 3NT

Tel: 01228 525101
Textphone: 01228 541384
Contact: Neil Robinson, Controller, Production

ITV franchise holder for Cumbria, the Scottish Borders and the Isle of Man.

Cable Communications Association

Artillery House, Artillery Row, London, SW1P 1RT

Carlton Television

101 St Martin's Lane, London, WC2N 4AZ

Tel: 020 7240 4000

ITV covers 15 regional licence holders including Carlton Television. Carlton Television comprises Carlton Broadcasting, Central Broadcasting and Westcountry. Carlton Broadcasting is responsible for the ITV regional licence for East, West and South Midlands. Carlton Productions produces network and regional programmes for both companies and for other national and international markets. Carlton Sales sells airtime and sponsorship for all three broadcasters. Carlton Television also operates two facilities: Carlton Studios in Nottingham, supplying studios and related services; and Carlton 02,1, the largest commercial operator of outside broadcast services in Europe.

Central Broadcasting

Central House, Broad Street, Birmingham, West Midlands, B1 2JP

Tel: 0121 643 9898
Textphone: 01908 270003
Fax: 0121 634 4898
E-mail: centraldutyoffice@centraltv.co.uk
Website: www.centraltv.co.uk

Channel Five Broadcasting Ltd

22 Long Acre, London, WC2E 9LY

Tel: 020 7550 5555
Fax: 020 7550 5554
Website: www.c5.co.uk

Channel Four Television Corporation

124-126 Horseferry Road, London, SW1P 2TX
Tel: 020 7396 4444
Textphone: 020 7306 8691
Fax: 020 7306 8347
E-mail: viewer-enqs@channel4.co.uk
Website: www.channel4.com
Contact: Sue Crockford, Advisor on Deaf
           Broadcasting
Tel: 020 7263 4199
Textphone: 020 7263 4199
Fax: 020 7281 6355

Channel 4 stands for innovation and independence. We are committed to increasing the inclusion of deaf and disabled people in all programmes, and to supporting the Deaf Film and Television Festival and the training of deaf/disabled people. A new database of deaf/disabled talent will be launched in Spring 1999.

Channel Television

The Television Centre, St. Helier, Jersey, Channel Islands, JE2 4YB
Tel: 01534 68999
Fax: 01534 816817
E-mail: ctv@itl.net
Website: www.channeltv.co.uk

Deaf Broadcasting Council

70 Blacketts Wood Drive, Chorleywood, Rickmansworth, Hertfordshire, WD3 5QQ
Tel: 01923 283127
Textphone: 01923 283127
Fax: 01923 283127
E-mail: dmyers@cix.co.uk
Website: www.waterlow.com.dbc
Contact: Ruth Myers, Honorary Secretary

The DBC is a consumer organisation to which all the major organisations for and on behalf of deaf, deafened and hard of hearing people are affiliated. Its aim is to ensure that the voice of the consumer is heard by broadcasters and that suitable access is provided to the full range of programmes.

Deaf Broadcasting Council Wales

Belvedere, Brynawel, Aberdare, Mid Glamorgan, CF44 7PF
Textphone: 01554 746161
Fax: 01554 746161
Contact: Alyson Griffiths, Honorary Secretary
Tel: 01554 746161

Deafview

RNID, 19-23 Featherstone Street, London, EC1Y 8SL
Tel: 020 7296 8145
Textphone: 020 7296 8029
Fax: 020 7296 8021
Contact: Tim Russell, Editor

Deafview is a Channel 4 Teletext news and information service updated twice a week - on Tuesdays and Fridays. It provides the latest news, information, forthcoming events and readers letters - but does not carry adverts. Send any details of events to the editor, at the above address.

GMTV Ltd

The London Television Centre, London, SE1 9TT
Tel: 020 7827 7000
Fax: 020 7827 7001

GMTV broadcasts a live, three-and-a-half hour magazine programme of news, features, show business and lifestyle items daily from 6.00am. Weekend programming is a mix of family viewing, with children's programming on Saturday mornings supplied by the Walt Disney Company and on Sundays, the agenda-setting Sunday Programme.

Grampian Television

Queen's Cross, Aberdeen, AB9 2XJ
Tel: 01224 646464
Fax: 01224 846805
Contact: Alistair Gracie, Controller

Television production in the largest region in the ITV Network. The main studio complex in Aberdeen is supported by studio centres in Dundee, Stornoway and Inverness.

23

Granada Television

Water Street, Manchester, Lancashire, M60 9EA
Tel: 0161 832 7211
Textphone: 0161 834 7789
Fax: 0161 827 2029
Website: www.itv.co.uk

HTV Wales

Culverhouse Cross, Cardiff, South Glamorgan, CF5 6XJ
Tel: 029 2059 0590
Textphone: 029 2059 0434
Fax: 029 2059 7183
Website: www.htv.co.uk

HTV has provided an independent television service to Wales for over 30 years as part of the ITV network. It transmits nearly 12 hours a week of regional programes and has bases all over Wales. HTV is part of the United News and media group of companies.

HTV West

The Television Centre, Bath Road, Bristol, Avon, BS4 3HG
Tel: 0117 972 2722
Fax: 0117 972 2400
E-mail: richard.lister@htv.co.uk
Website: www.htv.co.uk
Contact: Richard Lister, Press, PR and Community Relations Manager
Tel: 0117 972 2214

ITV broadcaster for West of England - part of United News and Media Group.

Independent Media Support Limited

21 Soho Square, London, W1V 5FD
Tel: 020 7440 5400
Fax: 020 7440 5410
E-mail: ims@dial.pipex.com
Contact: Sylvia Sheridan, Chief Executive

Independent Media Support provide subtitling for SKY, the BBC, the Disney Channel, and Granada SKY Broadcasting.

Independent Television Commission

33 Foley Street, London, W1P 7LB
Tel: 020 7255 3000
Textphone: 020 7306 7753

Independent Television Facilities Centre

28 Concord Road, Westwood Park Trading Estate, London, W3 0TH
Tel: 020 8752 0352
Fax: 020 8993 6393

Responsible for subtitling ITV network and Channel 5 programming for deaf and hard of hearing viewers.

Intelfax Ltd

Fifth Floor Lincoln House, 75 Westminster Bridge Road, London, SE1 7HS
Tel: 020 7928 2727
Fax: 020 7261 9961
E-mail: subtitling@intelfax.co.uk
Website: www.intelfax.co.uk

Intelfax produces all the subtitling for Channel 4 for both news and pre-recorded programmes. The company also produces some of the subtitles for both GMTV and the BBC. The company has a second office in Leeds which produces the subtitles for Yorkshire Television's regional programmes. Intelfax also regularly provides regional programme subtitles for other ITV companies. Intelfax's sister company, Intelfax Developments Ltd, makes and sells state-of-the-art subtitle transmission equipment which is currently in use with Channel 4 and the Irish national broadcaster, RTE. Additionally, Intelfax produces teletext information services for 18 other broadcasters.

Meridian Broadcasting Ltd

Television Centre, Southampton, Hampshire, SO14 0PZ
Tel: 023 8022 2555
Textphone: 023 8033 0561
Fax: 023 8071 2081
E-mail: dutyoffice@meridiantv.com
Website: www.meridian.tv.co.uk

Metro Cable TV

Honeyborough Industrial Estate, Neyland, Swansea, Milford Haven, Dyfed, SA73 1SE

Radius Television

37-39 Fitzwilliam Square, Dublin

23

Read Hear

CSV Media, 237 Pentonville Road, London, N1 9NJ
Tel: 020 7833 1894
Textphone: 020 7833 1894
Fax: 020 7833 5689

ReadHear is on BBC 2 every Saturday and covers news, views, topical debates, and issues relating to deaf and hard of hearing people. Please send events information, job adverts, etc to the above address.

Scottish Television

Cowcaddens, Glasgow, Lanarkshire, G2 3PR
Tel: 0141 300 3000
Textphone: 0141 300 3000
Fax: 0141 300 3030
E-mail: maystone@scottishmediagroup.com
Website: www.scottishmediagroup.com

See Hear!

Room 2374, BBC White City, 201 Wood Lane, London, W12 7TS
Tel: 020 8752 4703
Textphone: 020 8752 5292
Fax: 020 8752 6535
E-mail: seehear@bbc.co.uk
Website: www.bbc.co.uk/see_hear/
Contact: Bryn Brooks, Editor

See Hear is a magazine programme for deaf and hard of hearing people presented in BSL with open subtitles. It runs from October to March and is shown on Saturday mornings at 11.20am on BBC2.

Sign On

Tyne Tees Television, City Road, Newcastle-Upon-Tyne, Tyne and Wear, NE1 2AL
Tel: 0191 261 0181
Textphone: 0191 232 5523
Fax: 0191 261 7715
E-mail: bob.duncan@granadamedia.com
Contact: Bob Duncan, Executive Producer

Occasional documentary series for deaf people on Channel Four - usually transmitted at 12 noon on Saturdays.

Teletext Limited

101 Farm Lane, London, SW6 1QJ
Tel: 020 7386 5000
Fax: 020 7386 5751
Website: www.teletext.co.uk

Touchline Television

Glenfield Park Two, Blakewater Road, Blackburn, Lancashire, BB1 5QH
Tel: 01254 604200

Tyne Tees Television

The Television Centre, City Road, Newcastle, Tyne and Wear, NE1 2AL
Tel: 0191 261 0181
Textphone: 0191 232 5523
Fax: 0191 261 7715

Ulster Television

Havelock House, Ormeau Road, Belfast, County Antrim, BT7 1EB
Tel: 028 9032 8122
Fax: 028 9024 6695
Website: www.utvlive.com

Vision Text Subtitles

Cameo House, 11 Bear Street, London, WC2H 7AS
Tel: 020 7925 2121
Contact: Ron Eagle

Visual Motions

111 Wibsey Park Avenue, Wibsey, Bradford, BD6 3DQ
Tel: 01274 404919
Fax: 01274 406912
Contact: Gohar Nisar, Producer/Director

Visual Motions is a professional production company with an entirely deaf or hard of hearing crew. It was established to give an opportunity of management and production to professionally trained deaf people. It produces television dramas, documentaries, access videos for the deaf and training videos. It has up-to-date editing facilities and 3D graphics, suitalbe for the new digital and DVD technologies.

Westcountry Television

Western Wood Way, Language Science Park, Plymouth, Devon, PL7 5BQ
Tel: 01752 333333
Textphone: 01752 333030
Fax: 01752 333444

Regional ITV franchise-holder for Devon, Cornwall, The Isles of Scilly, West Dorset and South Somerset.

23

Yorkshire Television
The Television Centre, Leeds, West Yorkshire, LS3
1JS
Tel: 0113 243 8283
Fax: 0113 244 0213

Periodicals

This is an alphabetical list (not exhaustive) of journals and periodicals concerned with deafness and hearing loss for deaf and hard of hearing people and professionals. Details of subscription prices and how and where to obtain journals and periodicals are included.

ALS News

Flat 4, 21 Christchurch Avenue, London, NW6 7QP
Tel: 020 8459 7191
Contact: Lynn Jackson

ALS News is the bi-annual newsletter for members of the Association of Lipspeakers. ALS News includes information of developments in the lipspeaking profession, details on training courses and results, reports on exhibitions, workshops and conferences.

British Deaf News

P O Box 12, Carlisle, Cumbria, CA1 1HU
Tel: 01228 599994
            01594 833366 (Subscriptions)
Textphone: 01228 599994
Fax: 01228 541420
Contact: Sheila Gregory, Coordinator and
            Advertising Manager

Magazine of the British Deaf Association. Published monthly. Subscriptions: £15 (£12 for members of BDA); overseas rates available on request. Subscriptions are available from: Big D Company, P O Box 20, St John Street, Coleford, Gloucestershire, GL16 8YP. All correspondence, articles and advertisements should be sent to British Deaf News at the address above.

British Journal of Audiology

80 Brighton Road, Reading, Berkshire, RG6 1PS
Tel: 01189 660622
Fax: 01189 351915
E-mail: dbb29@can.ac.uk

The Journal of the British Society of Audiology. Published bi-monthly by Whurr Publishers, 19b Compton Terrace, London N1 2UN. Annual subscription including postage and packing: £155 UK and Europe; US$275 rest of world. Personal subscription rate: £85 UK and Europe; US$155 rest of world.

CACDP Standard

Pelaw House, School of Education, University of Durham, Durham, DH1 1TA
Tel: 0191 374 3607
Textphone: 0191 374 3607
Fax: 0191 374 3605
E-mail: durham@cacdp.demon.co.uk
Contact: Sarah Marshall, Publicity Officer
Tel: 0191 383 1155

CACDP membership magazine.

Child Language Teaching and Therapy

Turpin Distribution Services Ltd, Blackhorse Road, Letchworth, Hertfordshire, SG6 1HN
Tel: 01462 672555
Fax: 01462 480947
Contact: Maggie Woods, Manager

Published three times a year. Subscriptions: £42 (individuals, EU); £80 (organisations, EU); $82 (individuals, USA, Mexico and Canada); $159 (organisations, USA, Mexico and Canada; £47 (individuals, rest of world); £90 (organisations, rest of world). For enquiries contact the above address.

Clinical Otolaryngology and Allied Sciences

Journal Department, Blackwell Scientific Publications Ltd, Marston Book Services, P O Box 87, Oxfordshire, OX2 0DT
Tel: 01865 206206

Published bi-monthly. Subscriptions: £360 (UK and Europe); £395 (rest of world); $652 (USA and Canada). For enquiries contact the above address.

Deaf History Journal

49 Whitton Close, Doncaster, South Yorkshire, DN4 7RB

Journal produced three times a year by British Deaf History Society. Contact A J Boyce at the above address for more details.

Deaf Worlds

8 St John Street, Coleford, Gloucestershire, GL16 8AR
Tel: 01594 833858
Textphone: 01594 833446
Fax: 01594 833446
E-mail: deafbooks@forestbk.demon.co.uk
Contact: Mr McLean, The Forest Bookshop

Journal of Alliance of Deaf Service Users, Providers and Purchasers (ADSUP). Published three times a year by The Forest Bookshop. Subscriptions: £15

24

444

(individuals, UK); £25 (organisations, UK); £20 (individuals overseas); £30 (organisations overseas). For further details of subscriptions or advertisements, please contact The Forest Bookshop at the above address. Deaf Worlds is an international journal providing a focus for analysis and debate on social, cultural, political and psychological factors influencing the lives of individual deaf people, and their relationships with the communities and societies in which they live.

Deafblind Education

11-13 Clifton Terrace, Finsbury Park, London, N4 3SR

Tel:	020 7272 7774
Fax:	020 7272 6012
E-mail:	dbi@sense.org.uk
Contact:	Eileen Boothroyd, Editor

Deafblind Education is the journal of Deafblind International. It is published twice a year, the two editions are dated January-June and July-December.

Deafness

38 Victoria Place, Carlisle, Cumbria, CA1 1HU

The journal of the Association of Deaf Service Users and Providers (formerly the National Council of Social Workers with Deaf People), published three times a year.

Deafness and Education International

Whurr Publishers Ltd, 19b Compton Terrace, London, N1 2UN

Tel:	020 7359 5979
Fax:	020 7226 5290
E-mail:	info@whurr.co.uk
Website:	www.whurr.co.uk
Contact:	Lizzy Ewer, Advertising and Marketing

Deafness and Education International provides a forum for peer-reviewed scholarly papers on the education of deaf infants, children and young people and will report original research on their linguistic, educational, social and cognitive development, and on sign language, deaf culture and traditions, audiological issues, cochlear implants, educational technology, general child development, and relevant educational and legal issues.

Disability Now

6 Market Road, London, N7 9PW

Tel:	020 7619 7323
Textphone:	020 7619 7332
Fax:	020 7619 7331
E-mail:	editor@disabilitynow.org.uk
Contact:	Mary Wilkinson, Editor

ENT News

Pinpoint Scotland Ltd, 9 Gayfield Square, Edinburgh, Midlothian, EH1 3NT

Tel:	0131 557 4184

Hearing Concern Magazine

7-11 Armstrong Road, London, W3 7JL

Tel:	020 8743 1110
Textphone:	020 7742 9151
Fax:	020 8742 9043
E-mail:	hearing.concern@ukonline.co.uk
Website:	www.ukonline.co.uk/hearingconcern
Contact:	Phillip Baron, Editor

Magazine of Hearing Concern. Published quarterly and aimed at hard of hearing people. Subscriptions: £12.50 a year. This includes membership of Hearing Concern. Family membership £22.50; associate membership £35; 4-year covenant £45. Enquiries: Hearing Concern at the above address. Advertising rates on request.

Hearing Therapy

330-332 Grays Inn Road, London, WC1X 8DA

Tel:	020 7915 1643
Fax:	020 7278 5886
Contact:	Aniela Michalec, Hearing Therapist, Adult Auditory Rehabilitation

Journal of the British Society of Hearing Therapists. Published bi-annually. Subscriptions: £10 (UK); £12 (overseas). Enquiries to the above address.

International Journal of Language and Communication Disorders

Taylor & Francis, 1 Gunpowder Square, London, EC4A 3DE

Tel:	020 7583 0490
Fax:	020 7583 0581
E-mail:	info@tandf.co.uk
Website:	www.tandf.co.uk
Contact:	Customer Services

This is an academic peer-reviewed journal of international interest to those working with language and communication disorders.

Journal of Child Language

Subscriptions Department, Cambridge University Press, Edinburgh Buildings, Shaftsbury Road, Cambridge, CB2 2RU

Tel: 01223 325806
Fax: 01223 315052
E-mail: journals_information@cup.cam.ac.uk

Published three times a year. Subscriptions for 1999: individuals (print plus electronic) £47; Institutions (print plus electronic) £102.

Journal of Laryngology and Otology

Headley Bros Ltd, The Invicta Press, Ashford, Kent, TN24 8HH

Tel: 01233 623131
Fax: 01223 612345
Website: www.jlo.co.uk
Contact: Sheila Hubbard, Subscriptions Manager, Customer Services

A leading international journal, published monthly and containing original scientific articles and clinical records in otology, rhinology and laryngology. Includes occasional supplements.

Laserbeam

8 Church Lane, Kimpton, Hitchin, Hertfordshire, SG4 8RP

Tel: 01438 832676
Textphone: 01438 832676

Laserbeam is the membership magazine of Language and Sign as an Educational Resource. Membership is £10 a year (£5 unwaged). Each member receives a copy of the journal Laserbeam three times a year plus free copies of LASER's occasional conference reports.

Network

P O Box 50, Amersham, Buckinghamshire, HP6 6XB

Tel: 01494 723613
Fax: 01494 431932

Newsletter of the National Association of Deafened People (NADP). Published quarterly. Subscriptions: £10 a year. Enquiries to the Administrative Officer at the above address. Advertising rates on request at the above address.

NI Homes, Interiors and Living Magazine

P O Box 42, Bangor, County Down, BT19 7AD

Tel: 028 9147 4219
Fax: 028 9145 7226
Contact: Ruth Pringle, Editor

One in Seven

RNID, 19-23 Featherstone Street, London, EC1Y 8SL

Tel: 020 7296 8000
Textphone: 020 7296 8029
Fax: 020 7296 8021
E-mail: oneinseven@rnid.org.uk
Contact: Stephen Iliffe, Head of Membership Services

The membership magazine of the Royal National Institute for Deaf People. Includes news, human-interest features, TV specials, campaigns, consumer advice, product reviews, letters and a classified section. Published bi-monthly. Subscriptions: £16.50 (subscription included in membership): contact RNID Helpline at the above address. Editorial contributions: contact the Editor, Dawn Egan, at the above address. Advertising: contact Mark Harvey, Mongoose Communications, Victory House, London WC2H 7QH. Tel: 020 7306 0300; Textphone: 020 7312 0470; Fax: 020 7306 0301.

Papermates Journal

42 Winter Grove, Parr, St Helens, Merseyside, WA9 2JS

Papermates is a craft and pen-pal newsletter which enables deaf people to get information on craft by post. They can also place a pen-pal advertisement in the newsletter. The editor is profoundly deaf and would like to encourage other people, both deaf and hearing, to learn craft. Anyone is welcome to subscribe to the journal but unfortunately there are no facilities to make the journal available to deafblind people. If interested, please send a stamped addressed envelope for an information sheet and questionnaire.

Quiet

4th Floor, White Building, Fitzalan Square, Sheffield, South Yorkshire, S1 2AZ

Tel: 0114 273 0122/ 0114 279 6600 (Helpline)
Fax: 0114 279 6222
E-mail: tinnitus@dial.pipex.com
Contact: Val Rose, Editor

Magazine of the British Tinnitus Association (BTA). Published quarterly and aimed at people who experience tinnitus, and professionals working with them. Enquiries to the Editor at the above address. Subscriptions: £5 (membership fee includes subscription). Advertising: rates on request at above address.

24

Shape Magazine

LVS Resource Centre, 356 Holloway Road, London, N7 6PA

Tel:	020 7700 0100
Textphone:	020 7700 8144
Fax:	020 7700 8143

Speech and Language Therapy in Practice

Lynwood Cottage, High Street, Drumlithie, Stonehaven, Kincardineshire, AB39 3YZ

Tel:	01569 740348
Fax:	01569 740348
E-mail:	avrilnicoll@sol.co.uk
Website:	www.sol.co.uk/s/speechmag
Contact:	Avril Nicoll, Editor

Published quarterly. For subscriptions and enquiries please contact the above address.

Speech Therapy in Practice

Hexagon Publishing Ltd, Hexagon House, Surbiton Hill Road, Surbiton, Surrey, KT6 4TS

Published quarterly.

Spin

c/o Menieres Society, 98 Maybury Road, Woking, Surrey, GU21 5HX

Tel:	01483 740597
Textphone:	01483 771207
Fax:	01483 771207
Contact:	John Myall, Editor

Talk

c/o NDCS, 15 Dufferin Street, London, EC1Y 8PD

Tel:	020 7250 0123
Textphone:	020 7250 0123
Fax:	020 7251 5020
E-mail:	ndcs@netcomuk.co.uk
Contact:	Dan Tickle
Tel:	020 7490 8656
Textphone:	020 7490 8656

Founded in 1944, the National Deaf Children's Society is the leading UK charity to provide on-going support, advice and advocacy on all aspects of childhood deafness for deaf children, deaf young people, their families, carers and professionals working with them. Please contact the above address for subscription details and prices.

Talking Sense

11-13 Clifton Terrace, Finsbury Park, London, N4 3SR

Tel:	020 7272 7774
Textphone:	020 7272 9648
Fax:	020 7272 6012
E-mail:	talkingsense@sense.org.uk
Contact:	Colin Anderson, Editor

Sense is the national voluntary organisation supporting and campaigning for people who are deafblind, their families, their carers, and professionals who work with them. People of all ages and with widely varying conditions use Sense's specialist services. Founded as a parents' self-help group in 1955, Sense is now the leading national organisation working with deafblind people. HRH The Princess Royal is Sense's Patron. Contact the above address for details on subscriptions and advertising rates.

Transport

This is an alphabetical list of organisations providing support services for deaf travellers. It ranges from the RAC, through companies experienced in providing insurance services to deaf motorists, to organisations providing information on where to go and how to get there.

Abba Driving School

79 Botanic Avenue, Belfast, County Antrim, BT7 1JL

Tel: 028 9024 3353
Fax: 028 9031 4234
Contact: Mary Brackley, Driving Instructor

Theory and practical driving instruction.

Automobile Association

Norfolk House, Priestley Road, Basingstoke, Hampshire, RG24 9NY

Tel: 0800 444999
Textphone: 0800 262050
Website: www.theaa.co.uk

The AA can provide assistance to deaf road users in the event of vehicle breakdown. All emergency call centres are able to receive textphone messages. The AA also holds information on where deaf people can learn to drive. Anyone interested should phone the Disability Helpline which provides free advice for members of the AA.

Banstead Mobility Centre

Damson Way, Fountain Drive, Carshalton, Surrey, SM5 4NR

Tel: 020 8770 1151
Fax: 020 8770 1211
Contact: Elaine Hayes, Administrator

The Centre was established to "assist disabled people to achieve an optimum level of outdoor mobility which would enrich the quality of their working and social life". The main areas of activity are information and advice. The Centre maintains a register of driving instructors who have experience of teaching disabled people, including some who are deaf. The Mobility Centre cannot provide assistance in the event of vehicle breakdown.

Behind the Wheel

5 Mosse Gardens, Fishbourne, Chichester, West Sussex, PO19 3PQ

Tel: 01243 539106

Central London Dial-A-Ride

Hathaway House, 7D Woodfield Road, London, W9 2BA

Tel: 020 7266 6100
Fax: 020 7266 5079
Contact: Janet Cobill
               Hathaway House
               7D Woodfield Road
               London
               W9 2BA

Devitt Insurance Services Ltd

Central House, 32-66 High Street, Stratford, London, E15 2PF

Tel: 020 8522 3414
Fax: 020 8519 8780

Devitt Insurance Services offers car insurance to deaf people.

Disabled Drivers Association

National Headquarters, Old Hall Close, Ashwellthorpe, NORWICH, Norfolk, NR16 1EY

Tel: 01508 488173
Fax: 01508 488173

GMPTE Telephone Enquiry Unit

9 Portland Street, Piccadilly Gardens, Manchester, M60 1HX

Tel: 0161 228 7811
Textphone: 0161 228 7811
Fax: 0161 228 3291

The GMPTE Telephone Enquiry Unit provides information about buses, trains and trams in Greater Manchester, seven days a week from 8am to 8pm.

Grosvenor Autos

105 Grosvenor Road, Hyde, Cheshire, SK14 5AJ

Tel: 0161 366 6679
E-mail: mobppl@aol.com
Contact: M Mobey

Discount for deaf people.

London Transport

Training Department, Unit for Disabled Passengers, 172 Buckingham Palace Road, London, SW1W 9TN

Tel: 020 7918 3811
Fax: 020 7918 3451
E-mail: lt.udp@itbuses.co.uk
Contact: Gordon Harwood

The Unit for Disabled Passengers was set up in 1984 and has become a focal point within the transport world as a generator of practical solutions to mobility problems. The Unit's training course aims to increase awareness and understanding of 'Disability', to question attitudes and to identify and share helpful ways of meeting needs.

LTS Rail Ltd

6th Floor, Central House, Clifftown Road, Southend-On-Sea, Essex, SS1 1AB

Tel: 01702 357640
Textphone: 01702 357640
Fax: 01702 357823

LTS Rail operates the busy commuter route linking South Essex with London and is investing in new trains, upgraded stations and improved customer service to increase rail travel. Our 'Access for All' policy is opening the railway for the whole community, including disabled people, parents with buggies and the elderly.

Metropolitan Police Coach Advisory Service

HQ Traffic, New Scotland Yard, Broadway, London, SW1H 0BG

Tel: 020 7230 3072
Fax: 020 7230 3567

Advice on coach parking in London, including arrangements for picking up and setting down at theatres.

RAC Motoring Services Ltd

Great Park Road, Bradley Stoke, Bristol, Avon, BS32 4QN

Tel: 01454 208000 (membership)
Textphone: 0800 626389
Fax: 01454 208283
Contact: Helen Brunning, Planning and
            Communication Team, Customer
            Services
Tel: 01454 208132

The RAC provides assistance to members when their vehicles break down. Deaf drivers can use the textphone number to contact the RAC in the event of a breakdown. RAC members are also entitled to call on the RAC legal and technical service and receive discounts. The breakdown service operates 24 hours a day, and 365 days a year.

The Margaret Champney Trust

The Gatehouse, 9 Burkitt Road, Woodbridge, Suffolk, IP12 4JJ

Tel: 01394 388746

Can provide help for particular travel costs. Apply in writing for details.

Tickets Please

c/o The Attlee Foundation, 28 Commercial Street, London, E1 6LR

Tel: 020 7247 4876
Fax: 020 7375 3022
E-mail: attlee.foundation@virgin.net
Contact: Heléna Holt, Director

Tickets Please is a national scheme to assist disabled or disadvantaged people with travel costs for journeys which have some therapeutic value for either visitor or visited. For example, to enable a parent to visit a child in hospital away from home. Please phone or write for a leaflet.

Tripscope

The Courtyard, Evelyn Road, London, W4 5JL

Tel: 020 8994 9294

Information and help with planning and organising transport for elderly or disabled people in the UK and from abroad.

Tripscope South West

Pamwell House, Pennywell Road, Bristol, Avon, BS5 0TX

Tel: 0117 941 4094

Virgin Atlantic Airways Ltd

Virgin Flight Centre, Victoria Road, Horley, Surrey, RH6 7PX

Tel: 01293 444990
Fax: 01293 444820
Website: www.fly.virgin.com/atlantic/

Virgin Atlantic Airways trains all its cabin crew in the basics of deaf awareness. Virgin also offers, upon request and subject to availability, a signing crew member on its flights to the USA, Hong Kong, Japan, South Africa and the Caribbean.
Reservations: 01293 747747

25

Clubs and Societies

This section contains details of social clubs and societies in the UK. All clubs listed here have been contacted to ensure details are correct. However, old clubs cease to exist and new clubs open their doors with incredible speed and it is sometimes difficult to ensure that every club listed is still in business or to guarantee that every club in existence is listed. If you spot incorrect details or know that your club is not here, then please phone, fax or write to RNID at Featherstone Street and we will ensure that your club details go on the database. Clubs are listed alphabetically by name within country and county sections.

England

➤ Avon

Bath Deaf Club

Windows Arts Centre, Lower Borough Walls, Bath, Avon, BA1 1QR

Contact: H Norris, Chair

Bristol Centre for Deaf People

16-18 King Square, Bristol, Avon, BS2 8JL

Tel: 0117 924 9868

Textphone: 0117 944 1344

Fax: 0117 924 4884

Contact: William Martin, Principal Officer

Service provision for deaf people on information and advice, recreation and leisure, pastoral care, sports, British Sign Language and lipreading classes. Support for families, equipment service. Social work service on premises. All those people with hearing impairment, both adults and children, profoundly deaf, deafened, deafblind and deaf people with learning difficulties.

Keynsham Deaf and Hard of Hearing Club

33 Brockley Close, Little Stoke, Bristol, Avon, BS34 6HA

Tel: 01454 615646

Textphone: 0117 986 9638

Contact: Melanie Rowbottom, Secretary

E-mail: melmac.rowbottom@btinternet.com

A social club meeting once a month for deaf, hard of hearing and interested hearing people with or without British Sign Language skills. Members enjoy a chat, play bingo, skittles and socialise.

Weston-Super-Mare Deaf Club

Emmanuel Church, Oxford Street, Weston-Super-Mare, Avon, BS23 1TE

Tel: 01934 412875

Fax: 01934 412875

Contact: Derek Boardman, Reader

The social club is open on the first Saturday each month from 4.30pm to 7pm. A church service is also held on the first Saturday of each month 4.30pm to 7pm.

Yate Deaf Club

Yate Community Centre, 100 Station Road, Yate, Bristol, Avon, BS37 5DG

➤ Bedfordshire

Bedford Association of the Deaf

Elmstone Lodge, 116 Bromham Road, Bedford, MK40 2QP

Fax: 01234 325471

The Association meets on the first Friday of each month from 7 to 10pm for social activities. Deaf people of all ages are welcome. A mother and toddler group is due to start during 1999. Sign language and lipreading classes are organised as required. Social services are provided by appointment and information on the following services are available: general social work services, communication support and services for deafblind people plus British Sign Language tutoring.

Leighton Buzzard Deaf Club

Duncombe Drive, Leighton Buzzard, Bedfordshire, LU7 8SD

Contact: E Newman
             72 Bideford Green, Leighton Buzzard, Bedfordshire, LU7 7TJ

Textphone: 01525 852192

Fax: 01525 853051

Luton Deaf Centre

Alban Neve Centre, 49 Old Bedford Road, Luton, Bedfordshire, LU2 7NX

Tel: 01582 483417

Textphone: 01582 483417

Videotel: 01582 450096

Fax: 01582 720679

Contact: Mike Webster, Centre Manager and Videophone contact

Berkshire

Reading Centre for the Deaf

79 London Road, Reading, Berkshire, RG1 5BY

Tel: 01189 574535

Fax: 01189 574535

Contact: Clifford Powell, Secretary/Treasurer
          94 Bath Road, Reading, Berkshire,
          RG30 2EU

Tel: 01189 597680

Centre for deaf people providing spiritual and social activities. Information and help with problems regarding hearing aids.

Buckinghamshire

Amersham and Chesham Hard of Hearing Club

Wymondley, Burtons Lane, Chalfont St Giles, Buckinghamshire, HP8 4BB

Tel: 01494 762159

Contact: Anne Marshall

Club meets in Red Cross Hall, Amersham at 7.30pm on alternate Tuesday evenings.

Aylesbury Deaf Social Club

54 Whaddon Chase, Aylesbury, Buckinghamshire, HP19 3QP

Tel: 01296 433594

Contact: Dorothy Pople, Secretary

We are a social club whose activities include bingo, whist, quizzes, etc.

Aylesbury Hard of Hearing Club

19 Abbey Road, Aylesbury, Buckinghamshire, HP19 3NP

Contact: Doris Sneath

High Wycombe Deaf Association

St Francis Church Hall, Amersham Road, Terriers, High Wycombe, Buckinghamshire, HP13 5AB

Textphone: 01494 438187

Fax: 01494 438187

Contact: Mary Fallon, Hon Secretary

We organise various events, such as children's Christmas party, German whist drive, indoor games, etc. If you need a current fixture please contact Mary Fallon on the number above.

Milton Keynes Hard of Hearing Group

11 High Street, Nash, Buckinghamshire, MK17 0EP

Tel: 01908 501881

Contact: Sue Mander

Tel: 01908 641731

Meets at Salvation Army Hall, Ransoms Avenue, Milton Keynes at 7.15pm on the second Thursday of each month.

Risborough and District Group for the Hard of Hearing

13 Little Ham Lane, Monks Risborough, Princes Risborough, Buckinghamshire, HP27 9JW

Tel: 01844 345605

Contact: Vera Manderson, Secretary

The group meets at 2.30pm on the second Monday of each month at the Baptist Church Hall in Princes Risborough.

Cambridgeshire

Cambridgeshire Deaf Association

8 Romsey Terrace, Cambridge, CB1 3NH

Tel: 01223 246237

Textphone: 01223 411801

Fax: 01223 246237

Contact: A Gordon

Monday Drop-In from 10am to 1pm; Thursday Drop-In from 12 noon to 4.30pm; OAP Group every second Thursday from 12.30pm to 4pm; Parent and Toddler Group from 10am to 11.30am every Thursday; Deaf Club from 7.30pm every second and fourth Saturday. Sign languages classes are also available here.

March and District Deaf Club

Trinity Church School Room, High Street, March, Cambridgeshire, PE15 9LH

Contact: Godfrey Palmer, Hon Secretary
          47 Creek Street, March,
          Cambridgeshire, PE15 8RE

Textphone: 01354 658111

Fax: 01354 658111

➤ Channel Islands

Guernsey Hard of Hearing Association

c/o Mrs Jean Roland, Santanda, Mandley Beech Estate, Collings Road, St Peter Port, Guernsey, Channel Islands, GY1 1GQ

Tel: 01481 710149

Contact: Jean Roland

Our Association gives help and support to persons with hearing impairment, and ensures adequate services are provided for them. We advise their families, and endeavour to educate the public about their needs, and also encourage businesses to make provision for deaf customers. We have a 'drop-in centre' fortnightly on Fridays, in addition to our other social occasions.

Jersey Society for the Deaf and Hard of Hearing

Beeches Old Boys Club, 31 Hill Street, St. Helier, Jersey, Channel Islands, JE2 4UA

Tel: 01534 853369

Fax: 01534 853369

Contact: Sonia Walker, Secretary

➤ Cheshire

Chester and Deeside Deaf Sports and Social Club

Centre for the Deaf, South View Road, Chester, Cheshire, CH1 4JG

Tel: 0151 355 1421 (evenings)

Textphone: 01244 371373

Contact: Pat Evans, General Manager

Congleton Deaf Club

Fellowship House, Park Road, Congleton, Cheshire, CH12 1DP

Crewe Deaf Club

Hilary Centre, Salisbury Avenue, Crewe, Cheshire, CW2 6JW

Northwich Vale Royal Deaf Club

144 London Road, Northwich, Cheshire, CW9 5HH

Stockport Centre for the Deaf

First Floor, Walthew House, 112 Shaw Heath, Stockport, Cheshire, SK2 6QS

Tel: 0161 428 1912

Textphone: 0161 480 4054

Fax: 0161 429 8603

Warrington and District Society for Deaf People

Centre for Deaf People, 13 Wilson Patten Street, Warrington, Cheshire, WA1 1PG

Tel: 01925 634640

Textphone: 01925 411628

Videotel: 01925 232551

Fax: 01925 626992

To contact the club (evenings only), the voice and textphone number is: 01925 411628.

➤ Cleveland

Cleveland Deaf Centre

3 Park Road South, Middlesbrough, Cleveland, TS5 6LD

Tel: 01642 819782

Textphone: 01642 820059

Fax: 01642 819782

Contact: Craig Jones, Vice-Chair

Textphone: 01642 852165

Fax: 01642 852165

Hartlepool Deaf Centre

26 Stockton Road, Hartlepool, Cleveland, TS25 1RL

Tel: 01429 222206

Textphone: 01429 222206

Langbaugh Hearing Impaired Club

Senior Citizens' Social Centre, Westmorland Road, Redcar, Cleveland, TS10 4BW

Contact: Elna Fitzhugh, Secretary
            94 Westmorland Road, Redcar,
            Cleveland, TS10 4BW

Social club having outings by coach. Helping deaf and hard of hearing people with information, filling in forms, etc. Communication with profoundly deaf.

Middlesbrough Deaf Club
3 Park Avenue South, Middlesbrough, Cleveland, TS3 0PB
Tel: 01429 222206
Textphone: 01429 222206

Stockton Deaf Centre
Alma Street Centre, 4 Alma Street, Stockton-on-Tees, Cleveland, TS18 2AP
Tel: 01642 391485

Contact: Pat Manton, Chair
                9 Burniston Drive, Thornaby, Stockton-on-Tees, Cleveland, TS17 0HB

Fridays from 7 to 9 pm. Please note that the Hard of Hearing Club has disbanded.

Thornaby Deaf Centre
Queen Street Community Centre, Gilmour Street, Thornaby, Stockton-On-Tees, Cleveland, TS17 6JR
Tel: 01642 604034

The number above is the Secretary's number. Please ring for details of club's activities.

➢ Cornwall
Camborne Deaf Club
5a East Charles Street, Camborne, Cornwall, TR14 8JF
Tel: 01209 711739

West Cornwall Hard of Hearing Club
St Keverne, Higher More Street, Truro, Cornwall, TR1 1BW

➢ County Durham
Bishop Auckland Deaf Centre
General Hospital Social Club, Cockton Hill Road, Bishop Auckland, County Durham, DL14 6BD

Darlington Deaf Club
Raby Terrace, Darlington, County Durham, DL3 7TW

Contact: P Doyle, Secretary
Tel: 01325 503050

Durham Active Deaf Club
The Barnfield Centre, Barnfield Road, Spennymoor, Durham, DL16
Tel: 01388 815281
Textphone: 01388 811239
Fax: 01388 815281
Contact: Christine Cooke, Secretary
                17 North Road, Spennymoor, County Durham, DL16 6EW

Durham and Derwentside Deaf Club
c/o Durham Community Association, Shakespeare Hall, North Road, Durham, DH1 4RR

Contact: I Rennison, Secretary
                1 Stanley Court, Betjeman Close, Stanley, County Durham, DH9 6UD
Tel: 0191 283668

Peterlee Deaf Club
Peterlee Day Centre, Essington Way, Peterlee, County Durham, SR8 3LD
Textphone: 0191 586 5325

Contact: William Johnson, Chair
                39 Grisedale Road, Peterlee, County Durham, SR8 5PG

Open every Thursday evening for 'Social' from 7pm to 10pm. Talk, bingo, indoor sport, drink and eat, etc.

Stanley Deaf Club
Stanley Day Centre, Wear Road, Stanley, County Durham, DH9 6LT

➢ Cumbria
Cumbria Deaf Association
217 Duke Street, Barrow-in-Furness, Cumbria, LA14 1XT
Tel: 01229 822620
Textphone: 01229 822620

Contact: Barry Carter

Duke Street Deaf Club
217 Duke Street, Barrow-In-Furness, Cumbria, LA14 1XT
Tel: 01539 729548
Textphone: 01539 732019

Support for Hearing Impaired People

5 Stonecross Gardens, Kendal, Cumbria, LA9 5TB

Tel: 01539 740515

Contact: Vera Coakley

➤ Derbyshire

Chesterfield Deaf Society

Community Centre, Tontine Road, Chesterfield, Derbyshire, S40 1QU

Tel: 01246 558891

Textphone: 01246 558891

Contact: Greta Hallam, Secretary
                     84 Church Side, Hasland, Chesterfield, Derbyshire, S41 0LB

Derby Deaf Club

Rycote Centre, Parker Street, Derby, DE1 3HF

Tel: 01332 202514

Textphone: 01332 202514

Fax: 01332 202514

Contact: Raymond Bacon, Secretary

Textphone: 01332 2025140

The Derby Deaf Club aims to provide social, recreational, educational, spiritual and personal development opportunities for deaf people who prefer to communicate through British Sign Language, and for their friends and families.

Hearing Help Amber Valley

The Hearing Help Centre, 156 Derby Road, Ripley, Derbyshire, DE5 8HU

Tel: 01773 570976

Textphone: 01773 570976

Fax: 01773 570976

Contact: E Richardson, Service Manager

➤ Devon

Bideford Hard of Hearing Club

The Centre, The Pill, Bideford, Devon, EX39

Contact: Josephine Jones, Secretary

The club meets on Mondays 2pm to 4pm for a range of social activities including talks, trips, teas and bingo.

Exeter Deaf Social Club

Palace Gate Centre, 3 Palace Gate, Exeter, Devon, EX1 1JA

Tel: 01392 499005

Textphone: 01392 499005

Fax: 01392 499005

Contact: C Norrish, Dean and Secretary

North Devon Deaf Club

NDDCS and Community, Charles Dart Crescent, Barnstaple, Devon, EX32 7EB

Contact: J Anderson

Social Club meets Saturdays from 7pm. Sports events are organised; the club is a member of both the British Deaf Sports Council and the Western Deaf Sports Council. Sign language classes for beginners and Stage I and 2 are held on Mondays, Tuesdays and Fridays 7.30pm to 9.30pm.

Plymouth and District Mission for the Deaf

Blake Lodge, Seymour Road, Mannamead, Plymouth, Devon, PL3 5AS

Tel: 01752 660769

Textphone: 01752 660769

Tiverton Deaf Club

The Day Centre, Old Road, Tiverton, Devon, EX16 4HL

Torbay Deaf Social Club

Abbey Hall, Rock Road, Torquay, Devon, TQ2 5SP

Tel: 01803 214673

Textphone: 01803 214673

Fax: 01803 215918

Contact: Margaret Ford, Secretary

Social and sports club meets on Wednesdays 6.30pm to 11pm and on the second and fourth Saturday of every month from 7pm to 11pm. Parents and Children Group is held on the second Saturday 10am to 12 noon for children up to 12 years old. A church service is held at 4pm on the first Sunday of the month. A group for older people is held on Wednesday 4pm to 6.30pm. Various sports activities are arranged.

Bournemouth Deaf Club
12 Forest Way, Stapehill, Wimborne, Dorset, BH21 7PB
Tel: 01752 660769
Textphone: 01752 660769

Concern with Hearing - East Dorset
2 Kennart Road, Poole, Dorset, BH17 7AP
Tel: 01202 686855

Concern with Hearing - East Dorset is a local group of people dedicated to the interests of those who have lost part or all of their hearing. No sign language users, but encourage use and development of lipreading as aid to communication. Membership open to all, currently £2 per year. Four meetings are held a year at which full communication support is available. Meetings are held either in Poole, Bournemouth or Christchurch. Speakers are arranged to give presentations on a variety of subjects, not necessarily associated with hearing loss, and there is an opportunity to socialise. Tea and coffee are provided.

Poole and Bournemouth Deaf Centre
Fourways Day Centre, Constitution Hill Road, Poole, Dorset, BH14 0QB
Tel: 01202 428717
Textphone: 01202 426373

Wimborne Deaf and Hard of Hearing Club
c/o Rose Day Centre, Leigh Road, Wimborne, Dorset

Meets first and third Monday of every month 7.30 to 9.30pm at Rose Day Centre, situated behind Elim Pentacostal Church in Leigh Road. Anyone interested in joining should turn up on club night.

WRVS Hard of Hearing Club
250 Lymington Road, Highcliffe, Christchurch, Dorset, BH23 5ET
Tel: 01425 278998
Fax: 01425 278998
Contact: Maureen Cocks, Club Leader
Tel: 01202 273055

This is a social group which meets on the second and third Monday and the third Friday of the month from 2pm to 4pm. Social Services display available equipment for deaf and partially sighted people one day a week at the Day Centre. Social Services also operate out of the Day Centre and provide the following services: general social

work, provision of equipment, services for deafblind people and rehabilitation services.

➢ East Sussex
Brighton Deaf Centre
Carlton Hill, Brighton, East Sussex, BN2 2GW
Tel: 01273 671899
Textphone: 01273 606425
Fax: 01273 625283
Contact: P Mitchell, Manager

The Sussex Diocesan Association for the Deaf is a voluntary charitable organisation providing services for deaf and deafblind people and their families in East and West Sussex.

Eastbourne and District Hard of Hearing Association
c/o 22 Abbey Road, Eastbourne, East Sussex, BN20 8TE
Tel: 01323 731206
Contact: Phyl Webb, Secretary

Eastbourne Deaf Club
St Mary's Church Hall, Decoy Drive, Eastbourne, East Sussex, BN22 0AB

Contact: Wendy Roseblade, Secretary
             Flat 2, Dixon Court, 16 Eversfield Road, Eastbourne, East Sussex, BN21 2AS

Hastings Deaf Centre
28 Stockleigh Road, St Leonards-on-Sea, East Sussex, TN38 0JP
Tel: 01424 421987
Textphone: 01424 421987
Fax: 01424 421987
Contact: C Attfield, Community Worker for the Deaf

The Sussex Deaf Association and Hastings Deaf Centre is a voluntary charitable organisation providing services for deaf and deafblind people in East and West Sussex.

Essex

Beverley Club for the Deaf and Hard of Hearing
2 Mansfield Towers, Marine Parade East, Clacton-On-Sea, Essex, CO15 1UU

Contact: Christine Stiffell, Secretary and Treasurer

Braintree and Essex Youth Organisation for the Deaf
Braintree Youth and Sports Centre, Alec Hunter High School, Stubbs Lane, Braintree, Essex, CM7 6XP

Tel: 01376 324363

Contact: Anne Joslin, Deaf Youth Worker

Youth Club for 7-25s is fortnightly on Saturdays 6.30pm to 10pm. Various activities are arranged including sports, crafts, indoor games, outings and music. Simple sign language is taught; the class includes young people doing Duke of Edinburgh awards.

Harlow Deaf Club
Latton Bush Centre, Southern Way, Harlow, Essex, CM18 7BH

Contact: Gladys Thomas, Hon Secretary
            11 Rectory Wood, Harlow, Essex, CM20 1RD

St Angela's Centre
The Cardinal Heenan Centre, 326 High Road, Ilford, Essex, IG1 1QP

Tel: 020 8553 2621

Textphone: 020 8553 2621

Fax: 020 8553 2631

Contact: Margaret Duffy, Coordinator

There is a social club and a youth club on the first Saturday in every month. A lunch club for deaf people is held on the first Tuesday of the month 12 noon to 4pm and a lunch club for hard of hearing people is held every Wednesday 11am to 1.30pm. There are regular signed masses at various churches and other religious activities are also arranged. A children's playgroup is held during the summer. St Angela's also offers advice, communication and advocacy support to adults and children.

Sumners Centre
Broadley Road, Harlow, Essex, CM19 5RD

This is a drop-in centre open fortnightly on Tuesdays 12 noon to 3pm.

Gloucestershire

Cheltenham and District Social Club for the Hard of Hearing
11 Broadway Close, Prestbury, Cheltenham, Gloucestershire, GL52 3EB

Tel: 01242 520461

Contact: Janet Stone, Club Secretary

To promote a social life, with friendship, help and support for any hearing impaired person. With connections to national organisations we can inform members of events, etc nationwide, also of the latest technology in hearing aids and other equipment.

Cirencester Association for the Hard of Hearing
43 Ashcroft Gardens, Cirencester, Gloucestershire, GL7 1RD

Forest of Dean and District Hard of Hearing Club
Foxes Bridge Centre, Valley Road, Cinderford, Gloucestershire, GL14 2LJ

Tel: 01594 825470

Contact: Barbara Knight, Secretary
            19 Old Dean Road, Mitcheldean, Gloucestershire, GL17 0BQ

Tel: 01594 542784

The club meets at Foxes Bridge Day Centre at 7pm on the fourth Tuesday of every month. Meetings are informal and include speakers, slide shows, socials and outings. Transport is available. New members of any age are always welcome. The aims of the club are to: raise awareness locally of the needs of people with hearing impairment; share and exchange information; provide mutual support; and maintain close links with Social Services in order to have access to equipment and information. The club receives much information and support from the Gloucestershire Deaf Association. The Association acts as an agent for the County Council in the provision of a social and welfare service for hearing impaired people.

➢ Hampshire

Havant Borough Deaf Club

13 Hedge End Walk, Havant, Hampshire, PO9 5LS

Contact: H Eastley, Club Secretary

Portsmouth Deaf Association

279 Arundel Street, Fratton, Portsmouth,
Hampshire, PO1 1LX

Tel: 023 9282 0936
Textphone: 023 9282 0936
Fax: 023 9275 1110

Social club meets on Wednesdays and Saturdays
7pm to 11pm. Social club for elderly people meets
Wednesdays 11am to 4pm. A church service is
held on the third Sunday in the month at 3pm. The
youth club meets on the fourth Friday of the
month from 7pm to 10.30pm and Thursdays 2pm
to 4pm. A hard of hearing club meets twice a week
on Tuesdays 7pm. Sign language classes for
beginners are on Fridays 7pm to 9pm; enrolment
is via the local college, Cosham Park House, tel:
023 9237 5075.

➢ Herefordshire

Hereford and District Deaf Club

Richmond Club, Edgar Street, Hereford, HR4 9JS

Contact: J Barlow, Chair
            2 Queensway College Estate,
            Hereford, HR1 1HE

➢ Hertfordshire

Hertford Social Club for the Deaf

Sele School Youth Wing, Welwyn Road, Hertford,
SG14 2DG

Tel: 01992 461300
Textphone: 01992 461300
Fax: 01992 302629
Contact: Jill Harris, Hon Secretary
            51 Stoneleigh Drive, Hoddesdon,
            Hertfordshire, EN11 9LN

This club is for profoundly deaf people. We
organise whist drives, bingo, quizzes, and a coach
trip in the summer. Christmas dinner outing for
members only. We have over 40 members.
Hearing people who wish to learn sign language
are very welcome. New faces are welcome.

Jewish Deaf Circle

70 Blacketts Wood Drive, Chorleywood,
Rickmansworth, Hertfordshire, WD3 5QQ

Textphone: 01923 283127
Fax: 01923 283127
E-mail: dmyers@cix.co.uk
Contact: Ruth Myers, Hon Secretary

Social club for deaf, deafened and hard of hearing
Jewish people. Meets at the West London
Synagogue, 33 Seymour Place, W1, on the last
Tuesday of every month. Everyone is welcome to
attend.

Stevenage Deaf Club

19 Harvey Road, Chells, Stevenage, Hertfordshire,
SG2 0BG

Tel: 01438 360700
Textphone: 01438 360700
Fax: 01438 360700
Contact: M Dent, Secretary

We provide a social environment, entertainment,
and a sports programme for deaf and hard of
hearing people and their families who live in north
Hertfordshire.

➢ Isle of Wight

East Cowes Hard of Hearing Club

The Red Cross Hall, York Avenue, East Cowes, Isle
of Wight, PO32 6BH

Contact: Dorothy Ebbatson, Secretary
            3 Birch Close, East Cowes, Isle of
            Wight, PO32 6QT
Tel: 01983 298056

Newport Hard of Hearing Club

The Meeting Room, Lord Louis Library, Newport,
Isle of Wight, PO30 5WL

Tel: 01983 567794

Contact: Violet Day, Secretary
            28 Arundel Close, Ryde, Isle of Wight,
            PO33 1BS

The club exists to give friendship and support to
mainly very elderly members, with various degrees
of hearing impairment, who normally lack social
activities. We have our own loop system. The club
has at least two outings a year plus special
Christmas luncheon. All members receive birthday
and 'get well' cards.

Ryde Hard of Hearing Club

Ryde Methodist Church, Garfield Road, Ryde, Isle of Wight, PO33 2PS

Contact: Olive Batchelor, Secretary
             20a Arundel Close, Ryde, Isle of Wight, PO33 1BS
Tel: 01983 611055

Our aim is to offer friendship, outings to the mainland and local trips. Interesting speakers at our meetings and also many forms of entertainment. Update on all matters relating to disability, financial benefits, etc.

➤ Kent
Bexley Deaf Centre

1a Vicarage Road, Bexley, Kent, DA5 2AL

Tel: 01322 550879
Textphone: 01322 550879
Fax: 01322 525583
Contact: Bernadette Ewen, Chief Officer

Bexley Deaf Centre aims to make a difference to the lives of deaf people through encouragement and empowerment whilst increasing deaf awareness wherever possible. Services provided: hearing aid advice, information, demonstration of aids and adaptations, deaf awareness training, lipreading classes, information videos, job club, mother and childrens club, advocates, tinnitus support group.

Bexley Deafblind Club

Fossett Lodge, Homer Close, Bexleyheath, Kent, DA7 6QE

Tel: 020 8303 7777 ext 2697
Fax: 020 8298 7372
Contact: Christopher Kane-Round, Team Leader Visual Impairment Team
             London Borough of Bexley
             Civic Offices (R49), Broadway, Bexleyheath, Kent, DA6 8DE

Bexley Young Deaf Club

Crayford Day Centre, 4-6 London Road, Crayford, Dartford, Kent, DA1 4DX

Textphone: 01322 555246

Birchington Hard of Hearing Club

5 Turner Court, Clarendon Road, Cliftonville, Kent, CT9 2UT

Bromley Chain

12 Nutfield Way, Orpington, Kent, BR6 8EU

Tel: 01689 851075
Textphone: 01689 851328
Fax: 01689 851075
Contact: Kathleen Hankinson, Chairperson

Bromley Chain is a registered charity whose aim is to publicise the needs of deaf, deafblind and hard of hearing people who live and work in the Borough of Bromley.

Dartford Deaf Club

Bridge Court Resource Centre, Brent Way, Dartford, Kent, DA2 6DA

Tel: 01322 229820
Textphone: 01332 290728

Contact: Mark Watson, Secretary
Meets on Saturdays.

Folkestone Youth Club

Shepnay Close, Dawson Road, Folkestone, Kent, CT19 5SJ

Tel: 01303 241701
Textphone: 01303 254417
Fax: 01303 254417
Contact: M Mohanie, Youth Worker
             4 Hythe Close, Folkestone, Kent, CT20 3QH
Tel: 01303 256017

➤ Lancashire
Blackpool, Fylde and Wyre Society for the Deaf

64 Cornwall Avenue, Blackpool, Lancashire, FY2 9QW

Tel: 01253 351369
Textphone: 01253 596556
Fax: 01253 355894
Contact: Carole Parr, General Manager

Bolton Deaf Society

Bark Street, Bolton, Lancashire, BL1 2AX

Tel: 01204 521219
Textphone: 01204 521219
Fax: 01204 521219
Contact: Gillian Gregory, Manager

Provides advice and information on all aspects of deafness, also advocacy, advisory, social, recreational and religious services for deaf people. Deaf awareness training and sign language courses are available. The Society assesses and provides equipment for daily living and maintains the Local Authority Register of deaf and hard of hearing people.

Burnley Deaf Group
Temple Street Centre, Temple Street, Burnley, Lancashire, BB11 3BD
Tel: 01282 429729

Contact: Bert Bradley, Chairman
             20 Hurstwood Avenue, Burnley, Lancashire, BB10 4JZ

Social events and mutual support and friendship for profoundly deaf people and their families.

Bury and District Deaf Society
8 Tenterden Street, Bury, Lancashire, BL9 0EG
Tel: 0161 797 2946

Contact: Jess Webb, Bury College of Further Education

Chorley Deaf and Hard of Hearing Club
27 Victoria Street, Chorley, Lancashire, PR7 2TX
Tel: 01257 267751

Contact: Nancy Banks

City of Salford Association for the Deaf
White Moth House, Bracken Avenue, Walkenden, Salford, Lancashire, M28 3SS
Tel: 0161 799 0880
Textphone: 0161 799 4402
Fax: 0161 799 1555
Contact: Barry Minorcroft, Secretary

East Lancashire Deaf Society
Tel: 01254 252620
Textphone: 01254 262460
Fax: 01254 693200
E-mail: eldeaf@aol.com
See entry under Regional Organisations.

Greater Manchester Deaf Asian Community Group
Manchester Deaf Centre, Crawford House, Booth Street East, Manchester, Lancashire, M13 9GH
Tel: 0161 273 3415
Textphone: 0161 273 3415
Fax: 0161 273 6698
Contact: Naina Mehta, Coordinator
Tel: 0161 428 9153

Provides services for specific needs of Asian deaf, hard of hearing and speech impaired people. Advice and information on current issues affecting them. Leisure activities, arts and crafts, advocacy, empowerment and encouragement of members to take control of their own lives. Families are welcome to join in activities.

Lancaster and Morecambe Deaf Club
3b Cable Street, Lancaster, Lancashire, LA1 1HD
Tel: 01524 846147
Textphone: 01524 846147

Contact: Gary Quinn, Chairman

Our aim is to provide a centre where deaf people can meet socially and for mutual support. Upper floor: snooker, pool, darts. Lower floor: bar, social functions. Tuesday and Friday evenings: general activities, Tuesday afternoons: OAP group, other times for special events. Members organize monthly 'special events'.

Manchester Central Club for the Hard of Hearing
62 Rodborough Road, Newall Green, Manchester, Lancashire, M23 2TP

Contact: Connie Troop, Hon Secretary

Manchester Deaf Club
Crawford House, Booth Street East, Manchester, Lancashire, M13 9GH
Tel: 0161 273 3415
Textphone: 0161 274 3642
Fax: 0161 273 6698

Deaf Sports and Social Club. Thursdays at 8pm. Badminton, table tennis, snooker, dominoes, darts, cards, bar.

Oldham Deaf Society
165 Park Road, Oldham, Lancashire, OL4 1SH
Tel: 0161 624 2195

Contact: Michael Howard, Steward

Activities: bowls, billiards, snooker, table tennis, indoor bowls, church service.

Oldham Hard of Hearing Group
New Vale House, Greaves Street, Lees, Oldham, Lancashire, OL4 3DL
Tel: 0161 911 4803
Textphone: 0161 911 4803

A British Sign Language group also meets at these premises.

Preston Deaf Sports and Social Club
Deafway, Brockholes Brow, Preston, Lancashire, PR2 5AL
Tel: 01772 796461
Textphone: 01772 652390 Wed/Fri evenings
Fax: 01772 654439
Contact: C Pritchard, Secretary
Textphone: 01772 652390 Wed and Fri pm

The club meets on Wednesday and Friday evenings from 7pm. Indoor sports facilities include snooker, pool and badminton, and are available to use as well as the swimming pool and sauna/gym. Church services held monthly, over 55s club meet fortnightly, deaf walking group, bingo sessions. For further information on these activities please telephone.

Rochdale District Deaf Society
23 Church Lane, Rochdale, Lancashire, OL16 1NR
Textphone: 01706 645022
Contact: Valerie Crane, Social Organiser
Tel: 01706 45022 Textphone

There is a social club on Mondays, Thursdays and Saturdays from 7 to 11pm.

Rossendale Valley Deaf Group
Oakenhead Day Centre, Hasslingden Old Road, Rossendale, Lancashire, BB4 8RR
Tel: 01706 211124

St Joseph's Mission to the Deaf
Henesy House, Sudell Street, Collyhurst, Manchester, Lancashire, M4 4JF
Tel: 0161 834 8828
Textphone: 0161 834 5888

Tameside Centre for the Deaf and Hard of Hearing
225 Mossley Road, Ashton-under-Lyne, Lancashire, OL6 6LY
Tel: 0161 330 3290
Textphone: 0161 330 4016
Fax: 0161 344 2915
Contact: Marion Lomas, Chairman

This is a social club for deaf and hard of hearing people. It meets on Thursday afternoons 12 noon to 4pm, and also on Friday evenings 7.30pm to 11.30pm. Hard of hearing club meets Wednesdays 12 noon to 4pm for social activities, talks, outings and demonstrations, etc. There is a church service every fourth Sunday.

Welfare Centre for the Deaf
Old Centenary Church, St Leonard's Gate, Lancaster, Lancashire, LA1 1NN

Wigan Deaf Club
41 Avondale Road, Wigan, Lancashire, WN1 2BE
Tel: 01942 242275
Textphone: 01942 242275

➤ Leicestershire
Leicester and District Social Club for the Hard of Hearing
Centre for Deaf People, 135 Welford Road, Leicester, LE2 6BE
Tel: 0116 254 5126
Textphone: 0116 255 6776
Videotel: 0116 254 7053
Fax: 0116 255 6940
Contact: Mollie Aucott, Rehabilitation Worker
Tel: 0116 255 1112
Textphone: 0116 254 5126

The social club meets on Mondays 10.30am to 3.30pm for a range of activities including lipreading sessions, keep fit, raffles and outings. Transport may be available in certain circumstances.

Leicester Centre for Deaf People

Centre for Deaf People, 135 Welford Road, Leicester, LE2 6BE

Tel: 0116 255 6776
Textphone: 0116 254 5126
Videotel: 0116 247 0626
Fax: 0116 255 6940
E-mail: knight@centrefordeafpeopleleicester.b
                 tinternet.com
Contact: Philip Kilgour, Director
E-mail: philip.kilgour@leicesterdeaf.freeserve.
                 co.uk

The Centre for Deaf People in Leicester provides a county-wide service to people with a hearing loss, their carers and families in Leicester, Leicestershire and Rutland. The Centre provides information, awareness training, a social work service, communication services, services to ethnic minorities with a hearing loss, their families, carers and friends; an advocacy service and help with rehabilitation and environmental aids. It has a monthly newsletter, 'Centre News'. The Centre's services are available to all. Social activities include social club Wednesdays, Saturdays and Sundays, Mother and Toddler Group, a drama group and English classes. Various sports activities are organised and computer training is available via the local college. A wide range of hard of hearing groups meet at the club and there is also a group for people with tinnitus, meeting fortnightly on Wednesdays, for talks and counselling if needed. Sign language and lipreading classes are available. Contact the centre for details of classes in the Leicestershire area. Independent interpreting agency.

Loughborough Deaf Club

17 Forest Road, Loughborough, Leicestershire, LE11 3HA

Tel: 01509 214586
Textphone: 01509 214586

Contact: Philip Kilgour, Director
                 Centre for Deaf People, 135 Welford
                 Road, Leicester, LE2 6BE
Tel: 0116 255 6776
Fax: 0116 255 6940
E-mail: philip.kilgour@leicesterdeaf.freeserve.
                 co.uk

The club provides a meeting place, social facilities and church services for deaf and hard of hearing people residing in Loughborough and district. Activities include a social club on the first Tuesday in the month from 7.30pm. Fortnightly church service on Sundays starting at 3.30pm. Hard of

Hearing club first and third Thursday of the month from 2pm to 4.30pm. Lipreading classes are on Thursday. Please telephone the office for details. Social Services provide general social work, provision of equipment, communication support services, specialist services for deaf people of ethnic minority origin and rehabilitation services. All are provided by the Mission under a service agreement with Leicestershire County Council, Leicester City Council and Rutland County Council.

Loughborough Hard of Hearing Club

17 Forest Road, Loughborough, Leicestershire, LE11 3HA

Tel: 01509 230041

Contact: Ray Dew , Secretary
                 175 Park Road, Loughborough,
                 Leicestershire, LE11 3BS

We are a club for hard of hearing people to meet together socially. We teach lipreading, share information, reach out to the district with hearing awareness events and take members on outings. There is also a fortnightly church service, and an information morning on Wednesdays 10am to 12 noon.

➢ Lincolnshire

Grantham Deaf Group

St Wulfram's Church Committee Room, Church Street, Grantham, Lincolnshire, NG31 6RR

Tel: 01522 751759
Textphone: 01522 751759
Fax: 01522 751759
Contact: Pauline Bacon
                 51 Dudley Road, Grantham,
                 Lincolnshire, NG31 9AA
Tel: 01476 574724
Textphone: 01476 574724
Fax: 01476 574724

To provide a meeting place for deaf people of all ages in the Grantham area and to provide monthly church services (second Sunday of the month, 11am at St Wulfram's Church Rooms, Church Street, Grantham).

Lincoln and District Deaf Social Club

St Matthias Centre for Deaf People, Burton Road, Lincoln, LN1 3TX

Tel: 01522 541561
Textphone: 01522 541561
Fax: 01522 541561
Contact: R Ingall

Lincoln Diocesan Deaf Association

Tel: 01522 541561
Textphone: 01522 544462
Fax: 01522 541561
Contact: John Clark, Chaplain with People who
                  are Deaf
Textphone: 01522 751759
See entry under Religious Organisations.

MC Deaf Club

Chapel Village Hall, Sea View Road, Chapel St
Leonards, Lincolnshire

Contact: Tracey White
                  5 Rawnsley Close, Alford, Lincolnshire,
                  LN13 9PZ

Meets on the third Thursday of the month from
October to April and then on the second and
fourth Thursday of the month from May to
September.

Spalding and South Lincolnshire Social Club

Ivo Day Centre, Albion Street, Spalding,
Lincolnshire, PE11 2AU
Tel: 01775 766109
Textphone: 01775 766109
Fax: 01775 766109
Contact: Neville Walkley
                  5 Fennell Road, Pinchbeck, Spalding,
                  Lincolnshire, PE11 3RP

Social club meets on first and third Saturday of
each month from 4.30 to 9.45pm.

➤ London

All Saints Centre for Deaf People

East Road, Off Portway, London, E15 3QR
Tel: 020 8552 8734

Another contact is the Chaplain Rev Chris Colledge
Tel: 020 8743 2209 (voice) 020 8810 8879 (text).
Social club meeting on Thursdays at 5pm and
every third Saturday at 5pm. Sports events
arranged are darts and golf. German whist is
played on the last Sunday in every month. Monthly
church services are held at the centre. A meeting
and dinner for elderly and deafblind people is held
every third Wednesday in the month 11.30am to
3.00pm.

Black Deaf Club

1 Bradenham Close, Walworth, London, SE17 2QA

Contact: Debbie Roberts, Coordinator
                  c/o Jack Hobbs Youth Centre,
                  Maddock Way, Brandon Estate,
                  London, SE17 2QA

Brent Deaf People's Group

The New Millennium Day Centre, 1 Robson
Avenue, Willesden, London, NW10 3SG
Tel: 0800 515152 (Typetalk) then ask for
                  020 8830 2577
Textphone: 020 8830 2577
Fax: 020 8830 4377
E-mail: BDPG@btinternet.com
Website: www.btinternet.com/~bdpg
Contact: Simon Hesselberg, Resource Worker

We provide the following: advice, advocacy,
information, deaf club, deaf issues book and
subtitles video library, drop-in centre for the
elderly deaf and hard of hearing, outings, trips,
parties, public meetings, support groups for
parents of deaf children, welfare benefits advice,
work with Brent Council, with deaf and disabilities
organisations and the health authorities,
education and social services.

Brothers and Sisters Club

25 Cruikshank Road, London, WC1X 9HF
Tel: 020 7837 5561
Textphone: 020 7689 6867
Fax: 020 7837 5561
E-mail: DEAF@bsclub.freeserve.co.uk

Deaf lesbian and gay social club. Meets first
Friday of every month. For details of venue,
contact the Honorary Secretary. We also offer
support on 'coming out'.

Camden Deaf People's Group

c/o Peckwater Centre, Peckwater Street, London,
NW5 2TY
Tel: 020 7530 6478
Textphone: 020 7387 0700
Fax: 020 7530 6479
Contact: Mervyn Williams
                  c/o Garden Flat, 75 Canfield Gardens,
                  London, NW6 3EA
Fax: 020 7624 2161

Newly established group. For details of activities
and objectives, please contact the number above.

D-Zone Youth Club

Crofton School, Manwood Road, London, SE4 1AG

Tel: 0800 515152 (Typetalk) then ask for 020 8690 6847

Textphone: 020 8690 6847

Fax: 020 8690 7214

Contact: Edward Vidler, Youth Leader

D-Zone Youth Club (formerly Scope) was founded in 1978. Funded by Community Education Lewisham, it is the only full-time youth club in London and caters for deaf and hard of hearing young people. There are two age groups: youth (14-25 years) and junior (8-14). With a full-time youth worker and a number of part-time staff, the club offers a place for young people to meet and enjoy various activities, but most of all, a warm environment where sign language can be used freely and where there are no communication barriers. D-Zone has staff and volunteers with varied communication skills to meet most members' requirements.

Deaf Women's Group

Winkfield Resource Centre, 33 Winkworth Road, London, N22 5RR

Tel: 020 8829 9381

Textphone: 020 8829 9381

The group meets on Wednesdays 1pm to 4.30pm. Contact the centre for further details.

English Deaf Lawn Bowls Association

155a Croydon Road, London, SE20 7TY

Fax: 020 8690 7214

The Association seeks to raise the standard of deaf bowlers to international levels and it has a busy calendar of various matches with hearing clubs throughout England. Deaf contests and national matches are arranged annually. English deaf teams compete in the World Championship once every three years.

Holloway Neighbourhood Youth Groups

Fire Station, 84 Mayton Street, London, N7 6QT

Tel: 020 7609 4059

Textphone: 020 7609 4059

Fax: 020 7609 4059

Contact: Steve Webster, Senior Youth Worker

Youth club meets Mondays 4 to 6pm. The age group is 9-13 years. Activities include sport and crafts, developing communicative skills, deaf culture, negotiating and trips. The group also offers a summer scheme for youngsters aged 9-

16. Contact HNG Youth Groups for details. HNG Youth Groups Services for deaf and hard of hearing young people is funded by the London Borough of Islington.

Koleinu

JDA Centre, Julius Newman House, Woodside Park Road, London, N12 8RP

Textphone: 020 8446 0579

Fax: 020 8445 7451

Contact: Mira Goldberg, Coordinator

The project is aimed at supporting Jewish deaf children and their families, but non-Jewish people are welcome to use the library and take part in sign language courses and outings. Outings are arranged in school holiday time and it is hoped to start a youth club in the near future. The library contains books on topics relating to deafness, deaf issues and sign language. A Stage 1 sign language course takes place on Wednesday, 7.30pm to 9.30pm.

Lambeth Deaf Image

19 Stanthorpe Close, London, SW16 2EB

Multi-Cultural Deaf Club

Winkfield Resource Centre, 33 Winkfield Road, London, N17 8EA

Tel: 020 8829 9381

Textphone: 020 8829 9381

Contact: June Hippolite

Textphone: 020 8801 5715

The club meets on Monday evenings, 7.30pm to 10.30pm.

National Deaf Club

Frank Barnes School, Harley Road, London, NW3 3BX

Tel: 020 7586 4665

Textphone: 020 7586 4665

Fax: 020 7722 4415

Contact: Sandra David, Secretary

For information on the Club please write to or fax Mrs Sandra David, c/o Frank Barnes School, in the first instance. The club is held at the school on Saturdays.

Options

St John's Undercroft, Landsdowne Crescent, London, W11 2NS

Tel: 020 7792 8227

A meeting place where physically disabled or sensory-impaired young adults can make new friends and find common interests. For residents of Kensington and Chelsea aged 18 to 30 years. Various activities proposed. £1.00 per session includes tea and biscuits. Open Wednesday 2pm to 5pm.

Royal Association in Aid of Deaf People, Clapham

412 Clapham Road, London, SW9 9DA

Tel: 020 7622 4969

Fax: 020 7622 4969

Contact: Richard Edwards, Regional Manager

Mondays and Thursdays: table tennis 7pm to 11pm. Tuesdays: over-60s group meets 1pm to 6.30pm. Wednesdays: deafblind group meets 10.30am to 3pm. First Saturday in every month: Bingo 5pm to 11pm. Sunday: church service 3pm.

St John of Beverley Centre for Deaf People

258 Green Lanes, London, N4 2HE

Tel: 020 8800 5556

Contact Chaplain, Rev Chris Colledge, Tel:020 8743 2209/ 020 8810 8879 (Voice/Text). The centre is owned by the Royal Association in Aid of Deaf People. Various social and sports activities are managed locally. For further details contact the centre. A church service is held every second Wednesday of the month at 1pm.

Tottenham Hard of Hearing Club

Kemble Hall, Kemble Road, London, N17 9UE

Tel: 020 8365 9596

Contact: Chris Armitage

➢ Merseyside

30 Plus Group

Darwin Cottage, 71 Sefton Road, Litherland, Merseyside, L21 9HE

Tel: 0151 920 9420

Fax: 0151 920 9420

Contact: Dee Davies

Founded in 1994, the group caters for people with hearing loss who are aged between 30 and 55 who use lipreading and listening skills as a means of communication rather than sign language. It is hoped that a group may be formed for younger people.

Sefton Centre for the Deaf

The Esplanade Centre, The Esplanade, Waterloo, Liverpool, Merseyside, L22 5PT

Southport Centre for the Deaf

19a Stanley Street, Southport, Merseyside, PR9 0BY

Tel: 01704 537001

Textphone: 01704 537001

Contact: Bernadette Stokes, Secretary/Warden

A social club is held on alternate Saturday mornings from 10am to 12 noon, it is open to all, this is a general get-together. A church service is held on the first Tuesday of every month for deaf and hard of hearing people who lipread or use sign language. A hard of hearing club meets on Tuesdays from 10am to 12 noon for bingo, outings and other social get-togethers. An audiologist attends the club from 11am to 12 noon every Tuesday. Information for members is displayed on notice boards at the club. The emphasis of the club is on members organising activities themselves.

St Helens and District Society for the Deaf

32-40 Dentons Green Lane, Dentons Green, St Helens, Merseyside, WA10 6BQ

Tel: 01744 23887

Textphone: 01744 23887

Fax: 01744 611540

Contact: L Bewley, Secretary

The Society is established for charitable objectives and purposes only and to promote services for the benefit of deaf, deaf and speech impaired, and deafblind people in the St Helens area.

Wirral Centre for the Deaf

Tel: 0151 201 2552

Textphone: 0151 201 2552

Videotel: 0151 650 0737

Fax: 0151 201 2557

Contact: Ian Duncan, Centre Organiser

See entry under Regional Organisations.

➤ Middlesex

Crown Centre for Deaf and Hard of Hearing

The Pavilion, Kingston Playing Fields, Chestnut Avenue, West Drayton, Middlesex, UB7 8BT

Tel: 01895 436833

Fax: 01895 434809

The club runs a range of activities including a social club from 1pm on Saturdays, OAP club on Tuesdays from 1pm to 5pm and sports throughout the week. A sign language class for all levels is held on Mondays 5.30pm to 7pm. The club offers a free communicator/interpreter service to members. We now have approximately 12 different groups and clubs within the Crown Centre offering a range of activities.

Enfield Highway Deaf (OAP) Club

Enfield Highway Community Centre, 117 Hertford Road, Enfield, Middlesex, EN3 5JG

Contact: K Stelling, Organiser

We provide social activities for OAPs such as talks, bingo, coach outings and games, and any personal help, if our members require a service, such as interpreting or help with letters, etc.

Hayes Deaf Social Club

The Pavilion, Kingston Playing Fields, Chestnut Avenue, West Drayton, Middlesex, UB7 8BT

Tel: 01895 436833

Fax: 01895 434809

Contact: Vera Hunt, Secretary

Social club meeting for various activities every Saturday from approximately 1pm to 11pm.

Twickenham Hard of Hearing Group

United Reform Church Hall, First Cross Road, Twickenham, Middlesex, TW2 5QA

Contact: Kathleen Harris, Secretary
162 Twickenham Road, Feltham, Middlesex, TW13 6HD

➤ Norfolk

Great Yarmouth Deaf Club

Northgate Hospital Social Club, Northgate Street, Great Yarmouth, Norfolk, NR30 1BU

Tel: 01493 721312

Textphone: 01493 721312

The club meets on Saturdays 7.30pm to 11.30pm.

King's Lynn Deaf Club

Lynnsports, Park View, King's Lynn, Norfolk

Tel: 01553 674635

Textphone: 01553 674635

Fax: 01533 763850

Contact: J Rye, Secretary
9 St. Annes Crescent, Clenchwarton, King's Lynn, Norfolk, PE34 4AU

Meets on third Saturday of each month 7 to 10pm. Social and indoor sports.

➤ North East Lincolnshire

Chatterbox Club for Hard of Hearing People

Curzon Centre, Coulbeck Drive, off Curzon Avenue, Cleethorpes, North East Lincolnshire, DN35 9HW

Tel: 01472 325222

Textphone: 01472 325234

Contact: Janet Atkinson, Technical Officer with Deaf People, North East Lincolnshire Social Services
William Molson Centre, Kent Street, Grimsby, North East Lincolnshire, DN32 7DJ

Fax: 01472 325430

The club meets for social activities on Tuesdays from 7.30pm. Adult education provides lipreading classes which are flexible and take place in the club setting on Tuesdays. Janet Atkinson visits the club on a weekly basis and gives advice and information on a wide range of social services including provision of equipment and communication support.

➤ North Lincolnshire

Scunthorpe Deaf Club

Alvingham Road Day Centre, Alvingham Road, Scunthorpe, North Lincolnshire, DN16 2DP

Tel: 01724 851946

Fax: 01724 277657

Meets Thursdays and Saturday evenings.

➤ North Yorkshire

Centre for the Deaf Harrogate

Devonshire Place, Harrogate, North Yorkshire, HG1 4AA

Tel: 01423 879466

Textphone: 01423 527524

Scarborough and District Deaf Society

Elders Street Day Centre, Elders Street, Scarborough, North Yorkshire, YO11 1DZ

Tel: 01723 516203
Textphone: 01723 516203

Contact: Kathleen Halifax, Secretary
            9 Almond Grove, Filey, North
            Yorkshire, YO14 9EH

York Deaf Society

Centre for the Deaf, Bootham House, 61 Bootham, York, YO3 7BX

Tel: 01904 623459
Textphone: 01904 623459
Fax: 01904 623459

Contact: Robert Hofschröer, Administrator

A social club is held on Thursday and Saturday nights starting at 7.30pm. There is a bar and various activities are arranged. A church service is held on the third Sunday in the month at 3.30pm. Deaf youth club is held on Fridays 7pm to 9.30pm. A British Sign Language Stage II class is held on Thursdays 7pm to 9pm. Lipreading classes are held on Tuesdays 1.30pm to 3.30pm and Fridays 10.30am to 12.30pm.

➤ Northamptonshire

Daventry and District Hard of Hearing Club

Welfare Foundation Centre, New Steet Day Centre, New Street, Daventry, Northamptonshire, NN11 4BS

Tel: 01327 79508

Contact: Mildred Gale, Secretary
            1 Ashby Road, Daventry,
            Northamptonshire, NN11 5QD

Kettering Deaf Sports and Social Club

St Andrew's Hall, Rockingham Road, Kettering, Northamptonshire, NN16 9AN

Northamptonshire and Rutland Mission to the Deaf

St Mark's Centre for Deaf People, Green Street, Northampton, NN1 1SY

Tel: 01604 250303
Textphone: 01604 636828
Fax: 01604 239041
E-mail: northants-deaf.demon.co.uk

Contact: Frank Tanner, Chaplain
            St Marks Centre for Deaf People,
            Green Street, Northampton, NN1 1SY

See entry under Regional Organisations.

➤ Northumberland

Delaval Sign Club

Forte House Deaf Centre, Links Road, Blyth, Northumberland, NE24 3PQ

Tel: 01670 352528
Textphone: 01670 352528

Contact: D Booth, Secretary
            3 Ambleside Close, Seaton Delaval,
            Whitley Bay, Tyne and Wear, NE25 0JD

Tel: 0191 237 5358

Provides social activities for deaf people, 24-hour helpline, transport, etc.

➤ Nottinghamshire

Long Eaton and District Club for the Hard of Hearing

Granville Social Centre, Granville Avenue, Long Eaton, Nottingham, NG10 4HD

Contact: Kathleen Beams, Secretary
            15 Queens Drive, Brinsley,
            Nottingham, NG16 5DF

Mansfield Society for Deaf People

1 Wood Street, Mansfield, Nottinghamshire, NG18 1QB

Tel: 01623 652029
Textphone: 01623 652029
Fax: 01623 652029

Contact: Ian Brown, Centre Organiser

Aims to support the needs of the hearing impaired community in north Nottinghamshire.

West Bridgford Hard of Hearing Club

South Notts Campus for the Physically
Handicapped, Wilford View, Loughborough Road,
West Bridgford, Nottinghamshire, NG2 7FA

Tel: 0115 923 2353

Contact: M Conacher, Secretary

We are a social club for the hard of hearing.

> Oxfordshire

Oxford Deaf and Hard of Hearing Centre

Deaf and Hard of Hearing Centre, St Ebbes,
Oxford, OX1 1RL

Tel: 01865 243447

Textphone: 01865 243447

Fax: 01865 249823

The aim of the centre is to provide a central
meeting place in Oxford for all deaf and hard of
hearing people. Each 'club' - deaf club, hard of
hearing club, deaf children's society and church -
are independently managed but share central
services. There is also a sign language
interpretation service.

Wantage Deaf Club

Stirlings Day Centre, Garston Lane, Wantage,
Oxfordshire, OX12 7AR

> Shropshire

Shrewsbury Deaf Social Club

Brierley House, Abbey Foregate, Shrewsbury,
Shropshire, SY2 6AO

Textphone: 01743 248086

Fax: 01743 248086

Contact: Kathleen Jones, Chair

            151 Mount Pleasant Road, Heath
            Farm, Shrewsbury, Shropshire, SY1
            3EY

Meetings about club issues, bingo every month,
social activities.

Telford Deaf Social Club

Dawley Bank Community Centre, Bank Road,
Dawley-Bank, Telford, Shropshire

Contact: B Anderson, Secretary

            30 Audley Avenue, Newport,
            Shropshire, TF10 7DP

Tel: 01952 404367

The club meets fortnightly on Saturdays 7pm to
10pm. Provides social life and involvement in
other clubs, eg. friendly sports matches, some
education.

> Somerset

Bridgwater and Taunton Deaf Club

St Marks Centre, Bridgwater College, College Way,
Bridgwater, Somerset, TA6 4PZ

Tel: 01278 455464

Textphone: 01278 444363

Contact: Derek Grabham, Honorary Secretary

            61 Pollard Road, Bridgwater,
            Somerset, TA6 4YA

Textphone: 01278 428892

Club meetings twice a week: Tuesdays at Taunton,
Halion Centre, Hamilton Road, 7.30pm to 10pm.
Thursdays at Bridgwater College, Bath Road,
7.30pm to 10pm. Various events arranged such as
barbecues, Christmas party, bingo, indoor games
on Saturdays at Bridgwater Club.

Yeovil Deaf Centre

Addlewell Lane, Yeovil, Somerset, BA20 1QW

Contact: D Perkins

> South Humberside

Grimsby Deaf Club

30 Hainton Avenue, Grimsby, South Humberside,
DN32 9BB

> South Yorkshire

Barnsley Centre for the Deaf

Social Centre, Moorland Centre, Barnsley, South
Yorkshire, S70 6PQ

Doncaster Centre for the Deaf

Milton Walk, Doncaster, South Yorkshire, DN1 5QG

Tel: 01302 852124

Contact: George Hiley, Treasurer

Rotherham Deaf Sports and Social Club

c/o Social Services Department, Crinoline House,
Effingham Square, Rotherham, South Yorkshire,
S65 1AW

Tel: 01709 382121

Textphone: 01709 379954

Contact: Tony Bond, Social Worker with Deaf
            People

Tel: 01709 382121 ext 3962

Social club meets every Wednesday from 7pm to
9.30pm at the Resource Centre, Badsley Moor

26

Lane Hospital. Mother and toddler group meets on Tuesdays 1pm to 3pm. There is an organised indoor games league. For more details of this and other available services contact Rev Arnold, Chaplain for the Deaf, 01742 31672 (Textphone). A hard of hearing club meets on the third Wednesday of every month, 7pm to 9pm at the Arts Centre. A tinnitus support group meets 1.30pm to 3pm on the third Wednesday of the month at St Johns Ambulance HQ, Downs Row. Sign language classes are held on Mondays 6.30pm to 8.30pm at College of Art and Technology. Lipreading classes are held on Wednesdays during term time 6.30pm to 8.30pm at the Rockingham College Annexe, Rawmarsh Hill, Park Gate. Social Services can provide equipment.

Sheffield Central Deaf Club

2 Surrey Place, Sheffield, South Yorkshire, S1 2LP
Tel: 0114 275 5307
Textphone: 0114 275 5738
Videotel: 0114 276 0142
Fax: 0114 272 7632
Contact: C Marcroft, Trustee

Daily social snack bar open 10am to 2.45pm. Pool and snooker available. Social evenings Wednesday and Saturday 6.30pm to 11pm. Bingo Saturdays. Ladies' group Tuesday evenings. Mother and toddler group bi-weekly. OAP bingo Thursday afternoons. Sign language for beginners Wednesday 7.30pm to 9pm and Fridays 1pm to 2.30pm. Summer months: bowls and walking club. Church service first Sunday of every month.

Sheffield Sport and Social Deaf Club

105 Grange Crescent, Sheffield, South Yorkshire, S11 8JZ
Tel: 0114 255 1954
Textphone: 0114 255 1954

The club meets at 7pm on weekday evenings and at weekends.

➢ Staffordshire

North Staffordshire Hard of Hearing and Tinnitus Group

15 Elmwood Drive, Blythe Bridge, Stoke-On-Trent, Staffordshire, ST11 9NE
Tel: 01782 393879

Contact: A Davies, Secretary

South and Mid Staffordshire Club for the Deaf and Hard of Hearing

76 Dunedin Crescent, Winshill, Burton-on-Trent, Staffordshire, DE15 0EJ

Contact: B Hankey, Secretary

The club is for both deaf and hard of hearing people 55 years and over. Sign language training is available at the club. Social club is held on Thursday from 12 noon to 3pm.

Staffordshire Society for the Deaf Lichfield

Lombard Court, Lombard Street, Lichfield, Staffordshire, WS13 6DP
Tel: 01543 415308
Textphone: 01543 415308

Contact: Margaret Bunting, Senior Social Worker

Stoke-on-Trent and Staffordshire Deaf Society

Tel: 01782 219161
Textphone: 01782 281125
Videotel: 01782 206575
Fax: 01782 281125
E-mail: christopher.harrison@dial.pipex.com
Contact: Tom Wordley, Chief Executive

See entry under Regional Organisations.

➢ Suffolk

Bungay and District Hearing Impaired Club

c/o Community Wing, Bungay High School, Queens Road, Bungay, Suffolk, NR35 1RW
Tel: 01986 893817

Contact: Rosie Finch, Secretary

Ipswich Deaf Social Club

49 Fonnereau Road, Ipswich, Suffolk, IP1 3JN
Tel: 01473 251179
Textphone: 01473 251179
Fax: 01472 251179
Contact: H Hamblin, Administrator

The following clubs meet here: Hard of Hearing Club, Social Club, Tinnitus Group, Youth Club and lipreading classes. Contact us for more details.

Suffolk Deaf Association Bury St Edmunds

28 Northgate Street, Bury St Edmunds, Suffolk, IP33 1HY
Tel: 01284 754749

Suffolk Deaf Association Lowestoft

Tel: 01502 512504

Contact: R Bonner, Chairman

See entry under Regional Organisations.

➤ Surrey

Bookham Hard of Hearing Group

Old Barn Hall, Great Bookham, Leatherhead, Surrey, KT23 3PQ

Tel: 01372 373484

Contact: Richard Pankhurst, Chairman
4 Elmfield, Great Bookham, Surrey, KT23 3LQ

This is a social meeting place for hard of hearing people. A loop system and overhead projector are provided for aids in communication. The club meets every third Thursday in the month from 2.15pm to 4pm approximately. Talks and outings are arranged. Transport may be provided. The club is contactable by Minicom through the Treasurer, Mr Harvey West, on 01372 373484.

Croydon Hard of Hearing Project

Community Care Office, 138 Addington Road, South Croydon, Surrey, CR2 8LA

Tel: 020 8657 4881

Textphone: 020 8657 4881

Fax: 020 8651 5598

Contact: Francesca Crosskey, Coordinator

DeafMail

47 Bennetts Way, Shirley, Croydon, Surrey, CR0 8AE

Tel: 0800 515152
020 8777 2994 via Typetalk

Textphone: 020 8777 2994

Fax: 020 8777 2994

E-mail: deafmail@cix.co.uk

Website: www.deafmail.org.uk

Contact: Roy Staines, Coordinator

Deaf Mail is an E-mail orientated deaf organisation which is respected for the quality of its services and information content. Deaf Mail provides facilities for its members to meet electronically in a friendly and helpful atmosphere and represents them on their consumer issues as well as providing whatever assistance that is needed.

Spurs Club for the Deaf

156 Addiscombe Road, Croydon, Surrey, CR0 7LA

Textphone: 020 8662 6799

Fax: 020 8662 0523

Contact: C Goulden, Secretary and Treasurer

A social club for all ages meets once a month on a Saturday evening. In addition, there is tennis during the summer, one Sunday a month in Putney

➤ Tyne and Wear

Fountain View Deaf Club

Armstrong Street, Bensham, Gateshead, Tyne and Wear, NE8 4XS

Gateshead Deaf Club

c/o Trinity Centre, West Street, Gateshead, Tyne and Wear, NE8 1ED

Tel: 0191 478 6181

Gateshead Hard of Hearing Club

c/o 95 Meadow Lane, Gateshead, Tyne and Wear, NE11 9PP

Hexham and Newcastle Diocesan Deaf Centre

Tel: 0191 261 8888

Textphone: 0191 261 8888

Videotel: 0191 233 1074 (9am-4.30pm)

Fax: 0191 233 2122

Contact: Barbara Lyon, Administrator

See entry under Religious Organisations.

Newcastle and District Hard of Hearing Club

Quaker Meeting House, Jesmond Road, Newcastle upon Tyne, Tyne and Wear, NE2 1LB

Contact: C Wallace

Tel: 0191 420 4668

We are an organisation of hearing impaired people who communicate in spoken English, aided by lipreading. We meet every Monday 4pm to 8pm at the Quaker Meeting House, Jesmond. We have a lipreading class 5pm to 5.30pm, which is followed by bingo, games, quizzes or talks on interesting subjects. Tea, coffee and biscuits are available.

North Tyneside Deaf Club

Vine Street, Wallsend, Tyne and Wear, NE28 6JE

26

Northumbria Deaf Social Club

c/o Butlers, 18 Nun Street, Newcastle upon Tyne, Tyne and Wear, NE1 5AQ

Contact: Peter Knox
                   47 Umfraville Dene, Prudhoe,
                   Northumberland, NE42 5JF

Tel: 0191 221 0397

Meets on Saturday evenings at Butlers Pub.

South Tyneside Deaf Club

Companions Club, Brigham Place, South Shields, Tyne and Wear, NE33 2DL

Textphone: 0191 456 3448 Secretary

Open every Friday 12 noon to 3pm and every Saturday 7pm to 10.30pm. The Deaf Club, The John Wright Centre, Flagg Court, South Shields, NE33 2LS.

Sunderland Deaf Society

35 North Bridge Street, Sunderland, Tyne and Wear, SR5 1AH

Tel: 0191 510 0579
Textphone: 0191 510 0579
Videotel: 0191 510 0592
Fax: 0191 510 5692
E-mail: deafsociety@sunderland.com.
Contact: Peter Kendall, Coordinator

The aim of the Society is to promote the rights and welfare of people who are deaf, deafened or hard of hearing in Sunderland and the surrounding district.

Worcester Green OAP Deaf Club

Worcester Green Day Centre, Worcester Green, Gateshead, Tyne and Wear, NE8 1NH

➢ Warwickshire

Rugby and District Hard of Hearing Club

Hamilton House, 12 Bilton Road, Rugby, Warwickshire, CV22 7AL

Contact: Tracy Pawsey, Secretary
                   43 Bilton Road, Rugby, Warwickshire,
                   CV22 7EJ

Lipreading classes are held on Wednesday evenings from 7pm to 8.30pm.

➢ West Midlands

Asian Deaf Youth Club

Newtown Community Centre, Newtown Shopping Centre, Birmingham, West Midlands, B19 2SW

Tel: 0121 359 1219
Fax: 0121 359 1371

Meets Saturdays 10am to 12 noon. Contact Abi Mahmood at the Centre for Deaf People Birmingham, 0121 246 6100 (Voice) 0121 246 6101 (Textphone).

Birmingham Deaf Chess Club

Centre for the Deaf, Ladywood Road, Birmingham, West Midlands, B16 8SZ

Tel: 0121 246 6100
Textphone: 0121 246 6101

Birmingham Deaf Sports and Social Club

Ladywood Road, Birmingham, West Midlands, B16 8SZ

Tel: 0121 246 6100
Textphone: 0121 246 6101
Fax: 0121 246 6125
Contact: Sheila Kinsella, Club Secretary

Birmingham Hard of Hearing Club

Centre for the Deaf, Ladywood Road, Birmingham, West Midlands, B16 8SZ

Tel: 0121 246 6100
Textphone: 0121 246 6101
Fax: 0121 246 6125
Contact: D Storey, Hon Secretary
                   50 Riley Road, Yardley Wood,
                   Birmingham, West Midlands, B14 4JH

Centre for Deaf and Hard of Hearing People West Bromwich

Dagger Lane, West Bromwich, West Midlands, B71 2EB

Tel: 0121 525 5347
Fax: 0121 580 3088
Contact: Mike Chappel, Team Manager

26

Coventry Deaf Sports and Social Club

Henry Fry Centre, Hertford Place, Off Queens Road, Coventry, West Midlands, CV1 3JZ

Tel: 024 7622 2321
Textphone: 024 7622 2321

Contact: Jeanne Brown, Secretary
Tel: 024 7667 6821 (Home)
E-mail: wboswell@covdeaf.vonet.com

Coventry Youth Deaf Group

c/o 7 Prior Row, Coventry, West Midlands, CV1 5EE

Contact: Rita Mistry

Dudley Deaf Sports and Social Club

Queens Cross Centre, Wellington Road, Dudley, West Midlands, DY1 1RB

Tel: 01384 813460
Textphone: 01384 813460
Fax: 01384 813461
Contact: Helen Wrighton, Chair

East Birmingham and Solihull Hard of Hearing Club

Woodlands Farm, Back Lane, Meriden, Coventry, West Midlands, CV7 7LD

Tel: 01676 522317
Fax: 01676 522317
Contact: Alma Russell, Hon Secretary

Club meets on first Thursday in the month from 1pm to 3pm at Saltley Centre, Broadway Avenue, Birmingham, B9, for friendly, social, informal afternoons. Varied programmes throughout the year, including speakers, quizzes, outings, fundraising, lipreading, tea and biscuits.

Loud and Clear Hard of Hearing Group

Western Road, Birmingham, West Midlands, B18 7QQ

Tel: 0121 554 3801 ext 4875/6
Textphone: 0121 554 3801 ext 4875/6

A monthly support group for hearing impaired people, their friends and family.

Sandwell Deaf Sports and Social Club

Dagger Lane, West Bromwich, West Midlands, B71 4BB

Tel: 0121 525 5347
Textphone: 0121 525 5347
Fax: 0121 580 3088
Contact: Horace Styles, Chair
Textphone: 0121 588 5041

Walsall Deaf People's Centre

59a Lichfield Street, Walsall, West Midlands, WS4 2BX

Tel: 01922 614794
Textphone: 01922 614795
Videotel: 01922 614808
Fax: 01922 614795
E-mail: colin.sanders@virgin.net
Contact: Colin Sanders, Development Officer

Wolverhampton Hard of Hearing Club

38 Rupert Street, Wolverhampton, West Midlands, WV3 9NU

Tel: 01902 420904
Textphone: 01902 420904

Contact: Richard Gillis, Secretary

The club runs various social activities.

Wolverhampton Independent Deaf Club

38 Rupert Street, Wolverhampton, West Midlands, WV3 9NU

Contact: P Halliwell
            565 Griffiths Drive, Wolverhampton, West Midlands, WV11 2LH

Hard of Hearing Club held on Mondays, social evening on Saturdays. Church services are held one Sunday a month.

➢ West Sussex
Chichester Deaf Club

Common Room, Chichester High School for Girls, Stockbridge Road, Chichester, West Sussex, PO19 2EB

Tel: 01243 787014
Textphone: 01243 787014

Contact: R Parker, Secretary

Crawley Deaf Club

Brunel Hall Day Centre, Brunel Place, Station Way, Crawley, West Sussex, RH10 1JB

Tel:	01293 525486 (Hall)
Contact:	Christopher Agent, Secretary
	95 Warren Drive, Crawley, West Sussex, RH11 0DT
Textphone:	01293 6163371
Fax:	01293 6163371

The club meets on the third Saturday in the month from 6pm to 11pm.

Worthing Deaf Centre

Worthing Deaf Centre, Methold House, North Street, Worthing, West Sussex, BN11 1DU

Tel:	01903 528600
Textphone:	01903 528603
Fax:	01903 528603
Contact:	Sue Standing, Manager, Sussex Deaf Association
	Brighton Deaf Centre, Carlton Hill, Brighton, East Sussex, BN2 2GW

Social Club is held on the second and fourth Saturday in the month 6pm to 11pm. OAP Deaf Friendship Club meets on the first and third Wednesday in the month 12.30pm to 4.30pm at The Sydney Walter Centre, Sussex Road. Worthing Young Deaf Group meets on the first and third Saturday in the month from 2pm to 6pm. Mother and Toddler Group meets every Wednesday from 10am till 12 noon at the Sidney Walter Centre, Sussex Road, Worthing, BN11 1DS. Talking Hands Communication Club, Maybridge Fellowship Church Hall, The Strand, Goring-by-Sea every Tuesday 7.30pm. Youth Group, The Lavinia Norfolk Unit, Angmering School, Station Road every Monday at 6.30pm.

➤ West Yorkshire

Bradford Centre for Deaf People

25 Hallfield Road, Bradford, West Yorkshire, BD1 3RP

Tel:	01274 729280
Textphone:	01274 722752
Fax:	01274 370482
Contact:	Mary Hammond, Secretary

Social club meets every Wednesday, Friday and Saturday 7pm to 11pm.

Calderdale Association for the Deaf

c/o 2 Woodhall Crescent, Copley, Halifax, West Yorkshire, HX3 0UN

Contact:	V Jacklin, Hon Secretary
	2 Woodhall Crescent, Copley, Halifax, West Yorkshire, HX3 0UN
Tel:	01422 365959
Textphone:	01422 835924

Please contact the Hon Secretary for details of the Association's aims and activities.

Castleford Deaf Centre

Airedale Social Centre, Holywell Lane, Castleford, West Yorkshire

Tel:	01977 554657
Contact:	Pat Toney, General Secretary
	39 Netherfield Close, Whitwood, Castleford
Tel:	01977 558226

Dewsbury, Batley and Spenborough Centre for the Deaf

10 Oxford Road, Dewsbury, West Yorkshire, WF1 3QA

Tel:	01924 461940
Textphone:	01924 461940
Fax:	01924 461940
Contact:	Stephen Truelove, Centre Manager

The social club for all ages meets on Wednesdays and Saturdays from 7pm onwards. An OAP club meets Wednesdays from 2 to 6pm. Indoor sports are available on alternate Saturdays and Wednesdays and a church service is held on the first Sunday of every month.

Huddersfield Deaf Club

Oldgate House, 2 Oldgate, Huddersfield, West Yorkshire, HD1 6QF

Leeds Deaf Social Club

Centenary House, North Street, Leeds, West Yorkshire, LS2 8AY

Textphone:	0113 245 2512
Fax:	0113 242 3666
Contact:	Margaret Waterhouse, Administration Secretary

Wakefield City and District Society for the Deaf

7 South Parade, Wakefield, West Yorkshire, WF1 1LR

Tel: 01924 375958
Textphone: 01924 371106
Fax: 01924 371106
E-mail: wcd.sd04mb@aol.com

Books, videos and leaflets are available on loan from our information service.

➤ Wiltshire

Swindon and District Hard of Hearing Club

54 Tweed Close, Greenmeadow, Swindon, Wiltshire, SN2 3PX

Tel: 01793 725860

Contact: Jean Chapman, Secretary

Meetings first and third Monday of every month 7.30 to 8.30pm currently. These times are liable to change, please contact Secretary for up-to-date details.

Swindon Deaf Club

c/o Savoy Pub, Swindon, Wiltshire, SN2 1HR

Swindon Deaf Club has had to move out of the Football Ground and as of December 1998 people are meeting in the Savoy Pub in town on Thursday evenings from 8pm to 11pm.

➤ Worcestershire

Redditch Deaf Club

The Halcyon Centre, Easemore Road, Redditch, Worcestershire, B98 8HA

Tel: 01527 584302

Contact: Geraldine Tibbetts, General Secretary
             39 Meadow Road, Henley in Arden, Solihull, West Midlands, B95 5LB

Textphone: 01564 793206
Fax: 01564 793206

The Club is open every Saturday from 4pm to 10pm, unless otherwise stated. To help and protect the interests of deaf people within the local community. To bring together deaf and hearing people. To encourage deaf members in sporting and social activities. To encourage members with their educational advancement (eg through outings and visits).

Northern Ireland

➤ County Antrim

Ballymena Hard of Hearing Club

6 Gortin Heights, Ballymena, County Antrim, BT42 2ND

Contact: Roberta Boyd

Meets on 2nd Wednesday at 7.00pm.

Ballyowen Hard of Hearing Club

c/o Ballyowen Day Centre, Belfast, County Antrim, BT11 9AF

Contact: Bridie Hawkins

Meets on Wednesdays at 7pm.

Belfast Hard of Hearing Lunch Club

Flat 1, Marsden Gardens, Belfast, County Antrim, BT15 5AN

Contact: Margaret O'Brien

Carrickfergus/Larne Deaf Club

13 Hillside Park, Whitehead, Carrickfergus, County Antrim, BT38 9LJ

Textphone: 028 9337 3138

Contact: Eileen Leslie

The aims of our organisation are to promote communications between deaf people and to teach signing skills to hearing people by organising activities including day trips, barbecues and meetings with other groups in all parts of Ireland.

Hearing Impaired Young Adults Belfast

Beechbank House, 11 Derryvolgie Avenue, BELFAST, County Antrim, BT9 6FL

Tel: 028 3839 4088
Textphone: 028 3839 4088
Fax: 028 3839 4095
Contact: Ken Taylor, Chairman

North Belfast Hard of Hearing Club

18 Waveney Heights, Belfast, County Antrim, BT15 4FA

Wednesday Club is mostly senior citizens. Would like younger people to attend, also men would be welcome. We try to have a visitor once a month. Fun, bingo, Christmas dinner. Runs September to end of May.

26

St Joseph's Centre for the Deaf

321 Grosvenor Road, Belfast, County Antrim, BT12 4LP

Tel: 028 9032 2256
Textphone: 028 9032 2256
Fax: 028 9032 2256
Contact: Alex McCord

Meets second Thursday of the month.

➢ County Armagh

Cherrytrees Hard of Hearing Group

Cherrytrees Resource Centre, 1a Edenderry Gardens, Portadown, County Armagh, BT63 5EA

Tel: 028 3839 4088
Textphone: 028 3839 4088
Fax: 028 3839 4095
Contact: Sadie Robinson, Senior Social Worker

Meets on Thursdays 11am to 2pm (lunch provided). Contact Mr S Rooney or Sadie Robinson at address given.

➢ County Down

Bangor Deaf Club

103 Ballycrochan Road, Bangor, County Down, BT19 6NS

Contact: Joan McWhinney

Newry Deaf Club

Conifers Resource Centre, Dromalane Road, Newry, County Down, BT35 8AP

Tel: 028 3025 0800
Contact: Mavis Gorman
Textphone: 028 3025 0768

Ages from 12 to 80 years, mixed females and males.

➢ County Londonderry

Hard of Hearing Club Coleraine and District

1 Waterside, Coleraine, County Londonderry, BT51 3DP

Tel: 028 7035 7966
Fax: 028 7035 7966
Contact: Victoria Bryson, Correspondence Secretary
Tel: 028 7035 7966 ext 22

An organisation committed to the well-being of people with hearing difficulties through the provision of support, information, advocacy and entertainment.

474

North West Deaf Association

Glenbrook Day Centre, Glenbrook Terrace, Londonderry, BT48 0JQ

Contact: Robert Devine

Meets on Fridays at 8.30pm.

➢ County Tyrone

Dungannon Deaf Club

The Square, Stewartstown, County Tyrone, BT71 5HX

Contact: Brian Kelly

North West Association of Hearing Concern

6 Ballycolman Road, Strabane, County Tyrone, BT82 9BZ

Contact: Robert Devine
               Glenbrook Day Centre, Glenbrook Terrace, Londonderry, BT48 0JQ

Omagh Deaf Club

50 O'Kane Park, Omagh, County Tyrone, BT78 5AB

Tel: 028 8224 7560
Contact: Lucinda Hunter

Meets on Fridays at 8pm at CKS Hall, Omagh.

Omagh Deaf Youth

Sperrin Park, Omagh, County Tyrone, BT78 5BA

Contact: Peggy Tierney, Hon Treasurer

Eire

➢ Co Cork

Cork Association for the Deaf

5 McCurtin Street, Cork

Contact: Siobhan O'Sullivan

Scotland

➢ Angus
Tayside Association for the Deaf
36 Roseangle, Dundee, Angus, DD1 4LY
Tel: 01382 221124
Textphone: 01382 227052
Fax: 01382 200025
Contact: Lynn Grant, Manager of Social Work
                     Services

Contact for further information about sign
language classes in Scotland. Tayside Community
Education Department holds sign language
classes at different times and venues. For up-to-
date information please telephone: 01382
644622. Tayside are also the agents for social
work department.

➢ Ayrshire
Ayrshire Mission to the Deaf
10 Clark Street, Kilmarnock, Ayrshire, KA1 3AJ
Tel: 01563 524118

➢ Dumfriesshire
**Dumfries and Kircudbright Society for the
Deaf**
26 Rae Street, Dumfries, DG1 1HY
Tel: 01563 524118

➢ Inverness-Shire
**Fort William and Lochaber Friends of the Deaf
Association**
Deaf Care Centre, Shopping Square, Caol, Fort
William, Inverness-Shire, PH33 7DS
Tel: 01397 704889

Contact: Hester Munro, Secretary

The Centre provides support, equipment, training,
information and advice to deaf and hard of hearing
people of all ages in the Fort William area. The
Association also undertakes campaigning
activities.

Highland Society for the Deaf
15 Kenneth Street, Inverness, IV3 5NR
Tel: 01463 222898

➢ Lanarkshire
St Vincent's Centre for Deaf People
51 Tobago Street, Bridgeton, Glasgow,
Lanarkshire, G40 2RH
Tel: 0141 554 8897
Textphone: 0141 550 1616
Fax: 0141 551 8904
Contact: Elizabeth Lafferty, Project Manager

The Centre provides professional services/social
and recreational services/pastoral services. These
include information/advisory service, community
work, sign language and deaf awareness training,
deaf tutor group, advice on health issues, senior
citizens' group, social club, sport and recreation,
family days, signed mass (weekly), religious
celebration services/communion.

➢ Lothian
Edinburgh and East of Scotland Deaf Society
Tel: 0131 556 3128
Textphone: 0131 557 4202
Fax: 0131 557 0419
E-mail: admin@escotdeafsoc.demon.co.uk
See entry under Regional Organisations.

➢ Strathclyde
Deaf Connections
Tel: 0141 420 1759
Textphone: 0141 429 6682
Videotel: 0141 418 0597 (office hours)
Fax: 0141 429 6860
See entry under Regional Organisations.

Wales

➢ Clwyd
Barraclough Deaf Club
Barraclough House, Castle Street, Mold, Flintshire,
CH7 1NL
Tel: 01352 759479 Friday evenings
Textphone: 01352 759479

Contact: Gordon Evans, Chairman
                     110 Crogen, Lodgevale Park, Chirk,
                     Wrexham, LL14 5BJ
Textphone: 01244 531131

Clwyd Deaf Sports and Social Club

Centre for the Deaf, Barraclough House, Daniel Owen Precinct, Mold, Clwyd

Contact: C Hutton
           13 St David's Drive, Connah's Quay, Deeside, Clwyd, CH5 4SP

The club meets Friday evenings 7pm to 11pm, fortnightly in winter and weekly in summer.

Conwy Deaf Society

7 Hillside, St. Asaph, Clwyd, LL17 0SB
Textphone: 01745 583274

Contact: Joanna Hale

Meets every Saturday at Brickfield Youth and Community Centre, Brickfield Terrace, Llandudno Junction, Conwy, from 7pm to 11pm.

Mold Deaf Club

110 Crogan, Lodgevale Park, Chirk, Clwyd, LL14 5BY

Contact: Elaine Sturman

Meets on Fridays 7pm to 11pm.

Rhyl Hard of Hearing Club

Apostolic Church, Sisson Street, Rhyl, Clwyd, LL18 2DE

Contact: Jackie Cladon
Textphone: 01492 580016

Meets third Monday of every month from 10am to 2pm. Temporarily on hold (as of January 1999) for a few months while looking for new venue. Contact Jackie Claydon for updates.

Wrexham Deaf Club

41 Greengate Farm Estate, Coedpoeth, Wrexham, Clwyd, L11 3PS
Tel: 01978 291422
Textphone: 01978 261173

Social meetings for deaf people who use sign language to communicate. Meets Thursdays 10am to 1pm, Fridays 7pm to 9pm.

Wrexham Hard of Hearing Club

Capel y Croes, Bod Hyfryd, Wrexham, Clwyd

Contact: Alun Hughes
           Cae Garw, Bottom Road, Summer Hill, Wrexham, Clwyd, LL11 4TW
Tel: 01978 756920

Our group meets for social and support purposes. We have a mobile loop system and invite speakers on subjects of local cultural and hearing-related topics. We charge a small annual membership fee.

➤ Denbighshire

Rhyl Deaf Club

40 Gillian Drive, Weaverton, Rhyl, Clwyd, LL18 4TA
Tel: 01745 353080

Contact: Lindsay Gibson
Tel: 01492 536141
Textphone: 01492 536142

Provides a meeting place for deaf people to come together socially. Meets on the first Monday of every month from 7 to 10pm. Hafen Deg, Grange Road, Rhyl, Denbighshire.

➤ Dyfed

Carmarthen Deaf and Hard of Hearing Club

Day Centre, Cambrian Place, Carmarthen, Dyfed, SA31 1QH
Tel: 01267 235503

Contact: E Davies, Secretary
           75 Hafod Cwnin, Carmarthen, SA31 2AT

Ceredigion Deaf Club

c/o Maes-y-Dderwen, Cilgerran, Dyfed, SA43 2PG

Contact: J Allen, Secretary

Meets first Friday of each month in Penrhiwllan Village Hall excluding January to March, near Llandysul, Carmarthenshire. Table tennis, darts, billiards (mini table), etc or chat over a cup of tea.

Ceredigion Hearing Impaired Support Group

c/o Brynafon, Talybont, Ceredigion, SY24 5HD
Tel: 01970 832252
Fax: 01970 832252
Contact: Gill Belton, Hon Secretary

The group has a number of volunteers based mainly in the Aberystwyth area, who can visit the elderly in their own homes to advise on devices and equipment. We clean and maintain NHS aids and provide transport to the hearing aid clinics if necessary.

Llanelli Deaf Club

5 Tan-y-Coed, Burry Port, Carmarthenshire, SA16 0SN

Contact: Vaughan Williams, Secretary

Meets Thursdays 7pm to 9pm (social), Tuesdays 7pm to 9pm (meeting/presentation). Llanelli Deaf Centre, 54 New Road, Llanelli, Carmarthenshire SA15 3DR.

Llanelli Hard of Hearing Club

c/o 55 Robinson Street, Llanelli, Carmarthenshire, SA15 1TT

Tel: 01554 759618

Contact: M Sweet

Meets every Tuesday at 7.30pm in Coleshill Disabled Centre.

Llanelli Hearing Impaired Support Group

c/o 14 Tan-y-Bryn, Burry Port, Llanelli, Carmarthenshire, SA16 0HP

Tel: 01554 833604

Textphone: 01554 833604

Contact: O Jones

Our aim is to help NHS hearing aid users with any problems. If contacted we will visit the person and if unable to do minor repairs will take the hearing aid - or owner - to the audiology department. We also hold a clinic every Friday, with two members present, to advise about environmental aids, etc.

Pembroke Deaf Club

Old Rugby Football Club, Narbeth Road, Saundersfoot, Dyfed, SA69 9DS

Textphone: 01834 813066

Contact: Peter Williams, Chairman
2 New Buildings, Sardis, nr Saundersfoot, Dyfed, SA69 9AW

Offers mutual support for British Sign Language users, at a social evening once a month. Trips and other social events are arranged throughout the year. There is also regular contact with health and social services to plan services.

Talking Hands Hearing Impaired Support Group

c/o 9 Burgess Meadows, Jobswell Road, Carmarthen, SA31 3JL

Contact: Beryl Jones

Hearing Impaired, Tenby (HIT)

4 Rosemount Gardens Villas, Heywood Lane, Tenby, Dyfed, SA70 8BN

Tel: 01834 842239

Textphone: 01834 842239

Fax: 01834 842239

Contact: Glynn Price, Chairman
4 Rosemount Gardens Villas, Heywood Lane, Tenby, Pembrokeshire, SA70 8BN

Lipreading classes, hearing aid clinics, demonstrations, deaf awareness.

➢ Gwent

Brynmawr Deaf Club

30 Alexandra Street, Ebbw Vale, Blaenau, Gwent, NP3 6JF

Contact: Richard Williams

Meets at St Mary's Church, Dumfries Place, Brynmawr on Thursdays, 7 to 9pm.

Cardiff Deaf Club

c/o 30 Alexandra Street, Ebbw Vale, Blaenau, Gwent, NP3 6JF

Contact: Richard Williams, Secretary

Meets at 163 Newport Road, Cardiff, on Wednesdays 6 to 10pm.

Griffithstown Social Centre for the Deaf

Widdershins Centre, Greenhill Road, Griffithstown, Pontypool, Gwent, NP4 5BE

Contact: A Clark

Newport Deaf Club

Ladyhill Centre, Alway, Newport, Gwent, NP9 9SW

Contact: June Webb, Secretary
619 Monnow Way, Bettws, Newport, Gwent, NP9 6DJ

To provide a place for deaf people to meet their friends and to organise suitable events such as inter-deaf sports, children's parties, and adult outings. Meets Wednesdays 7 to 10pm at Ladyhill Centre, Alway, Newport.

Pill Harrier Rugby Deaf Club

47 Farmwood Close, Newport, Gwent, NP9 9BR

Contact: Richard Jones, Secretary

Meets at Pill Harrier Sports and Social Club, Courtybella Terrace, Pillgwenlly, Newport on Wednesdays approximately 8pm.

Risca Hearing Impaired Support Group
64 Waunfawr Gardens, Cross Keys, Newport, Gwent, NP1 7AJ
Tel: 01495 271175

Contact: S Davies

Thursday Club for the Deaf
37 Rupert Brooke Drive, Newport, Gwent, NP9 3HP

Contact: R Lewington
            51 Dan-y-Coed Road, Cyn Coed, Cardiff, CF2 6ND
Textphone: 029 2068 9283

Deaf and hard of hearing people meet at Alway Centre for the Deaf, Aberthaw Road, Newport on Thursdays between 11am and 3pm. It is a social club with varied activities. We arrange for speakers from outside the deaf community to speak about their work. There are coach outings and also a weekly church service.

➢ Gwynedd
Abercolwyn Hard of Hearing Club
c/o 26 Taverners Court, Lloyd Street West, Llandudno, Gwynedd, LL30 2DB
Tel: 01492 877733

Contact: Sue Deakin, Secretary

Meeting for a social afternoon with speakers on various subjects, and for people with same disability to discuss problems that they encounter in everyday life and if possible to visit where these problems occur, to try to sort things out. Members can have their hearing aids attended to by our own trained people.

Blaenau Ffestiniog Hard of Hearing Club
9 Maes y Plas, Blaenau Ffestiniog, Gwynedd, LL41 4DA

Contact: E Hughes

Dolgellau Hard of Hearing Club
The Ship Hotel, Dolgellau, Gwynedd, LL40 2YL
Tel: 01341 430639

Contact: Marion Humphries, Secretary
Tel: 01341 423199

Dyffryn Conwy
The Clinic, Watling Street, Llanrwst, Gwynedd, LL26 0LS
Tel: 01492 660741

Gwynedd Deaf Club
7 Station Road, Llanberis, Gwynedd, LL55 4TA

Contact: Judith Jones
            Awel y Mor, Borth-y-Gest, Porthmadog, Gwynedd, LL49 9TS
Textphone: 01766 512821
Fax: 01766 512821

Llanberis Deaf Club is a social club with a busy programme of events. We welcome visitors staying in the area.

Holyhead Deaf and Hard of Hearing Club
Community Centre, St. Seiriols Close, Holyhead, Gwynedd, LL65 1RD
Tel: 01407 769355
Textphone: 01407 769355
Fax: 01407 769355
Contact: Ann Hazell
            20 Holborn Road, Holyhead, Gwynedd, LL65 2AT

Llanberis Deaf Club
Awel-y-Mor, Borth-y-Gest, Porthmadog, Gwynedd, LL49 9TY
Textphone: 01766 512821
Contact: Judith Jones, Secretary
Fax: 01766 512821

A social club, meeting every other Saturday from 6pm to 9pm at Station Road, Llanberis.

Llandudno Deaf Centre
c/o Conservative Club, First Floor, Upper Mostyn Street, Llandudno, Gwynedd, LL30 2SW
Tel: 01492 876026
Contact: David Duller
            36 Glyndwr Road, Llysfaen, Colwyn Bay, Clwyd, LL29 8TA
Textphone: 01492 512508
Meets every Saturday 7pm to 11pm.

Marl Hard of Hearing Club

The Bungalow, Plas Tre Marl, Broad Street, Llandudno Junction, LL31 9HL

Contact: Harold Broadley
              65 Everard Road, Rhos-on-Sea, Conwy, LL28 4HA
Tel: 01492 543576

The club welcomes all hard of hearing, deaf and deafened people. Informal meetings with occasional speakers and lipreading practice.

Young Hard of Hearing and Deafened People's Club

The Bungalow, Plas Tre Marl, Broad Street, Llandudno Junction, LL31 9HL

Textphone: 01492 580016

Contact Jackie Claydon at the North Wales Deaf Association at the above address and telephone number.

➢ Mid Glamorgan

Bridgend and District Hearing Impaired Support Group

Glen Cottage, Coychurch, Bridgend, CF35 5HD
Tel: 01656 861370
Textphone: 01656 861370
Fax: 01656 861370

Meets first Tuesday every month at Evergreen Hall, Bridgend.

Bridgend Deaf Club

5 Taliesin Close, Pencoed, Bridgend, Mid Glamorgan, CF35 6JR

Contact: Alan Williams, Secretary

Meets at Coychurch Road, Bridgend, Tuesdays, 6pm to 10pm.

Caerphilly Deaf Club

31 Longfellow Gardens, Graig-y-Rhacca, Machen, Mid Glamorgan

Contact: Graham Caldicott, Secretary

Meets at Caerphilly Social Centre, Station Road, Caerphilly on Thursday evenings 7pm to 9pm.

Glamorgan Mission to the Deaf

1 Lan Park Road, Graigwen, Pontypridd, Mid Glamorgan, CF37 2DH
Tel: 01443 404222
Textphone: 01443 404222
Contact: David Roberts
Tel: 01443 402250

See entry under Regional Organisations.

Hawthorn Hard of Hearing Support Group

36 Ynyscorrwg Road, Hawthorn, Pontypridd, Mid Glamorgan, CF37 5AP
Tel: 01443 842307

Contact: Katie Davies

The group gets together to sort out the best way to cope with the disability and helps with information of what is available to this end, as well as keeping up with new environmental aids, etc. We also have lipreading classes regularly (once a fortnight). A social service worker also attends these classes.

Pontypridd Deaf Club

40 Herbert Road, Aberdare, Mid Glamorgan, CF44 7ND

Contact: Graham Baker, Secretary

Meets at 1 Lan Park Road, Pontypridd, Tuesdays and Saturdays 7pm to 10pm.

➢ Powys
Brecon Deaf Club

County Hall, Llandrindod Wells, Powys, LD1 5LG
Tel: 01874 623706

Contact: Sheila Clark, Social Worker with Deaf People

Meets every Wednesday 7pm to 9pm.

Llandrindod Wells Deaf Club

Community Room, Lant Avenue, Llandrindod Wells, Powys, LD1 5EH

Contact: C Taylor

Radnor Deaf and Hard of Hearing Support Group

Sefton House, Middleton Street, Llandrindod Wells, Powys, LD1 5DG

Tel: 01597 822191

Fax: 01597 824856

Contact: Cathy Taylor

Social and support group.

Welshpool Hearing Impaired Support Group

c/o School House, Buttington, Welshpool, Powys, SY21 8HD

Contact: Dorothy Rowlands

Tel: 01938 552654

➢ South Glamorgan

Barry Deaf Club

Vale Resources Centre, Hen Goleg, College Fields Close, Barry, South Glamorgan, CF6 6LF

Tel: 01446 730402

Textphone: 01446 742245

Fax: 01446 721980

Contact: Val Bardsley, Secretary

Meets on Tuesday evenings 7pm to 9pm.

Cardiff and District Hearing Impaired Group

9 Court Road, Whitchurch, Cardiff, CF4 1HN

Tel: 029 2069 1781

Contact: Cedrick Moon

➢ West Glamorgan

Neath Deaf Club

16 Rosser Street, Neath, West Glamorgan, SA11 3BX

Contact: William David, Secretary

Meets at Neath Deaf Club, Cadoxton Road, Neath, from 7pm to 9pm on Tuesdays.

Swansea Deaf Club

58 Rowan Tree Close, Neath, West Glamorgan, SA10 7SQ

Tel: 01792 470477

Contact: Helen Mort, Secretary

Meets at Swansea Mission for the Deaf, Ffynone Road, St James' Gardens, Uplands, Swansea, on Thursdays 7pm to 10pm.

Swansea Valley Sign Language Group

7 Elizabeth Close, Ynysforgan, Swansea, West Glamorgan, SA6 6RW

Tel: 01639 637949

Contact: P Powell

Ystradgynlais Hearing Impaired Support Group

14 Lluest, Ystradgynlais, Swansea, West Glamorgan, SA9 1HT

Tel: 01639 843528

Contact: J Martin

26

Arts and Leisure

This section contains information on theatres, arts venues, organisations related to the arts, sports and leisure who are able to provide services for people with a hearing loss.

This section lists organisations alphabetically under the following headings: holidays, leisure, museums and galleries, music, sport and finally theatre.

Holidays

British Deaf Naturist Club

P O Box 531, DAGENHAM, Essex, RM9 4AN

Tel: 020 8924 7145 (after 7pm)

Textphone: 020 8924 7145

Fax: 020 8924 7163

Contact: Peter Johnson, Secretary

Britain's first naturist club for deaf people. Provides deaf naturist caravans and camping club and private deaf naturist house parties. Hearing people using British Sign Language are also welcome. For details of how to join and dates of meetings, please contact the Secretary.

Butterfields

Pen Y Nant Cottage, Minera, Wrexham, Clwyd, LL11 3DA

Tel: 01978 750547

Textphone: 01978 750547

Fax: 01978 750547

Contact: Ken Butterfield, Partner

Butterfields provides the following resources: residential outdoor activity courses for deaf children, young people and adults. Respite care for deaf children and young people with or without additional special needs. (Registered and approved by Wrexham Social Services for foster care provision.) Social work support services through service level agreements with local authorities/voluntary organisations. Deaf awareness training courses. Communication support services: BSL interpretation, deafblind manual communication and guiding, lipspeaking.

Chalfont Line Ltd

4 Medway Parade, Perivale, Middlesex, UB6 8HA

Tel: 020 8997 3799

Fax: 020 8991 2892

Contact: Terry Reynolds, Chairman

Chalfont Line Holidays specialises in holidays for people with disabilities of all kinds. We have recently designed and built a specialised coach which has a personal loop system for hearing disabilities, wheelchair lift and clamping system, accessible toilet and three-monitor video enabling signed commentary from accompanying guide.

Deaf Caravan and Camping Club

102 Mansfield Road, Clipstone Village, Mansfield, Nottinghamshire, NG21 9AW

Tel: 01623 653102

Textphone: 01623 653102

Fax: 01623 653102

Contact: Clifford Brown, Hon Secretary

Formed in 1974, the club is an independent organisation run by deaf people for deaf people. Rallies are held throughout the year, usually from Easter to November on a monthly basis at various sites throughout England, Wales and possibly Scotland. The September rally is combined with the Annual General Meeting. Events at rallies can include family games, rambles, barbecues and sometimes visits to deaf centres. Membership forms are available from the Honorary Secretary.

Edgar Guest House for the Deaf

1 Wyndham Park, East Runton, Cromer, Norfolk, NR27 9NJ

Tel: 01263 513045

Textphone: 01263 513045

Fax: 01263 513045

Holiday Care Service

2nd Floor, Imperial Buildings, Victoria Road, Horley, Surrey, RH6 7PZ

Tel: 01293 774535 Information
                   01293 776943 Admin

Textphone: 01293 776943

Fax: 01293 784647

Contact: Derek Moore, Information Manager

Tel: 01293 776943

The Holiday Care Service was founded in 1980 to give disabled people the information and confidence they need to take a break. There is an information sheet specifically for deaf and hard of hearing people, including details of activity holidays as well as hotels and guest houses with facilities such as teletext television or signing staff. Information service on specialist organisations providing holidays in the UK and abroad, special interest holidays, accessible transport, accessible hotels, B&B, farmhouses and self-catering accommodation.

Kingfisher Barn
Rye Farm, Culham, Abingdon, Oxfordshire, OX14 3NN
Tel: 01235 527657
Textphone: 01235 527590

London Tourist Board Information Centre
Victoria Station Forecourt, London, SW1E 5JN

Southern Tourist Board
Chamberlayne Road, Eastleigh, Hampshire, SO50 5JH
Tel: 023 8062 0006
Fax: 023 8062 0010
Contact: Marilyn Fletcher, Head of Information

Tara Guest House
10 Hollywell Street, Oxford, OX1 3SA
Tel: 01865 202953/ 0800 515152
Fax: 01865 202953
Contact: Judith Goodwin

Bed and breakfast in the centre of Oxford, convenient for all the colleges.

West Country Cottages
The Geminids, Abbotskerswell, Devon, TQ12 5PP
Tel: 01626 333678
Textphone: 01626 333678
Fax: 01626 336678
E-mail: holidays@westcottages.u-net.com
Website: www.westcottages.u-net.com

Coastal, waterside and National Park locations. Lands End to the Cotswolds. Self-catering cottages in delightful settings. Thatched cottages, large family houses, cosy retreats for two. Some with pools and sports facilities. Most English Tourist Board-inspected and commended for quality.

West Country Tourist Board
60 St David's Hill, Exeter, Devon, EX4 4SY
Tel: 01392 425426
Fax: 01392 420891
E-mail: post@wctb.co.uk
Contact: Alison Full

The West Country Tourist Board Day Out Fairs offers information from a wide range of attractions and destinations to help those planning group outings.

Leisure - General

ADAPT Trust
8 Hampton Terrace, Edinburgh, Midlothian, EH12 5JD
Tel: 0131 346 1999
Fax: 0131 346 1991
E-mail: tat@adapttrust.co.uk
Contact: Stewart Coulter, Development Manager

The ADAPT Trust (Access for Disabled People to Arts Premises Today) works throughout the UK and is the only agency to deal solely with access to arts venues. The trust offers advice and undertakes consultancy, and access audit, commissions. It also offers training and makes grants for access improvements.

Arts and Disability Forum
Albany House, 73-75 Great Victoria Street, Belfast, County Antrim, BT2 7AF
Tel: 028 9023 9450
Textphone: 028 9032 5744
Fax: 028 9024 7770
E-mail: adf.dforum@dnet.co.uk
Contact: Avril Crawford, Development Officer

The Arts and Disability Forum is working for equal access to mainstream arts for disabled people, as both consumers and participants, and campaigns for better opportunities in arts education, training and employment. It promotes the work of disabled artists and administers a bursary to further their skills and chosen art form.

Artsline

54 Chalton Street, London, NW1 1HS

Tel: 020 7388 2227

Textphone: 020 7388 2227

Fax: 020 7383 2653

E-mail: artsline@dircon.co.uk

Website: www.dircon.co.uk/artsline

Information and advice is given on access to the arts in London - both physical access to mainstream arts events/venues and access to involvement in the arts/disability arts. It also produces access guides to arts venues, including theatres, cinemas, galleries, tourist attractions, museums and restaurants. Play access guide for disabled children. Runs a multi-cultural project for disabled and deaf people from all ethnic minority communities.

Dance For Everyone

30 Sevington Road, Hendon, London, NW4 3RX

Tel: 020 8202 7863

Fax: 020 8202 7863

Contact: Naomi Benari, Artistic Director

Workshops, videos, and performances to encourage deaf children to express themselves through movement. Includes workshops, lectures to assist their teachers.

Llanrumney Youth Centre

Llanrumney Youth Centre, Ball Road, Llanrumney, Cardiff, CF3 9YW

Tel: 029 2077 8931

Fax: 029 2077 8931

Contact: Chris Hole

National Subtitling Library for Deaf People

3rd Floor, Victoria Mill, Andrew Street, Compstall, Stockport, Cheshire, SK6 1DJ

Tel: 0161 449 9650

Textphone: 0161 449 9650

Fax: 0161 449 9650

Contact: Beryl Roberts, Administrator

The National Subtitling Library for Deaf People is a charity that aims to enhance educational and recreational opportunities for deaf and hearing impaired people by producing and distributing subtitled videotapes. Services include an educational service, a postal hire service, and a contract subtitling service.

Playmix

Playmix Studio 4, 47 Wharfdale Road, London, N1 9SE

Tel: 020 7837 0973

Textphone: 020 7837 9326

Contact: Helga McGilp

Royal Botanic Gardens, Kew

Outreach Education Officer, Education Department, Richmond, Surrey, TW9 3AB

Tel: 01444 894000

Fax: 020 8332 5610 (Enquiry Unit)

Contact: Andrea Vaillancourt-Alder

The Outreach Education Unit delivers two programme options. Option 1 offers a fully equipped mobile classroom which is erected in a central location for one week, allowing for three programme days with three workshops a day. The Mobile Education Unit is a seven-metre long exhibition unit, which incorporates an open stage, study benches, audio visual facilities, scientific field equipment and a small specialised library. Option 2 offers 'in-school' visits with the outreach education officer using school grounds and facilities. Both programmes offer a choice of five workshops.

Silentview

Centre for Deaf People, Queens Drive, Liverpool, Merseyside, L13 0DJ

Tel: 0151 228 0888

Textphone: 0151 252 1032

Videotel: 0151 220 2019

Fax: 0151 228 4872

E-mail: Bkirwan@silentview.demon.co.uk

Contact: Barry Kirwan

Encourages deaf people to be involved in video production, to work with others to promote equal opportunities for deaf people in television and video production at all levels (broadcast, corporate, community) and to produce programmes that provide equal access for deaf people with sign language and subtitles.

Museums and Galleries

British Museum

Great Russell Street, Bloomsbury, London, WC1B 3DG

Tel: 020 7323 8509
Textphone: 020 7323 8920
Fax: 020 7323 8855
E-mail: s.picton@british-museum.ac.uk
Website: www.british-museum.ac.uk
Contact: Kate Ramsden, Access Coordinator, Education Service
38-43 Russell Square, London, WC1B 5DA
Textphone: 020 7323 8731/ 8920

The museum organises monthly guided tours of specific areas of the museums collections with sign language interpretation. Sound enhancement and portable induction loops are available. The British Museum actively seeks the opinions of deaf and hard of hearing people about the services they would like to see implemented or developed within the museum.

Norton Priory Museum

Tudor Road, Manor Park, Runcorn, Cheshire, WA7 1SX

Tel: 01928 569895

The trust was set up to secure the preservation and interpretation of the historic site and gardens of Norton Priory. This beautiful site is open every afternoon, and at other times by arrangement, with a programme of family activities and events plus an award-winning education service.

Tate Gallery

Millbank, London, SW1P 4RG

Tel: 020 7887 8000
Textphone: 020 7887 8687
Fax: 020 7887 8007
E-mail: information@tate.org.uk
Website: www.tate.org.uk
Contact: Salvatore Rubbino
Tel: 020 7887 8725
Fax: 020 7887 8729

The Tate Gallery houses the national collections of British paintings and sculpture, including the Turner Collection in the Clore Gallery, and of international modern art. The gallery aims to make the collection accessible to all and is committed to meeting the diverse needs of all its many visitors.

The Photographers' Gallery

5 Great Newport Street, London, WC2H 7HY

Tel: 020 7831 1772
Textphone: 020 7379 6057
Fax: 020 7836 9704
E-mail: info@photonet.org.uk
Website: www.photonet.org.uk

The gallery runs BSL talks for deaf adults. A bi-monthly newsletter, 'Great', is available. Celebrates, investigates and communicates the nature of photography. Engages the widest possible public in understanding and enjoying the photographic image. Aims to be at the forefront of photographic creativity.

Music

Beethoven Fund for Deaf Children

P O Box 16975, London, NW8 6ZL

Tel: 020 7586 8107
Fax: 020 7722 7981
Contact: Ann Rachlin, Founder/Chair

The Beethoven Fund is the only charity devoted to providing musical speech therapy to the hundreds of schools and partially hearing units throughout the country as well as assisting in funding centres for hearing impaired infants and young children. The fund supplies specially designed musical instruments to assist the children with their breathing, as well as providing vibrations that enable them to produce the rhythm and melody of speech.

Enabling For Music

Unit for the Study of Musical Skill, Department of Psychology, Keele University, Keele, Staffordshire, ST5 5BG

Tel: 01782 583388
Fax: 01782 583387
E-mail: g.dalgarno@keele.ac.uk
Contact: Gordon Dalgarno, Chairman

Helps individuals, schools and organisations through scientific and technological means, so that people who are hard of hearing or deaf can listen to music more clearly and enjoyably. No charge is made but a modest donation (only if it can be afforded) will be gratefully accepted.

English National Opera

St Martins Lane, London, WC2N 9HU

Tel: 020 7632 8300
Textphone: 020 7836 7666
Fax: 020 7497 9052
Contact: Carol Watson, Theatre Manager
Tel: 020 7845 9440

The box office is equipped with a textphone. There is an infra-red system with 24 receiving units (for those with hearing aids) and headsets are available from a desk in the foyer. Reception is good throughout the theatre, but best in the stalls. Seats are reserved at the front of the stalls for the profoundly deaf. There is one signed performance per production during a season. Tickets for disabled patrons and one companion are £12.50 each (Monday to Thursday) and £15 (Friday to Saturday). Seats can be reserved close to the stage - please explain your requirements when booking. Information about forthcoming productions is available through the free mailing list. Synopses and cast lists are available free of charge.

London Diocese Deaf Choir

The Pavilion, Kingston Playing Fields, Chestnut Avenue, West Drayton, Middlesex, UB7 8BT

Tel: 01895 434809
Textphone: 01895 434809
Fax: 01895 434809
Contact: Vera Hunt
Tel: 01628 623909
Fax: 01628 623909

The choir aims to bring to deaf people more involvement and understanding of church services and also, by taking the choir into 'hearing' churches, gives more understanding and awareness of profoundly deaf people's problems.

Music and the Deaf

Kirklees Media Centre, 7 Northumberland Street, Huddersfield, West Yorkshire, HD1 IRL

Tel: 01484 425551
Textphone: 01484 425551
Fax: 01484 425560
E-mail: matd@architechs.com
Website: www.matd.org.uk
Contact: Paul Whittaker, Artistic Director

Helps hearing impaired people access music and performing arts through workshops, signed theatre performances and talks. Publications and regional contacts are also available.

Music and the Deaf Scotland

510 King Street, Aberdeen, AB24 5ST

Tel: 01224 486032
Textphone: 01224 486032
Fax: 01224 495261
Website: www.matd.org.uk
Contact: Anne and Mary Whittaker

Royal Opera House

Covent Garden, London, WC2E 9DD

Tel: 020 7240 1200

Website: www.royalopera.org

The Royal Opera House is currently closed for redevelopment, due to reopen in December 1999. In the interim, both the Royal Ballet and the Royal Opera are performing at various venues in London and throughout the UK. Please contact the access officer on 020 7240 9307 for more information.

St Anselms Hayes Deaf Choir

5 Crown Close, Hayes, Middlesex, UB3 3BJ

Textphone: 020 8573 6548

Wigmore Hall

36 Wigmore Street, London, W1H 0BP

Tel: 020 7935 2141

Sport

Deaf Mountaineering Club

22 Lady Brae Place, Gorebridge, Midlothian, EH23 4HR

Contact: K Burt

Disability Sport England

13 Brunswick Place, London, N1 6DX

Tel: 020 7490 4919
Fax: 020 7490 4914
E-mail: info@dse.org.uk
Website: www.euroyellowpages.com/dse/dispe
            ngl.html
Contact: Sharon Kyle, Membership Officer
Textphone: 020 7336 8721

A national governing body of sport for disabled people. Responsible for the promotion, development and organisation of sports opportunities for people with physical disabilities, learning disabilities and sensory impairments. Work is carried out at local, regional and national

English Deaf Chess Association

13 Broadwater Dale, Letchworth, Hertfordshire, SG6 3HQ

Textphone: 01462 679933

Fax: 01462 484043

Contact: Phillip Gardner, Secretary

Tel: Use Textphone or Typetalk

The association seeks to encourage and recognise the playing of chess, individual deaf chess players and the organisation of Deaf Chess Clubs in both England and Wales. The EDCA is a member of the International Committee of Silent Chess, and regularly participates in its World Team and Individual Championships as well as the Europa Cup Club Championships. The association is also a member of the British Chess Federation. An annual report, 'Silent Rook', and a bi-annual newsletter 'Silent Checkmate' are available from the association.

English Deaf Football League

68 Wyatts Green Lane, Wyatts Green, Brentwood, Essex, CM15 0PY

Tel: 01277 822748

Contact: Andrew Scolding, General Secretary

International Ski School for the Deaf

18e Sun Lane, Wakefield, West Yorkshire, WF1 1JD

Tel: 01924 298551

Textphone: 01924 298551

Fax: 01924 280232

Contact: Colin Macdonald, Director

The director is a member of the British Association of Ski Instructors. The aim of the organisation is to promote development in winter sports for deaf people. The organisation provides the following services: information, advice, education, research and training. It can also provide equipment and sports facilities for training. Also a member of CISS World Winter Games Alpine Technique Delegate. The organisation doubles as the winter/adventure section of the British Deaf Sports Council.

Mountain Bike (UK) for the Deaf

c/o Bank House Farm, Stoke Saint Milborough, Ludlow, Shropshire, SY8 2ES

Mountain Bike (UK) for the Deaf organises monthly weekend rides and trips to the Peak District, Derbyshire, Yorkshire Dales, the Lake District, Wales and other venues all over the UK from March to October. These trips are for deaf and hard of hearing people aged 13 upwards, and cater for beginners as well as experienced riders. Meetings can be arranged near to each member's home territory using youth hostels or camping and share travelling and accommodation expenses. Please write for information, enclosing an SAE.

Riding for the Disabled, Northern Ireland

62 Skeagh Road, Dromore, County Down, BT25 2QB

Tel: 028 9269 2236

Fax: 028 9269 2236

Contact: Grania Shillington, Regional Chairman

The aim of RDA is to provide the opportunity for people with disabilities to ride and/or carriage drive for the benefit for their health and well-being.

Royal Yachting Association Sailability

RYA House, Romsey Road, Eastleigh, Hampshire, SO50 9YA

Tel: 023 8062 7400

Fax: 023 8062 0545

E-mail: info@ryasailability.org

Contact: Julian Mandiwall

RYA Sailability promotes, fosters and integrates where possible sailing for people with disabilities. A programme of events is available and details of local clubs providing sailing opportunities.

Sport and Disability West Midlands

Birmingham Sports Centre, Highgate, Birmingham, West Midlands, B12 9DL

Contact: Dennis Hodgkins, Regional Manager c/o University College Worcester, Henwick Grove, Worcester, WR2 6AJ

Tel: 01905 855429

Develops sporting opportunities for disabled people. Actively promotes the mainstreaming of disability sport with the governing bodies of all sports. Offers an information service to everyone who has an interest in and wishes to participate or contribute to the projects.

UK Sports Association for People with Learning Disability

Ground Floor, Leroy House, 436 Essex Road, London, N1 3QP

Tel: 020 7354 1030

Fax: 020 7354 2593

Contact: Tracey McCillen, Administration Officer

Welsh Institute of Sport

Sophia Gardens, Cardiff, South Glamorgan, CF1 9SW

Tel: 029 2030 0584
Fax: 029 2030 0599

Theatre

Aberystwyth Arts Centre

Penglais, Aberystwyth, Ceredigion, SY23 3DE

Tel: 01970 622882
Fax: 01970 622883
E-mail: lla@aber.ac.uk
Contact: Maris Davies, Administrator
Tel: 01970 622884

Aberystwyth Arts Centre is the main venue for the arts in mid- and west Wales.

Adelphi Theatre

Maiden Lane, The Strand, London, WC2E 7NA

Tel: 020 7344 0055

At the Adelphi Theatre there is an infra-red system with seven headsets. Deposit of £10. Occasional sign language-interpreted performances. Contact box office for details. Information will soon be available in large print.

Albery Theatre

St Martin's Lane, London, WC2E 7NA

Tel: 020 7369 1730

Contact: Peter Faldon, Theatre Manager

West End Theatre showing commercial work. Currently West End home of the 'Almeida at the Albery' season until July 1999.

Aldwych Theatre

Alwych, London, WC2N 4DF

Tel: 020 7379 3367

No loop or infra-red system available. Please book early if you wish to sit near the front of the auditorium. Box D is also recommended.

Apollo Theatre

Shaftesbury Avenue, London, W1V 7DH

Tel: 020 7494 5470
Fax: 020 7494 5154

Apollo Victoria Theatre

17 Wilton Road, London, SW1V 1LG

Tel: 020 7828 7074
Fax: 020 7630 7716
Contact: Jamie Baskeyfield, Theatre Manager

Contact the theatre box office for details of signed performances. There is no loop or infra-red system. Occasional sign language interpreted performances. Please book early if you wish to sit near the front of the auditorium.

Arts Theatre

6 Great Newport Street, London, WC2H 7JA

Tel: 020 7836 3334

Barbican Theatre

Barbican Centre, Silk Street, Barbican, London, EC2Y 8DS

Tel: 020 7638 8891
Fax: 020 7382 7270

Twin track infra-red system with 30 headsets. Returnable deposit £5. Regular sign language interpreted perfomances. For details of Royal Shakespeare Company productions, join the free mailing list by writing to: Access Mailing List, Membership Department, RSC, Stratford-upon-Avon, Warwickshire, CV37 6BB. Telephone for details of the Barbican Centre mailing list. Regular audio described performances. For details of RSC productions, join the free mailing list and use the above address. Please arrive 45-60 minutes before the performance. Braille and large print plot synopses and cast lists are available. Touch tours of the stage and props can be arranged. Six house seats in row D near the front of the auditorium are kept until the day of the performance. The main lifts have tactile buttons and voice announcement. The Pit has a twin-track infra-red system with 10 headsets - more can be borrowed from the Barbican Theatre if necessary.You will be asked for a deposit of £5.

Buxton Opera House

Water Street, Buxton, Derbyshire, SK17 6XN

Tel: 01298 72050
Fax: 01298 27563
E-mail: admin@buxton-opera.co.uk
Website: www.buxton-opera.co.uk
Contact: Helen Dunnett, Marketing Manager

To provide quality entertainment for the people of Buxton, High Peak and the wider community. The opera house is a 937-seat venue which provides a wide variety of entertainment including opera, music, dance, comedy, pantomime and drama. The opera house also presents a range of associated education events.

Cambridge Theatre

Earlham Street, Seven Dials, London, WC2 9HH

Tel: 020 7494 5040

Fax: 020 7494 5154

As part of Stoll Moss Theatres Ltd the theatre has been installed with an infra-red system for which headsets are available upon request from the theatre manager.

Carmarthen Lyric Theatre

8 King Street, Carmarthen, Dyfed, SA31 1BD

Tel: 01267 232632

Fax: 01267 234559

Contact: Elizabeth Evans, Theatre Manager

Promotes the arts in all its forms in Carmarthen and encourages young people to take up performing arts.

Clwyd Theatr Cymru

Mold, Flintshire, CH7 1YA

Tel: 01352 755114 Box Office

Fax: 01352 758323

Theatre, music, dance, film and art exhibitions throughout the year, plus free parking, a restaurant, bar and bookshop. Sign language interpreted performances offered on most company productions.

Comedy Theatre

Panton Street, London, SW1Y 4DN

Tel: 020 7839 1731

Fax: 020 7839 3663

Comedy Theatre has an infra-red system.

Common Ground Sign Dance Theatre

4th Floor, Crane Building, Hanover Street, Liverpool, Merseyside, L1 3DY

Tel: 0151 707 8033

Textphone: 0151 707 8380

Fax: 0151 707 8033

E-mail: common.sign@dial.pipex.com

Website: www.dspace.dial.pipex.com/common.sign/

Contact: Barry Avison, Administrator

Our aims are both artistic and social. As an integrated company, we aim to promote ourselves as a positive role model of integration in action. Through our work and through performances, we further aim to create a clearer understanding and appreciation, between deaf and hearing people, and of each other's culture.

Crescent Theatre

Sheepcote Street, Brindley Place, Birmingham, West Midlands, B16 8AE

Tel: 0121 643 5859

Fax: 0121 643 5860

Contact: Paul Cooper

Criterion Theatre

2 Jermyn Street, Piccadilly Circus, London, W1V 9LB

Tel: 020 7839 8811

Fax: 020 7925 0596

E-mail: FIONA.CALLAGHAN@act-arts.co.uk

Contact: Fiona Callaghan, Theatre Manager

Dominion Theatre

Tottenham Court Road, London, W1 0AG

Tel: 020 7636 2293

A twin-track infra-red system is planned for the near future. Sign language interpreted performances are offered. Please ring for the details. Touch tours of the stage and props may be possible. Please enquire. Audio described performances are also being planned. Please indicate your requirements when booking.

Donmar Warehouse Theatre

41 Earlham Street, Covent Garden, London, WC2H 9LD

Tel: 020 7867 1150

Fax: 020 7240 4878

Contact: Julia Christie, Theatre Manager

Tel: 020 7836 3939

The Donmar Warehouse provides information on signed performances. An induction loop is fitted in the auditorium and reception is best in the centre stalls. Disabled patrons pay standby rate, bookable in advance. Programmes can be photocopied and enlarged on request. An infra-red hearing system has just been fitted. There is excellent reception from all seats in the auditorium. A deposit is required and will be returned at the end of the loan period. Ask at the box office for any further information.

Drill Hall

16 Chenies Street, London, WC1E 7ET

Tel: 020 7637 8270

Duchess Theatre

Catherine Street, London, WC2B 5LA

Tel: 020 7494 5040

Fax: 020 7494 5147

Website: www.stollmoss.com

Contact: Chris Isherman, Theatre Manager

Tel: 020 7379 5717

Theatre has an infra-red system. Headsets available from the theatre manager. You will be asked to sign the receipt. To book in advance call Customer Services on: 020 7494 5470. Lowest concessionary price available for that performance for disabled theatregoers and a companion. Also book well in advance if you wish to sit near the front of the auditorium.

Duke of York's Theatre

St Martins Lane, London, WC2N 4BG

Tel: 020 7836 4615

Fax: 020 7565 5001

Contact: Vikki Hayward, Theatre Manager

Tel: 020 7565 5050

There is an infra-red system. Eighteen headsets are available from the main foyer desk. A returnable deposit of £5.00 is required, except for special audio description performances. Disabled theatregoers plus one companion pay half price.

Fortune Theatre

Russell Street, Covent Garden, London, WC2B 5HH

Tel: 020 7836 2238

Fax: 020 7497 5551

Contact: Dorothy Freedman

Tel: 020 7836 6260

Garrick Theatre

Charing Cross Road, London, WC2H 0HH

Tel: 020 7494 5470

Fax: 020 7494 5154

Website: www.stollmoss.com

Contact: Phil Hawkeswood, Theatre Manager

Theatre has an infra-red system. Headsets available from the theatre manager. You will be asked to sign the receipt. To book in advance call

Customer Services on: 020 7494 5470. Lowest concessionary price available for that performance for disabled theatregoers and a companion. Also book well in advance if you wish to sit near the front of the auditorium. Sign language interpreted perfomances are offered. Please ask the box office.

Gielgud Theatre

Shaftesbury Avenue, London, W1V 8AR

Tel: 020 7494 5040

Fax: 020 7494 5156

Website: www.stollmoss.com

Theatre has infra-red system. Headsets available from the theatre manager. You will be asked to sign the receipt. To book in advance call Customer Services on 020 7494 5470. Lowest concessionary price available for that performance for disabled theatregoers and a companion. Also book well in advance if you wish to sit near the front of the auditorium.

Globe Theatre

Bear Gardens, Bankside, London, SE1 9ED

Tel: 020 7401 9919

There is no infra-red or induction loop system in the Yard.

Graeae Theatre Company

Interchange Studios, Dalby Street, London, NW5 3NQ

Tel: 020 7267 2703

Fax: 020 7267 2703

E-mail: graea@dircon

Grand Theatre

Singleton Street, Swansea, West Glamorgan, SA1 3QJ

Tel: 01792 475242

Fax: 01792 475379

Contact: Gary Iles

Swansea Grand Theatre provides entertainment across the spectrum: musicals; pantomime; drama; comedy; opera; dance. Sennheiser infra-red hearing system installed. Signed performances usually available for weekly productions.

Gulbenkian Theatre

University of Kent, Canterbury, Kent, CT2 7NB

Tel: 01227 764000/ 01227 769075 Box Office

Fax: 01227 827956

Contact: Pam Hardiman

Tel: 01227 833493

Theatre presenting a mixed programme of professional drama, dance and music. Thrust stages 340 seats.

Haymarket Theatre

Theatre Royal, Haymarket, London, SW1Y 4HA

Tel: 020 7930 8800

Fax: 020 7839 6478

There are no infra-red or loop facilities at present. Please indicate your requirements when booking.

Her Majesty's Theatre

Haymarket, London, SW1Y 4QD

Tel: 020 7494 5040

Fax: 020 7494 5154

Website: www.stollmoss.com

Contact: John Fitzsimmons, Theatre Manager

Tel: 020 7930 5343

Theatre has an infra-red system. Headsets available from the theatre manager.You will be asked to sign the receipt. To book in advance call Customer Services on: 020 7494 5470. Lowest concessionary price available for that performance for disabled theatregoers and a companion. Book well in advance if you wish to sit near the front of the auditorium.

King's Head Theatre

115 Upper Street, London, N1 1QN

Tel: 020 7226 1916

Textphone: 020 7226 1916

Fax: 020 7226 8507

Contact: Pam Mears, Administrator

The King's Head Theatre produce a vast mix of quality theatre, cabaret, musicals, comedy and more. Each main house production includes one signed performance and the auditorium is fitted with an induction loop system. Dinner in the theatre is also offered before each main house production.

Labatt's Apollo

Queen Caroline Street, Hammersmith, London, W6 9HQ

Tel: 020 8748 6045

Fax: 020 8748 9853

Please indicate your requirements when booking. There are no infra-red or loop facilities available. Please book early if you wish to sit near the front of the auditorium. Steps are highlighted.

Little Hands Theatre Company

1 Lyndhurst Avenue, Surbiton, Surrey, KT5 9LN

Tel: 020 8399 0946

Fax: 020 8399 0846

Little Hands is a company producing theatre and mime for deaf children.

London Bubble

5 Elephant Lane, London, SE16 4JD

Tel: 020 7237 4437

Textphone: 020 7231 2366

Fax: 020 7231 2366

The London Bubble Theatre tours productions and participating projects London-wide, year-round. When touring with its tent, there is a loop system installed.

London Palladium

Argyll Street, London, W1V 1AB

Tel: 020 7494 5020

Fax: 020 7734 9380

Contact: Gareth Parnell, Theatre Manager

Tel: 020 7734 6846

To book call Stoll Moss Customer Service on:020 7494 5470. There is an infra-red system with 10 headsets, available from the theatre manager. You will be asked to sign a receipt. For details of signed performances contact the above address. Lowest concession available for disabled theatregoers and one companion. One sign language interpreted performance per production. Please check with the box office.

London Theatre Guide

The Society of London Theatre, Bedford Chambers, The Piazza, Covent Garden, London, WC2E 8HQ

Tel: 020 7836 0971

Fortnightly listing of all West End shows including starting time and approximate running time, prices, a map of Theatreland, an indication of access for disabled theatregoers and discounts for senior citizens. Available free from theatres, tourist information centres, libraries and arts centres, or by annual subscription (£12.50 in the UK).

Lyceum Theatre

Wellington Street, London, WC2E 7DA

Tel: 020 7420 8112

Fax: 020 7240 4346

Please indicate your requirements when booking. Infra-red system with 10 headsets. You will be asked to leave a deposit of £10.

Lyric Theatre

55 Ridgeway Street, Belfast, County Antrim, BT9 5FB

Lyric Theatre

Shaftesbury Avenue, London, W1V 7HA

Tel: 020 7494 5470

Fax: 020 7437 5443

Website: www.stollmoss.com

Contact: Alison Hayes, Theatre Manager

Tel: 020 7437 3694

Theatre has an infra-red system. Headsets available from the theatre manager. You will be asked to sign the receipt. To book in advance call Customer Services on the number above. Lowest concessionary price available for that performance for disabled theatregoers and a companion. Also book well in advance if you wish to sit near the front of the auditorium.

National Theatre

Upper Ground, London, SE1 9PX

Tel: 020 7452 3000/ 7452 3400
            Information Desk

Textphone: 020 7620 0741 (3-5pm)

Fax: 020 7452 3030

Website: www.nt-online.org

Contact: John Langley, Theatre Manager

Tel: 020 7452 3333

There are three separate theatres within this complex: the Olivier, the Lyttleton and the Cottesloe. All three theatres have a twin-track infra-red system with headsets or neck loops. A £5.00 minimum deposit is charged, which is returnable. All three theatres also have one signed performance for most productions. Written

plot synopses are available. Backstage tours are also occasionally accompanied by signing. Please ask for information. Sign language interpreted performances are offered approximately every six weeks. To join the free mailing list with details of these performances, write to: Marketing Department, Signed/Audio Described Performance Mailing List, use the above address. Several members of staff, including the chef, can sign. A limited number of seats are kept at the front - please ask when booking.

Neti Neti Theatre Company

George Orwell School, Turle Road, London, N4 3LS

Tel: 020 7483 4239

Fax: 020 7483 4239

Contact: Rita Mishra, General Manager

Neti Neti Theatre Company aims to produce innovative work for young people and adults with an emphasis on the experience and perception of disability, particularily hidden disability and difference. The company can provide information, advice and education through performance. It also holds workshops, presentations and training sessions. It holds signed performances and produces subtitled and signed videos of all of its productions. Neti Neti also sells books and badges

New London Theatre

Drury Lane, London, WC2B 5PW

Tel: 020 7242 9802

Contact: Douglas Hinton, Customer Liaison
            Manager for 'Cats'

The Theatre has an infra-red system with six headsets available, and loop system with six headsets for use with a T-switch. A deposit of £5.00 is required. The signal may be stronger in some parts of the theatre. Please ask for advice when you book. Occasional sign language interpreted performances. This theatre is currently showing 'Cats'. Touch tours of the stage and props are available - please contact the box office for details. An audio description service is being planned. Steps between levels are highlighted. Book early if you wish to sit near the front of the auditorium.

New Theatre

Park Place, Cardiff, CF1 3LN
Tel: 029 2087 8787
Textphone: 029 2087 8881
Fax: 029 2087 8888

The New Theatre, Cardiff, presents the best in musicals, drama, dance, children's shows, opera and pantomime to the people of the Welsh capital and surrounding areas. It regularly presents shows by the Royal Shakespeare Company, the National Theatre, Welsh National Opera, Northern Ballet Theatre, and Clwyd Theatr Cymru.

New Venture Theatre

Bedford Place, Brighton, East Sussex, BN1 2PT
Tel: 01273 746118
E-mail: tonyloveless@pavilion.co.uk
Contact: Tony Loveless, Administrative Director

New Venture Theatre is the area's major non-professional theatre with two theatre spaces and presenting non-professional productions each running 7 to 14 performances during the 1998/9 season. The company actively encourages new writing and this year is premiering two new plays. New members are always welcome. Both theatre spaces have induction loop systems.

Old Vic Theatre

The Cut, Waterloo Road, London, SE1 8NB
Tel: 020 7928 7616
Fax: 020 7928 3608

There are no loop or infra-red facilities available at this theatre. Please book early if you wish to sit near the front of the auditorium.

Open Air Theatre

Inner Circle, Regents Park, London, NW1 4NU
Tel: 020 7486 2431
Fax: 020 7487 4562

The Open Air Theatre in Regent's Park is London's premier outdoor venue serving predominantly Londoners with a repertory summer season of two Shakespeare plays, a musical and a children's play. The theatre is open from May until September and information on signed performances may be found on the season's leaflet, available from April.

Palace Theatre

Shaftesbury Avenue, London, W1V 8AY
Tel: 020 7343 0909
Fax: 020 7734 6157

An induction loop system is planned. Sign language interpreted performances are offered. Please contact the box office for details. Information in large print is available. Most steps are highlighted.

Parc and Dare Theatre

Dyfodwg Street, Treorchy, Rhondda, Cynon, Taff, CF42 6NL
Tel: 01443 773112
Fax: 01443 776922

Provides first-class live entertainment together with all the newest films on release.

Phoenix Theatre

Charing Cross Road, London, WC2H 0JP
Tel: 020 7465 0211
Fax: 020 7465 0212

No loop or infra-red facilities available. Please book early if you wish to sit near the front of the auditorium. Steps are highlighted.

Piccadilly Theatre

Denman Street, Piccadilly, London, W1V 8DY
Tel: 020 7836 1443

No loop or infra-red facilities available at this theatre. Touch tours of the stage and props may be possible. Please ask to speak to the theatre manager. Also book early if you wish to sit near the front of the auditorium.

Playhouse Theatre

Northumberland Avenue, London, WC2N 5DE
Tel: 020 7839 4401
Fax: 020 7839 1195

The theatre has a loop system, operating for the stalls. (Reception is best in the centre stalls.) Please turn your hearing aid to the 'T' switch. Information in large print available on request.

Polka Theatre for Children

240 The Broadway, London, SW19 1SB

Tel: 020 8543 4888 Box Office

Contact: Judith Howard

Polka is the only theatre building in Britain which produces and presents work exclusively for children. Open all year (except September) Tuesdays to Saturdays offering inspirational plays in two theatre spaces for ages 3 to 13. Show-related exhibitions, clubs and workshops, a playground, cafe and souvenir shops enhance the visit.

Prince Edward Theatre

Old Compton Street, London, W1V 6HS

Tel: 020 7447 5400

Prince of Wales Theatre

31 Coventry Street, London, W1V 8AS

Tel: 020 7930 1867

Fax: 020 7930 5108

Contact: John Causebrook, Manager

Queen's Theatre

Shaftesbury Avenue, London, W1V 8AS

Tel: 020 7494 5041

Fax: 020 7494 5154

Website: www.stoll-moss.com

Contact: Nicholas Shaw, Theatre Manager

Tel: 020 7734 1348

Plays, musicals, comedy. Function rooms available for hire. Conferences, product launches. Television broadcasts.

Royal Court Theatre Downstairs

Duke of York's Theatre, 104 St Martin's Lane, London, WC2N 9HN

Tel: 020 7565 5000

Fax: 020 7565 5001

The Royal Court organises signed performances of its productions. There is a quarterly publication detailing their future productions. Infra-red system with 18 headsets. There is limited access to this facility in the auditorium - please ask the box office when booking. There are plans to provide an audio description service in the future.

Royal Court Theatre Upstairs

Ambassador's Theatre, West Street, London, WC2H 9ND

Tel: 020 7565 5000

Fax: 020 7565 5001

The Royal Court organises signed performances in its productions. There is a quarterly publication detailing its future productions. There is an induction loop available. There are plans to provide an audio description service in the future.

Royal Shakespeare Company - Barbican

Barbican Centre, Silk Street, London, EC2Y 8BQ

Tel: 020 7628 3351

Textphone: 020 7382 7297

Fax: 020 7374 0818

Website: www.rsc.org.uk

There is an infra-red system with 20 headsets, available from the box office for a deposit of £5.00. Sign language interpreted performances and backstage tours are available in the Barbican Theatre. Contact the box office for details.

Sadler's Wells Theatre

Rosebery Avenue, London, EC1R 4TN

Tel: 020 7863 8000

Fax: 020 7314 9004

Contact: Nadia Stern, Theatre Administrator

There is a loop system for use with T-switch. Sound quality may vary according to stage equipment brought in by visiting companies. There are occasionally signed performances and other activities for deaf and hearing impaired people.

Savoy Theatre

The Strand, London, WC2B 5LD

Tel: 020 7836 8888 Box Office/ 7836 8817 Admin

Contact: Kevin Chapple, Theatre Manager

The Savoy Theatre hosts assorted shows ranging from plays and comedies to musicals. Seats approximately 1,100. The theatre is built underground so there are many seats in the stalls. It is a no-smoking theatre. There is an infra-red system with 10 headsets. Please indicate your requirements when you book.

Shaftesbury Theatre

210 Shaftesbury Avenue, London, WC2H 8DP

Tel: 020 7379 5399

There is no loop or infra-red system, but there are plans to install a twin-track Sennheisser infra-red system. There are some sign language interpreted performances and the theatre hopes to increase the number of interpreted performances per production. Information in large print and on tape will soon be available. Book early if you wish to sit near the front of the auditorium, or in a box so that a companion can describe for you.

Shape London

LVS Resource Centre, 356 Holloway Road, London, N7 6PA

Tel: 020 7700 8139

Textphone: 020 7700 8139

Fax: 020 7700 8143

Contact: Maggie Woolley, Director

Shape opens up access to the arts, enabling greater participation by disabled, deaf and older people. Key services comprise: ticket scheme, education, training, arts development, deaf arts programme and advice, information and consultancy. Reduced price tickets and volunteer escorts/drivers for a wide range of London arts and entertainment events. Membership open to disabled people or people over 60. Individuals £10, Groups £20 per annum. Bi-monthly ticket scheme magazine listing events and access details.

Sherman Theatre

Senghenydd Road, Cardiff, South Glamorgan, CF2 4YE

Tel: 029 2023 0451

Textphone: 029 2034 5610

Fax: 029 2066 5581

The Sherman is the only producing theatre in Cardiff and has commissioned more new plays than any other theatre in Britain. It has an exciting and often challenging programme, which includes drama, opera and comedy, attracting audiences of more than 125,000 people each year. To join the Sherman's mailing list contact the theatre on the numbers listed above.

SPIT

P O Box 6028, London, NW4 2ZB

Tel: 020 8202 1731

Fax: 020 8202 1731

Contact: Sarah Sills, Editor, 'SPIT News'

Provides information on signed performance in theatres around the country. Listings of sign language interpreted performances by member theatres.

St Martin's Theatre

West Street, Cambridge Circus, London, WC2H 9NA

Tel: 020 7836 1443

Induction loop and single track infra-red systems with four headsets. You will be asked for a deposit. Please book in advance and indicate your requirements when you book. Programmes can be enlarged on the theatre's photocopier or read to customers on request.

Stephen Joseph Theatre

Westborough, Scarborough, North Yorkshire, YO11 1JW

Tel: 01723 370541

Fax: 01723 360506

E-mail: response@sjt.onyxnet.co.uk

Website: www.webart.co.uk/client/sjt/

Contact: Stephen Ward, General Manager

Strand Theatre

Aldwych, London, WC2B 5LD

Tel: 020 7930 8800

There are no loop or infra-red facilities at this theatre. Visually impaired customers should book early if they wish to sit near the front of the auditorium. Please indicate your requirements when you book.

Theatr Ardudwy

Harlech, Gwynedd, LL46 2PU

Tel: 01766 780667

Fax: 01766 780778

Contact: Valerie Wynne-Williams, Director

Theatr Felinfach

Felinfach, Dyffryn Aeron, Ceredigion, SA48 8AF

Tel: 01570 470697

Fax: 01570 471030

E-mail: swyddfa@theatrfelinfach.demon.co.uk

Website: www.theatrfelinfach.demon.co.uk

Contact: Euros Lewis, Lecturer in Charge

Community education and development through the medium of the arts in general, and the performing arts and community radio and television in particular.

Theatr Gogledd Cymru/North Wales Theatre

The Promenade, Llandudno, Conwy, LL30 1BB

Tel: 01492 879771

Fax: 01492 860790

Contact: Nick Reed, General Manager

1,500-seat multi-purpose theatre housing one of the largest stages in the UK. Featuring a year-round programme of number one productions including opera, ballet, orchestral music, West End shows, comedy, popular music and variety. Situated on Llandudno's Victorian promenade.

Theatr Gwynedd

Ffordd Deiniol, Bangor, Gwynedd, LL57 2TL

Tel: 01248 351707

Fax: 01248 351915

E-mail: theatr@globalnet.co.uk

Contact: Dafydd Thomas, Director

A varied arts venue providing entertainment for the people of north-west Wales. The programme includes drama, varied musical concerts, opera, dance, pantomines and films in both English and Welsh languages. Theatr Gwynedd also has its own Welsh language producing company. There is a loop system for films, and occasional signed performances.

Theatr Hafren

Llanidloes Road, Newtown, Powys, SY16 4HU

Tel: 01686 625007

Fax: 01686 625446

E-mail: boxoffice@coleg-powys.ac.uk

Theatre and gallery on campus of Coleg Powys offering comprehensive year-round programme of drama, music, dance and entertainment. Ample free parking, and loop system in auditorium.

Theatr Mwldan

Theatr Mwldan, Bath House Road, Cardigan, Ceredigion, SA43 1JY

Tel: 01239 621200

Fax: 01239 613600

Contact: Dilwyn Davies, Director

Theatre Royal Drury Lane

Catherine Street, London, WC2B 5JF

Tel: 020 7494 5040

Fax: 020 7379 6836

Website: www.stollmoss.com

Contact: Rupert Bielby, Theatre Manager

Tel: 020 7240 0115

Theatre has an infra-red system. Headsets available from the theatre manager. You will be asked to sign the receipt. To book in advance call Customer Services on: 020 7494 5470. Lowest concessionary price available for that performance for disabled theatregoers and a companion. Also book well in advance if you wish to sit near the front of the auditorium.

Unicorn Theatre for Children

6-7 Great Newport Street, London, WC2H 7JB

Tel: 020 7379 3280

Fax: 020 7836 5366

Contact: Sarah Scott, Deaf Development Officer

Tel: 020 7379 3280 (Tuesdays only)

The Unicorn Theatre is a professional theatre company dedicated to performing theatre for audiences of children between the ages of 4 and 12 years. The theatre can provide information and advice, education and workshops in drama. Theatre productions are put on and competitions in playwriting are organised. Plays are chosen on the basis of relevance and interest. The intention is to create a theatre for children as an audience now, and not to create the audiences of the future - except as an additional gain. Work for deaf and partially hearing children is an extension of the company's desire to make the work as accessible as possible. It provides a number of particular activities for deaf and partially hearing children both on the premises and in schools. Signed interpretation of each production is provided. They also provide occasional productions through 'Little Deaf Unicorn' Company. NOTE: From April 1999, Unicorn will be moving to temporary accommodation elsewhere. Contact The Arts Council (Sarah Scott) on 020 7333 0100 for updates and location, etc.

Vaudeville Theatre

The Strand, London, WC2R 0NH
Tel: 020 7836 9987

There are no loop or infra-red facilities at present at this theatre. Please indicate your requirements when you book.

Victoria Palace Theatre

Victoria Street, London, SW1E 5LA
Tel: 020 7834 1317

Induction loop and single track infra-red system with four headsets. You will be asked for a deposit. Please book in advance. There is a member of staff in the box office who can sign.

Westminster Theatre

Palace Street, London, SW1E 5JB
Tel: 020 7834 7882
Fax: 020 7828 7609
Contact: Juliet Adams, Theatre Manager
The theatre has a loop system.

Whitehall Theatre

Whitehall, London, SW1A 2DY
Tel: 020 7369 1735
Fax: 020 7839 3462

There are no loop or infra-red facilities at this theatre.

Wyndham's Theatre

Charing Cross Road, London, WC2H 0DA
Tel: 020 7867 1125/ 1116
Fax: 020 7240 3492
Contact: William Ingrey, Theatre Manager
The theatre is equipped with Sennheiser infra-red transmitters with 12 headsets and receivers which are available for patrons on payment of a small deposit.

Religious Organisations

This is a new section which gives coverage of organisations that are able to provide spiritual support and opportunities for worship to deaf people. The list of organisations is by no means exhaustive. As new organisations make themselves known they will be included in the directory. Organisations are listed alphabetically by name.

Bath and Wells Diocesan Council of Deaf People

The Old Deanery, Wells, Somerset, BA5 2UG
Tel: 01749 670777
Fax: 01749 674240
Contact: Brenda Feltham

To make contact with all deaf people in the Diocese of Bath and Wells. To assist deaf people to overcome the effects of their disabilities by the provision of interpreters in cases of special needs. To give advice and guidance to deaf people on personal problems and in connection with any services which appear to be available to them and of which they wish to take advantage, whether provided under any enactment or rendered by any other voluntary organisation. To provide religious services for deaf people in their own manual language or orally. To facilitate equal opportunities for deaf people.

Belfast Deaf Christian Fellowship

Beersbridge Road, Belfast, County Antrim, BT5 5DY
Contact: Jimmy Steadman

Correspondence address: 11 Manderille Avenue, Newtownards, County Down BT23 3XA

Catholic Deaf Association

Our Lady and St Joseph, New Hartley, Whitley Bay, Tyne and Wear, NE25 0RT
Tel: 0191 237 0455
Fax: 0191 237 0455
Contact: Father Austin Tomaney, Organising Secretary

The CDA is an organisation of deaf and hearing people who support each other and promote services within the community. At diocesan level the Association creates awareness among bishops and diocesan communities of the needs and rights of deaf people and works with dioceses to establish services with appropriately qualified personnel. The Association also seeks to support existing services and to promote working partnerships with other agencies. At national level, the Association provides support groups for chaplains, heads of diocesan services, pastoral workers and deaf people; organises events and programmes such as training days, annual conferences, pilgrimages and holidays; establishes working committees such as the Development Committee, Bishops' Committee and Millennium Committee.

Catholic Deaf Service

Marian House, 48 Talbot Street, Cardiff, South Glamorgan, CF1 9BX
Tel: 029 2022 3352
Textphone: 029 2022 3352
Fax: 029 2038 8108
E-mail: ccd@globalnet.co.uk
Contact: Tony Hodges

The service is a pastorally based church organisation, offering services to deaf and hard of hearing people and their families. We offer Catholic church services in sign language and interpreting for other Christian services. Counselling is also offered in sign and speech. Training is also provided for deaf people who wish to participate in the various ministries of the Church.

Christian Deaf Link UK

29 Summerfield Street, London, SE12 0NH
E-mail: DeafLink01@aol.uk.com

Formerly the London Christian Deaf Link, Deaf Link UK has changed its name, logo and slogan in order to broaden its work and funding support in the UK. Deaf Link aims to develop innovative Christian work, meeting the spiritual needs of deaf people. Events include Saturday Fellowship every two months, and two Sunday services a month. Other major activities are outreach/drama, weekend conferences, Bible training days, etc. A 1999 Programme Fixtures list can be requested. Anyone interested can pay £3.50 subscription for the Deaf Link magazine (quarterly).

Christian Fellowship Church

171-177 Holywood Road, Belfast, County Antrim, BT4 2DJ
Contact: K Blair

Christian church with hearing and deaf members. Correspondence address: 18 Ballyfore Avenue, Ballyduff, BT36 6XE.

Church Action on Disability (CHAD)

50 Scrutton Street, London, EC2A 4PH
Tel: 020 7452 2085
Fax: 020 7452 2001
E-mail: mlpfcm@aol.com
Contact: Martyn Pope, CHAD Coordinator

Church of Ireland Mission to the Deaf

Wilton House, 5 College Square North, Belfast, County Antrim, BT1 6AR
Contact: Wil Murphy

Committee for Ministry Among Deaf People

Advisory Board of Ministry, Church House, Great Smith Street, London, SW1P 3NZ
Tel: 020 7233 1153
Textphone: 020 7233 1153
Fax: 020 7898 1421
E-mail: 106575.2374@compuserve.com
Contact: June Bellinger, Secretary

The Committee has a responsibility to represent the interests of deaf people to the church and vice versa. Its aim is that all deaf people shall have access to church membership and pastoral care offered in their own languages. The Committee works in three main fields: (i) among congregations of deaf people, (ii) with the diocesan chaplains for deaf people, (iii) with the structures of the Church of England. The Committee also offers an advice and counselling service to those in the Church who deal with deafened and hard of hearing people. All churches and church halls are encouraged to provide loop facilities for their members and a leaflet 'Is the gospel really heard in your church?' has been published to enhance this.

Communicating Christians

14 Pelham Lane, Canwick, Lincoln, LN4 2RR
Tel: 01522 522854 (after 6pm)
Contact: Heather Dawson

Promotes sign language use and supports Christians who wish to support deaf people in their fellowship.

Deaf Evangelical Fellowship

Shalom, 4 Swallow Avenue, Skellingthorpe, Lincolnshire, LN6 0XL
Textphone: 01522 500614
Contact: Frank Carter, Missioner/Secretary
Tel: 01522 500614

Religious organisation for deaf and hard of hearing people. Church services are held on Sundays 3pm to 5pm. Sign language and lipreading classes are held on Fridays 7.30pm to 9pm.

Diocese of Exeter Chaplaincy to the Deaf

Glenn House, 96 Old Tiverton Road, Exeter, Devon, EX4 6LD
Tel: 01392 427227
Textphone: 01392 427227
Fax: 01392 427227
Contact: Rev Gill Behenna, Chaplain with Deaf People

The Chaplaincy seeks to provide spiritual and pastoral care for deaf people, their families and friends. It can provide information, advice, educational services, workshops, conferences and training. The Chaplaincy also undertakes campaigning activities. A quarterly newsletter, 'The Messenger', is produced.

Hands Together

P O Box 212, Doncaster, South Yorkshire, DN2 5XA
Tel: 01302 369684
Textphone: 01302 369684

A Deaf Christian network providing training, videos in British Sign Language and information for deaf church-goers on where they can find signed services.

Hard of Hearing Christian Fellowship

P O Box 91, Reading, Berkshire, RG1 5YR
Tel: 01379 652951
Contact: Richard Livermore, Development Officer

            High Gables, Hall Road, Winfarthing, Diss, Norfolk, IP22 2EJ

The Fellowship seeks to support hard of hearing Christians in their local churches. It provides pastoral care by means of home groups, weekend conferences, and the 'Hearing Eye' magazine. Churches are encouraged in deaf awareness, use of loop systems and non-verbal means of communication. Used hearing aids are sent overseas.

Hexham and Newcastle Diocesan Deaf Centre

2 Summerhill Grove, Summerhill Square,
Newcastle upon Tyne, NE4 6EE

Tel: 0191 261 8888
Textphone: 0191 261 8888
Videotel: 0191 233 1074 (9am-4.30pm)
Fax: 0191 233 2122
Contact: Barbara Lyon, Administrator
2 Summerhill Grove, Summerhill
Square, Newcastle Upon Tyne, Tyne
and Wear, NE4 6EE

Youth Service for 5 to 25 year olds (Francis
Murphy, Youth Worker). Sign language
communication classes. Spiritual and pastoral
services. Conference centre. Thursday luncheon
club. Recreational facilities: social club, sports
club, drama and youth club.

Kinghan Church for the Deaf

13 Botanic Avenue, Belfast, County Antrim, BT7
1JG

Tel: 028 9032 2588
Textphone: 028 9032 2588
Fax: 028 9032 9348
Contact: George Grindle

Formerly the Kinghan Mission to the Deaf which
was founded in 1857, we have now become a
church and Christian centre for deaf people. As
well as Sunday services, there are various week-
night activities for deaf people.

Lincoln Diocesan Deaf Association

St Matthias Centre for Deaf People, Burton Road,
Lincoln, LN1 3TX

Tel: 01522 541561
Textphone: 01522 544462
Fax: 01522 541561
Contact: John Clark, Chaplain with People who
are Deaf
Textphone: 01522 751759

Aims: to provide spiritual and pastoral care for
deaf people, to ensure deaf people receive their
rights under current legislation, to provide and
promote the use of sign language, to provide
advocacy, to assist deaf people in need. Activities
include deaf churches, deaf clubs, drama, and
indoor games.

National Chaplaincy for the Deaf

St Vincents Centre for the Deaf, 31 Richmond Hill,
Rathmines, Dublin 6

Tel: 00353 1 897 2256
Textphone: 00353 1 830 5744
Contact: Diarmuid O'Farrell
Textphone: 010 353 18 305744

Northumbria Deaf Mission

Tel: 0191 221 0397
Textphone: 0191 221 0397
Fax: 0191 221 0444
Contact: Jennifer Bell, Secretary
Tel: 0191 221 0444

See entry under Regional Organisations.

Rye Lane Baptist Chapel

59 Rye Lane, London, SE15 5EX

Tel: 020 7639 7098
Contact: Gwen Richards

Some hard of hearing people attend this church,
and a loop system is installed.

Salisbury Diocesan Association for the Deaf and Hard of Hearing

Church House, Crane Street, Salisbury, Wiltshire,
SP1 2QB

Tel: 01722 411977 ext 205
Textphone: 01722 411977 ext 205
Fax: 01722 331159
Contact: Diana James, Administrator

The Association provides ministry and pastoral
care to all deaf and hard of hearing people in the
Diocese of Salisbury, which covers the two
counties of Wiltshire and Dorset. The services of
the Association are also available to professionals
working with deaf people and the general public.
It produces a quarterly magazine, 'News and
Notes'.

Southwark Cathedral

Montague Close, London, SE1 9DA

Tel: 020 7407 3708
Contact: Roy White, Vice Provost

We are an Anglican cathedral serving the Diocese
of Southwark and the area covering south London
and north Surrey. The Hard of Hearing Group is
open to those who minister in any Christian
church. Its task is one of mutual support and
raising awareness of the needs of hard of hearing
people in churches.

St Clement with St Peter Church of England Church

140 Friern Road, East Dulwich, London, SE22 0AY
Tel: 020 8693 1890
Fax: 020 8693 1890
Contact: Rev Peter Macan, Vicar

Ten hard of hearing people attend this church and a loop system is installed. They are in touch with the Southwark Diocese Hard of Hearing Group.

St James Catholic Church

45 Elm Grove, Peckham, London, SE15 5DD
Tel: 020 7639 1947
Contact: Rev R Brennan

Weekly Mass. Loop system in use.

St John With St Andrew Church of England Church

Meeting House Lane, Peckham, London, SE15 2UN
Tel: 020 7639 0084
Contact: Rev Johnson

Ten hard of hearing people attend this church and a loop system is installed.

The Most Holy Trinity Church

Dockhead, London, SE1 2BS
Tel: 020 7237 1641
Fax: 020 7237 1641
Contact: Rev Alan McLean

We are a lively worshipping community who try to support all those who are in need. Between 10 and 12 hard of hearing people attend this church and a loop system is installed.

The Norwegian Church

1 St Olave's Square, Albion Street, London, SE16 7JB
Tel: 020 7237 5587
Textphone: 020 7237 7280
Contact: Father Petterson

Morning Mass service. Ten hard of hearing people attend this church and a loop system is installed.

Union Chapel

255 Tooley Street, London, SE1 2LA
Tel: 020 7403 6192
Fax: 020 7403 5380
Contact: David Nunn, Minister

A Christian Church in association with New Frontiers International and a member of the Evangelical Alliance. Meeting on Sundays at 10.30am, at Drummond Christian Centre, Drummond Road, London, SE16. Sign language interpretation is available as is a loop system. Visitors are very welcome.

Westminster Diocese Deaf Service

Vaughan House, 46 Francis Street, London, SW1P 1QN
Tel: 020 7798 9026
Textphone: 020 7798 9026
Fax: 020 7799 9010
Contact: Suzanne Line, Director

Westminster Diocese Deaf Service works with deaf and hard of hearing people of all ages, to facilitate and enable them to participate fully in the life of the church, sharing their own gifts. It provides the range of services and activities that would be found in any parish.

Wolverhampton Church Association for the Deaf

38 Rupert Street, Wolverhampton, West Midlands, WV3 9NU
Tel: 01902 420904
Textphone: 01902 420904
Contact: H M Palmer, Secretary

Religious/Educational/Service/Social. Please contact the centre for details of days and times of meetings.

500

The RNID helpline – we're here to help!

Whatever your query is – from hearing aids to lipreading, telephone aids to sign language classes – give us a call. The RNID Helpline is equally accessible to all, whatever your degree of hearing loss. Our Helpline staff can assist you in any of these ways.

By phone: telephone our national RNID Helpline number – 0870 60 50 123, between the hours of 9.30am and 5.00pm. Calls cost less than 7p a minute. An answerphone service will be available outside office hours.

By textphone: call 0870 60 33 007 between the hours of 9.30am and 5.00pm or leave a message at all other times.

In writing: write to: RNID Helpline, The Royal National Institute for Deaf People, PO Box 16464, London EC1Y 8TT or send a fax to 020 7296 8199.

In person: please feel free to drop in to our national head office – 19-23 Featherstone Street, London EC1Y 8SL. Our reception staff will make you feel welcome and will help you with your enquiry. A signer will also be available.

Whatever your query, give us a call...

0870 60 50 123

THE ROYAL NATIONAL INSTITUTE FOR DEAF PEOPLE

RNID

Information for deaf and hard of hearing people and anyone who works with them

Single copies of these leaflets are free. Prices only apply if you want to order more than one copy of any leaflet. Members get a 10 per cent discount on the prices shown.

Basic British Sign Language – An illustrated introduction focusing on words that may be useful in the workplace   30p

Look after your ears – Practical information on how to protect your hearing   30p

Questions about tinnitus – General information about tinnitus, where to get advice and treatment, and how you can help yourself if you have tinnitus   30p

All about hearing aids – A guide to getting and using a hearing aid, privately or through the NHS   30p

Benefits and services for deaf and hard of hearing people – Help for anyone who has a hearing loss, from disability benefits and communication support to equipment and specialist telephone services   30p

Common ear problems – Basic information about some of the most common ear conditions and their causes   30p

Deaf and hard of hearing people – General information about deafness, deaf people and issues related to deafness 30p

Equipment for deaf people – Special equipment available for deaf and hard of hearing people to use at home or at work   30p

Help with TV and audio – Information for deaf people on getting the most of out your television or audio system, including subtitles on television   30p

How your ears work – A clear, concise description of the different parts of the ear and what they do, with a detailed diagram   30p

Age-related hearing loss – What to do if you begin losing your hearing as you get older   30p

Available from RNID HelpLine, PO Box 16464, London EC1Y 8TT
Tel: 0870 60 50 123 Textphone: 0870 60 33 007
Fax: 0171 296 8021

THE ROYAL NATIONAL INSTITUTE FOR DEAF PEOPLE

Index

E

M

Wolverhampton Church Association for the Deaf 500
Wolverhampton Education Service 330
Wolverhampton Hard of Hearing Club 471
Wolverhampton Independent Deaf Club 471
Wolverhampton Social Services 33
Wolverhampton Tinnitus Support Group 129
Women's Health Information and Support Service 430
Woodcote County Primary School 295
Woodham Comprehensive School 286
Woodlands Community School 288, 360
Woodlands County Infant School 283
Woodlands County Junior School 311
Woodside Community School 310
Woolley Wood Primary School 322
Worcester and Hereford Association for Deaf People 234
Worcester and Hereford Interpreting Service 160
Worcester College of Technology 377
Worcester Green OAP Deaf Club 470
Worcester Royal Infirmary 108
Worcester Tinnitus Support Group 130
Worcestershire Education Service 336
Worcestershire Social Services 34
Working Party on Signed English 220
World Federation of the Deaf 246
World Federation of the Deaf France 247
World Recreation Association of the Deaf, Inc. 267
Worthing Deaf Centre 472
Worthing Hospital 107
Worthing Social Services 33
Wren Centre 430
Wrexham Deaf Club 476
Wrexham Education Service 347
Wrexham Hard of Hearing Club 476
Wrexham Maelor Hospital 112
Wrexham Social Services 42
Wrexham Special Education Centre 347
Wrexham Tinnitus Support Group 131
Write Away 220
WRVS Hard of Hearing Club 455
WS Steele Ltd 190
WSP Environmental 190
Wulfrun College 376
Wycombe General Hospital 76, 92
Wye College 364, 390
Wyndham's Theatre 496

Wynfield House Home for the Deaf 146
Wyre Forest Citizen Advocacy 430
Wythenshaw Hospital 99

Y

Yardley Green Hospital 88, 106
Yate Deaf Club 450
Yeatman Hospital 78
Yeovil College 372
Yeovil Deaf Centre 467
Yeovil District Hospital 104
Yeovil Tinnitus Self-Help Group 127
YWCA 147
Ynys Mon Voluntary Services 430
Ynysawdre Comprehensive School 351
Ynysowen Junior School 351
York College of Further and Higher Education 369, 393
York Deaf Society 466
York District Hospital 103
York Social Services 26
York Tinnitus Support Group 126
Yorkshire Coast College of Further and Higher Education 369
Yorkshire Cochlear Implant Programme 116
Yorkshire Residential School for Deaf Children 273
Yorkshire Television 443
Young Hard of Hearing and Deafened People's Club 479
Young Women's Christian Association 147
Youth Exchange Council 246
Youth Information Project 430
Ysbyty Gwynedd 112
Ysbyty Gwynedd 90
Ysgol Dewi Saint (Primary) 349
Ystrad Mynach Hospital 72, 113
Ystradgynlais Hearing Impaired Support Group 480

Z

Zambia National Association of the Deaf 267
Zveza Drustev Slusno 254
Zveza Glumim in Naglusnih Slovenije 254

For deaf people it's the key to a whole new way of life

To a deaf person that 'GA' key stands for much more than 'go ahead' - it means additional independence and the benefits of the phone network that hearing people take for granted.

Typetalk's 22,000 textphone users rely on our confidential relay service to put them in contact with hearing people. A textphone is a special phone with a screen and keyboard.

Users speak directly to the hearing person or they may type their messages which are translated into speech by highly trained operators who relay them to the hearing person. Their response is then typed back to the textphone user and appears on their screen.

The service, of course, is highly confidential and FREE to join. Calls are charged at standard BT rates and customers may qualify for 60% off their Typetalk and BT phone bills up to £160 each year.

If you could benefit from using Typetalk, or you know someone who would, then call us or fill in the form and take your first step towards improving your, or someone else's, quality of life.

typetalk

BT **RNID**
working together

TO FIND OUT MORE OR REGISTER FREE OF CHARGE CALL:
0800 500 888 (text) or 0800 7 311 888 (voice)
between 9am – 5pm, Monday to Friday **OR**, complete this coupon and return it in an envelope (no stamp needed) to:
Typetalk, Registration Department, FREEPOST, Liverpool L3 5BR

✂

I WOULD LIKE TO KNOW MORE ABOUT TYPETALK. PLEASE SEND ME MORE INFORMATION

Full name (Mr/Mrs/Miss/Ms)
_____

Address _____

_____

Postcode _____

Tel. _____

Send to: **Typetalk, Registration Department, FREEPOST, Liverpool L3 5BR** (no stamp needed)

HFA 1